EARTH & SPACE SCIENCES

FOR NGSS

THIS BOOK IS THE PROPERTY OF

Name ____________________

Class ____________________

School ____________________

Earth & Space Sciences

FOR NGSS

About the Authors

Jillian Mellanby *Editor*

Jill began her science career with a degree in biochemistry and, after a short spell in research labs, became a science teacher both in the UK and then New Zealand. She spent many years managing the Royal Society of New Zealand's academic publishing programme of eight science journals which allowed her to hone her project management and editorial skills. She was also a part of the Expert Advice writing team at the Royal Society of New Zealand, producing science pieces for a public audience. She joined the BIOZONE team in late 2021, as editor.

Kent Pryor *Author*

Kent has a BSc from Massey University, majoring in zoology and ecology and taught secondary school biology and chemistry for 9 years before joining BIOZONE as an author in 2009.

Sarah Gaze *Author*

Sarah has 16 years' experience as a Science and Chemistry teacher, recently completing MEd. (1st class hons) with a focus on curriculum, science, and climate change education. She has a background in educational resource development, academic writing, and art. Sarah joined the BIOZONE team at the start of 2022.

Lissa Bainbridge-Smith *Author*

Lissa graduated with a Masters in Science (hons) from the University of Waikato. After graduation she worked in industry in a research and development capacity for eight years. Lissa joined BIOZONE in 2006 and is hands-on developing new curricula. Lissa has also taught science theory and practical skills to international and ESL students.

Cover photograph

NASA's Mars Perseverance rover and Ingenuity helicopter

The Perseverance rover touched down on Mars on 18 February 2021. It used a rocket powered descent stage and sky crane to slow the descent and lower it to the surface, similar to the Curiosity rover's descent stage. Perseverance also carried and deployed a mini helicopter, Ingenuity, which is the first powered aircraft to fly on another planet. Perseverance is an evolution of the Curiosity rover, with upgrades to make it more robust and a new instruments package. One of Perseverance's missions is to collect rock samples for return to Earth for future study.

PHOTO: https://photojournal.jpl.nasa.gov/jpeg/PIA23764.jpg
Public domain

ISBN 978-1-98-856693-1

Second Edition 2022

Published by BIOZONE International Ltd

Third printing
Printed by BR Printers

Acknowledgements:

BIOZONE wishes to thank and acknowledge the team for their efforts and contributions to the production of this title.

Purchases of this book may be made direct from the publisher:

BIOZONE Corporation
USA and Canada
FREE phone: 1-855-246-4555
FREE fax: 1-855-935-3555
Email: sales@biozone.com
Web: www.biozone.com/us

Contents

CODING: Activity is marked: ☐ to be done ☑ when completed ● Practical investigation

Contents

CODING: **Activity** is marked: ☐ to be done ☑ when completed ● Practical investigation

Using This Book

Each chapter begins with a broad **anchoring phenomenon**. This is something you may have seen, heard about, or experienced but may not necessarily be able to explain. Activities make up most of this book. As you work through the activities in each chapter, you will build a deeper understanding of scientific concepts. You can then test your understanding in the Summing Up activity at the end of the chapter.

Structure of a chapter

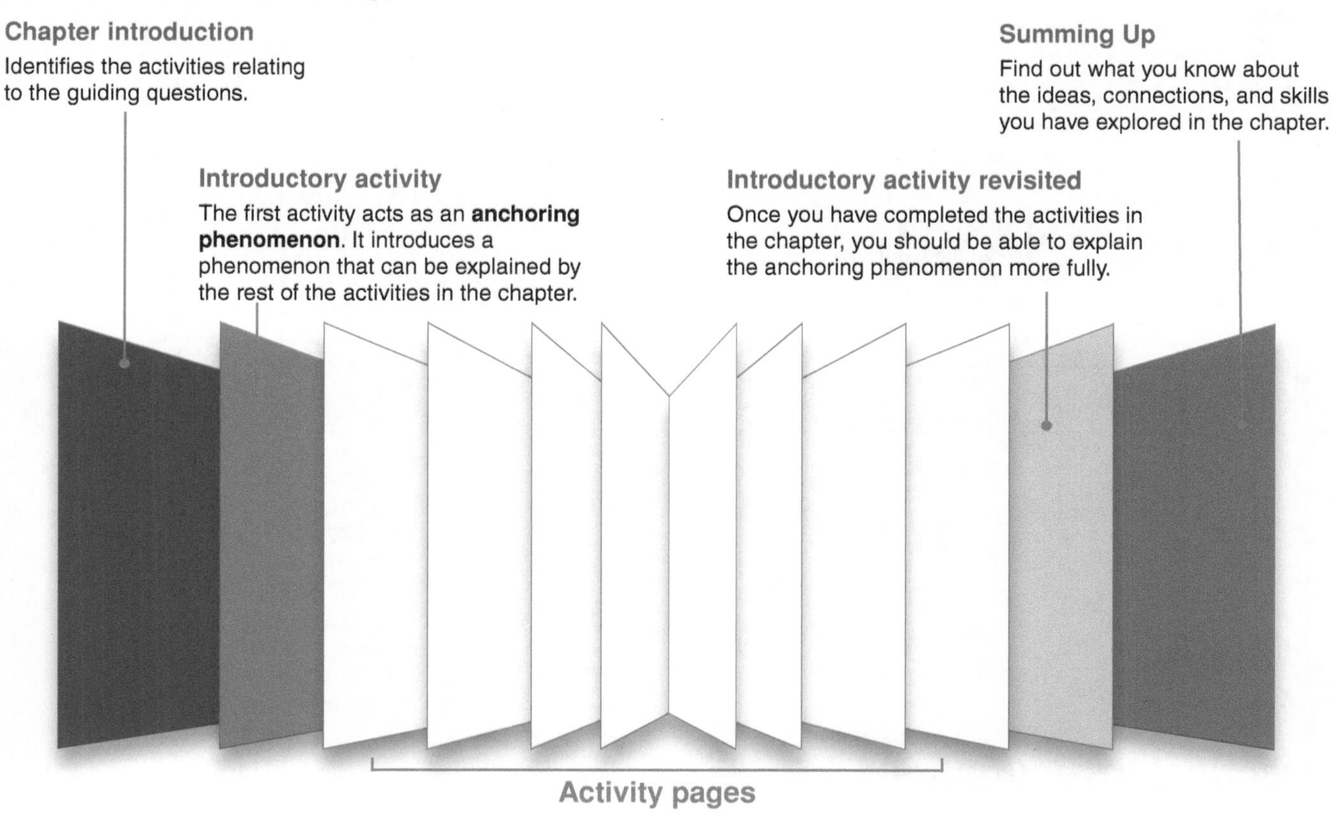

Chapter Introductions

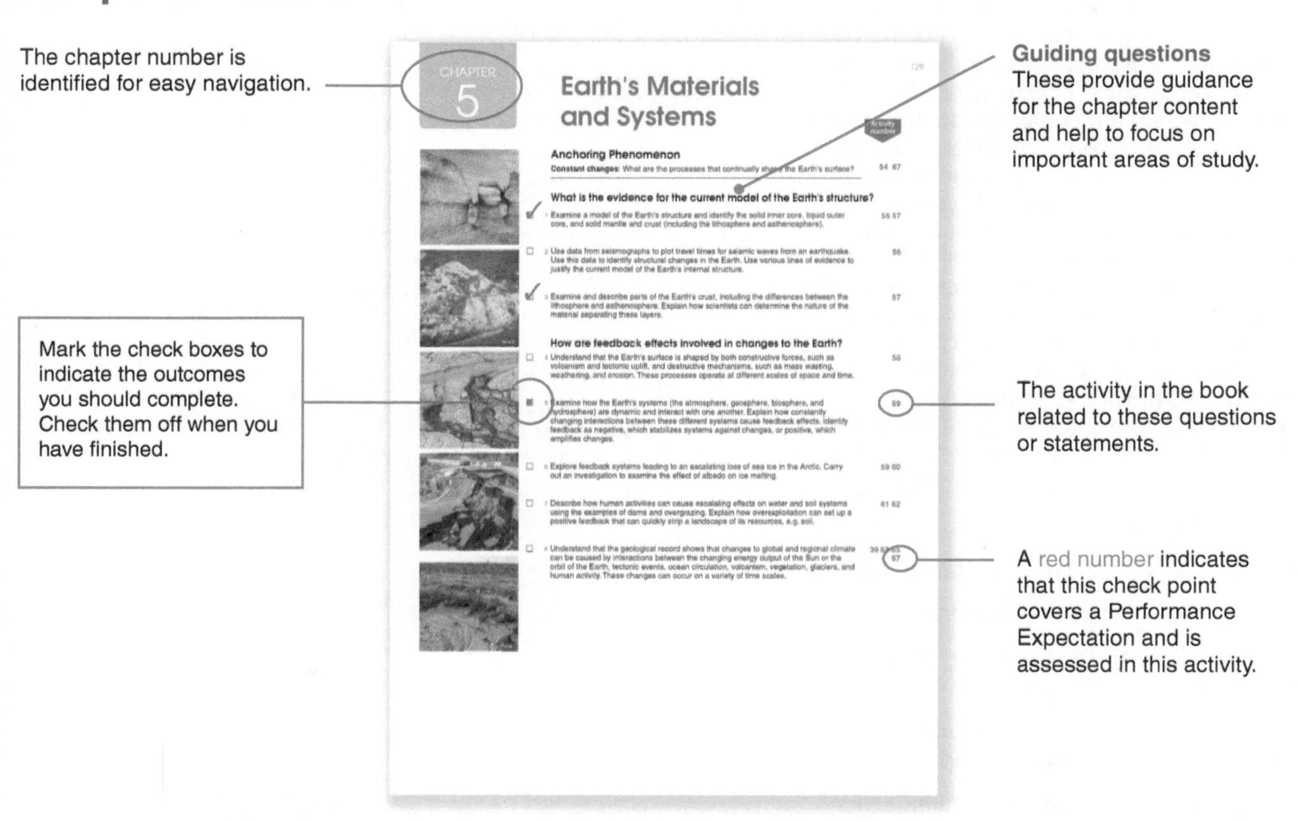

Glossary Terms

Building communication skills and scientific literacy is an important feature of any science course. By speaking with, listening to your peers and teachers, and writing answers, you naturally practice and develop communication skills. To help develop **scientific literacy**, we have included a **glossary** at the back of this worktext (pages 316-322). The glossary provides a definition in English and also in Spanish. Refer to the glossary to help you understand the meaning of a key term. It is easy to see which key terms are in the glossary, the terms have been **bolded** within an activity (see below). Note: key terms are only bolded the first time they appear within an activity.

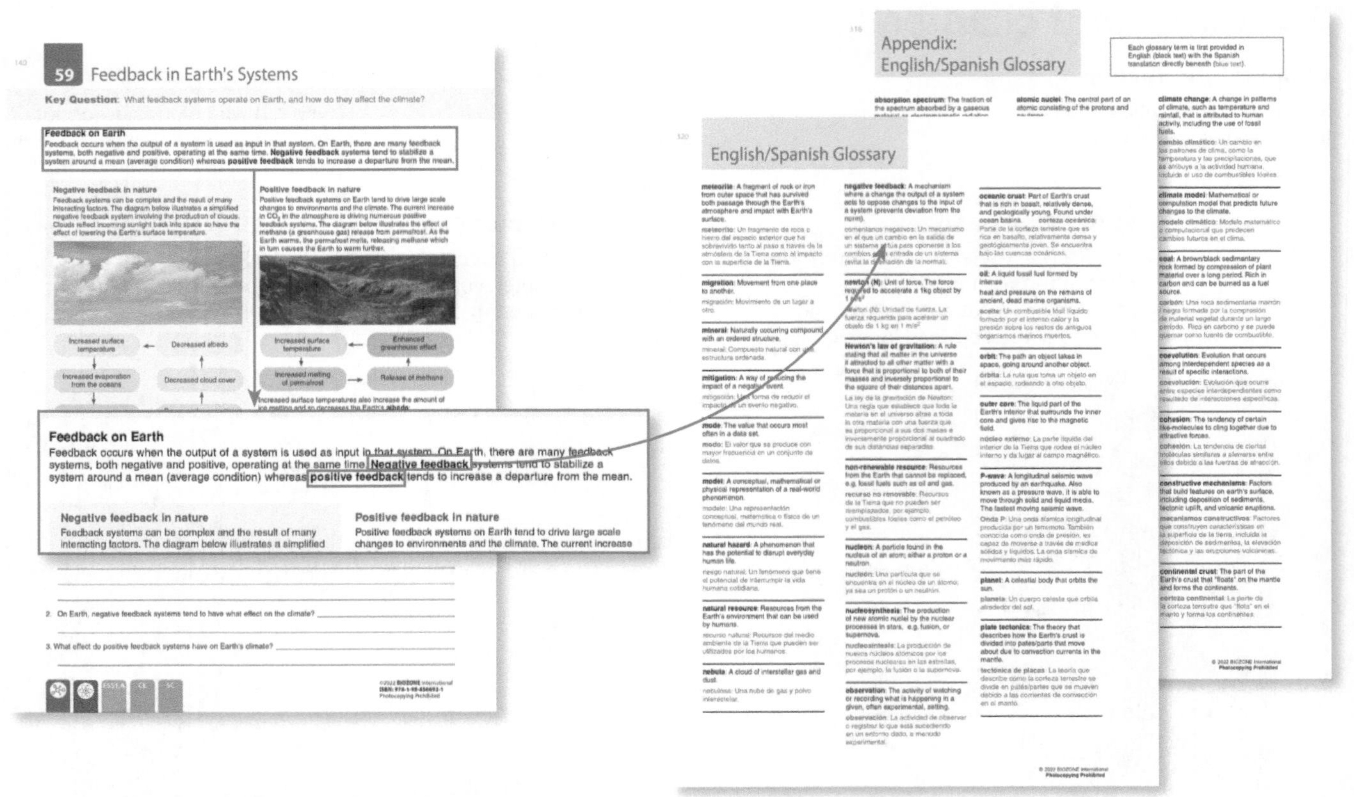

Practical Investigations

An important part of Earth and Space Sciences involves carrying out investigations and carefully observing and recording what occurs during them. Throughout the book, you will notice green investigation panels (like the one shown right). Each investigation has been designed using simple equipment found around the home or in most high school laboratories. The investigations provide opportunities for you to investigate phenomena for yourself. The investigations have different purposes depending on where they occur within the chapter. Some provide stimulus material or ask questions to encourage you to think about a particular phenomenon before you study it in detail. Others build on work you have already carried out and provide a more complex scenario for you to explain. Equipment lists are provided as an appendix at the back of the book. The investigations will help you develop:

- Skills in observation
- Skills in critical analysis and problem solving
- Skills in mathematics and numeracy
- Skills in collecting and analyzing data and maintaining accurate records
- Skills in working independently and collaboratively as part of a group
- Skills in communicating and contributing to group discussions

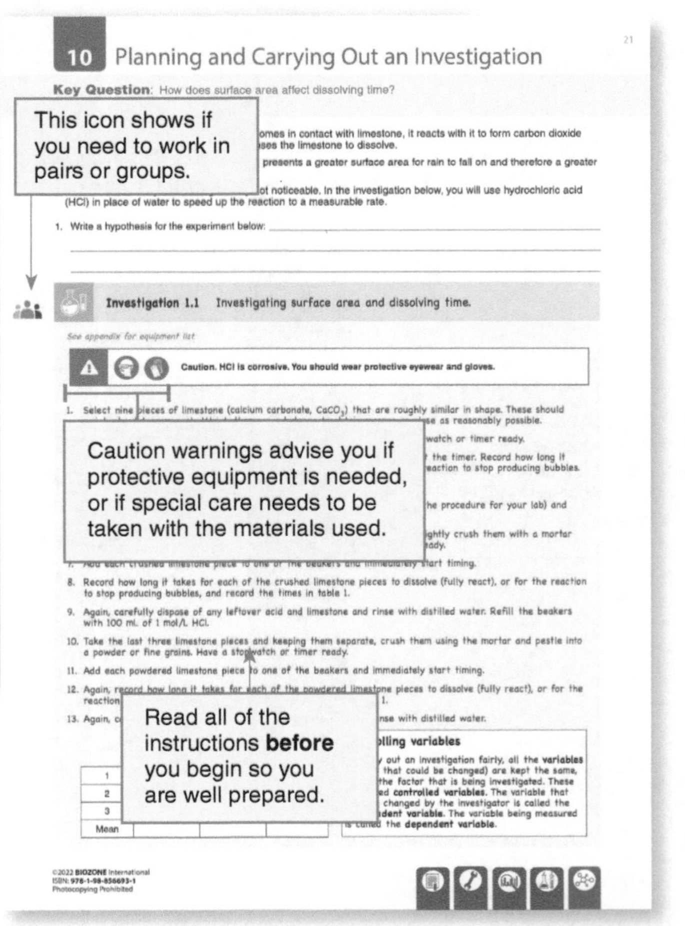

Using the Tab System

The tab system is a useful way to quickly identify the Disciplinary Core ideas, Crosscutting concepts, and Science and Engineering Practices embedded within each activity. The tabs also indicate whether or not the activity is supported online on BIOZONE's **Resource Hub**.

The gray hub tab indicates that the activity is supported online at the **BIOZONE RESOURCE HUB**. Online support may include videos, animations, games, simulations, articles, 3D models, and computer models.

The orange Disciplinary Core Idea (DCI) tabs indicate the core ideas that are covered in the activity. These are covered in the introduction to each chapter, under the guiding questions. The code itself is just a guide for your teacher.

The ETS icon indicates an engineering design DCI is included in the activity.

The **blue** Science and Engineering Practices tabs use picture codes to identify the Science and Engineering Practices (SEPs) relevant to the activity. You will use science and engineering practices in the course of completing the activities.

The green Crosscutting Concepts tabs indicate activities that share the same crosscutting concepts. You will become familiar with the concepts that connect all areas of science.

Science and Engineering Practices

Asking questions (for science) and defining problems (for engineering)

Asking scientific questions about observations or content in texts helps to define problems and draw valid conclusions.

Developing and using models

Models can be used to represent a system or a part of a system. Using models can help to visualize a structure, process, or design and understand how it works. Models can also be used to improve a design.

Planning and carrying out investigations

Planning and carrying out investigations is an important part of independent research. Investigations allow ideas and models to be tested and refined.

Analyzing and interpreting data

Once data is collected, it must be analyzed to reveal any patterns or relationships. Tables and graphs are just two of the many ways to display and analyze data for trends.

Using mathematics and computational thinking

Mathematics is a tool for understanding scientific data. Converting or transforming data helps to see relationships more easily while statistical analysis can help determine the significance of the results.

Constructing explanations (for science) and designing solutions (for engineering)

Constructing explanations for observations and phenomena is a dynamic process and may involve drawing on existing knowledge as well as generating new ideas.

Engaging in argument from evidence

Scientific argument based on evidence is how new ideas gain acceptance in science. Logical reasoning based on evidence is required when considering the merit of new claims or explanations of phenomena.

Obtaining, evaluating, and communicating information

Evaluating information for scientific accuracy or bias is important in determining its validity and reliability. Communicating information includes reports, graphics, oral presentation, and models.

Crosscutting Concepts

Patterns

We see patterns everywhere in science. These guide how we organize and classify events and organisms and prompt us to ask questions about the factors that create and influence them.

Cause and effect

A major part of science is investigating and explaining causal relationships. The mechanisms by which they occur can be tested in one context and used to explain and predict events in new contexts.

Scale, proportion, and quantity

Different things are relevant at different scales. Changes in scale, proportion, or quantity affect the structure or performance of a system.

Systems and system models

Making a model of a system, e.g. physical, mathematical, provides a way to understand and test ideas.

Energy and matter

Energy flows and matter cycles. Tracking these fluxes helps us understand how systems function.

Structure and function

The structure of a substance or object determines many of its properties and functions.

Stability and change

Science often deals with constructing explanations of how things change or how they remain stable.

Using BIOZONE's Resource Hub

- BIOZONE's Resource Hub provides links to online content that supports the activities in the book. From this page, you can also check for any corrections or clarifications to the book since printing.
- The Resource Hub provides a range of different resources to help explain or support the activity in the worktext. They provide great support to help your understanding of a topic.

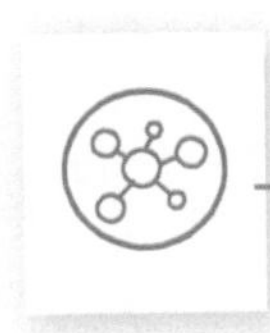

www.BIOZONEhub.com

Then enter the code in the text field **NES2-6931**

Or scan this QR code

Earth and Space Sciences for NGSS

BIOZONE's Resource Hub provides links to online content that supports the activities in the book. From this page, you can also check for any errata or clarifications to the book or model answers since printing.

The external websites are, for the most part, narrowly focused animations and video clips directly relevant to some aspect of the activity on which they are cited. They provide great support to help your understanding.

Chapter number and title

Chapter 1 - Science Practices

- 1. The Nature of Science
- 2. Systems and Models
- 3. Mathematics and Computation
- 4. Useful Concepts in Earth and Space Science
- 5. Observations and Assumptions
- 6. Tables and Graphs
- 7. Correlation vs Causation
- 8. Analyzing and Interpreting Data
- 9. Descriptive Statistics and the Spread of Data
- 10. Planning and Carrying out an Investigation

Click on an activity title to go directly to the resources available for that activity.

View resources →

BIOZONE

Using BIOZONE's Resource Hub

BIOZONE's Resource Hub provides links to online content that supports the activities in the book. From this page, you can also check for any errata or clarifications to the book or model answers since printing.

The external websites are, for the most part, narrowly focused animations and video clips directly relevant to some aspect of the activity on which they are cited. They provide great support to help your understanding.

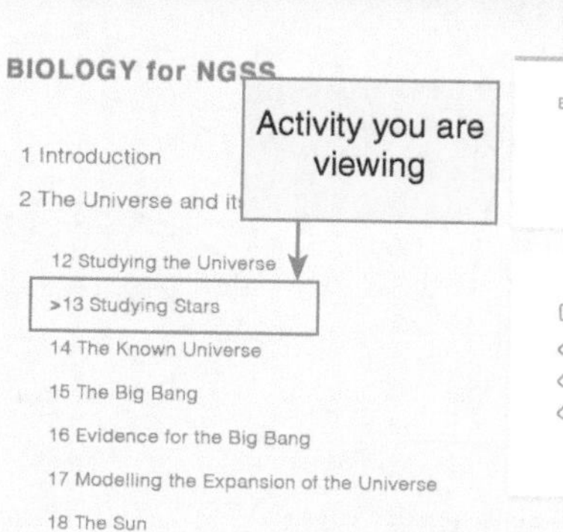

Activity

Activity you are viewing

BIOLOGY for NGSS

1 Introduction
2 The Universe and its Stars
12 Studying the Universe
>13 Studying Stars
14 The Known Universe
15 The Big Bang
16 Evidence for the Big Bang
17 Modelling the Expansion of the Universe
18 The Sun
19 Life Cycles of Stars
20 Interpreting Hertzsprung-Russell Diagrams
21 Red Giants
22 Supernovae

BIOZONE Resource Hub / The Universe and its Stars / Studying Stars

13 Studying Stars

- Black body radiation
- Emission and absorption spectra
- Absorption spectrum of stars
- How many stars are there?

Resources available for this activity. Hyperlink to an external website. Resources are tagged if they are teacher-only or specifically for gifted students.

The Resource Hub icons

Games

Simulations

Weblinks

Slideshow

3D Models

PDF

Spreadsheet

Video

Reference

Explore videos

Explore spreadsheet modeling

BIOZONE Modeling changes to the carbon cycle

© 2019 BIOZONE International Ltd

Explore web based resources

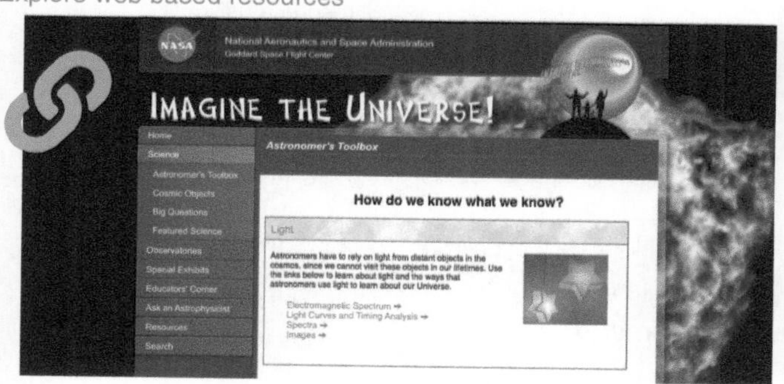

Explore 3D models

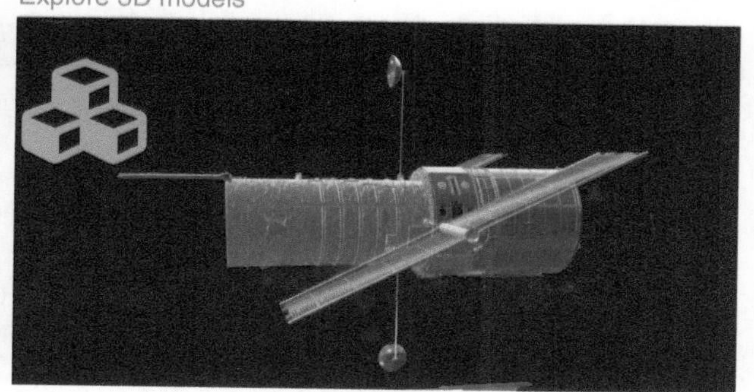

Earth and Space Sciences: A Flow of Ideas

This map shows the structure of the NGSS Earth and Space Sciences program, as represented in this worktext. The dark blue boxes indicate the book sections, each of which has its own concept map. The blue ovals are the chapters in each section. We have placed some major connections between topics. You can make more of your own.

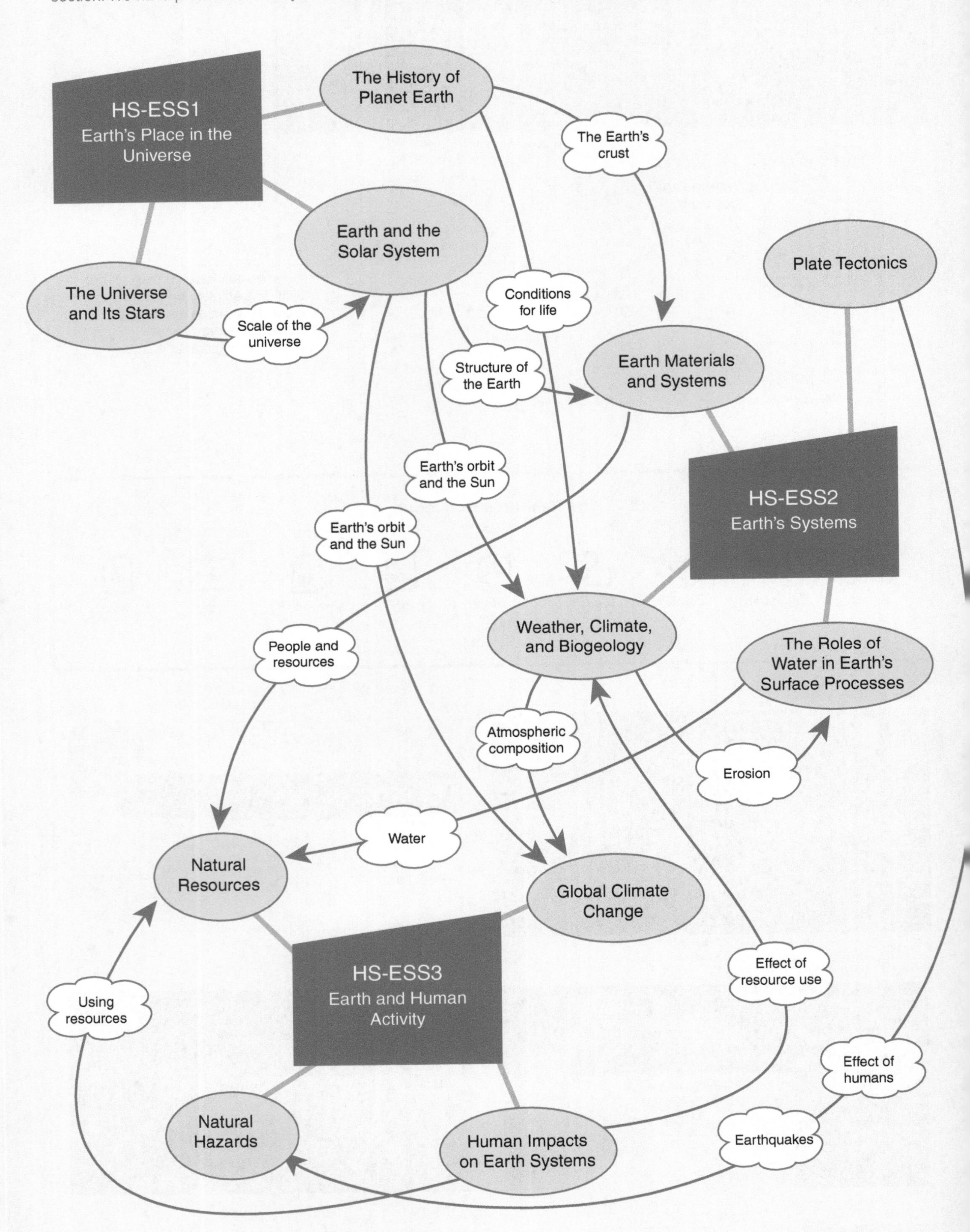

CHAPTER 1

Science Practices

Activity number

Science and engineering practices

Background in activities noted. Covered in following chapters in context.

Asking questions and defining problems

		Statement	Activity number
☐	1	Demonstrate an understanding of science as inquiry. Appreciate that unexpected results may lead to new questions and new discoveries.	1
☐	2	Formulate and evaluate questions that you can feasibly investigate.	5

Developing and using models

		Statement	Activity number
☐	3	Develop and use models, based on evidence, to describe systems or their components and how they work.	1 2 4

Planning and carrying out investigations

		Statement	Activity number
☐	4	Plan and conduct investigations to provide data to test a hypothesis based on observations. Identify any assumptions in the design of your investigation.	10
☐	5	Consider and evaluate the accuracy and precision of the data that you collect.	9 10
☐	6	Use appropriate tools to collect and record data. Data may be quantitative (continuous or discontinuous), qualitative, or ranked.	10
☐	7	Variables are factors that can change or be changed in an experiment. Make and test hypotheses about the effect on a dependent variable when an independent variable is manipulated. Understand and use controls appropriately.	10

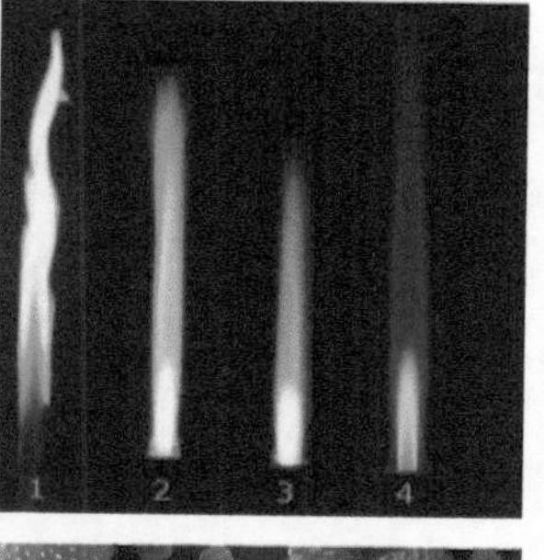

Analyzing and interpreting data

		Statement	Activity number
☐	8	Use appropriate graphs to visualize data and identify trends.	8 10
☐	9	Summarize data and describe its features using descriptive statistics.	9 10
☐	10	Apply concepts of statistics and probability to answer questions and solve problems.	9 10

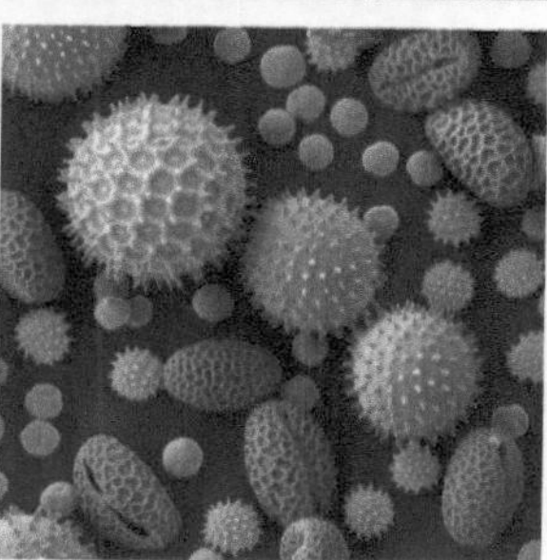

Using mathematics and computational thinking

		Statement	Activity number
☐	11	Demonstrate an ability to use mathematics and computational tools to analyze, represent, and model data. Recognize and use appropriate units in calculations.	3 4 6
☐	12	Demonstrate an ability to apply ratios, rates, percentages, and unit conversions.	3 4

Constructing explanations and designing solutions

		Statement	Activity number
☐	13	Explain results based on evidence and application of scientific ideas and principles.	8 10

Engaging in argument from evidence

		Statement	Activity number
☐	14	Use evidence to defend and evaluate claims and explanations about science.	8

Obtaining, evaluating, and communicating information

		Statement	Activity number
☐	15	Evaluate the validity and reliability of designs, methods, claims, and evidence.	10

1 The Nature of Science

Key Question: How does science help us explore and understand the underlying principles of natural phenomena?

- Science is a way of understanding the universe we live in: where it came from, the rules it obeys and how it changes over time. Science distinguishes itself from other ways of understanding the universe by using empirical standards, logical arguments, and skeptical review. What we understand about the universe changes over time, as the body of knowledge increases.
- Science is a human endeavor and requires creativity and imagination. New research and ways of thinking can be based on the well argued idea of a single person.
- Science influences, and is influenced by, society and technology. As society's beliefs and desires change, what is or can be researched is also affected. As technology advances, what is or can be researched changes. Scientific discoveries advance technology and can change society's beliefs.
- Science can never answer questions about the universe with absolute certainty. It can be confident of certain outcomes, but only within the limits of the data. Science might help us predict with 99.9% certainty that a system will behave in a certain way, but that still means there's one chance in a thousand it won't.

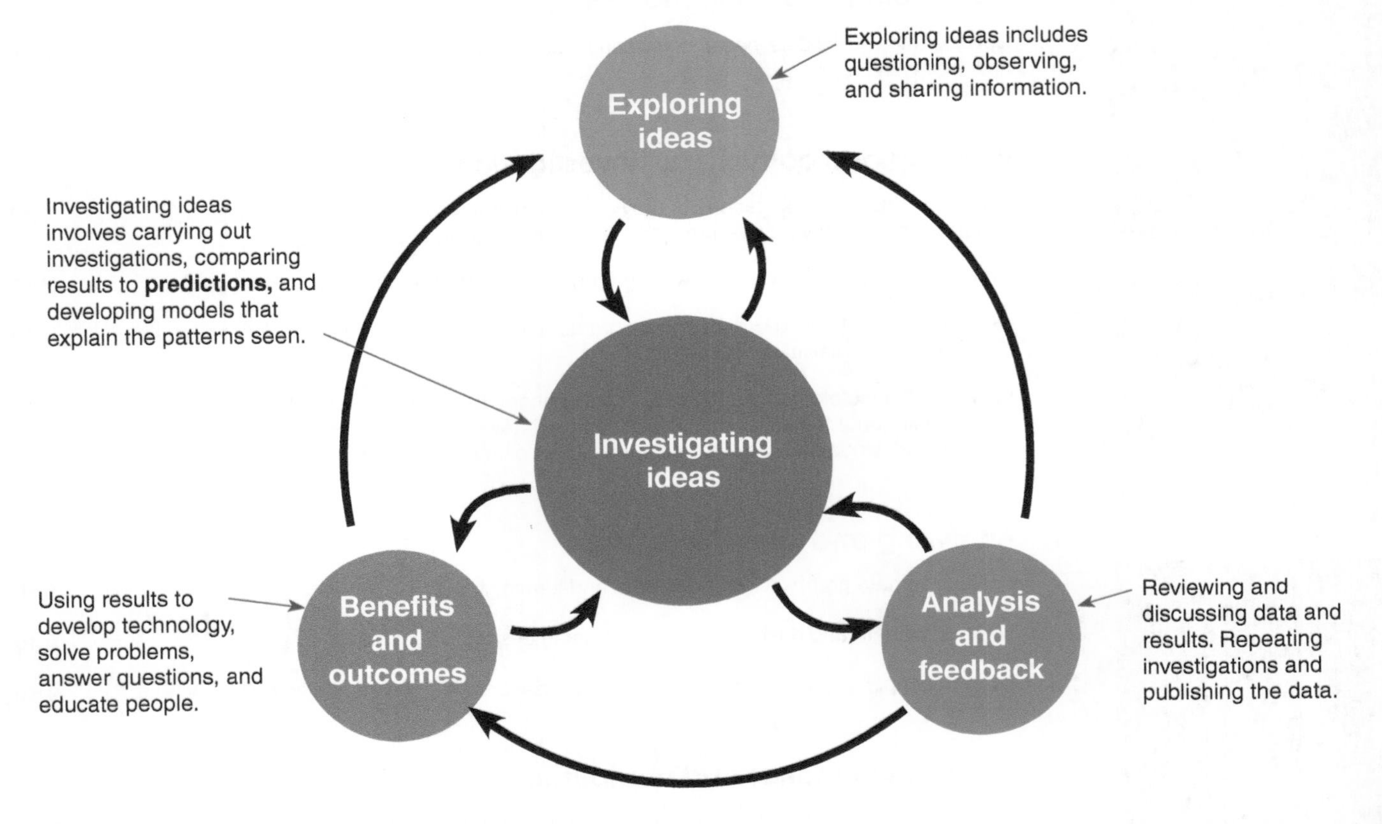

Science is a way of exploring the world

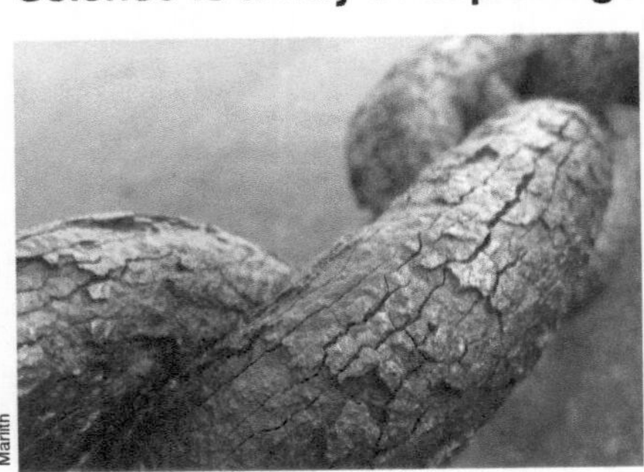

Observing
Observations cause questions: iron appears to lose mass when rusting (rusted objects are crumbly and worn). Where does the mass go?

Carrying out investigations
Investigations seek to answer a question, or part of it. An iron object kept in a container can be weighed before and after rusting. Mass is gained during rusting.

Interpreting results and exploring further
How does the result change our understanding of iron and rusting? Why is it apparently different from what we think we see? What process is occurring here?

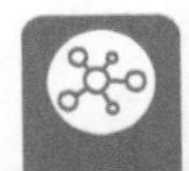

SSM

ISBN: 978-1-98-856693-1

Gravity and orbiting objects - the nature of science

Science and apparently everyday observation often come into conflict.

Knowledge was based on observation and experience. Ideas were not tested under controlled conditions.

Aristotle (Greece) (384–322 BC) taught that the Earth was the center of the universe, and that the Sun and planets orbited it. This seemed plainly obvious as it is what we see standing here on Earth.

Aristotle also expressed the idea that light objects, such as a feather, fall more slowly than heavy objects, such as a stone. It was accepted, until at least the 15th century, precisely because it appeared to match everyday observation.

Many ideas that were at odds with social and political beliefs were oppressed, often ruthlessly.

Around 1514, **Nicolaus Copernicus** (Poland) proposed that the Earth and planets orbited the Sun (heliocentric model). This was at odds with the geocentric (Earth centered) model supported by the Church.

In the 16th century, **Galileo** slowed down the motion of falling objects by using an inclined plane, and balls made of different materials and masses. He used a water clock to accurately measure the time it took for the balls to roll set distances. He found that the amount of time it took for the ball to roll down the entire length of the ramp was independent of its mass. This led him to believe that all objects fall at the same rate, no matter their mass.

The testing of ideas under controlled conditions allows the underlying principles to be discovered.

In 1610, **Galileo** (Italy) published his observations of the moons of Jupiter, arguing that the idea of everything orbiting the Earth was wrong because here were objects orbiting something else. His ideas were at odds with the Church and he spent the rest of his life under house arrest.

Importantly, **Galileo** explained his conclusion using mathematics. A physical law expressed as a mathematical equation allows for predictions that can then be tested experimentally.

As new ideas based on facts obtained by controlled experiment became more widely accepted, social and political ideas began to change.

Around the same time, **Johannes Kepler** (Germany) published his laws of planetary motion around the Sun, based on observational data collected by astronomer Tycho Brahe. In contrast to Galileo, his ideas were accepted relatively quickly.

As more information becomes available, phenomena that were once thought to be separate, e.g. falling objects and planetary orbits, can now be described under one over-arching principle, e.g. gravity.

In 1687, **Isaac Newton** (England) realized that falling bodies and orbiting planets were following the same principles, which he described in his laws of motion. Under Aristotle, different motions were explained by different causes. Under Newton, different motions were explained by the same causes. Falling objects fall because of the Earth's gravity pulling on them. Planets follow their orbital path because of the Sun's gravity pulling on them; they are continually falling towards the Sun, while also moving at 90° relative to the Sun.

New mathematics, knowledge, and inspiration can redefine whole areas of science and society. Einstein's theory of relativity was revolutionary and has stood up to every scientific test, including gravitational waves.

Observations of the orbits of planets, such as Mercury, didn't always match predictions based on Newton's law. In 1905, **Albert Einstein** (Germany) explained gravity as the curving of the fabric of space due to the mass of an object. Planets orbit a star because they are following the curve of space created by the enormous mass of the star.

1. Describe how science is a tool for understanding the universe: ______________________

2. Why can science not predict with absolute certainty how a system will behave? ______________________

3. New discoveries on other planets and moons, including Mars, the moons of Jupiter and Saturn, and exoplanets, suggest that the elements and conditions for life are more common than was believed, even just a decade ago. The chance of finding life, of some kind, somewhere other than Earth seems increasingly possible. As a group, discuss the social changes that might occur if life (even simple life) was found somewhere in the solar system other than Earth. What would this mean for us as humans, and as members of the population of the solar system?

ISBN: **978-1-98-856693-1**

2 Systems and Models

Key Question: What is the difference between a system and a model?

- **Systems** are groups of inter-related components working together by way of a driving force. A simple example of a system is our eight-planet solar system. Each of the planet's orbits represents a single component of the system. The driving force of the system is gravity from the Sun.
- Modeling systems helps us to understand how they work. A **model** is a representation of an object or system that shares important characteristics with the object or system being studied. A model does not necessarily have to incorporate all the characteristics or be fully accurate to be useful. It depends on the level of understanding required.

NASA

Modeling data

- Models are extremely important when trying to understand how a system operates. Models are useful for breaking complex systems down into manageable parts, and often only part of a system is modeled at a time. As understanding of the system progresses, more and more **data** can be built into the model so that it more closely represents the real world system or object.
- A common example is the use of models to represent atoms. The three illustrations below become more complex from left to right.

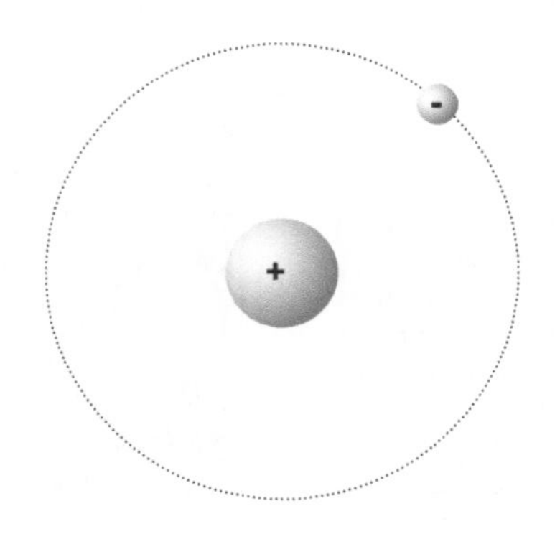
Rutherford's atomic model showing position of charge.

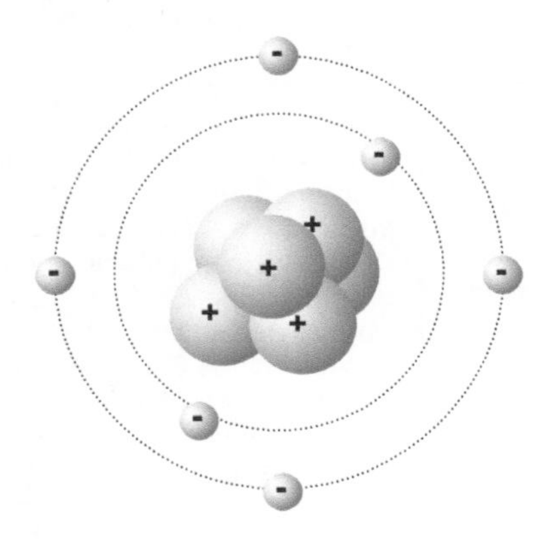
Bohr atomic model showing electron orbitals (2D).

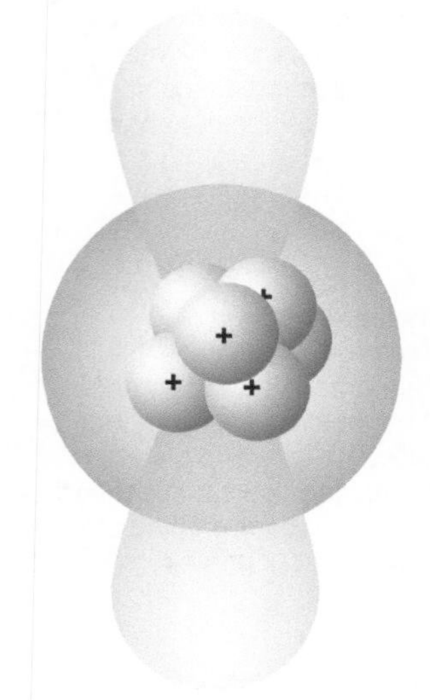
Atomic model using quantum mechanics to show 3D electron clouds.

Modeling the weather
Weather systems are modeled in order to predict future weather. A weather model has several parts to it where current weather data can be entered. Computers are used to run the model under different scenarios. The outcomes are used to predict the most likely weather pattern in the future.

Modeling the Earth's structure
The Earth's structure can be modeled using data from earthquakes, Earth's magnetic field, and volcanic activity. The Earth's magnetic field suggests an iron core surrounded by molten material. The bending of earthquake waves suggests a thin solid crust. Volcanic activity shows there is molten material below the crust.

Modeling the evolution of stars
Models of stellar evolution are based on visual **observation** of numerous stars, their luminosity, measured surface color, and mass. Models of nuclear fusion are added to this data. Based on these observations, we can predict how a star of a certain mass will behave and develop, over millions to billions of years.

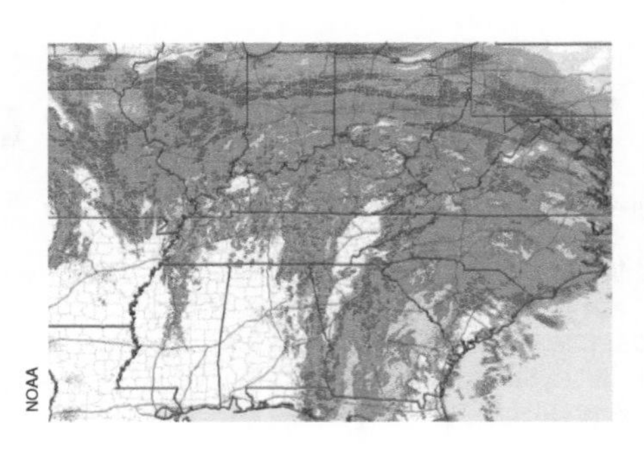
NOAA

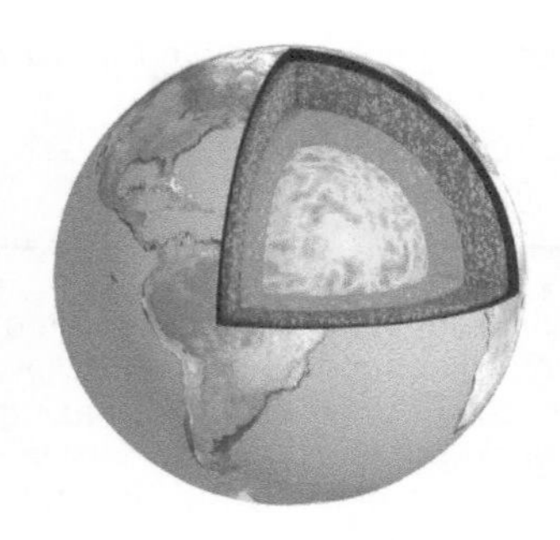

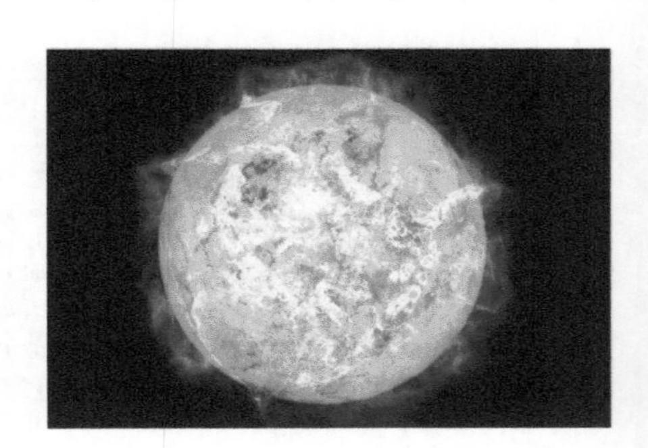

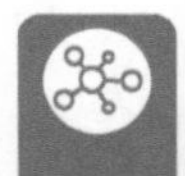

SSM

ISBN: **978-1-98-856693-1**

Closed, open, and isolated systems

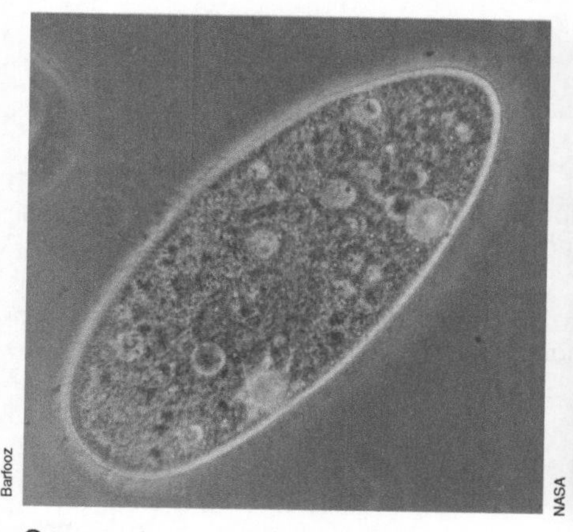

Open systems are able to exchange matter, energy, and information with their surroundings. This causes them to be constantly changing, although the overall processes and outcomes remain relatively constant. Open systems are the most common type in natural systems. Examples include ecosystems, living organisms, and the ocean.

Closed systems exchange energy with their surroundings, but not matter. Closed systems are uncommon on Earth, although the cycling of certain materials, such as water and nitrogen, approximates them. The Earth itself is essentially a closed system. It receives energy from the Sun but exchanges virtually no matter with the universe, apart from the occasional meteorite.

Isolated systems exchange no energy, information, or matter with their surroundings. No such systems are known to exist, except possibly the entire universe. Some natural systems approximate isolated systems, at least for certain lengths of time. The solar system is essentially isolated, as is the Milky Way galaxy, if gravity from nearby stars or galaxies is ignored.

1. (a) What is a system? ____________________

   (b) What is a model? ____________________

   (c) Explain why models are never 100% accurate representations of the system being studied: ____________________

   (d) Discuss the advantages and disadvantages of using models to explain a system: ____________________

   (e) Why is it easier to use a series of simple models, rather than a single, complex one, to explain a complex system?

   ____

2. Identify each of the following as either an open, closed, or isolated system:

   (a) Reef ecosystem: ____________________

   (b) Nitrogen cycle: ____________________

   (c) Earth: ____________________

   (d) Biosphere: ____________________

   (e) Solar system: ____________________

   (f) Digestive system: ____________________

   (g) A national park: ____________________

   (h) A large lake: ____________________

ISBN: **978-1-98-856693-1**

3 Mathematics and Computation

Key Question: How and why do we use standard mathematical notation, and why is it important to be familiar with these?

- Mathematics is used in Earth and space sciences to analyze, interpret, and compare **data**. It is important that you are familiar with mathematical notation (the language of mathematics) and can confidently apply some basic mathematical principles and calculations to your data.
- Much of our understanding of Earth and space sciences is based on our ability to use mathematics to interpret the patterns seen in collected data, and express the laws of the universe in simple notation.

Commonly used mathematical symbols

- In mathematics, universal symbols are used to represent mathematical concepts. They save time and space when writing. Some commonly used symbols are shown below:

= Equal to

$<$ The value on the left is **less than** the value on the right

$>$ The value on the left is **greater than** the value on the right

$\propto$ Proportional to. $A \propto B$ means that A = a constant × B

~ Approximately equal to

∞ Infinity

$\sqrt{b}$ The square root of b

b^2 b squared (b × b)

b^n b to the power of n (b × b... n times)

Δ The change in. For example $\Delta T / \Delta d$ = the change in T ÷ the change in d (see rates, below right).

Length

Kilometer (km) 1000 m

Meter (m) 1000 mm

Volume

Liter (L) 1000 mL

Milliliter (mL) = 1 mm^3

Area

Square kilometer 1,000,000 m^2

Hectare 10,000 m^2

Square meter 1,000,000 mm^2

Temperature

0°C = freezing point of pure water

100°C = boiling point of pure water

Kelvin scale (K) and °C have the same magnitude. Kelvin scale starts at absolute zero (–273.15 °C).

Decimal and standard form

- Decimal form (also called ordinary form) is the longhand way of writing a number, e.g. 15,000,000. Very large or very small numbers can take up too much space if written in decimal form and are often expressed in a condensed standard form. For example, 15,000,000 is written as 1.5×10^7 in standard form.
- In standard form, a number is always written as $A \times 10^n$, where A is a number between 1 and 10, and n (the exponent) indicates how many places to move the decimal point. n can be positive or negative.
- For the example above, A = 1.5 and n = 7 because the decimal point moved seven places (see below).

$$15\,000\,000 = 1.5 \times 10^7$$

- Small numbers can also be written in standard form. The exponent (n) will be negative. For example, 0.00101 is written as 1.01×10^{-3}.

$$0.00101 = 1.01 \times 10^{-3}$$

Adding numbers in standard form

- Numbers in standard form can be added together so long as they are both raised to the same power of ten. E.g. $1 \times 10^4 + 2 \times 10^3 = 1 \times 10^4 + 0.2 \times 10^4 = 1.2 \times 10^4$

Rates

- **Rates** are expressed as a measure per unit of time and show how a **variable** changes over time. Rates are used to provide meaningful comparisons of data that may have been recorded over different time periods.
- Often, rates are expressed as a mean rate over the duration of the measurement period, but it is also useful to calculate the rate at various times to understand how rate changes over time. The table below shows the distance traveled by a rolling ball. A worked example for the rate at 4 seconds is provided below.

Time (s)	Distance traveled (m)	Rate of movement (speed) (m/s)
0	0	0
2	34	17
4	42	4*
6	48	3
8	50	1
10	50	0

* meters moved between 2 - 4 seconds: 42 m – 34 m = 8 m

Rate of movement (speed) between 2 - 4 seconds
8 m ÷ 2 seconds = 4 m/s

1. Use the information above to complete the following calculations:

(a) $\sqrt{9}$: ______________________

(b) 4^3: ______________________

(c) Write 6,340,000 in standard form: ______________________

(d) Write 0.00103 in standard form: ______________________

(e) Convert 10 cm to millimeters: ______________________

(f) Convert 4 liters to milliliters: ______________________

(g) Write 7.82×10^7 as a number: ______________________

(h) $4.5 \times 10^4 + 6.45 \times 10^5$: ______________________

ISBN: 978-1-98-856693-1

Dealing with large numbers

- Earth and space sciences often deal with very large numbers or scales. Numerical **data**, indicating scale, can often increase or decrease exponentially. Large scale changes in numerical data can be made more manageable by transforming the data using logarithms.

Exponential function

- Exponential growth or decay occurs at an increasingly rapid rate in proportion to the increasing or decreasing total number or size.
- In an exponential function, the base number is fixed (constant) and the exponent is variable.
- The equation for an exponential function is $y = c^x$ (where c = constant).
- An example of exponential decay is radioactive decay. Any radioactive element has a half-life, the amount of time required for its radioactivity to fall to half its original value.
- Here, the amount of radioactivity (y) is dependent on a constant (c) to the power of the time passed (x).

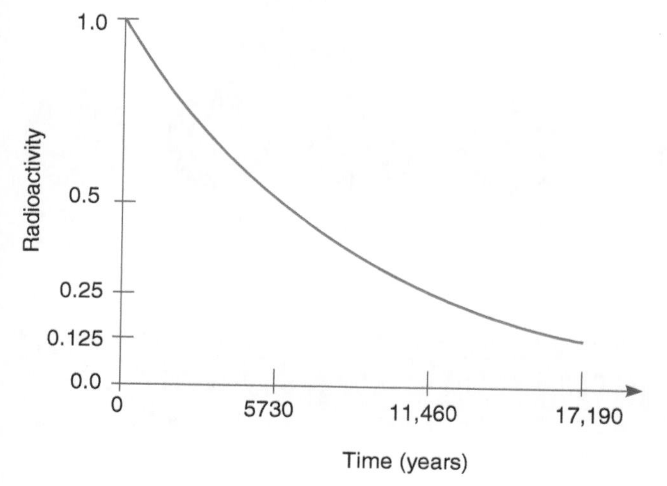

Example above: Carbon-14 (^{14}C) has a half life of 5730 years. If a sample with a mass of 10 g was left for 5730 years half the sample will have decayed, leaving 5 g of radioactive material. After another 5730 years, 2.5 g of radioactive carbon will be left.

Log transformations

- A log transformation can make very large numbers easier to work with.
- The log of a number is the exponent to which a fixed value (the base) is raised to get that number. So $\log_{10}(1000) = 3$ because $10^3 = 1000$.
- Both $\log_{10}$ and $\log_e$ (natural logs or *ln*) are commonly used.
- Log transformations are useful for data where there is an exponential increase or decrease in numbers. In this case, the transformation will produce a straight line plot.
- To find the log10 of a number, e.g. 32, using a calculator, key in log 32 = The answer should be 1.51.
- An example of a log scale is the Moment Magnitude scale used to measure the energy released during earthquakes. Each step of the scale is approximately $10^{1.5}$ times greater than the step below it. Calculating the difference in energy released between earthquakes can be done by finding the inverse $\log_{10}$ of the difference in magnitude ($10^{(1.5 \times (m1-m2))}$).
- Also, the number of earthquakes around the world at each magnitude follows a negative logarithmic spread (below).

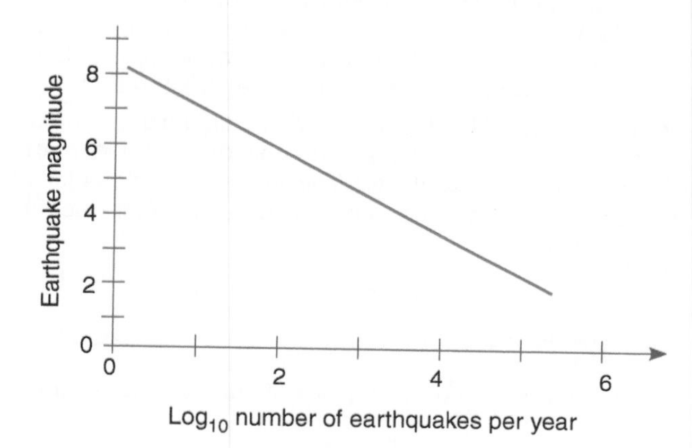

2. The Moment Magnitude scale is a measure of the energy released during an earthquake.

   (a) How many times more energy is released by the magnitude 6 earthquake than a magnitude 4 earthquake?

   (b) How many times more energy is released by the magnitude 7.5 earthquake than a magnitude 4.3 earthquake?

3. The pH scale measures the acidity of a substance. It is a negative logarithmic scale. A pH of 3 has a hydrogen ion concentration (which is responsible for acidity) ten times greater than a pH of 4.

   How many times greater is the hydrogen ion concentration of a pH 2 solution than a pH 6 solution?

4. Carbon-14 (^{14}C) is found in living organisms. It has a half life of 5730 years. When an organism dies, it stops taking in ^{14}C and the ratio of ^{14}C to ^{12}C changes.
   Using these pieces of information, explain how we can calculate how long ago an organism died:

ISBN: **978-1-98-856693-1**

4 Useful Concepts in Earth and Space Science

Key Question: What useful concepts can help explain how certain systems behave?

Energy

- Energy is the ability of a system to do work. It may be transferred between systems and transformed into different forms, but it cannot be created or destroyed. The amount of energy in a closed system is the same before and after a transformation. Energy is measured in joules (J).
- Energy can be classified as potential (stored) or kinetic (movement) (right).
- Energy can be transformed. For example, a ball at the top of a hill has gravitational potential energy. As it rolls down the hill, the ball loses gravitational potential energy and gains kinetic energy. Some of the energy is also lost as heat and sound as it rolls down the hill.

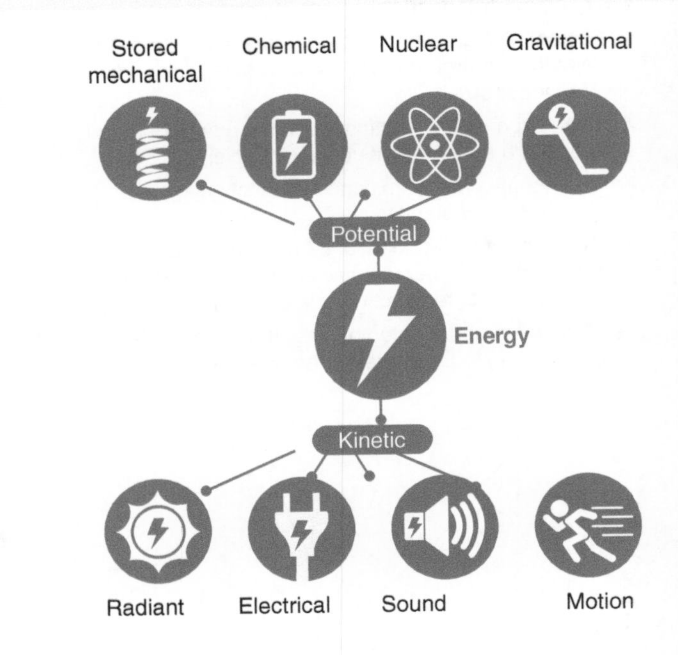

Light

- Visible light is part of the spectrum of electromagnetic radiation. Visible light is defined as the part of the electromagnetic spectrum with a wavelength between 400 and 700 nanometers. Light waves near 400 nm appear blue, while light at 700 nm appears red. Light travels in a vacuum at around 299,792,458 m/s.
- The speed of light is sometimes called the universal speed limit. Nothing that we know of can travel at or above the speed of light. This speed limit stops logical paradoxes occurring, e.g. arriving somewhere before your image.

Short = blue
Long = red
400 nm
700 nm

1. What is energy? ____________________

2. What are the two main types of energy? Give examples of each:

   (a) ____________________

   (b) ____________________

3. Energy cannot be created or destroyed, but only transformed. Explain this statement: ____________________

4. What kind of energy is light? ____________________

5. (a) What is the wavelength of blue light? ____________________

   (b) What is the wavelength of red light? ____________________

6. Why is the universal speed limit of the speed of light important in our understanding of the universe?

ISBN: **978-1-98-856693-1**

Temperature

- Temperature is a measure of the energy of an object. Molecules constantly vibrate (kinetic energy) and temperature is a measure of these vibrations. The faster and larger the vibrations, the higher the object's temperature. Temperature rises as heat is added to a system, and lowers when heat is removed.
- There are many temperature scales used throughout the world, but the most common are the Celsius, Fahrenheit, and Kelvin scales. The Kelvin scale is commonly used in science although, because it uses the same magnitude of scale as the Celsius scale, Celsius is also commonly used.
- Temperature can be inferred from color. A heated piece of iron will initially glow red, then orange-yellow as it gets hotter, then white.

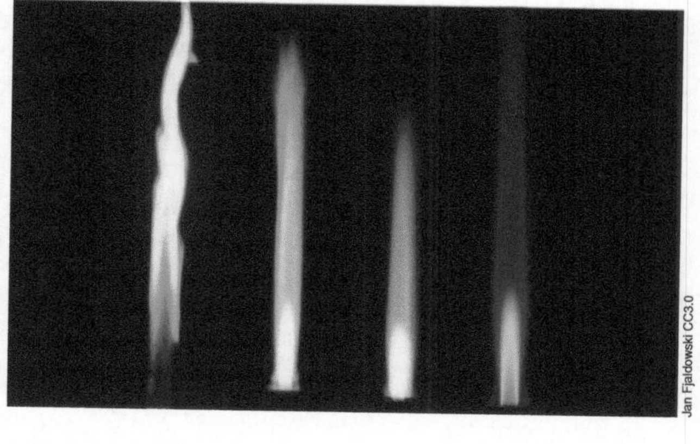
Jan Fjaldowski CC3.0

- In chemistry, the color of a Bunsen flame gives an indication of temperature. A yellow (or safety) flame is the coolest, at 300°C. With increasing oxygen supply, a hotter, blue flame is produced, with a temperature of ~1500°C (right). A blue-colored flame indicates that there is no soot (uncombusted material) in the flame.

Pressure

- Pressure is an important concept in Earth and space science. Pressure is a measure of the force being applied per unit surface area. The pressure of the air pressing on the surface of the Earth is 101.3 Pa (pascals). Pressure is important in the formation of rocks, the weather, and stars. Pressure and temperature are related by Gay-Lussac's Law, formulated in 1809, which states P (pressure) $\propto$ T (temperature) for a given mass and volume of gas.

Low temperature - slow movement of gas particles

High temperature - fast movement of gas particles

7. What is temperature measuring? ______________________________

____

____

8. Explain how heated metal's temperature can be inferred from its color: ______________________________

____

____

____

____

9. What is pressure?______________________________

____

10. (a) Explain why the pressure in a sealed container of gas increases when heat is added to the system: ______________________________

____

____

____

____

(b) Explain why the pressure in a sealed container of gas decreases when the system is cooled: ______________________________

____

____

____

ISBN: **978-1-98-856693-1**

Density

- The density of a substance is the relationship between the mass of the substance and how much space it takes up (volume). In other words, density is the amount of matter contained in a particular volume. An element such as lead is extremely dense because its particles are very close together.
- Density can be used to identify pure substances, and to determine the composition of mixed substances.
- Water and oil provide an easy example of observing differences in density (right). An object's relative density to water will determine whether it floats or sinks. Oil has a lower density than water so it floats above the water. An object with a higher density will sink. In glass A, to the right, the density of the water is greater than that of the cork, but less than that of the metal.

Distance

The units used to measure distance depend greatly on the distance being measured. The distances between objects in space are vast and so units of measure are used that make working with these distances simpler.

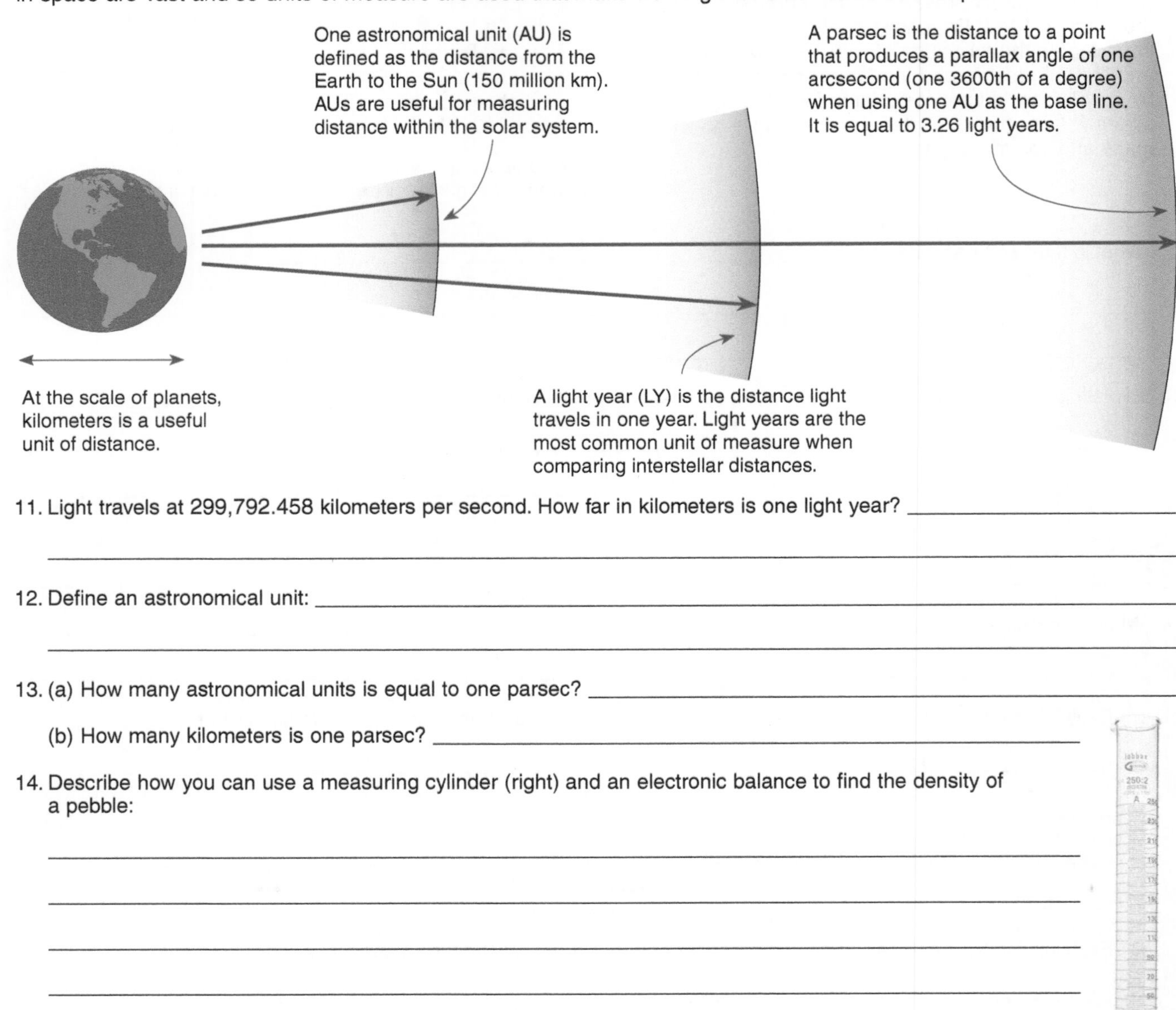

11. Light travels at 299,792.458 kilometers per second. How far in kilometers is one light year? ____________________

____

12. Define an astronomical unit: ____________________

____

13. (a) How many astronomical units is equal to one parsec? ____________________

(b) How many kilometers is one parsec? ____________________

14. Describe how you can use a measuring cylinder (right) and an electronic balance to find the density of a pebble:

____

____

____

____

15. What is the density of an object with a mass of 12 grams and a volume of 22mL? ____________________

____

ISBN: **978-1-98-856693-1**

Inverse square law

The inverse square law describes how the intensity of an effect varies with distance. Specifically, the intensity of an effect, e.g. light, changes in inverse proportion to the square of the distance from the source. To put it simply, the further the distance between two objects, the less intense the effect (see diagram below).

A number of physical properties reduce in magnitude as they become more distant in a way that can be represented by an inverse square law. These include:

- Gravity
- Electric field
- Light intensity
- Radiation
- Sound intensity

The inverse-square law can be written as:

Intensity is proportional to: $\frac{1}{\text{distance squared } (d^2)}$

If the intensity at one distance is known, the intensity at a second distance can be calculated using the following equation:

$$\text{intensity}_1 \times \text{distance}_1^2 = \text{intensity}_2 \times \text{distance}_2^2$$

Where:

I_1 = Intensity 1 at D_1
I_2 = Intensity 2 at D_2
D_1 = Distance 1 from source
D_2 = Distance 2 from source

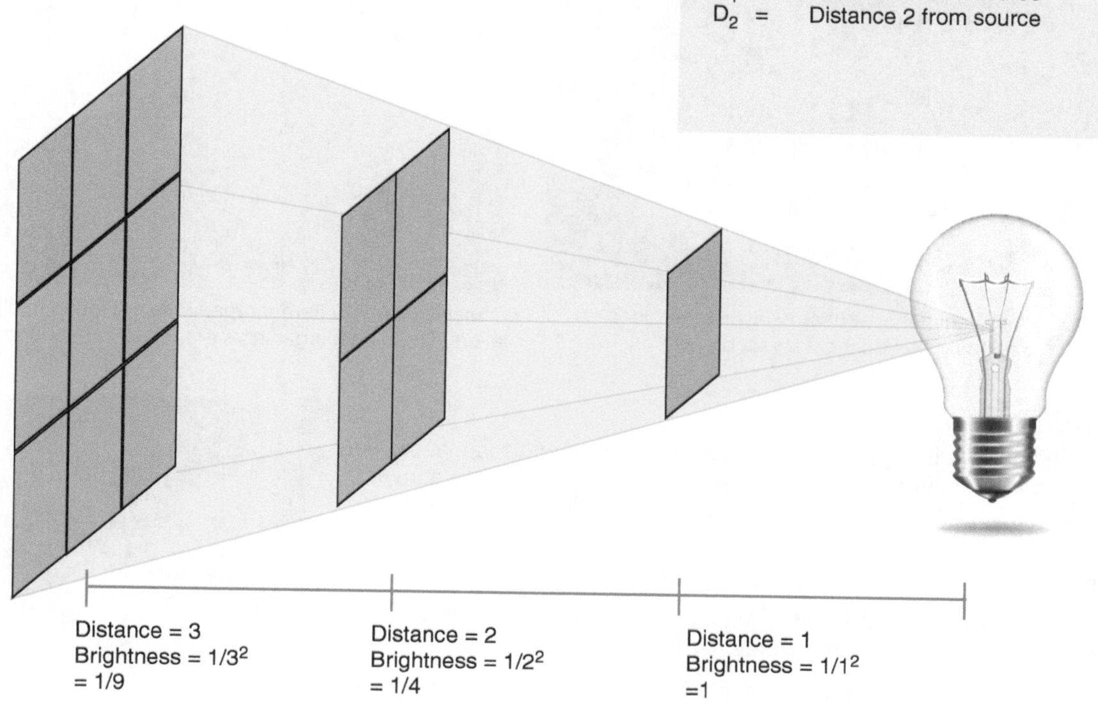

16. (a) For simplicity, the acceleration due to gravity produced by the mass of Sun at the radius of the Earth's orbit (1 AU) has a value of 1 (ignoring any units). Using the inverse square law, what would be the value of the of the acceleration of gravity at the radius of the orbit of Jupiter, at approximately 5 AU? Show your working:

(b) The acceleration due to gravity at the photosphere of the Sun (6.96×10^8 meters from the center) is 274 m/s^2. Using the inverse square law, what would be the expected value for the acceleration due to gravity at the radius of Earth's orbit (1.50×10^{11} meters)? Show your working:

(c) Using the inverse square law, what would be the value of the acceleration of gravity at the radius of the orbit of Jupiter (approximately 7.43×10^{11} meters)? Show your working. Is this what you would have expected?

ISBN: **978-1-98-856693-1**

5 Observations and Assumptions

Key Question: What assumptions must be made in Earth and space science in order to make sense of the universe we live in?

Observations and hypotheses

- An **observation** is watching or recording what is happening. Observation is the basis for forming hypotheses and making **predictions**. An observation may generate a number of hypotheses (tentative explanations for what we see). Each **hypothesis** will lead to one or more predictions, which can be tested by investigation.
- A hypothesis can be written as a statement to include the prediction: "If X is true, then if I do Y (the experiment), I expect Z (the prediction)". Hypotheses are accepted, changed, or rejected on the basis of investigations. A hypothesis should have a sound theoretical basis and should be testable.

Observation 1: Sediments appear in layers, the oldest layers at the bottom, the youngest layers on top.

Brocken Inaglory

Observation 2: Different organisms are found in different rock layers. The oldest organisms are found in the deepest layers.

Assumptions

Any investigation requires you to make **assumptions** about the system you are working with. Assumptions are features of the system you are studying that you assume to be true, but that you do not (or cannot) test. Some assumptions about the geological systems described above include:

- Layers of sediment are always laid down horizontally.
- Layers of sediments are ordered youngest on top to oldest on the bottom, unless disturbed after formation.
- Organisms in the rock are there because they died at the same time as the sediments were being laid down (they weren't put there afterwards).

1. Read the two observations on sediments and fossils above, and then answer the following questions:

   (a) Generate a hypothesis to explain the observation that plant A is found above animal B in rock strata:

   Hypothesis: ______________________________

   ____

   ____

   (b) Describe one of the assumptions being made in your hypothesis: ______________________________

   ____

   ____

   (c) Generate a prediction about the relative age of fossils found in rock strata: ______________________________

   ____

   (d) How could you test your prediction? ______________________________

   ____

2. Form a group with three other classmates. Discuss what you would do if your test of the prediction did not support your hypothesis. Summarize your response and attach it to this page.

ISBN: **978-1-98-856693-1**

Occam's razor

- Occam's razor is a problem solving method which, at its simplest states that, among competing hypotheses, the one with the least number of assumptions should be used. Occam's razor helps rule out hypotheses or explanations that contain too many assumptions.
- For example, there are two possible models explaining how the solar system is organized. The geocentric model states that the Sun and planets orbit the Earth. The heliocentric model states that all the planets, including Earth, orbit the Sun. Both can be used to calculate the position of the planets as we see them in the sky. However, the geocentric model makes many more assumptions, including that the laws of gravity don't apply to the Earth and Sun, and that the planets all have secondary "epicycles" along their orbits.

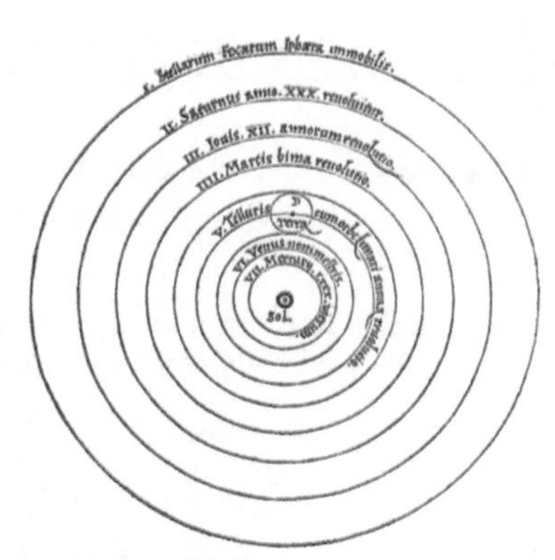

Copernicus' heliocentric model has just seven assumptions.

Assumptions and the wider universe

For our universe to make sense, and for us to make sense of the universe, we have to assume that certain ideas hold true everywhere in the universe and, if they don't, we have to be able to explain why not. There are essentially two rules that are assumed to be true in science.

1 All of existence, i.e. the universe, is governed by rules (laws) that are the same everywhere, and they are inviolable (they cannot be broken).

- This is essential for us to discover and understand the laws of the universe. There can't be one set of laws that apply in our universe today and a different set of laws tomorrow. Nor can there be different laws that apply to different parts of the universe. For example, the movement of light in a vacuum must behave the same way today, as it did yesterday, as it does everywhere in the universe.

2 These laws can be determined by observation of the universe around us.

- The second rule is equally important. What if the laws that govern the universe were not able to be understood? What if the number of laws was essentially infinite? No matter how carefully you observed something or how general your equations, you would never be able to write down a law that could be applied reliably to more than one situation.

NASA

Applying assumptions

It has been observed that, at the center of our galaxy, about a dozen stars are orbiting a common point that appears empty. Some of the stars are moving through space at speeds of over 5000 km/s (the Sun moves at about 220 km/s). Assuming that the laws of gravity apply in the center of the galaxy the same as they apply here on Earth, then it can be calculated that there must be an unseen object (called Sagittarius A*) with a mass of 4 million times the Sun holding the stars in their orbits.

3. (a) How does Occam's razor help to simplify explanations? ______________________

____

____

(b) Two students observed that two trees had toppled over in the night and that the grass around the trees was apparently undisturbed. Student A hypothesized that the wind had blown them over. Student B hypothesized that the trees had been knocked over by a large truck and the grass repaired after the truck had been removed.

Decide which of these two hypotheses is more likely, and explain your choice: ______________________

____

____

____

4. Explain why it is important in science to assume that the laws of nature are universal, behaving in the same way everywhere and at every time:

____

____

____

ISBN: **978-1-98-856693-1**

6 Tables and Graphs

Key Question: How can we use tables and graphs to provide a way to organize and visualize data in a way that helps to identify trends?

- **Tables** and **graphs** are ways to present **data** and they have different purposes. Tables provide an accurate record of numerical values and allow you to organise your data so that relationships and trends are apparent.
- Graphs provide a visual image of trends in the data in a minimum of space. It is useful to plot your data as soon as possible, even during your experiment, as this will help you to evaluate your results as you proceed and make adjustments, as necessary, e.g. to the sampling interval.
- The choice between graphing or tabulating in the final report depends on the type and complexity of the data, and the information that you want to convey. Sometimes, both are appropriate.

Presenting data in tables

Table 1: Population, land area, and calculated population density in four US states.

State	Population	Land area (km^2)	Population density (people km^{-2})
Alabama	4,871,547	135,754	35.9
Florida	20,636,975	170,307	121.2
Montana	1,032,949	380,847	2.7
Texas	27,469,114	695,662	39.5

- Tables provide a way to systematically record and condense a large amount of information. They provide an accurate record of numerical data and allow you to organise your data, making it easier to see patterns, trends, or anomalies.
- Table titles, and row and column headings must be clear and accurate so the reader knows exactly what the table is about.
- Columns can be added for calculated values such as density, rate, and summary statistics, e.g. **mean** and standard deviation. For large data sets, it is often the summary statistic, e.g. mean temperature each year, that is plotted.
- Summary statistics make it easier to identify trends and compare different treatments. Rates are useful in making multiple data sets comparable, e.g. if recordings were made over different time periods.

Presenting data in graphs

Fig. 1: Mean annual temperature in New Hampshire and Arizona

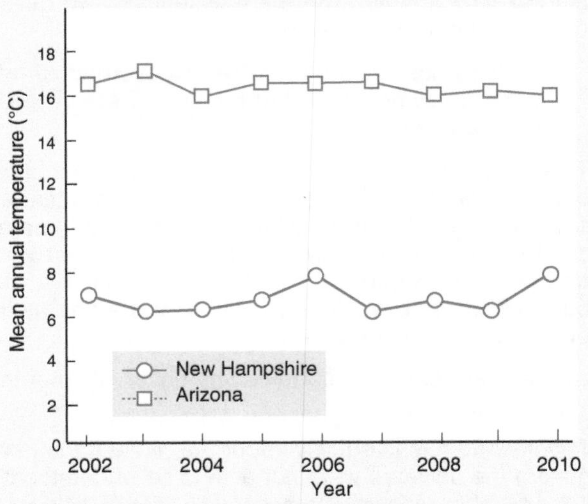

- Graphs are a good way of visually showing trends, patterns, and relationships without taking up too much space. Complex data sets tend to be presented as a graph rather than a table.
- Presenting graphs properly requires attention to a few basic details, including correct orientation and labeling of the axes, accurate plotting of points, and a descriptive, accurate title.

1. Describe the advantages of using a table to present information: ______________________

2. What is the benefit of including summary information, e.g. means or processed data, on a table? ______________________

3. What are the main advantages of presenting data in a graph? ______________________

4. Why might you include both graphs and tables in a final report? ______________________

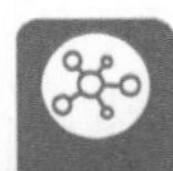

ISBN: 978-1-98-856693-1

7 Correlation or Causation?

Key Question: What is the difference between correlation and causation, and why does correlation not necessarily imply causation?

- Researchers often want to know if two variables have any **correlation** (relationship) to each other. This can be achieved by plotting the **data** as a scatter **graph** and drawing a line of best fit through the data, or by testing for correlation using a statistical test.
- The strength of a correlation is indicated by the correlation coefficient (r or R), which varies between 1 and -1. A value of 1 indicates a perfect (1:1) relationship between the variables. A value of -1 indicates a 1:1 negative relationship, and 0 indicates no relationship between the variables.

Correlation does not imply causation

You may come across the phrase "correlation does not necessarily imply causation". This means that even when there is a strong correlation between variables, i.e. they vary together in a predictable way, you cannot assume that change in one variable caused change in the other.

Example: When data from the organic food association and the office of special education programs is plotted (below), there is a strong correlation between the increase in organic food and rates of diagnosed autism. However, it is unlikely that eating organic food causes autism, so we cannot assume a causative effect here.

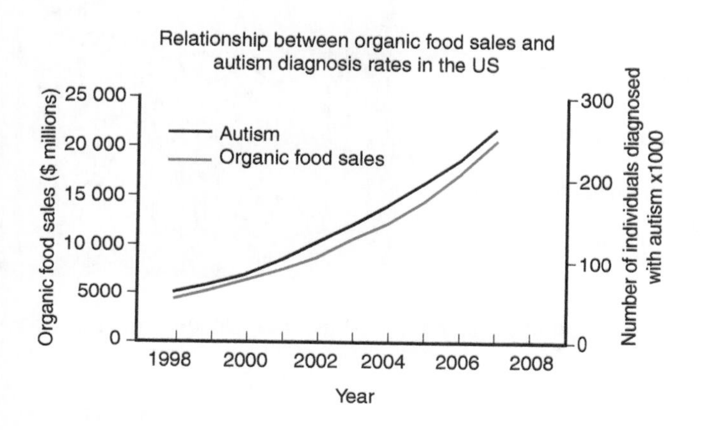

Drawing the line of best fit

Some simple guidelines need to be followed when drawing a line of best fit on your scatter plot.

- Your line should follow the trend of the data points.
- Roughly half of your data points should be above the line of best fit, and half below.
- The line of best fit does not necessarily pass through any particular point.
- The line of best fit should pivot around the point which represents the **mean** of the x and the mean of the y variables.

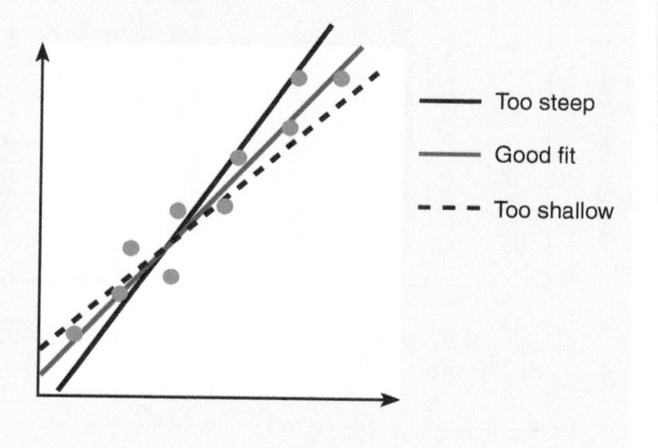

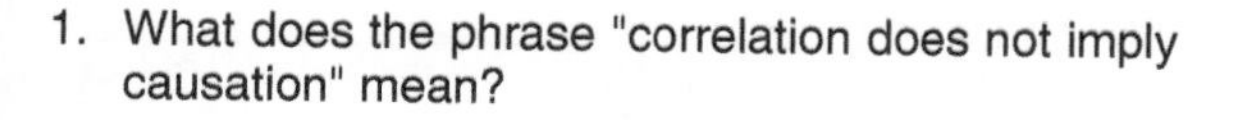

1. What does the phrase "correlation does not imply causation" mean?

2. A student measured the length of eruptions of Old Faithful and the time between the eruptions for a day, and plotted a scatter graph of the results (right).

   (a) Draw a line of best fit through the data:

   (b) Using your line of best fit as a guide, comment on the correlation between eruption length and the time between eruptions:

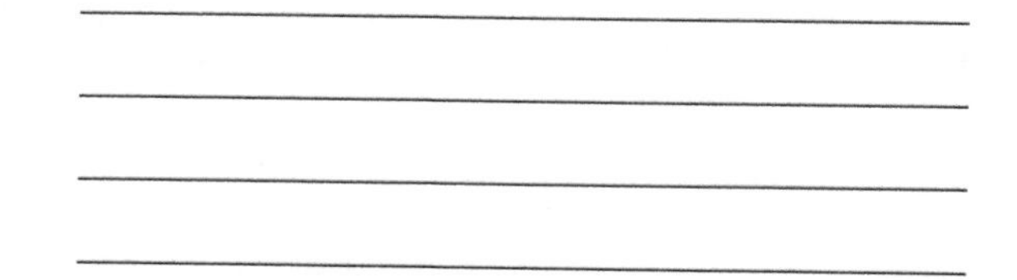

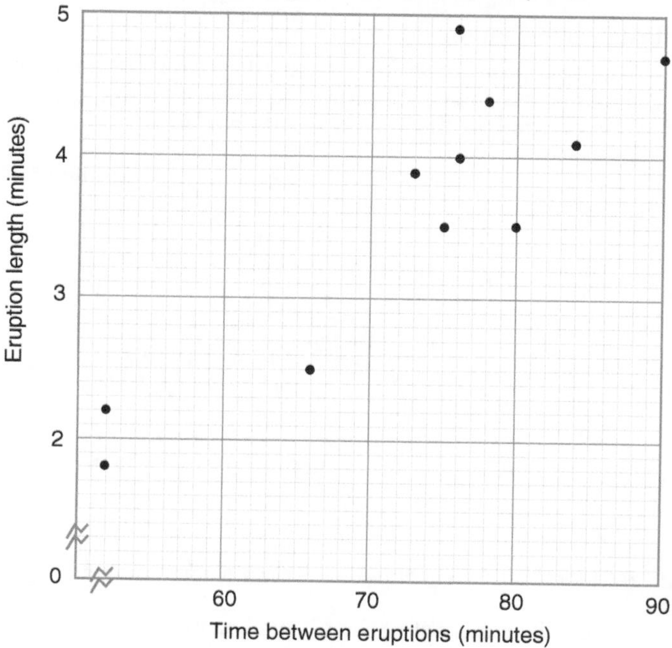

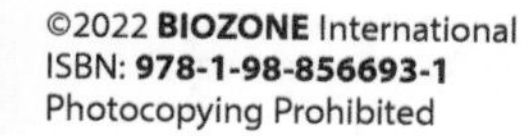

ISBN: 978-1-98-856693-1

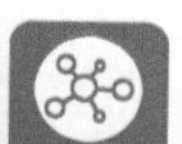
CE

8 Analyzing and Interpreting Data

Key Question: How can data be analyzed and displayed to provide meaningful information?

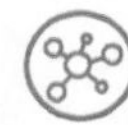

Displaying processed data

Processed **data** is usually displayed in a table or **graph**. Tables, and especially graphs, can help make any trends in the data easier to see. Graphs can be used to predict values that do not appear in the original data. Sometimes, many different data points may be plotted on the one graph so that a large amount of information is shown in a compact way.

Pollen in sediments

- The data below shows the percentage of pollen in sediments from a region in northeastern United States, laid down over 15,000 years. By graphing the percentages of pollen from different plants beside each other and matching the pollen type to known trees and landscapes, we can develop a picture of what the land looked like at any particular time in the last 15,000 years.
- We can see from the graph that about 5000 years ago, the land was mostly hardwood forest, including oak and beech trees. However, 15,000 years ago, we can see that the land was covered mostly by tundra. This is consistent with what is known about the climate conditions 15,000 years ago.

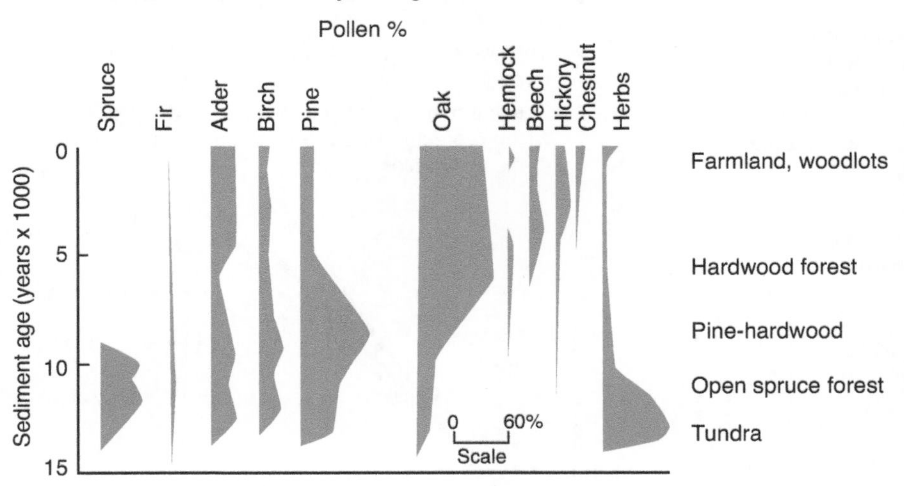

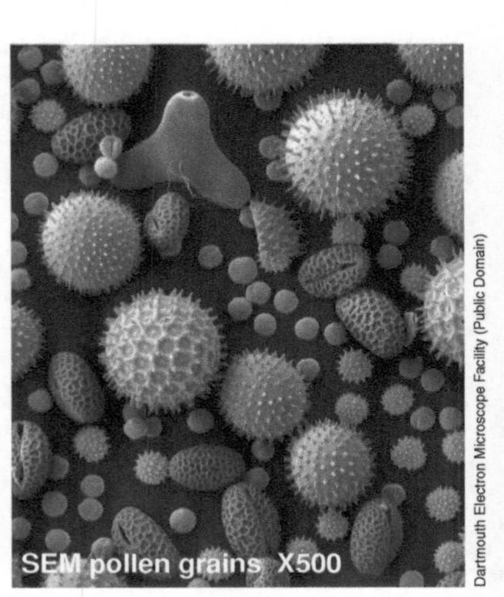

1. (a) Using the pollen graph above, determine the predominant type of plant cover in the northeastern United States 10,000 years ago:

 ____

 (b) What appears to be the most common tree in the area from 10,000 years ago to present? ______________

 (c) Which type of tree went into steep decline between 10,000 and 5000 years ago? ______________

Stalactite formation

- Stalactites grow down from the top of cave roofs as rainwater deposits minerals on to them. The more rain there is, the faster the stalactites grow. They also tend to grow in annual rings as there is usually more rain in winter than in summer. Analyze the stalactite data below:

Stalactite thickness

Thickness (mm): 0.0, 0.1, 0.2, 0.3

Time (years before present): 450, 400, 350, 300, 250, 200

2 (a) Identify the wettest period of time before present: ______________

 (b) Identify the driest period of time before present: ______________

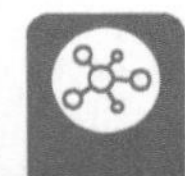

ISBN: **978-1-98-856693-1**

Analyzing oxygen isotopes in ice cores

- Oxygen comes in two common isotopes: oxygen-16 (^{16}O) (light) and oxygen-18 (^{18}O) (heavy). In water, this causes water molecules with ^{18}O to be heavier than water containing ^{16}O. Heavy water evaporates less than light water. Therefore, there is less ^{18}O in the atmosphere and in rain than in seawater. Temperature affects the amount of ^{18}O in the atmosphere. The data below measure the difference in ^{18}O in rainwater compared to the ocean, at different temperatures.

3. Plot the isotope data on the grid below. Temperature is on the x axis:

Difference ^{18}O (%) in rainwater compared to seawater	Temp °C
-4.2	-36
-3.8	-34
-2.8	-27
-3.5	-19
-2.7	-19
-1.6	-10
-1.5	0
-1.9	4
-1.2	1
-0.6	5
-1.0	8
-0.6	11
-0.5	20

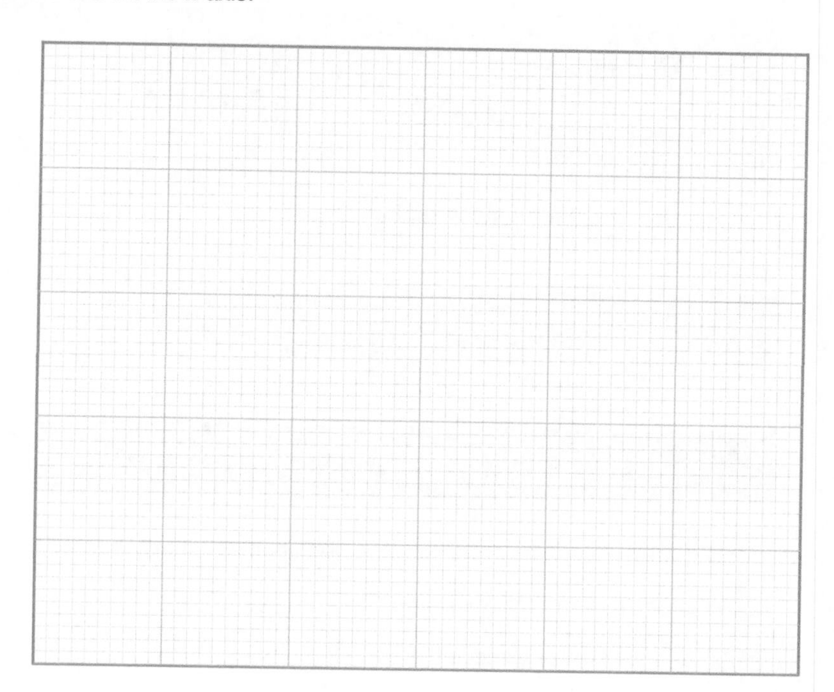

4. (a) Once a reference has been established (as above), it is then possible to measure oxygen isotopes in ice cores and determine what the temperature must have been at the time the ice was laid down. The data below is taken from ice cores on the Gomez Plateau in Antarctica. Use the data below and above to complete the table, and work out how the temperature of the Gomez Plateau has changed over time.

(b) Plot a graph of temperature change over time for the Gomez Plateau. Draw a line of best fit through the points:

Year	Difference ^{18}O (%) in rainwater compared to seawater	Temp °C
2005	-2.10	
1995	-2.30	
1985	-2.28	
1975	-2.25	
1965	-2.30	
1955	-2.03	
1945	-2.06	
1935	-2.26	
1925	-2.19	
1915	-2.31	
1905	-2.23	
1895	-2.27	
1885	-2.24	
1875	-2.16	

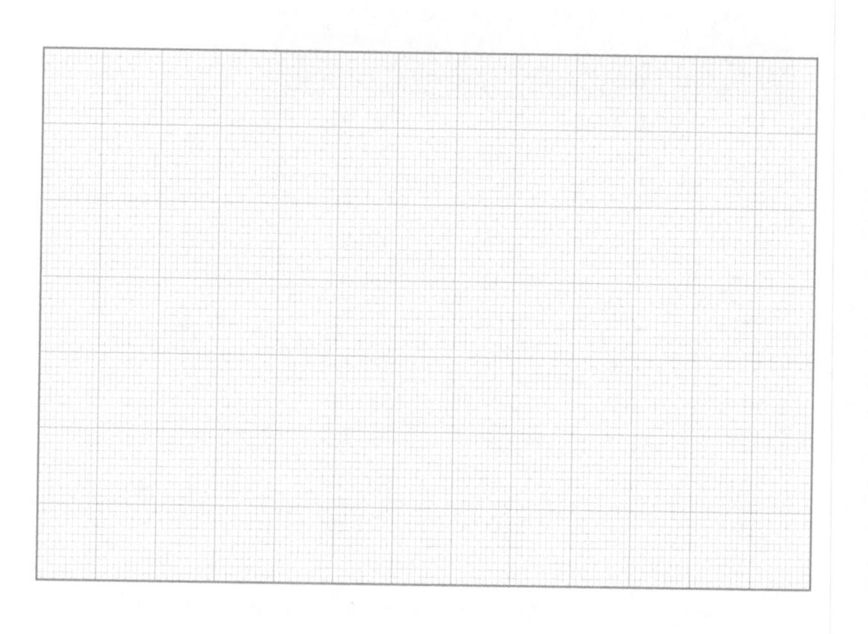

(c) Describe the trend in temperature over time on the Gomez Plateau: ______________________________

____

ISBN: **978-1-98-856693-1**

Displaying and analyzing data on volcanic rock types

5. The graph below displays information on different rock types. Study the graph and answer the questions below:

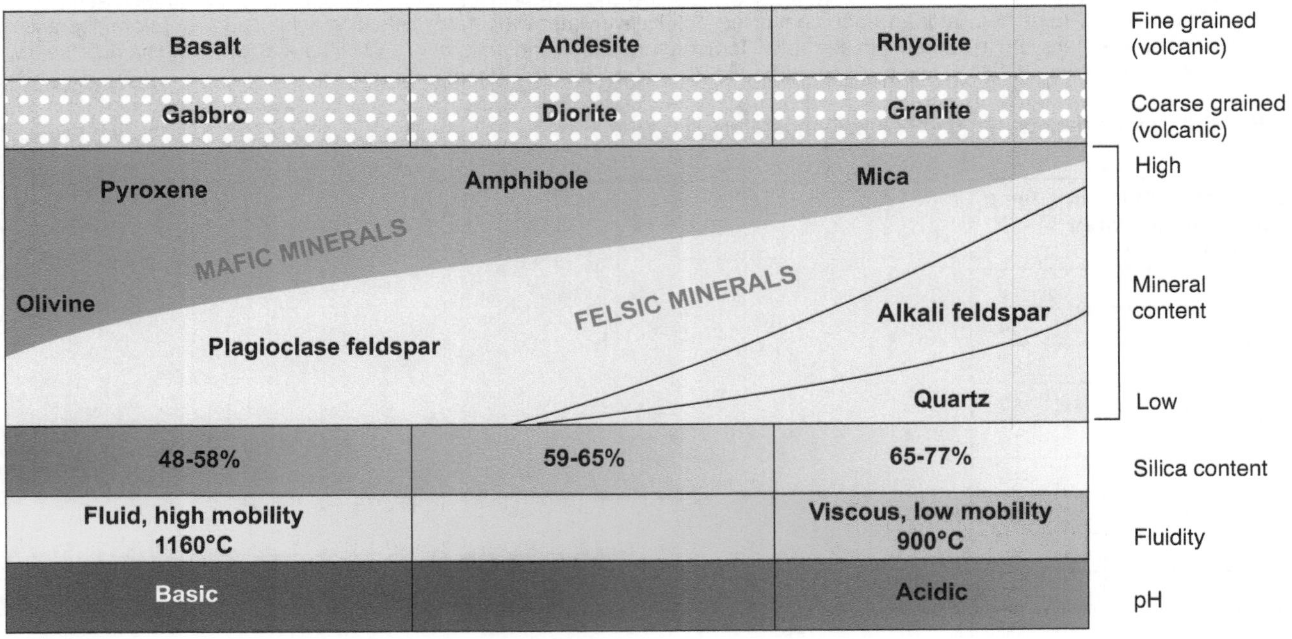

(a) Identify the fine grained rock with a silica content of between 48-58%: ____________________

(b) What is the pH of this rock type? ____________________

(c) Is the rock fluid or viscous? ____________________

(d) Identify the coarse grained, highly acidic rock: ____________________

(e) What is the most common mineral in the highest pH example of this rock? ____________________

Analyzing tree ring data and rainfall

- Trees produce annual rings. In dry years, the rings are narrow and closer together. In wet years, the rings are larger and further apart. Using specific formulae, the width of the tree rings can be used to reconstruct rainfall. The data for an area of eucalyptus forest in Australia is shown in the table below:

Year	Tree ring (mm)	Actual rainfall (mm)	Reconstructed rainfall (mm)
1910	1.672	115.20	301.36
1920	0.378	193.80	165.53
1930	0.432	163.80	171.20
1940	0.600	121.80	188.83
1950	0.433	148.40	171.30
1960	1.288	320.80	261.06
1970	0.726	160.30	202.06
1980	2.147	420.40	351.23
1990	0.197	199.20	146.53
2000	3.902	627.60	535.45
2010	0.122	102.30	138.66

6. (a) Plot the actual rainfall data and the reconstructed rainfall data on the graph above. Remember a key:

(b) Does the reconstructed data accurately represent the actual data? What does this mean for reconstructing rainfall when we do not know the actual rainfall?

____

____

ISBN: 978-1-98-856693-1

9 Descriptive Statistics and the Spread of Data

Key Question: What are descriptive statistics and how are they used?

Descriptive statistics

When we describe a set of data, it is usual to give a measure of central tendency. This is a single value identifying the central position within that set of data. **Descriptive statistics**, such as **mean**, **median**, and **mode**, are all valid measures of central tendency, depending of the type of data and its distribution. They help to summarize features of the data, so are often called summary statistics. The appropriate statistic for different types of data variables and their distributions is described below.

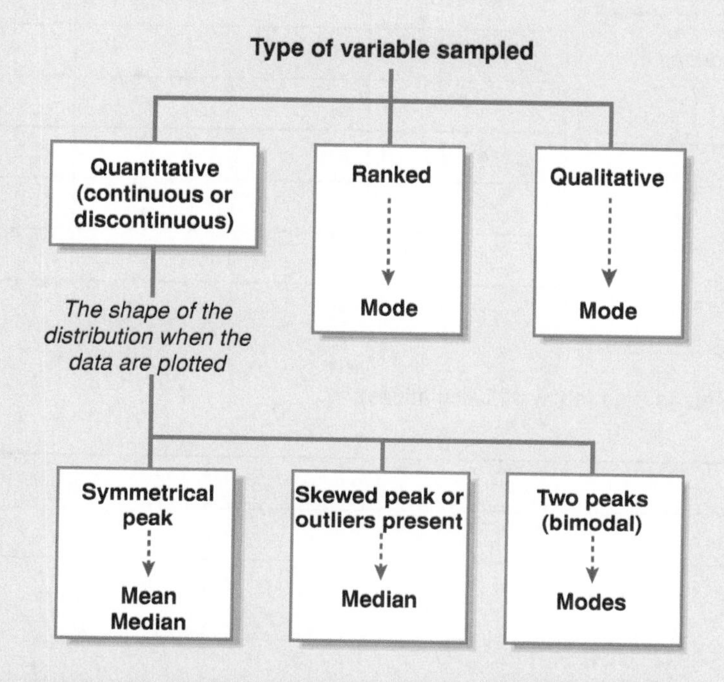

Statistic	Definition and when to use it	How to calculate it
Mean	• The average of all data entries. • Measure of central tendency for normally distributed data.	• Add up all the data entries. • Divide by the total number of data entries.
Median	• The middle value when data entries are placed in rank order. • A good measure of central tendency for skewed distributions.	• Arrange the data in increasing rank order. • Identify the middle value. • For an even number of entries, find the mid point of the two middle values.
Mode	• The most common data value. • Suitable for bimodal distributions and qualitative data.	• Identify the category with the highest number of data entries using a tally chart or a bar **graph**.

Distribution of data

Variability in continuous data is often displayed as a frequency distribution. There are several types of distribution.

- Normal distribution (A): data is spread symmetrically about the mean. It has a classic bell shape when plotted.
- Skewed data (B): data is not centered around the middle but has a "tail" to the left or right.
- Bimodal data (C): data which has two peaks.

The shape of the distribution will determine which statistic (mean, median, or mode) should be used to describe the central tendency of the sample data.

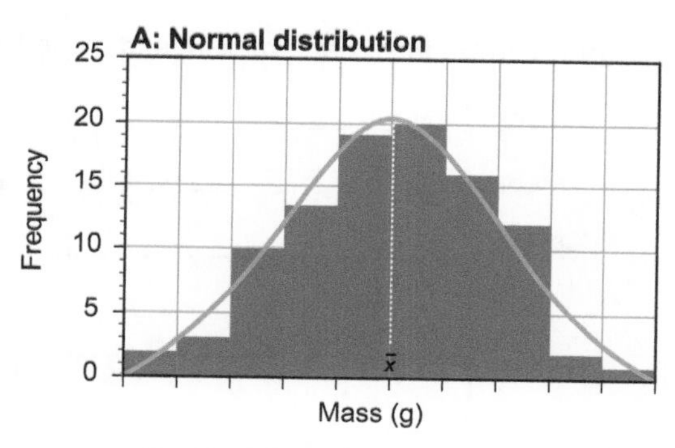

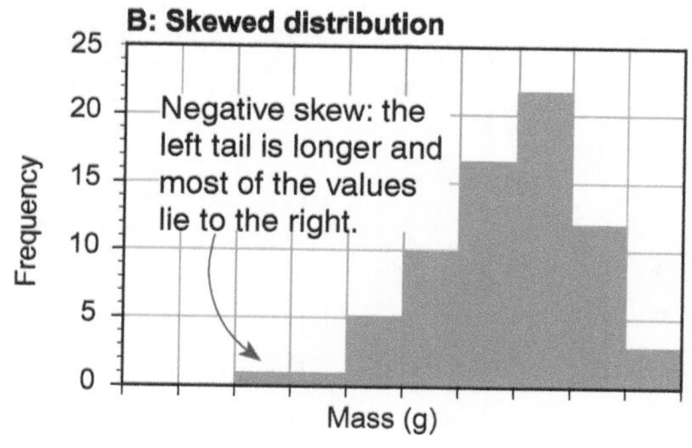

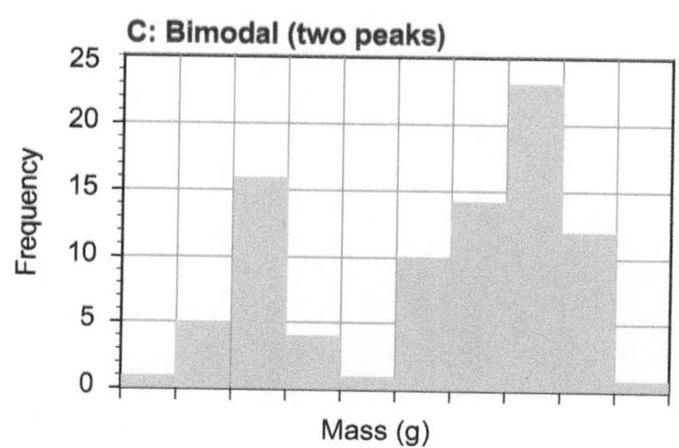

ISBN: 978-1-98-856693-1

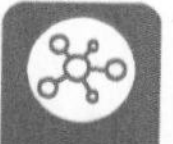

1. A sample of stones on a beach was taken and their individual masses recorded, as part of a study on beach stability.

Stone mass (g)									
881	335	909	632	706	359	881	284	607	290
795	439	229	182	383	719	509	322	578	686
488	375	143	204	161	160	419	147	68	91
167	459	151	135	197	180	115	314	414	83

(a) Draw up a tally chart in the space provided on the right for the stone masses.

(b) On the graph paper at the bottom of the page, draw a frequency histogram for the stone data.

(c) What type of distribution does the data have?

(d) Is this what you would expect?

(e) What would be the best measure of central tendency in the stone data set (mean, median, or mode)?

(f) Explain why you chose your answer in (e):

Mass (g)	Tally	Total
1-100		
101-200		
201-300		
301-400		
401-500		
501-600		
601-700		
701-800		
801-900		
901-1000		

(g) Calculate the mean, median, and mode for the stone data (show all calculations):

Mean:

Median:

Mode:

ISBN: **978-1-98-856693-1**

10 Planning and Carrying Out an Investigation

Key Question: How does surface area affect dissolving time?

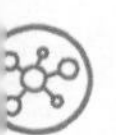

- Rainwater is very slightly acidic. When it comes in contact with limestone, it reacts with it to form carbon dioxide gas, and calcium ions in solution. This causes the limestone to dissolve.
- Limestone that is already partially eroded, presents a greater surface area for rain to fall on and therefore a greater surface area for reaction.
- This reaction is very slow, and generally not noticeable. In the investigation below, you will use hydrochloric acid (HCl) in place of water to speed up the reaction to a measurable rate.

1. Write a hypothesis for the experiment below: ______________________________

____

____

Investigation 1.1 Investigating surface area and dissolving time.

See appendix for equipment list.

Caution. HCl is corrosive. You should wear protective eyewear and gloves.

1. Select nine pieces of limestone (calcium carbonate, $CaCO_3$) that are roughly similar in shape. These should weigh about 1 gram each. Weigh them on a balance to obtain masses as close as reasonably possible.
2. Fill each of three 200 mL beakers with 100 mL of 1 mol/L HCl. Have a stopwatch or timer ready.
3. In each beaker, place one piece of limestone (leaving six). Immediately start the timer. Record how long it takes for each of the limestone pieces to dissolve (fully react), or for the reaction to stop producing bubbles.
4. Record these times in table 1.
5. Carefully dispose of any leftover acid and limestone (you teacher will tell the procedure for your lab) and rinse with distilled water. Refill the beakers with 100 mL of 1 mol/L HCl.
6. Take three of the remaining limestone pieces and, keeping them separate, lightly crush them with a mortar and pestle into smaller pieces (not a powder). Have a stopwatch or timer ready.
7. Add each crushed limestone piece to one of the beakers and immediately start timing.
8. Record how long it takes for each of the crushed limestone pieces to dissolve (fully react), or for the reaction to stop producing bubbles, and record the times in table 1.
9. Carefully dispose of any leftover acid and limestone and rinse with distilled water. Refill the beakers with 100 mL of 1 mol/L HCl.
10. Take the last three limestone pieces and keeping them separate, crush them using the mortar and pestle into a powder or fine grains. Have a stopwatch or timer ready.
11. Add each powdered limestone piece to one of the beakers and immediately start timing.
12. Again, record how long it takes for each of the powdered limestone pieces to dissolve (fully react), or for the reaction to stop producing bubbles and record the times in table 1.
13. Carefully dispose of any leftover acid and limestone and rinse with distilled water.

	Table 1: Dissolving time for limestone (s)		
	Single piece	Crushed	Powdered
1			
2			
3			
Mean			

Controlling variables

To carry out an investigation fairly, all the **variables** (factors that could be changed) are kept the same, except the factor that is being investigated. These are called **controlled variables**. The variable that is being changed by the investigator is called the **independent variable**. The variable being measured is called the **dependent variable**.

ISBN: **978-1-98-856693-1**

2. Calculate the mean dissolving time for the single, crushed, or powdered limestone. Record on the table (previous page):

3. Which limestone has the lowest and which has the highest surface area? ______

4. What assumption is this experiment based on? ______

5. Identify the independent variable for the experiment: ______

6. Identify the dependent variable for the experiment: ______

7. Use your calculations to plot a column graph on the grid below:

8. Write a conclusion based on the findings: ______

9. Discuss how this experiment relates to chemical erosion and how the experiment could be improved:

Temperature and weathering

10. Some students decided to investigate the effect of temperature on erosion processes. They again used calcium carbonate chips and hydrochloric acid to simulate rainwater and rock but this time placed the $CaCO_3$ and acid into water baths to control the temperature of the solutions.

    Write a hypothesis for this investigation: ______

ISBN: **978-1-98-856693-1**

11. The students carried out the investigation using water bath temperatures of 15°C, 20°C, 25°C, and 30°C as their independent variable.

(a) Explain why the temperature range of 15°C to 30°C is appropriate for this investigation: ______

(b) Identify some important variables that would be controlled in this investigation: ______

12. Draw a diagram that outlines the method used by the students to carry out the investigation. Include labels for the equipment used:

13. For each temperature, the students carried out the procedure three times (three samples). Produce a table that would be appropriate for them to record and process their data in:

14. The students wanted to graph their results. What part of the results should the students graph and what would be the most appropriate type of graph to produce and why?

ISBN: **978-1-98-856693-1**

Earth's Place in the Universe

Concepts and connections
Use arrows to make connections between related concepts in this section of the book

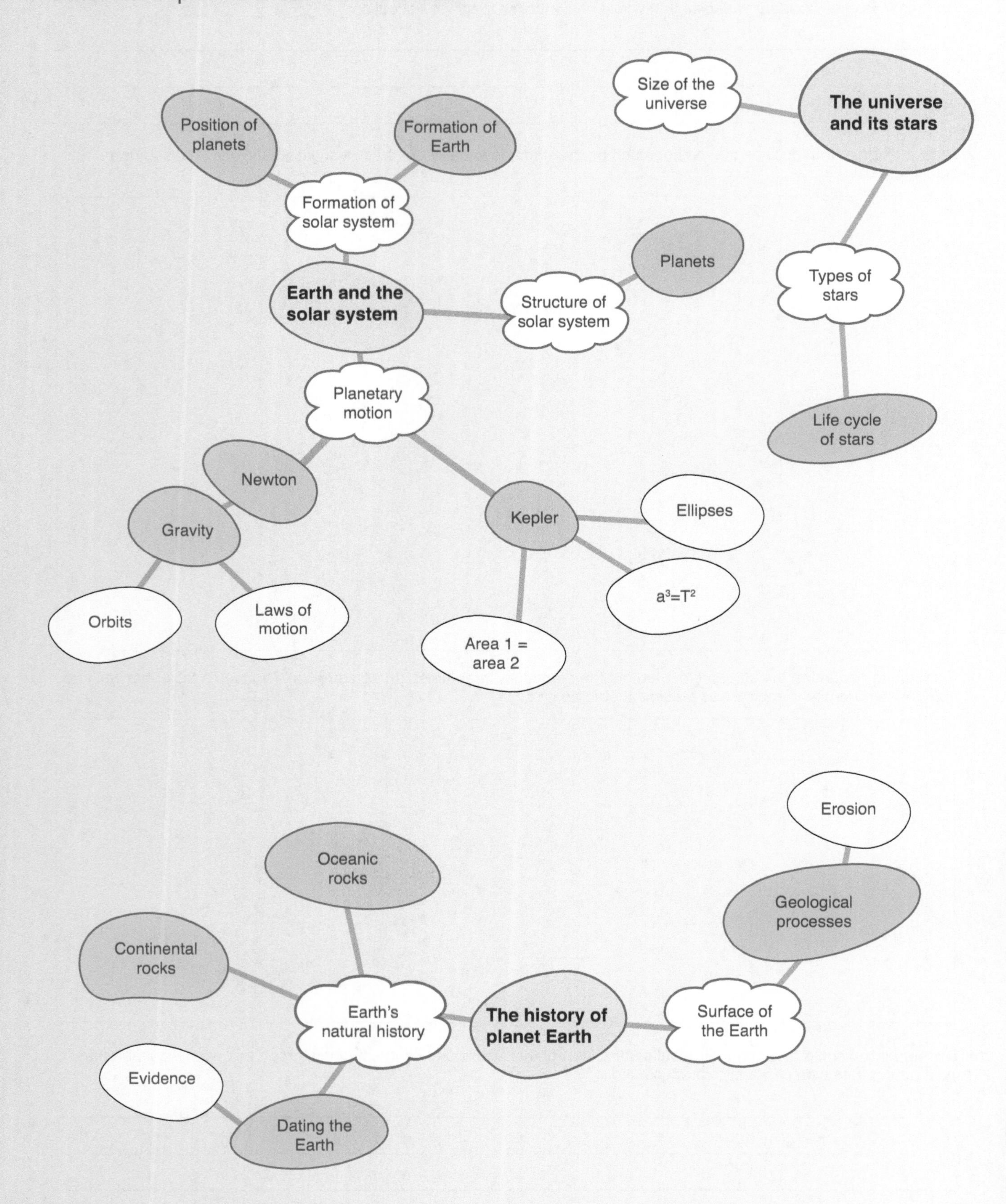

ISBN: 978-1-98-856693-1

CHAPTER 2

The Universe and its Stars

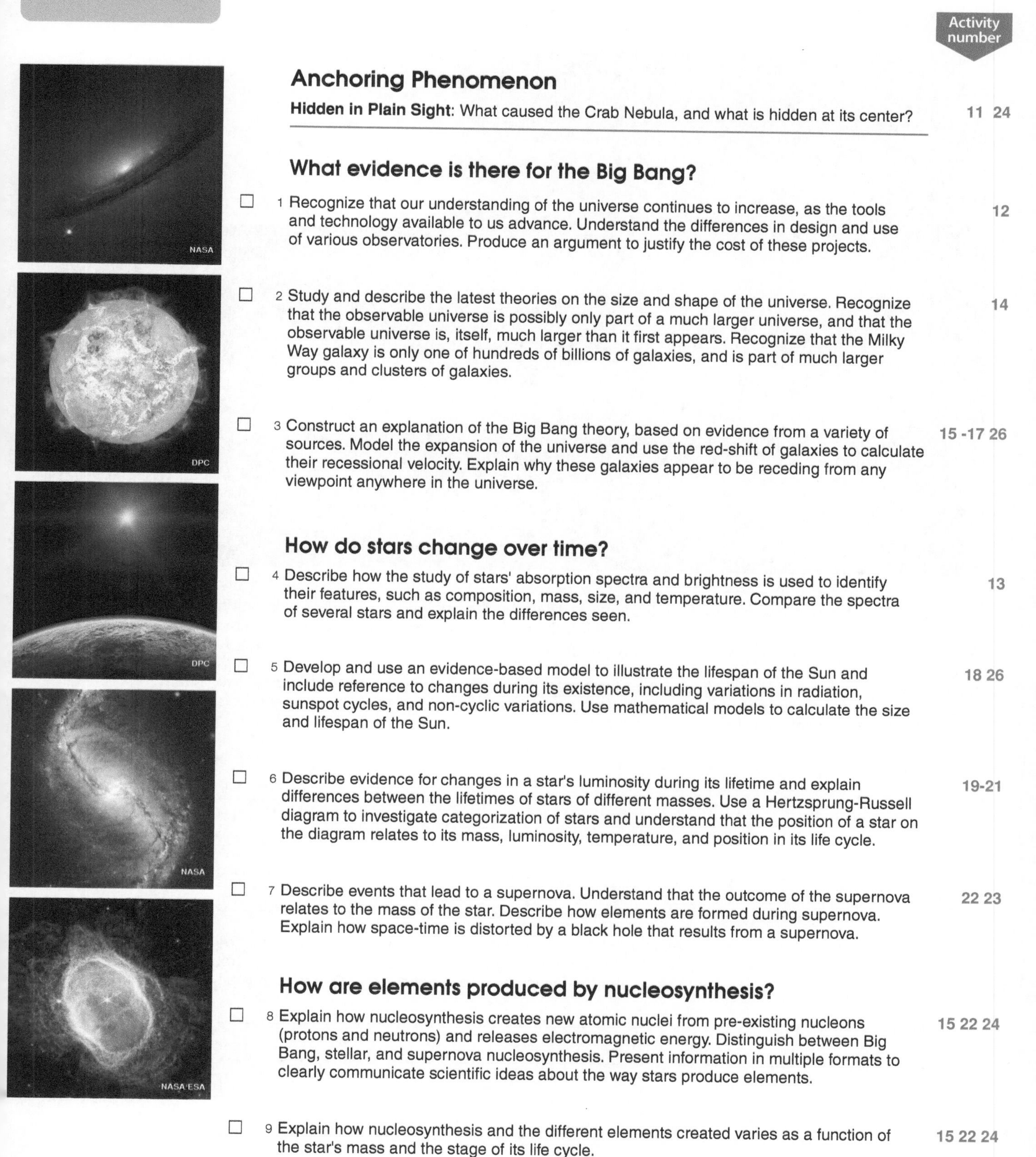

Activity number

Anchoring Phenomenon

Hidden in Plain Sight: What caused the Crab Nebula, and what is hidden at its center? 11 24

What evidence is there for the Big Bang?

- ☐ 1 Recognize that our understanding of the universe continues to increase, as the tools and technology available to us advance. Understand the differences in design and use of various observatories. Produce an argument to justify the cost of these projects. 12

- ☐ 2 Study and describe the latest theories on the size and shape of the universe. Recognize that the observable universe is possibly only part of a much larger universe, and that the observable universe is, itself, much larger than it first appears. Recognize that the Milky Way galaxy is only one of hundreds of billions of galaxies, and is part of much larger groups and clusters of galaxies. 14

- ☐ 3 Construct an explanation of the Big Bang theory, based on evidence from a variety of sources. Model the expansion of the universe and use the red-shift of galaxies to calculate their recessional velocity. Explain why these galaxies appear to be receding from any viewpoint anywhere in the universe. 15 -17 26

How do stars change over time?

- ☐ 4 Describe how the study of stars' absorption spectra and brightness is used to identify their features, such as composition, mass, size, and temperature. Compare the spectra of several stars and explain the differences seen. 13

- ☐ 5 Develop and use an evidence-based model to illustrate the lifespan of the Sun and include reference to changes during its existence, including variations in radiation, sunspot cycles, and non-cyclic variations. Use mathematical models to calculate the size and lifespan of the Sun. 18 26

- ☐ 6 Describe evidence for changes in a star's luminosity during its lifetime and explain differences between the lifetimes of stars of different masses. Use a Hertzsprung-Russell diagram to investigate categorization of stars and understand that the position of a star on the diagram relates to its mass, luminosity, temperature, and position in its life cycle. 19-21

- ☐ 7 Describe events that lead to a supernova. Understand that the outcome of the supernova relates to the mass of the star. Describe how elements are formed during supernova. Explain how space-time is distorted by a black hole that results from a supernova. 22 23

How are elements produced by nucleosynthesis?

- ☐ 8 Explain how nucleosynthesis creates new atomic nuclei from pre-existing nucleons (protons and neutrons) and releases electromagnetic energy. Distinguish between Big Bang, stellar, and supernova nucleosynthesis. Present information in multiple formats to clearly communicate scientific ideas about the way stars produce elements. 15 22 24

- ☐ 9 Explain how nucleosynthesis and the different elements created varies as a function of the star's mass and the stage of its life cycle. 15 22 24

11 Hidden in Plain Sight

Key Question: What caused the Crab Nebula, and what is hidden at its center?

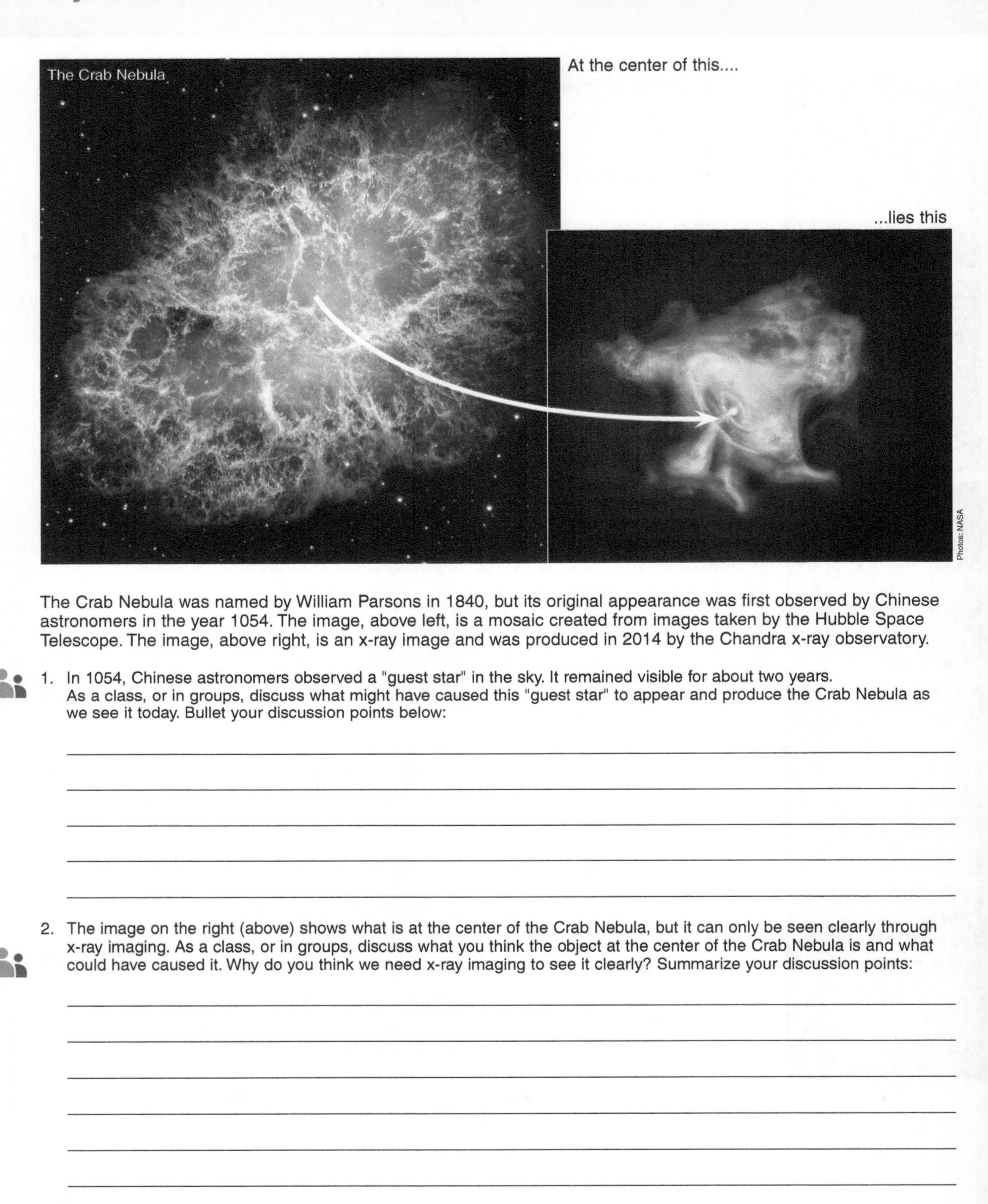

The Crab Nebula was named by William Parsons in 1840, but its original appearance was first observed by Chinese astronomers in the year 1054. The image, above left, is a mosaic created from images taken by the Hubble Space Telescope. The image, above right, is an x-ray image and was produced in 2014 by the Chandra x-ray observatory.

1. In 1054, Chinese astronomers observed a "guest star" in the sky. It remained visible for about two years. As a class, or in groups, discuss what might have caused this "guest star" to appear and produce the Crab Nebula as we see it today. Bullet your discussion points below:

2. The image on the right (above) shows what is at the center of the Crab Nebula, but it can only be seen clearly through x-ray imaging. As a class, or in groups, discuss what you think the object at the center of the Crab Nebula is and what could have caused it. Why do you think we need x-ray imaging to see it clearly? Summarize your discussion points:

ISBN: 978-1-98-856693-1

12 Studying the Universe

Key Question: How can scientists and astronomers study different aspects of the universe by using various devices for gathering data?

Studying the universe

- People have studied the universe for millennia. To begin with, people studied the sky visually, using only their eyes and noting how the stars, Moon, and **Sun** moved across the sky. Accurate study and mapping of the **stars** and Sun helped people keep track of the seasons, and important (usually religious) events. With the beginning of the Renaissance in Western Europe, studying stars became more academic and accurate as instrumentation became more advanced.

1

Simple devices such as Tycho Brahe's quadrant (left), in 1597, allowed the accurate measurement of the angle of the stars and planets above the horizon. Brahe produced an enormous amount of data on the movements and positions of stars and planets which was later used by Johannes Kepler to develop the laws of planetary motion.

2

In 1610, Galileo Galilei used a refracting telescope (above) to view the moons of Jupiter and became the first person to see objects orbiting another planet. He used his observations as part of his argument that the planets orbited the Sun instead of the Earth.

3

Once developed, optical telescopes became progressively sophisticated and larger. They included both refracting (using lenses) and reflecting (using mirrors) telescopes. However, they only allowed observation of visible light. During the early 20th century, optical telescopes were used to confirm that the universe extended beyond the Milky Way galaxy.

The VLT (Very Large Telescope) in Chile

ESA

4

The use of radio telescopes to view the sky began in earnest after the Second World War. The use of radio astronomy allowed astronomers to see parts of the universe that had been invisible to optical devices. Radio telescope observatories may have one huge radio telescope (right) or many smaller ones joined together in an array (below).

Dicklyon CC 4.0

ISBN: 978-1-98-856693-1

ESS1.A

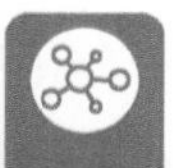

Space telescopes

- Because of the distorting effect of Earth's atmosphere, it is difficult with ground based optical telescopes to produce clear images of astronomical phenomena. There have been major advances in optical telescopes in the last few decades, such as the introduction of adaptive optics which compensate for the atmosphere's distortion. However, a major problem for ground based telescopes of any kind is the fact that the Earth rotates, and so there can be many hours in every twenty four in which the telescope is facing away from the target.
- This has been solved by the development of spaced based observatories. There have been a large number of these over many decades. Different observatories are designed to detect different kinds of **electromagnetic radiation**, from gamma rays to infrared. The most famous of these space observatories is the Hubble Space Telescope (HST).

The Hubble Space Telescope

- Work on the Hubble Space Telescope (HST) began in 1979, with the grinding of the primary mirror. It was launched into space by the space shuttle Discovery in 1990, but flaws in the primary mirror meant a mission to add an optics package was needed. Although the HST was producing better images than ground based telescopes at the time, it wasn't until the end of 1993 that a corrective optics package was installed and the full ability of the HST was realized. Since then, the HST has produced the most spectacular images of the universe ever made. The HST has now been operating for more than thirty years and is expected to operate until somewhere between 2030 and 2040.

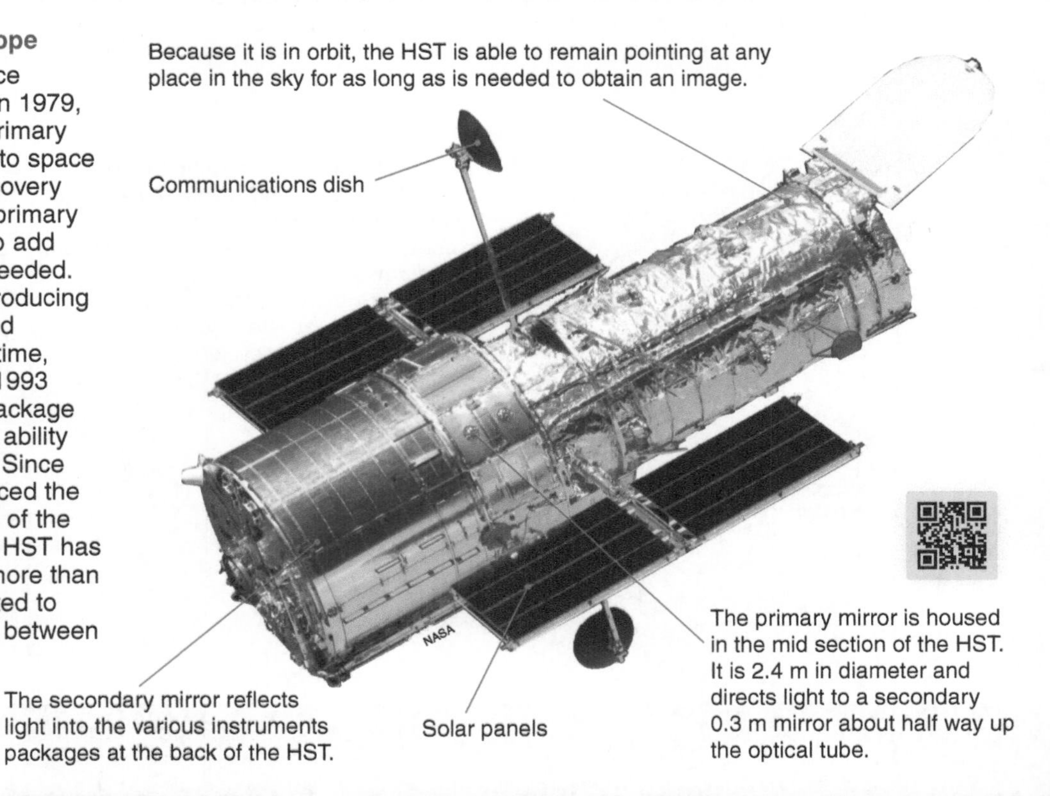

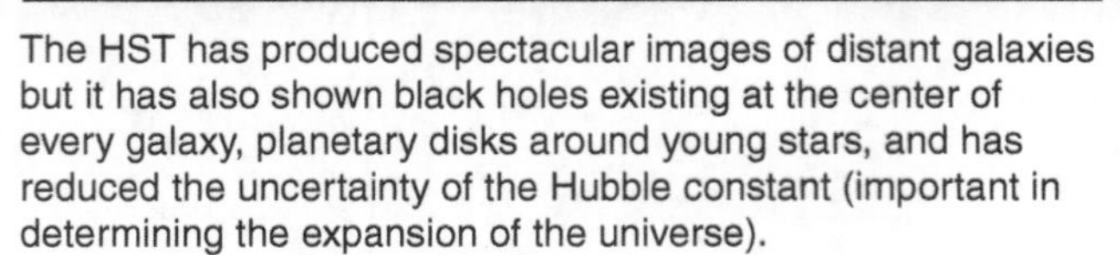
The HST has produced spectacular images of distant galaxies but it has also shown black holes existing at the center of every galaxy, planetary disks around young stars, and has reduced the uncertainty of the Hubble constant (important in determining the expansion of the universe).

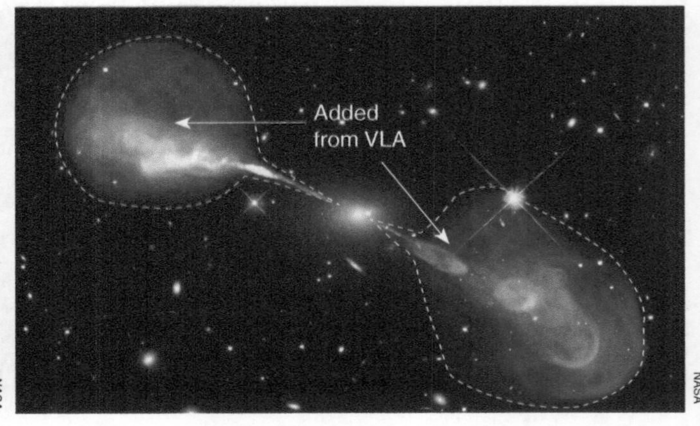

Combining images and information from different observatories, allows us to gain a different view of celestial objects. The image above is a composite of an optical image taken from the Hubble Space Telescope, and a radio image taken from the Very Large Array (VLA) in New Mexico.

1. Identify some reasons for needing to accurately map objects in the night sky: ______________________

____

____

2. What advantages do space telescopes have over ground based telescopes? ______________________

____

____

ISBN: 978-1-98-856693-1

The James Webb Space Telescope

- Planning for the James Webb Space Telescope (JWST) began in 1990. Initially intended to be launched around 2007, the JWST was beset with cost overruns and development issues. Much of the technology for the JWST didn't exist to a high enough precision when its development began. Also, the fact that the JWST would be orbiting far beyond the reach of crewed spacecraft meant that, if errors occurred (as with the HST), there would be no recovery available.
- Although the US$10 billion cost may initially seem high the JWST has a far higher resolution and magnification than the HST. Images that once took the HST days or weeks to produce can be produced by the JWST in hours or days. This means far more science can be done in less time.

The secondary mirror is held on three arms that swung down and locked into place during unfolding.

The 6.5 m diameter primary mirror of the JWST is so big that it had to be folded to fit inside the nose cone of the Ariane 5 launch rocket.

Each of the 18 segments of the mirror can be individually adjusted so that a perfectly focused image can be produced.

The primary mirror, made of beryllium (making it lightweight and strong) is coated with gold. The gold reflects infrared light and allows the JWST to capture light waves from the very earliest galaxies and stars.

NASA

The Integrated Science Instrument Module (ISIM) includes The Near-Infrared Camera, the Near-Infrared Spectrograph, Mid-Infrared Instrument, and the Fine Guidance Sensor/Near-Infrared Image.

The tennis court sized sun shield is made of 5 layers of Kapton. It keeps the mirror in the shade and reduces the temperature of the instrument package to 39 K (-234°C).

The spacecraft bus provides the support equipment for the JWST, including electricity, communications, propulsion, and attitude control

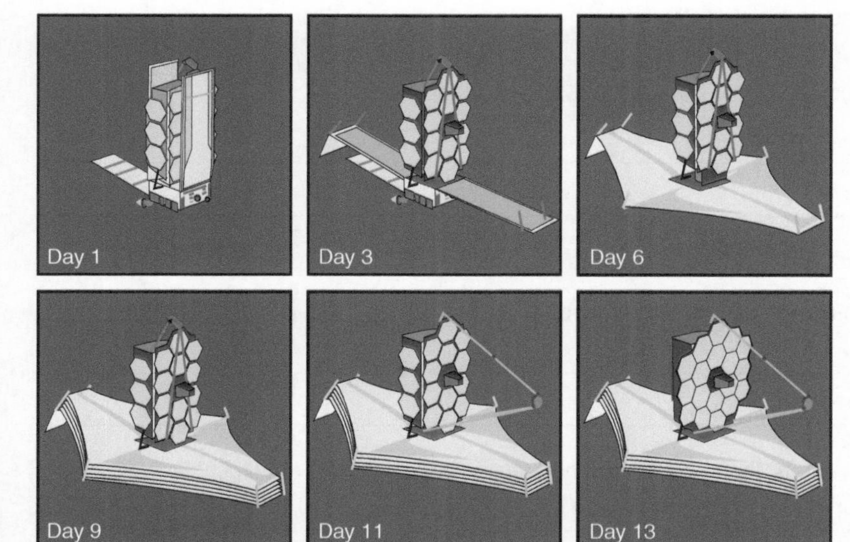

The JWST unfolded over about 2 weeks. Day 1: the solar panel unfolded to provide power. Day 3: the sun-shield pallets folded down. Day 6-9: the sun-shield expanded to full size. Day 11: the secondary mirror deployed. Day 13: the primary mirror unfolded. A further 6 months allowed for cooling the JWST, and aligning and testing the mirror and the instruments.

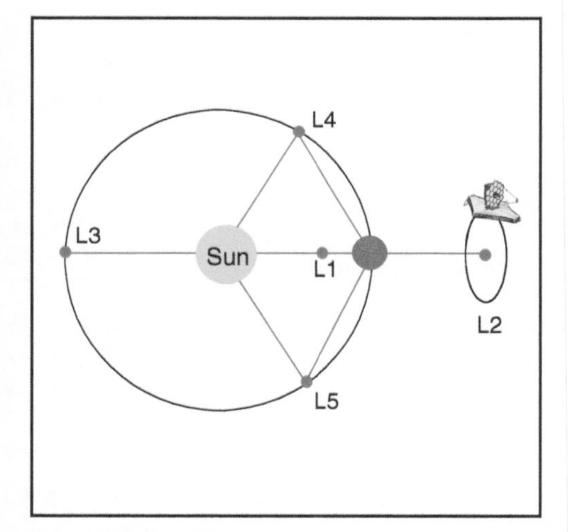

The JWST is positioned 1.5 million kilometers from Earth and orbits a gravitational point called the second Lagrange point, or L2. Here, the gravity of the Sun and Earth combine to pull the JWST along with the Earth, so that it has an orbit that always puts it directly in line with the Sun and Earth, with the Earth in the middle

3. As a class, debate the cost of projects such as the Hubble Space Telescope and the James Webb Space Telescope. Are they really worth their enormous cost? Form groups (these could be chosen by your teacher: either two large groups or multiple smaller groups), those for the telescopes, and those against. Research and present your argument for or against. At the end, write a short paragraph stating your viewpoint, with justification.

ISBN: 978-1-98-856693-1

Observing electromagnetic radiation

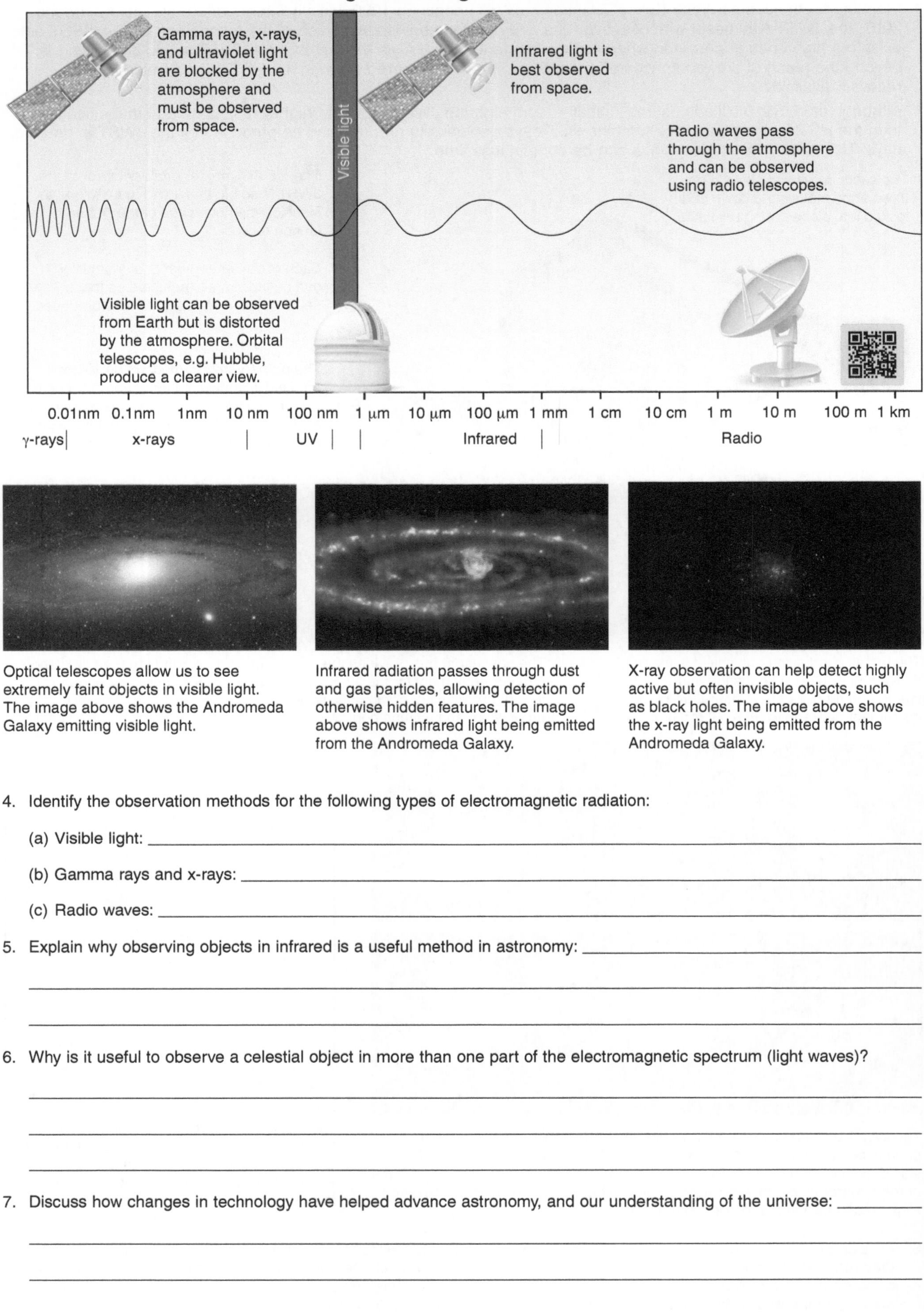

Optical telescopes allow us to see extremely faint objects in visible light. The image above shows the Andromeda Galaxy emitting visible light.

Infrared radiation passes through dust and gas particles, allowing detection of otherwise hidden features. The image above shows infrared light being emitted from the Andromeda Galaxy.

X-ray observation can help detect highly active but often invisible objects, such as black holes. The image above shows the x-ray light being emitted from the Andromeda Galaxy.

4. Identify the observation methods for the following types of electromagnetic radiation:

   (a) Visible light: ______________________________

   (b) Gamma rays and x-rays: ______________________________

   (c) Radio waves: ______________________________

5. Explain why observing objects in infrared is a useful method in astronomy: ______________________________

6. Why is it useful to observe a celestial object in more than one part of the electromagnetic spectrum (light waves)?

7. Discuss how changes in technology have helped advance astronomy, and our understanding of the universe: ______________________________

ISBN: 978-1-98-856693-1

13 Studying Stars

Key Question: How do we know what stars are made of?

- The sizes of the **stars** are almost incomprehensible. The Sun is a small to mid-sized star and has a diameter of 1,392,000 km. It is difficult to imagine the size of a star such as VY Canis Majoris, one of the largest known stars, with a mass around 17 times greater than the Sun, and a diameter around 1420 times that of the Sun.

Measuring the mass and size of a star

- The mass and sizes of stars can be measured by observing their effect on other objects, their absolute luminosity, i.e. the total amount of energy emitted, which is related to brightness, and their temperature.
- A binary or planetary system is needed for an accurate assessment of mass. In a such a system, Kepler's laws of motion can be used to relate the mass of the stars to the period of orbit of the planets around them.
- The size of the star is related proportionally to its luminosity (large stars are usually brighter than small stars). Luminosity can be calculated based on a star's distance from Earth (measured by parallax) and the use of the inverse square law (luminosity decreases in proportion to distance).

Canis Majoris (above) is a red hypergiant and one of the largest stars known. In comparison, the Sun, with a diameter of more than 1 million km, is the size of the dot shown with the arrow above.

Magnitude and luminosity

- A star's apparent magnitude is how bright the star is to the naked eye. The scale is "backwards" and logarithmic: a magnitude 1 star is 2.5 times brighter than a magnitude 2 star. The absolute magnitude is the apparent magnitude the star would have if placed at a distance of 10 parsecs (32.6 light years) from Earth. If the distance to the star is known, then the absolute magnitude can be calculated from the apparent magnitude.
- Luminosity and absolute magnitude are related. The more luminous a star is, the smaller its absolute magnitude. In astronomy, luminosity is the total energy emitted over all wavelengths per unit of time (synonymous with watts (W, power)).
- The table below shows the apparent and absolute magnitudes, and the luminosity of several stars:

Star	Apparent magnitude	Absolute magnitude	Luminosity (Sun = 1)	Distance (light years)
Sun	-26.8	4.83	1	0
Aldebaran	0.75	-2.1	518	65
Betelgeuse	0.42	-2.9	150,000	640
VY Canis Majoris	7.9	-9.4	2.7 billion	3900
Vega	0.03	0.58	50	25

1. Identify two ways of calculating a star's mass: ______

2. What is the apparent magnitude of the Sun? ______

3. The star Sirius has an apparent magnitude of -1.46 and an absolute magnitude of 1.4. What is meant by apparent magnitude and absolute magnitude?

______

4. (a) Which star appears brighter to a person on Earth, Aldebaran, or VY Canis Majoris? ______

   (b) Which star is actually brighter? ______

ISBN: 978-1-98-856693-1

SPQ PS4.B ESS1.A

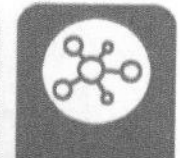

How do we know what a star is made of?

- The composition of a star can be determined by its **absorption spectrum**.
- The very hottest, inner layers of most stars emit an almost continuous spectrum of electromagnetic (EM) radiation. When the visible section of this radiation passes through the outer layers, gaseous elements there absorb certain wavelengths, leaving dark bands in the EM spectrum that is finally emitted from the star. This pattern of dark bands can be compared with the absorption spectra, determined in laboratories, for specific elements, as each **element** has a unique "spectral fingerprint".
- When reaching the Earth, the light can be passed through a prism to split it up into the spectrum of colors (ROYGBIV). Within this spectrum, black lines will indicate the "missing" wavelengths of light, i.e. those absorbed by elements in the star being observed (below and right).

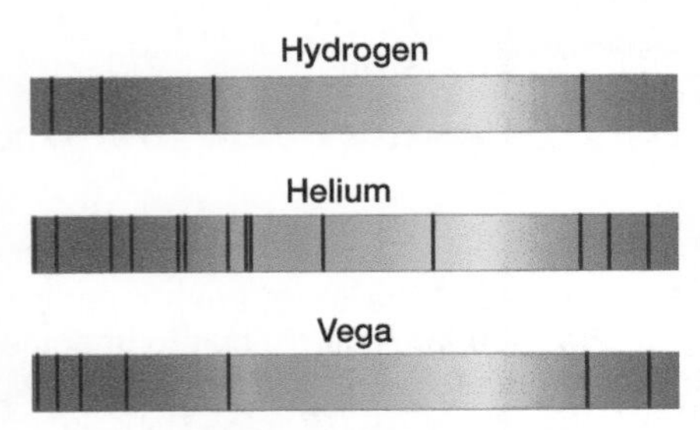

The absorption spectra of hydrogen and helium and the star Vega. Vega shows hydrogen absorption lines and weaker helium lines.

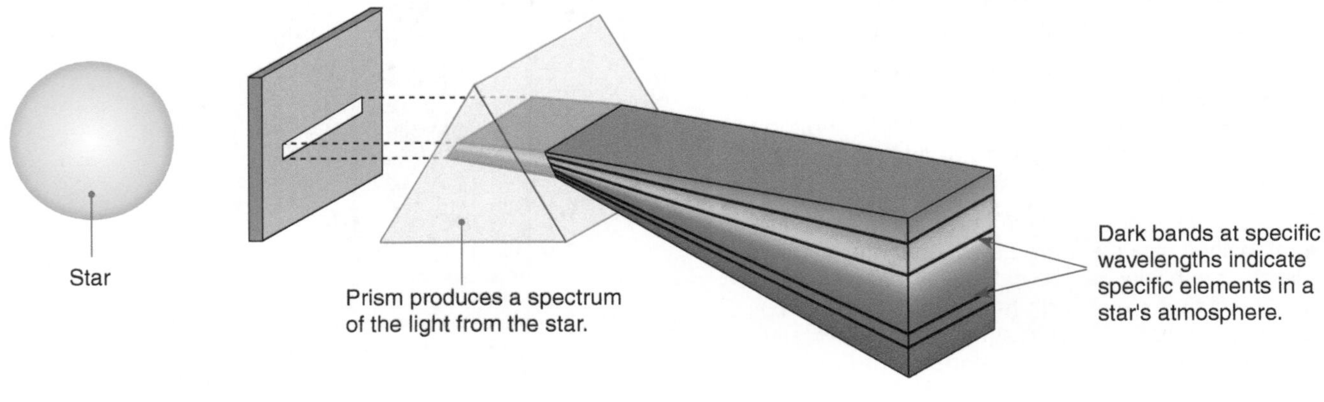

Absorption by atoms

- The lines in a star's light spectrum are at specific wavelengths. These wavelengths correspond to the energy absorbed and re-emitted by electrons orbiting atoms in a star's atmosphere.

Early in the 20th century, it was established that the electrons in atoms (and ions) can only be found at certain energy levels around the nucleus. The symbol **n** represents the level number with n = 1 level being the ground state (lowest level). Any energy absorbed or released by an atom must match the difference in energy between two energy levels. This is why only certain wavelengths of light (the photons corresponding to each wavelength have a unique energy) can be absorbed or emitted.

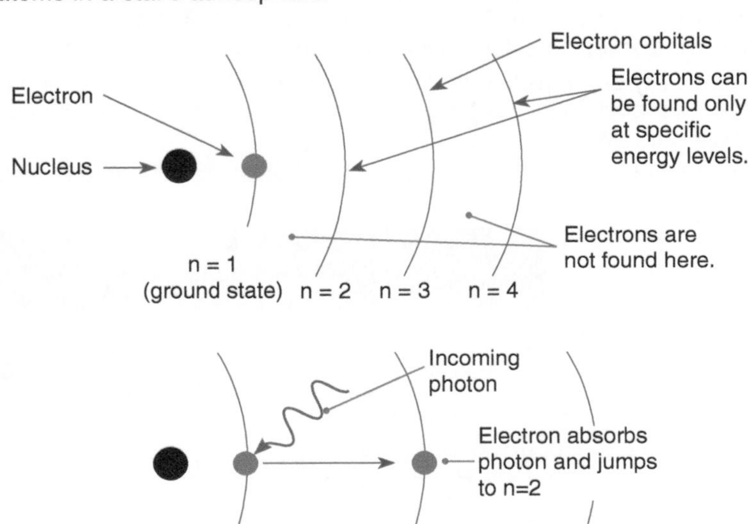

A hydrogen atom has one electron. Normally, it orbits the nucleus at an energy state of n = 1 (the ground state). If a photon of light with the right wavelength hits it, the electron will jump to the next level n = 2 (an excited state). The wavelength of the photon needed to do this is 121.4 nanometers. A photon with a wavelength of 103 nm will make the electron jump from n = 1 to n = 3 (remember shorter wavelengths of light carry greater energy).

Incoming photon

Electron absorbs photon and jumps to n=2

n = 1 n = 2 n = 3

As the electron returns to the ground state from n = 2, it emits a photon equal to what it absorbed (121.4 nm). The photon will be emitted in a random direction (likely in a different direction from its original travel). This results in the missing wavelength of light, and so causes the dark bands seen in an absorption spectrum.

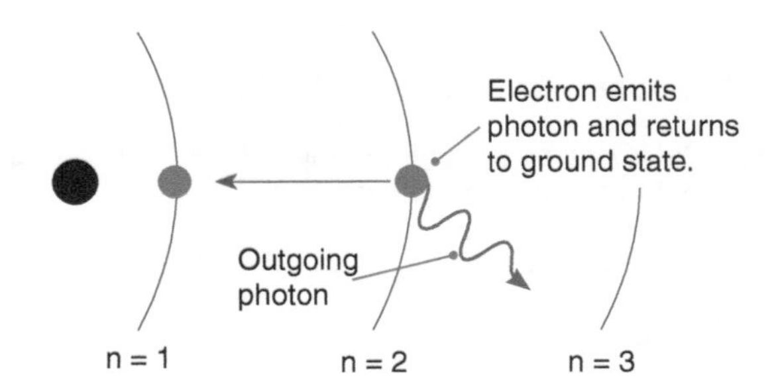

5. What causes the lines in the a star's absorption spectrum? ______________________________

____

ISBN: 978-1-98-856693-1

Comparing absorption spectra

- The graph below shows the absorption curves for the star Vega, the Sun, and the star Aldebaran. Vega is a blue-white star with a surface temperature of about 9600 K, the Sun is a yellow star with a surface temperature of about 6000 K, and Aldebaran is a orange giant with a surface temperature of about 3900 K.
- The large dips indicated in the spectrum of Vega are consistent with the absorption lines in the visible hydrogen spectrum. The dip at 410 nm (H_δ) indicates an electron jumping from n = 2 to n = 6. Although the Sun also has large amounts of hydrogen, the dips are not as prominent. These differences are due to the stars having different temperatures and luminosities. Photons flowing from the Sun generally do not have enough energy to bump electrons in hydrogen up to higher energy states.

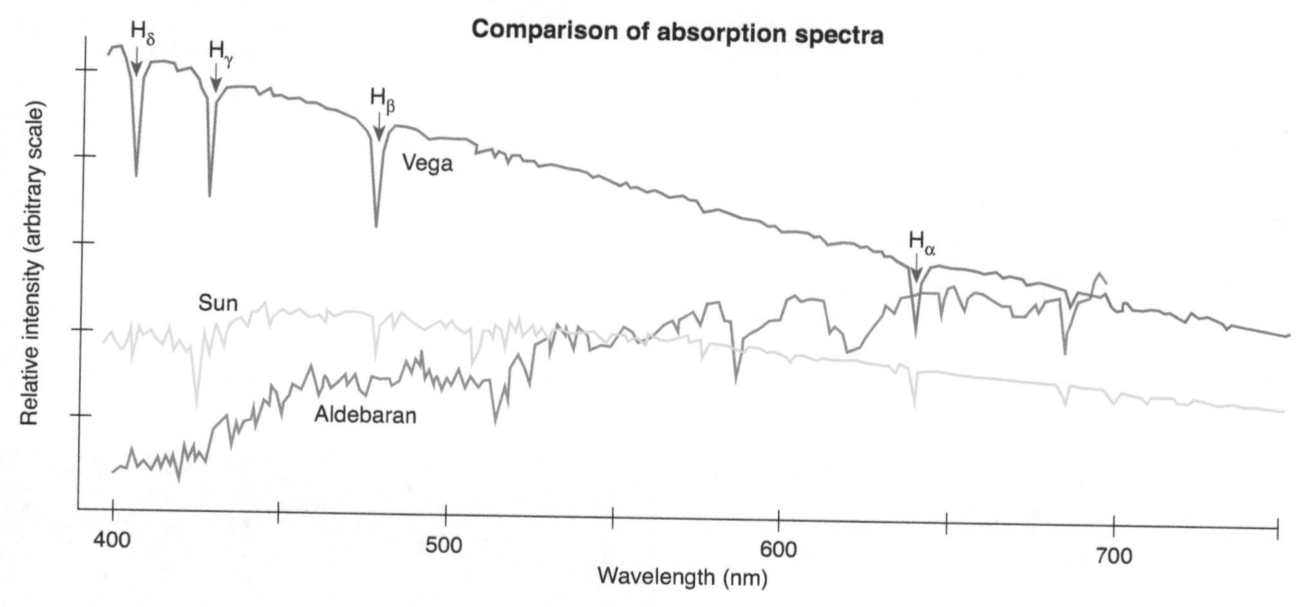

6. Explain briefly how the composition of a star can be determined: ______________________________

7. The diagram, below left, shows the absorption spectra of four different elements. Use them to identify the elements present in the two hypothetical stars, A and B, below right:

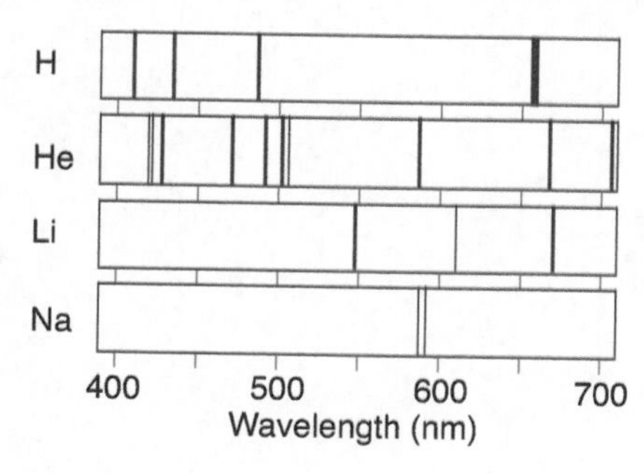

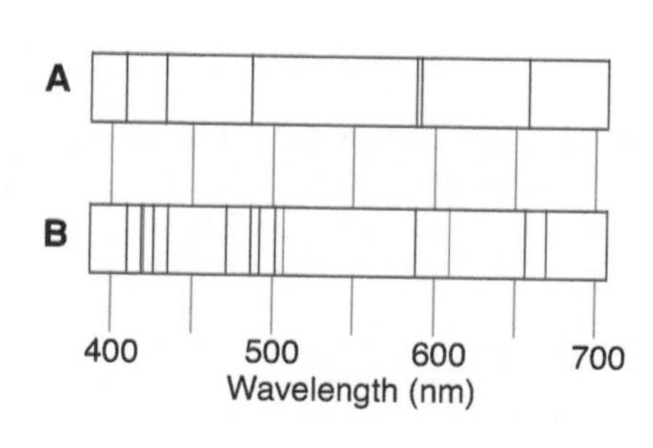

(a) A: ______________________________

(b) B: ______________________________

8. All stars are made up of mostly hydrogen and helium, with small amounts of heavier elements. Explain why the absorption spectra of very hot, blue stars do not generally show hydrogen lines in the visible spectrum, whereas blue-white stars, such as Vega, show prominent hydrogen lines, and yellow stars like the Sun show only small hydrogen lines:

ISBN: 978-1-98-856693-1

Star color and temperature

- Recall that temperature can be inferred, in part, from color. For example, a piece of iron heated in a hot flame will initially glow red, then orange-yellow as it gets hotter, and finally may reach white hot.
- The temperature of stars can be determined from their color in a similar way (below). Remember, short wavelengths produce blue colors, whereas long wavelengths produce redder colors.

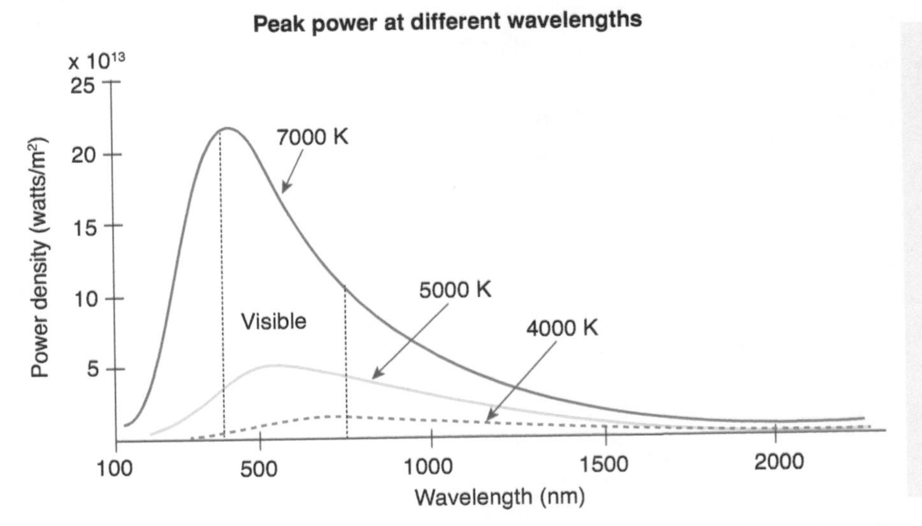

By measuring the wavelength at a star's peak power density, the star's temperature can be determined using the **Wien Displacement Law**.

$$\text{Wavelength } \lambda_{max} \text{ (m)} = \frac{b}{T}$$

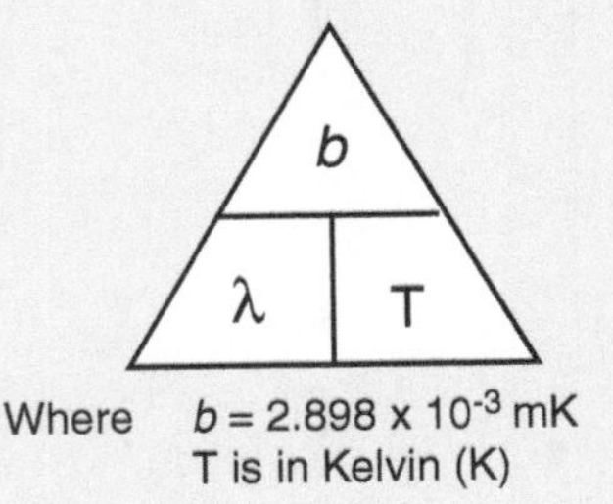

Where $b = 2.898 \times 10^{-3}$ mK
T is in Kelvin (K)

9. The image on the right shows a sparkler as it is burning.

   (a) Identify and label the three bright distinct colors that can be seen on the shaft of the burning sparkler:

   ____

   ____

   (b) List the colors from hottest to coolest:

   ____

   ____

10. The image on the right shows stars of various colors. List the circled stars in order of their temperature, from hottest to coldest:

    ____

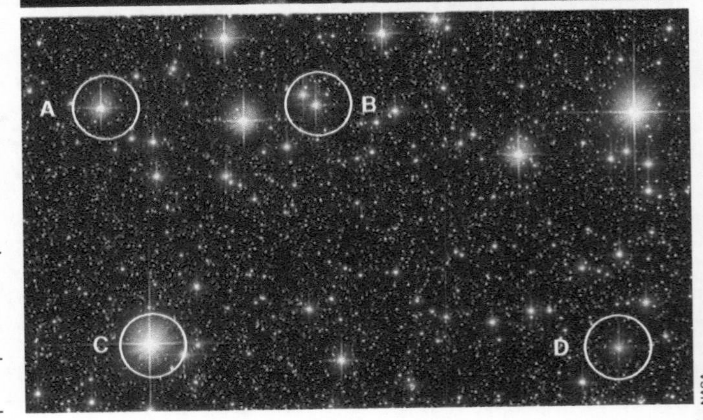

11. (a) What color would a star emitting its peak energy at a wavelength of 300 nm appear?

    ____

    (b) Why? ______________________

    ____

    ____

12. Use the Wien Displacement Law to determine the temperature of the following stars:

Star	Wavelength (nm) at peak power density	Wavelength (m) at peak power density	Temperature (K)
Antares	934		
Vega	311		
Regulus	223		
OTS-44 brown dwarf	1260		
Sun	502		

ISBN: 978-1-98-856693-1

14 The Known Universe

Key Question: Where exactly are we in the universe, and what is its shape and size?

Our place in the universe

1. (a) What is the distance to the Sun's nearest star? ______________________

   (b) What percentage of the diameter of the Milky Way Galaxy is this? ______________________

   (c) What is the distance to the nearest major galaxy? ______________________

ISBN: 978-1-98-856693-1

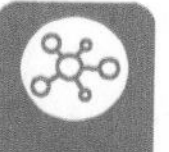

Just how big is big?

- One of the problems when studying space phenomena, is the human limitation of visualizing the distances between galactic and intergalactic objects. Comparisons are usually made by analogy, and compressing scales into distances we can understand. Here's an example:
- If the Sun was the size of a marble 1 cm in diameter then:
  - The Earth would be 0.09 mm in diameter and 1 m from the Sun.
  - Jupiter would be 1 mm in diameter and 5.5 m from the Sun.
  - Proxima Centauri (the nearest star to the Sun) would be 289 km away.
  - The distance to the center of the Milky Way galaxy would be 1.7 million km.
- Even if we scaled the entire Milky Way galaxy (100,000 light years across) down to 1 cm in diameter then:
  - The Large Magellanic Cloud (a small galaxy orbiting the Milky way) would be 1.63 cm away.
  - The Andromeda galaxy (the nearest large galaxy) would be 2.5 m away.
  - The cosmic horizon (as far as we can see with the most powerful telescopes) would be 1.3 kilometers away.
  - The estimated diameter of the observable universe would be 9.3 km.

The size of the universe

- From the Earth, the furthest objects we can see in space emitted light over 13 billion years ago. We are seeing them as they were 13 billion years ago.
- While light from these furthest objects has taken 13 billion years to reach us, that does not mean they are 13 billion light years away. The universe has been expanding during that time.
- This means the most distant objects are now much further away than would be expected if the universe was not expanding. The most distant objects seen so far have been calculated to be more than 30 billion light years away.
- Taking the expansion of the universe into account, it is estimated that the edge of our observable universe is actually 46.6 billion light years away, and from our viewpoint the universe is about 93 billion light years in diameter.

Apparent distance to UDFy38135539 = 13.1 billion LY

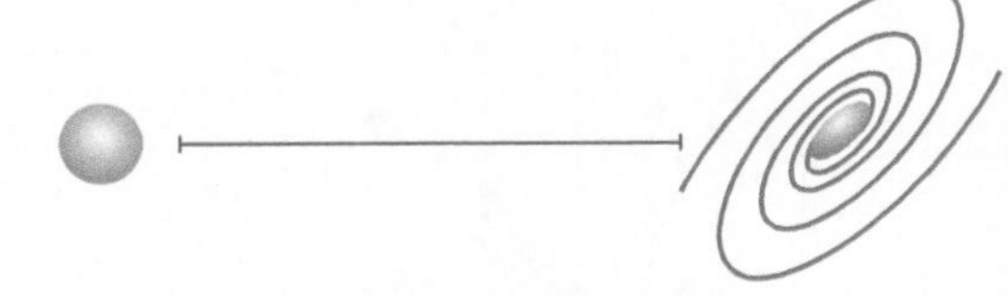

Actual distance to UDFy38135539 = 30 billion LY

What is the universe made of?

- The universe we can actually see and measure makes up only around 4% of the actual matter and energy in the universe.
- It is estimated that 26% of the universe is dark matter, and a massive 70% is dark energy. Both dark matter and dark energy are currently unobservable. We know they must exist because of the motions of the stars and galaxies, but neither dark matter nor dark energy appear to interact with any "normal" matter as we know it.
- The composite image (right) shows a merging cluster of galaxies (Abell 520). The blue colored area in the middle indicates where most of the mass appears to be, which is likely dark matter.

2. In groups, discuss the scales shown on the previous page. Do they have any real meaning to you? Work out some other scales to compare the sizes of the solar system, distance to the galaxies etc., and write them in the space below:

ISBN: 978-1-98-856693-1

3. What is diameter of the observable universe? ___

4. Explain why the galaxy UDFy38135539 appears 13.1 billion light years away but is actually about 30 billion light years away:

___

___

5. (a) What are the three components that make up the universe? ___

   (b) What percentage of the universe comprises normal visible matter? ___

6. How do we know dark matter and dark energy exist, when they cannot be observed directly? ___

___

___

The shape of the universe

If you draw a triangle on a flat piece of paper, the internal angles of the triangle add up to 180°, but what happens if you draw a triangle on the surface of a ball? The internal angles add up to more than 180°. And what about the surface of a saddle? The internal angles of a triangle add up to less that 180°. Now, imagine drawing a huge triangle on the "surface" of the universe. What would the internal angles of the triangle be? The answer depends on whether the universe is curved or flat. The answer has important consequences for the shape and fate of the universe.

If the internal angles of your triangle add to be greater than 180°, then the universe is positively curved like a sphere. In this case, the universe is finite but has no edge. It will eventually slow its expansion and collapse back in on itself.

If the triangle's internal angles add to be equal to 180°, then the universe is flat. In this case it will continue to expand forever, although the expansion will slow over an infinite amount of time. Current evidence suggests the universe is flat.

If your triangle has internal angles that add to less than 180°, then the universe is negatively curved, like the shape of a saddle. It is infinite and will expand forever at an ever increasing rate.

7. (a) Describe the path of two parallel light beams in a flat universe: ___

___

___

   (b) Describe the path of two parallel light beams in a positively curved universe: ___

___

___

   (c) Describe the path of two parallel light beams in a negatively curved universe: ___

___

___

8. Describe how the possible fates of the universe are related to the shape of the universe: ___

___

___

___

___

ISBN: 978-1-98-856693-1

15 The Big Bang

Key Question: How did the universe begin, and what events occurred as it formed?

- It is not known exactly what triggered the expansion of the universe, but it is known that 13.8 billion years ago, an infinitely dense, infinitely hot, and infinitely small ball of matter and energy called a **singularity** suddenly expanded to form the universe we know today. The event is commonly called the **Big Bang**.

The expanding universe

- A common misconception about the Big Bang is that it was an immense explosion, moving outwards into a void of empty space. In fact, before the Big Bang, there was no space. As far as humans are concerned, there was no anything.
- When the Big Bang occurred, an infinitesimal point expanded and, importantly, space expanded with it, i.e. space went from infinitely small, to (now) almost infinitely large. Think of a deflated balloon. As it is blown up it expands and the space inside it grows. Draw some dots or galaxies on the balloon and they move further apart as the balloon is blown up because the balloon is expanding, not because more material is being added to the balloon.

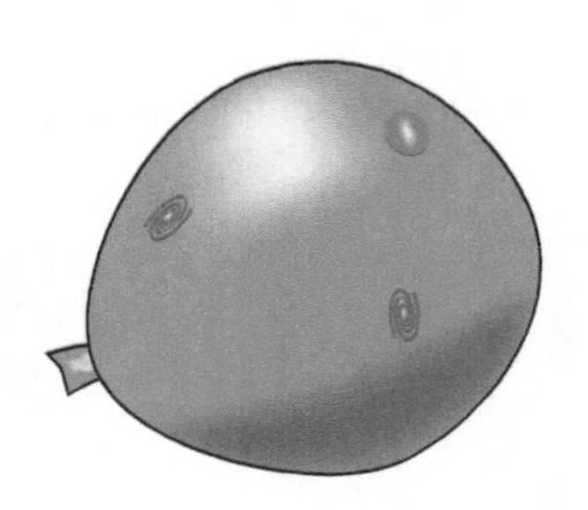

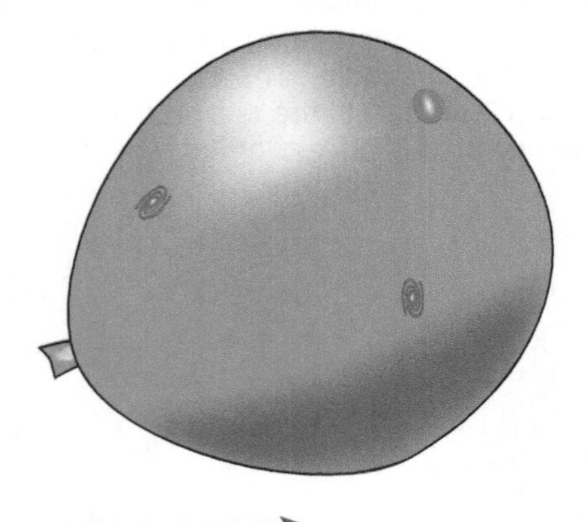

Time

The universe begins at time 0. Everything that currently exists in the universe was compressed to an infinitely small point called a singularity.

10^{-43} seconds after the Big Bang (that's a decimal point (.) followed by 42 zeros, then a 1) the temperature of the universe was 10^{32} °C. At this temperature, there is only one unified force. It is too hot for even elementary particles to form.

Between 10^{-38} and 10^{-35} seconds a process called inflation occurs. The universe grows by 10^{62} times. Inflation stops when the energy causing it is transformed into the matter and energy known today. The temperature drops to 10^{29} °C. Gravity separates from the other three fundamental forces.

0

10^{-43} seconds

10^{-38} seconds

The very early universe was filled with simple elementary particles and antiparticles, including high energy photons (gamma rays), electrons, and positrons.

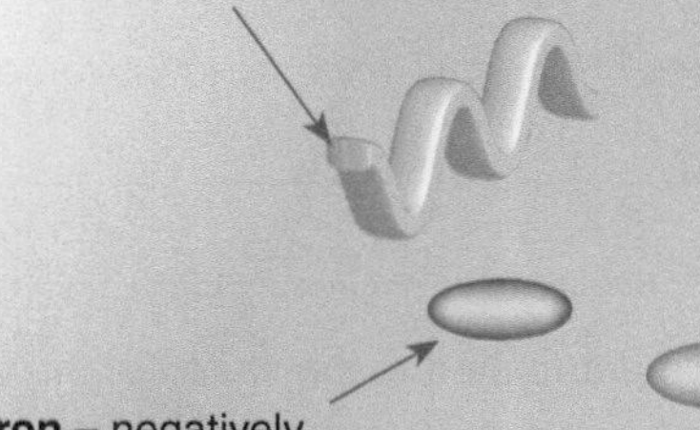

Photon – particles of light

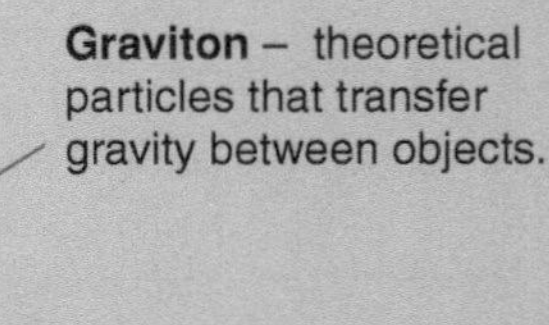

Graviton – theoretical particles that transfer gravity between objects.

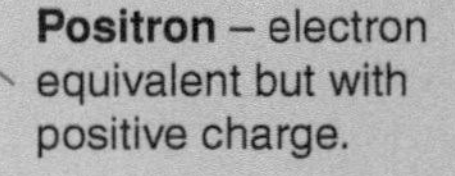

Electron – negatively charged particle. For an unknown reason, more electrons than positrons were produced in the Big Bang.

Positron – electron equivalent but with positive charge.

ISBN: 978-1-98-856693-1

An overview of the Big Bang and the evolution of the universe

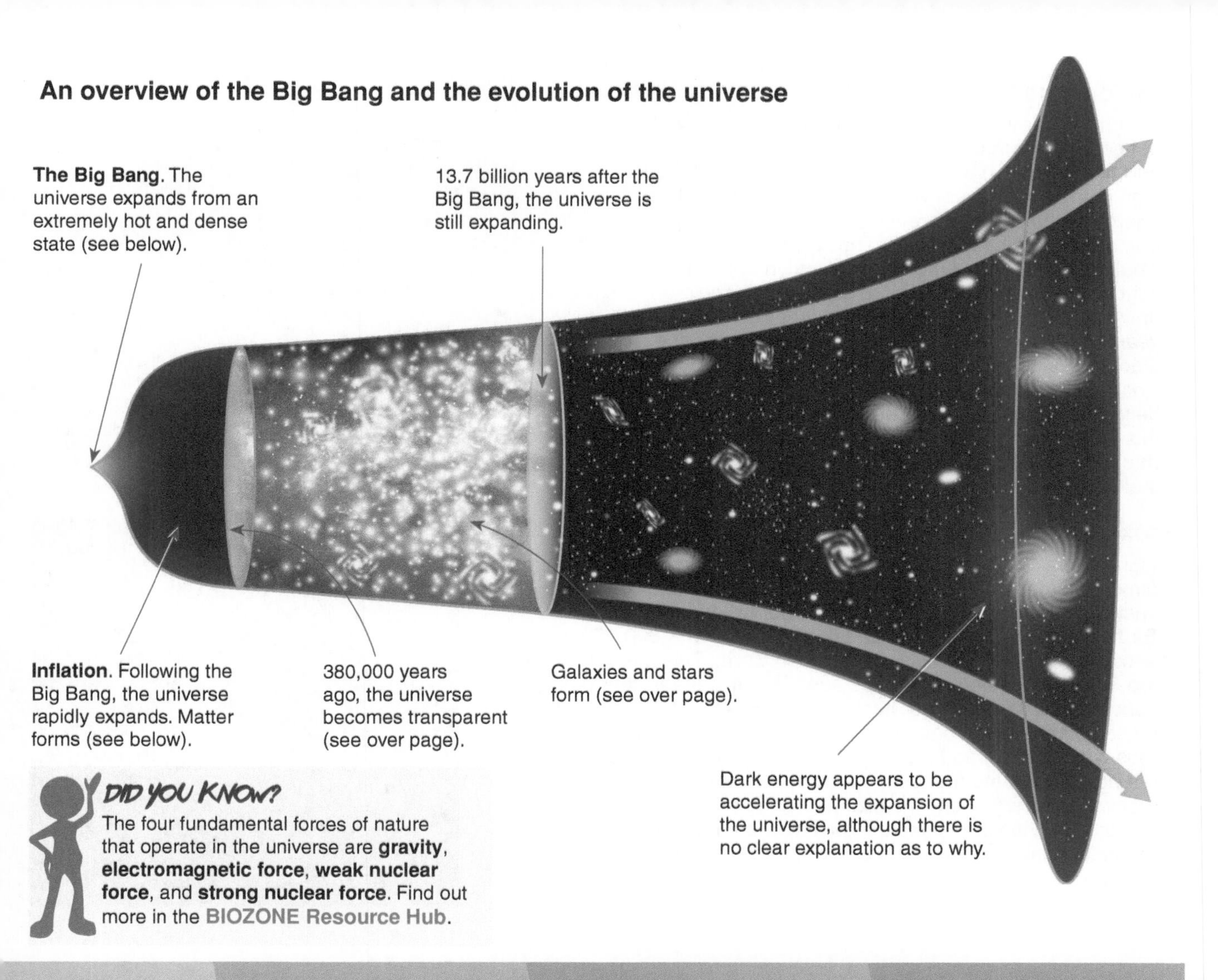

DID YOU KNOW?
The four fundamental forces of nature that operate in the universe are **gravity**, **electromagnetic force**, **weak nuclear force**, and **strong nuclear force**. Find out more in the **BIOZONE Resource Hub**.

e temperature of the iverse drops to 10^{15} °C. e four fundamental ces of the universe parate, and particles ch as gluons, and quarks m.

)$^{-12}$ seconds

The temperature of the universe drops to 1 trillion °C. Quarks combine to form protons and neutrons.

10^{-4} seconds

The universe continues to expand (but more slowly). The temperature drops to 5 billion °C. All positrons have been annihilated in collisions with electrons.

5 seconds

The universe's temperature reaches 1 billion °C, cool enough for protons and neutrons to join to together to form helium nuclei. Photons of light are still too energetic to let electrons join nuclei to form atoms.

3 minutes

Quarks are elementary particles and fundamental components of matter. There are six different types of quarks.

Gluons are particles that hold quarks together.

Proton

There are six different types of quarks. The combinations of three specific quarks produces protons and neutrons.

Proton

Neutron

ISBN: 978-1-98-856693-1

From opaque to transparent

- Seconds after the Big Bang, the universe was a very hot soup of **atomic nuclei** (hydrogen nuclei (protons) and helium nuclei) and free electrons, along with very high energy photons of light called gamma rays. The energy of the photons prevented the atomic nuclei from capturing the electrons. These free electrons would have scattered the photons, much like visible light is scattered by water droplets in a fog. The universe would have been opaque. After 380,000 years the photons had lost most of their energy and electrons were able to be captured by atomic nuclei. Photons were no longer scattered and the universe became transparent. The photons of light from this time make up what is now called the **cosmic microwave background** (CMB). It is the oldest light that we can detect.

The CMB can be detected throughout the sky in every direction.

Looking back in time

- Light travels at about 300,000 km/s. However, even at this almost unimaginable speed, light still takes time to travel the vast distances of space. The Sun is 150 million km away from Earth. Thus, light from the Sun takes 150 million ÷ 300,000 = 500 seconds (about eight minutes) to reach Earth. This means we see the Sun as it was eight minutes ago. Similarly, the further out into space we look, the further back in time we see. The light from the most distant objects has taken around 13 billion years to reach us, thus we see them as they were 13 billion years ago. The image to the right shows the first deep field image released from the JWST. It covers an area of sky the size of a grain of sand held at an arms length. Every point of light is a galaxy. The image contains some of the oldest galaxies yet seen. Some are estimated to be 35 billion light years away. We see them as they were just 200 million years after the Big Bang.

The temperature of the universe reaches about 3000 °C. Photon energies are low enough for electrons to join **atomic nuclei** and form atoms. Photons are no longer scattered by these electrons and the universe becomes transparent.

380,000 years

Gravity has had long enough to pull clumps of matter together into huge structures called filaments. Galaxies will form along these filaments, along with the first generation of stars. The explosion of first generation stars produces the elements heavier than carbon.

300–500 million years

The majority of the hydrogen and helium present in the universe today was formed during the early stages of the universe.

Hydrogen

Helium

Carbon

ISBN: 978-1-98-856693-1

1. How long ago did the Big Bang occur? ______

2. How long after the Big Bang did the following form:

   (a) Quarks: ______

   (b) Protons: ______

   (c) Atomic nuclei: ______

   (d) Atoms: ______

   (e) Galaxies: ______

3. Explain why the universe was opaque until around 380,000 years after the Big Bang: ______

4. What does the cosmic microwave background represent? ______

5. Read the following statement: "The universe was formed when a dense ball of material exploded into space, forming the universe we see today". Identify and comment on any errors in this statement:

The Sun forms as a second generation star. The heavy elements formed by the explosions of first generation stars form the planets orbiting it. The temperature of the universe is now -258°C. The Earth forms about 500,000 years after the Sun.

9 billion years

The planets of our solar system formed from the dust around the proto-Sun.

Presently, the temperature of the universe is -270°C, just a few degrees above absolute zero. The universe is still expanding, and evidence suggests the expansion is accelerating.

13.7 billion years

Andrew Pontzen and Fabio Governato

At the largest scale, the galaxies are collected together along huge filaments. It is suggested that these filaments formed as a result of ordinary matter interacting with dark matter.

ISBN: 978-1-98-856693-1

16 Evidence for the Big Bang

Key Question: What evidence is there for the Big Bang, and the beginning of the universe?

- When Albert Einstein published his equations for the General Theory of Relativity, they allowed for several solutions to how the universe could behave. In 1924, Alexander Friedmann solved the equations, to show that the universe could be expanding (it also could be contracting, or static). Before the end of the decade, observations by Edwin Hubble of the movement of distant galaxies confirmed that the universe was expanding. Since then, the discovery of the **cosmic microwave background**, and the hydrogen and helium composition of early **stars** has added weight to the theory that the universe was once much smaller, hotter, and denser than it is now.

1: Red-shifted galaxies

- Light travels at a constant speed, no matter whether an object is moving towards or away from you. What changes, is the wavelength of the light. Light waves emitted from an object moving towards you are compressed into the blue part of the spectrum. Light waves emitted from an object moving away from you are expanded into the red part of the spectrum. This is called the **Doppler effect**.

The Doppler effect

- It is likely that you have encountered the Doppler effect out on the street. Cars moving at speed towards you always appear to produce higher pitches (frequency) of sound than when they are moving away.
- The diagrams below shows the effect of a moving object on the sound waves its creates.

If the car is stationary, observer A and B hear the same frequency of sound.

If the car is moves towards observer B, then observer B hears a higher frequency of sound than normal, and observer A hears a lower frequency of sound than normal.

- The same thing happens for light waves. In this case the light waves in front of a moving object will be compressed or shorted. Short wavelengths of light are towards the blue end of the visible light spectrum so to an observer, an object moving towards them will appear bluer than normal and it appears blue-shifted.
- Light waves behind a moving object will be stretched out. Longer wavelengths of light are towards the red end of the visible light spectrum, so to an observer, an object moving away from them will appear redder than normal and it would appear red-shifted.

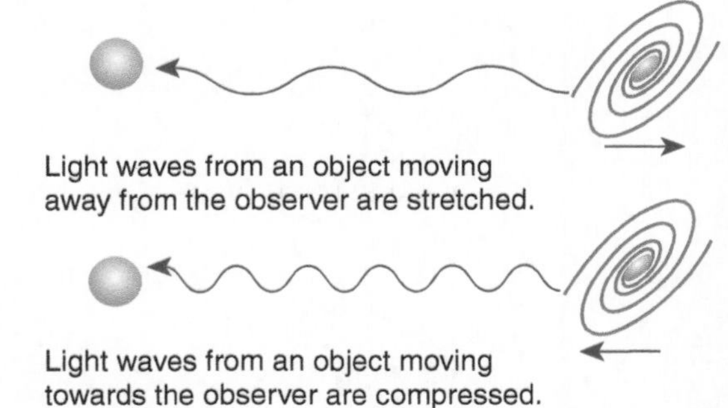

Light waves from an object moving away from the observer are stretched.

Light waves from an object moving towards the observer are compressed.

Red-shifted spectrums

- In the same way that light from stars can be separated into its spectrum, so too can light from galaxies. Elements in the galaxy absorb some of the wavelengths of light in this spectrum and produce dark bands. The spectrum of a galaxy moving towards us will have these characteristic bands shifted towards the blue end of its spectrum, while a galaxy moving away from us will have these bands shifted towards the red end of its spectrum and be red-shifted.
- In 1929, Edwin Hubble measured the red-shift of various galaxies. Hubble found that all but the very nearest galaxies were red-shifted, meaning they were moving away from us. Importantly, he also found that the further away they were, the more red-shifted they were and the faster they were moving away.

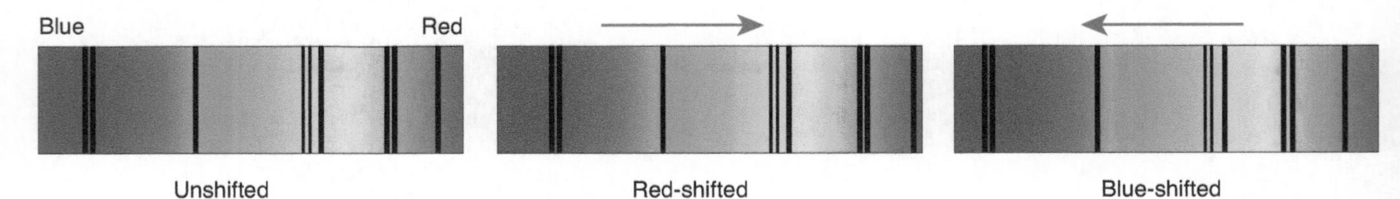

Unshifted

The spectral lines of a stationary galaxy are represented above.

Red-shifted

The spectral lines of a galaxy moving away from us will beshifted towards the red end of the spectrum.

Blue-shifted

If the galaxy is moving towards us the spectral lines will be shifted into the blue end of the spectrum.

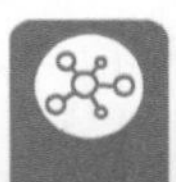

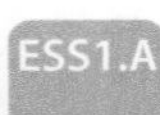

ESS1.A EM SC

ISBN: 978-1-98-856693-1

1. Explain what is meant by red-shifted: ______________________________

____

____

2. Study the spectral diagrams of galaxies A and B, below right. Compare them to the unshifted spectral diagram on the left. What can you say about galaxy A and galaxy B?

Blue

Red

Unshifted

A

B

____

____

____

3. How does the red-shifting of galaxies provide evidence for the Big Bang:?______________________________

____

____

2: Composition of early galaxies and stars

- The Big Bang theory states that, during the few seconds after the Big Bang, a small number of protons and neutrons fused to produce helium and a trace amount of lithium. Heavy elements were not formed because the conditions for the formation of heavier elements require a much greater time (tens of thousands of years) than the Big Bang lasted for. Therefore, when we measure the elements in distant young galaxies, we should expect to see large amounts of hydrogen (about 75% of all elements), smaller amount of helium (about 24%), and trace amounts of lithium and other elements.
- Measurements of these elements in young galaxies and stars match these predictions precisely.
- Because light takes billions of years to cross the vast distances between us and the most distant galaxies, we see them as they were just a few hundreds of millions of years after the Big Bang. This means we see the distant galaxies as being very young, compared to nearby galaxies, which we see as being very old.
- The absorption spectra of these young and old galaxies are very different, showing that the universe changes over time. This fits with the idea that the universe had a beginning.

NASA/ESA

Young gas clouds, stars, and galaxies comprise 75% hydrogen and 25% helium by mass, exactly what would be expected if hydrogen and helium were formed during the Big Bang.

4. Why could heavy elements not form during the Big Bang? ______________________________

____

5. (a) Why do nearby stars and galaxies have different compositions from the very distant stars and galaxies?

____

____

____

(b) How is this evidence for the Big Bang? ______________________________

____

____

ISBN: 978-1-98-856693-1

3: Cosmic microwave background

- It was realized as far back as the late 1940s that the heat and energy left over from the Big Bang should still be present and able to be detected. Astrophysicists, Ralph Alpher and Robert Herman, reasoned that the expansion of the universe since the Big Bang should have stretched the wavelength of the high energy radiation to somewhere in the microwave region of the electromagnetic spectrum, with a temperature of about 5 K (5°C above absolute zero).
- About 15 years later, Arno Penzias and Robert Wilson, working for Bell Telephone Laboratories found that the communications equipment they were working with produced a steady background radio noise, no matter how much they cleaned it or what direction they pointed it in. Inspection of the background noise showed it to have a "noise temperature" of 4.2 K. The wavelength of this radio noise was measured at 7.35 cm, within the microwave region of the spectrum. Refinements of measurements have now placed the average temperature at 2.728 K.

NASA

The Horn Antenna used by Arno Penzias and Robert Wilson.

Darker regions in the image of the Cosmic Microwave Backgound (CMB), shown right, show cooler temperatures; brighter regions show higher temperatures. The contrast of the image is 30,000 times (the temperature fluctuations are *very* small. Between the "hot" and "cold" regions there is a temperature difference of 0.0002 K). Fluctuations in the temperature indicate precursors to the large scale structures we see in the universe today.

NASA

6. (a) What is the cosmic microwave background? ______________________________

____

____

(b) Explain how the discovery of the CMB provided evidence for the Big Bang: ______________________________

____

____

____

7. The universe is about 13.7 billion years old. Describe how the CMB would have been different 2 billion years ago, and how it will have changed by 2 billion years in the future:

____

____

8. Study the three pieces of evidence for the Big Bang in this activity carefully. What is common to all these pieces of observable evidence, and why does this make them much more powerful than if they did not have this common feature?

____

____

____

____

ISBN: 978-1-98-856693-1

17 Modeling the Expansion of the Universe

Key Question: What actually happens during the expansion of space, and what does it look like to us on Earth?

The motion of galaxies

- The spectrum below shows a simplified reference spectrum. It shows the absorption for hydrogen (4 lines) plus one line each for sodium (Na) and magnesium (Mg). Below the reference spectrum, there are spectra for two different galaxies. You can explore many more of these using the Sloan Digital Sky Survey – Plate Browser, an online resource with data from hundreds of galaxies. Find the link on the **BIOZONE Resource Hub**.

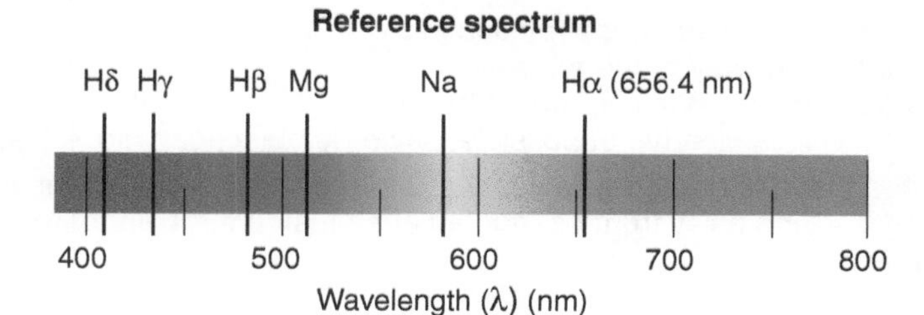

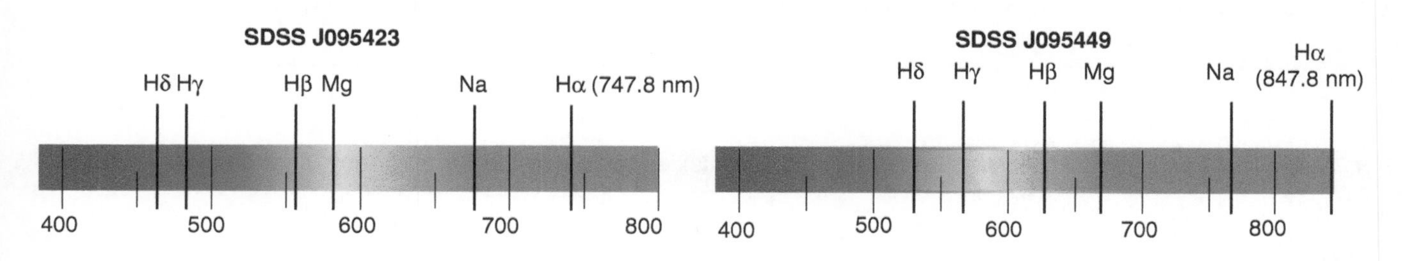

- The shift in wavelength (λ) caused by the **Doppler effect** can be used to calculate a z value. The greater the z value, the greater the distance the object or galaxy is from Earth. z values can also be used to calculate the recessional velocity of the object (the rate at which it is moving away). z is dimensionless, so it has no units. It can be calculated by:

$$z = \frac{(\lambda \text{ observed} - \lambda \text{ rest})}{\lambda \text{ rest}}$$

$\Delta\lambda$ / z | λ_r

- The table on the right shows some examples of recession velocities for a selection of z values. The third column expresses these velocities as a percentage of the speed of light. The fourth column gives the distance to the source of redshifted light at the time the light is received.

z	v (x10^5 km/s)	% of c	d (x 10^9 ly)
0.001	0.003	0.10	0.02
0.01	0.030	1.00	0.11
0.05	0.146	4.88	0.64
0.15	0.416	13.89	2.22
0.20	0.541	18.03	2.96
0.30	0.769	25.65	4.24
0.50	1.153	38.46	6.64
1.00	1.799	60.00	12.04
2.00	2.398	80.00	18.89
4.00	2.767	92.31	28.03
6.00	2.878	96.00	32.48
8.00	2.925	97.56	33.96

Note: **v** = recession velocity
c = speed of light
d = distance to the source of redshifted light

1. (a) Study the spectra of the galaxies above. What can be said about the position of the absorption lines in all the spectra compared to the reference spectrum?

____

(b) What does this mean about the movement of these galaxies? ____________________

(c) Use the Hα values to calculate the z value for the two galaxies. Which has the greatest redshift? ____________

____

____

(d) Use the table to give an approximate value for each galaxy's recession velocity:

(i) SDSS J095423: ____________________ (ii) SDSS J095449: ____________________

ISBN: 978-1-98-856693-1

SC EM ESS1.A

- In 1929, Edwin Hubble published a paper examining the relationship between the redshift of distant galaxies (from which recession velocity can be calculated) and their distance.
- The data he and his colleagues gathered can be plotted on a graph (right). It was the first observational evidence of what has become known as **Hubble's law**.
- Hubble's law can be expressed mathematically as **v = Hd**, where v is velocity, d is distance, and H is the Hubble constant. Since 1929, astronomers have used different methods to try to measure the Hubble constant more accurately. The most recent techniques put its value at around 70 km/s/Mpc plus or minus a few percent.

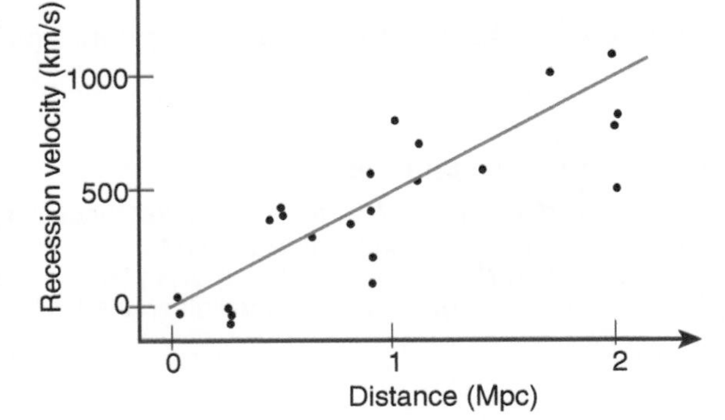

- The data produced an interesting problem. If the relationship shown by the graph held true all the way to the furthest galaxies, then those galaxies must be travelling away from us faster than the speed of light. This is clearly not possible, since no object can move faster than the speed of light.

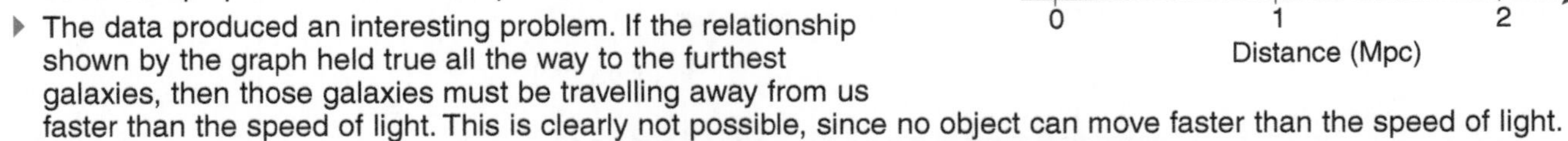

- Hubble's data led to the idea that it is not the galaxies that are moving. It is in fact the space between them that is expanding. The galaxies are moving away from us, not because they are moving through space, but because the space between them and us is expanding.

2. Describe the relationship between recession velocity of a galaxy and its distance from an observer:

___

___

- A simple investigation can illustrate the motion of the galaxies relative to the Earth (or any other observer), below.

Investigation 2.1 Modeling expansion.

See appendix for equipment list.

1. Set up a thick rubber band, held by a pin, on top of a sheet of paper, as shown in the drawing below.
2. Draw 4 marks on the band. Hold the rubber band tight (but not stretched) and record the positions of your marks, the end, and the pin's position on the paper. These are the start (original) positions.
3. Stretch the rubber band to double its length.
4. Use a different colored pen to record the 5 new positions of the marks on the paper. Measure the distances from the pin to the marks and record them in the first two columns of the table below.

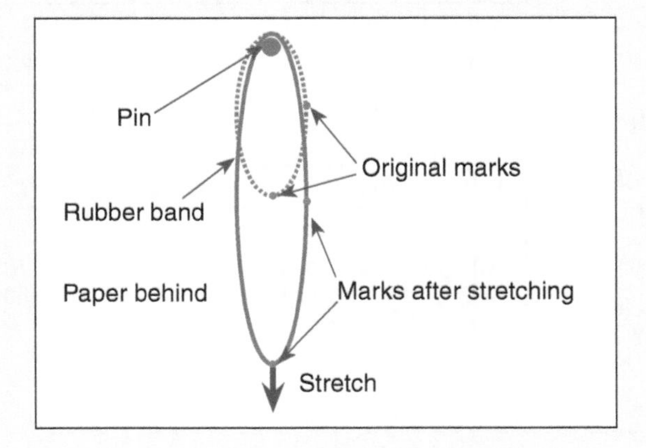

Mark	Original distance to pin (cm)	Stretched distance to pin (cm)	Speed (cm/s)
Pin			
1			
2			
3			
4			
End			

3. (a) Assume the movement of the band took one second. Using speed = distance ÷ time, calculate the speed the mark on the rubber band was moving while the rubber band was being stretched. Record this in the table above:

   (b) Which point was moving slowest relative to the pin (the observer)? ___

   (c) Which point was moving fastest relative to the pin (the observer)? ___

4. Is this consistent with the current model of the expansion of the universe? ___

___

ISBN: 978-1-98-856693-1

5. (a) On the grid below, plot the speed of each mark on the rubber band against the original distance from the pin. Draw a line of best fit through the points.

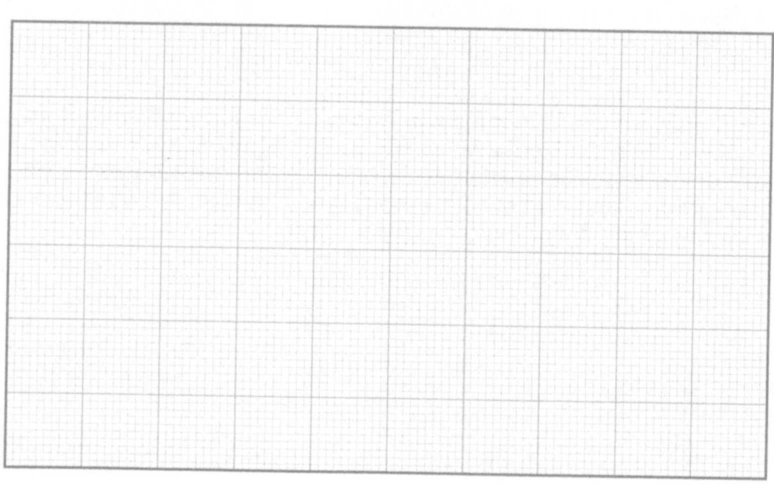

(b) Calculate the slope (gradient) of the line (include units). This produces the constant for the expansion of the rubber band universe - we will call this the "Rubble" constant.

____

(c) If the end of the band moves 3 cm, how far does the middle of the band move? ______________

(d) If the original rubber band was 200 cm long, how fast would the end be moving, assuming the Rubble constant you calculated holds true to that distance in the rubber band universe?

____

The expanding universe

- When we look out into space in any direction, we see distant galaxies are moving away from us. The expansion of space appears to be centered on us. How is that possible? Is the Earth the center of the universe?
- Not quite. The diagrams below show two sets of dots representing galaxies in an expanding universe. Set 2, on the right, is expanded 20% compared to set 1, on the left.
- Observe what happens below when different equivalent galaxies (marked A, B, and C) are matched up:

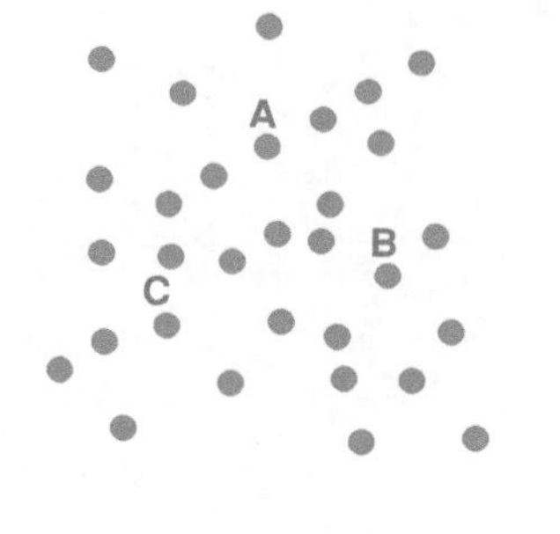

Set 1

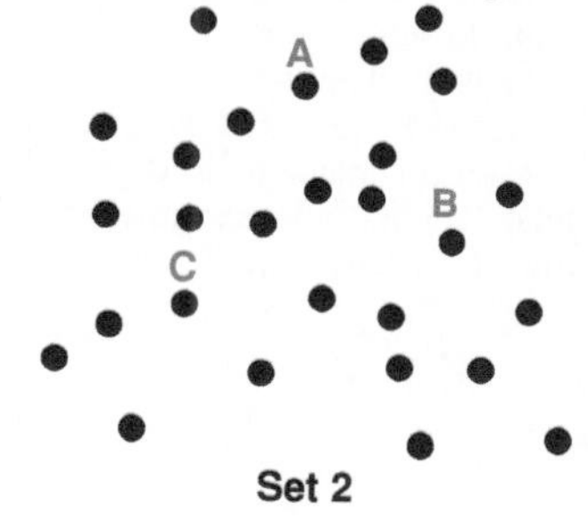

Set 2

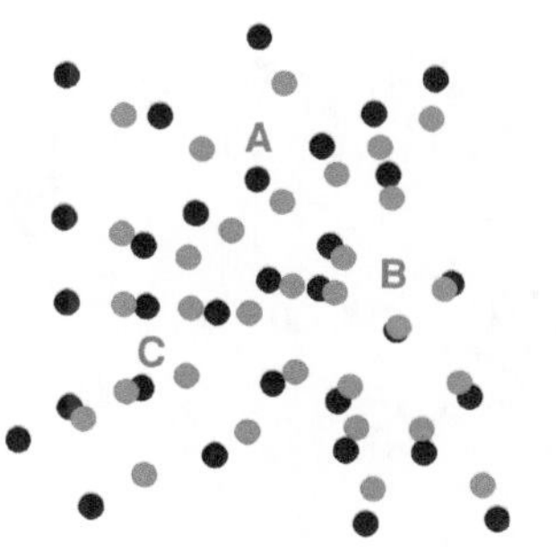

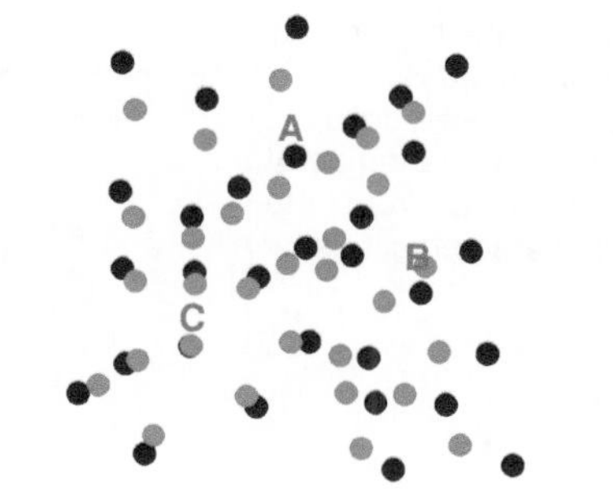

6. What appears to happen when A coincides, B coincides, or C coincides? ______________

____

____

7. What does this tell us about the expanding universe, and our apparent position in it? ______________

____

____

ISBN: 978-1-98-856693-1

18 The Sun

Key Question: What is the structure of the Sun, and what keeps it shining?

▶ The Sun contains 99.8% of all the mass in the solar system. It has a diameter of 1,392,000 km and is more than 330,000 times more massive than the Earth, with a mass of 1.99×10^{30} kg. The **Sun** formed about 4.5 billion years ago and will continue to shine, with little change, for at least another 4 billion years. When the Sun reaches about 10 billion years old, the hydrogen in its core will be exhausted. The core will shrink and the Sun will swell to form a red giant, with a diameter reaching out to the orbit of the Earth.

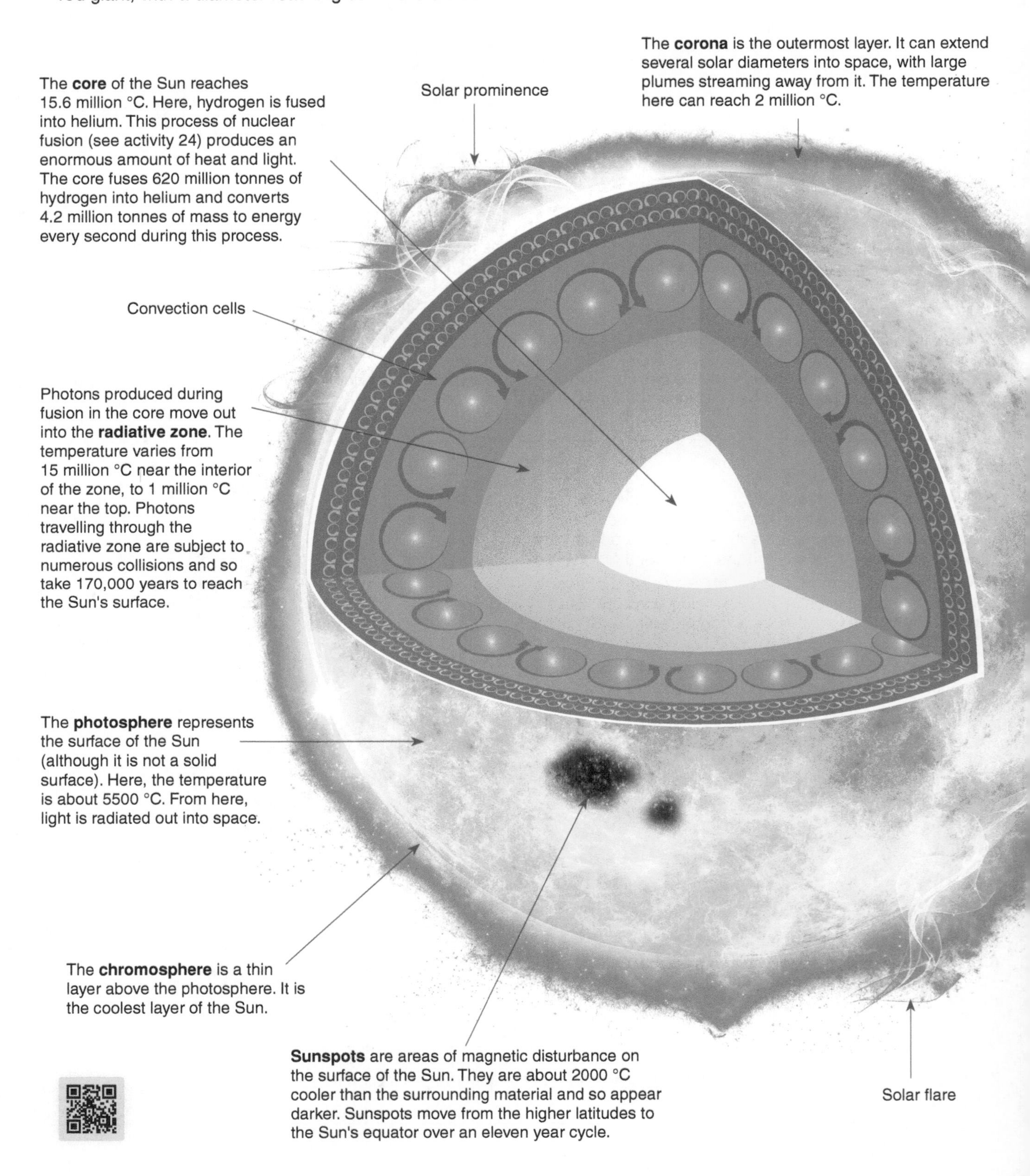

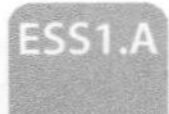

ESS1.A PS3.D SPQ EM

ISBN: 978-1-98-856693-1

1. (a) What type of reaction produces the Sun's energy? ______

   (b) Which two elements are involved in this process? ______

2. Why do sunspots appear darker than the rest of the Sun's surface? ______

3. Why is the photosphere considered the "surface" of the Sun? ______

Just how big is the Sun?

- The Sun is a massive object. It has about 99.8% of the mass of the solar system in it. Imagining its true size can be difficult, given that there's clearly nothing on Earth even remotely that large.
- We can do a simple experiment to measure the diameter of the Sun using a simple pinhole camera arrangement.

Investigation 2.2 Measuring the size of the Sun.

See appendix for equipment list.

1. Set up a pinhole camera by using a pin to punch a small hole through piece of aluminum foil. The foil can be held flat by taping it to a cardboard frame.
2. In a sunny place, hold the aluminum foil up to the Sun allowing light to pass through the pin hole onto a sheet of paper. Move the paper back and forth until a sharp image of the Sun is formed (this image may be quite small).
3. Measure the distance between the pinhole and paper where the image formed. Measure the diameter of the Sun's image.

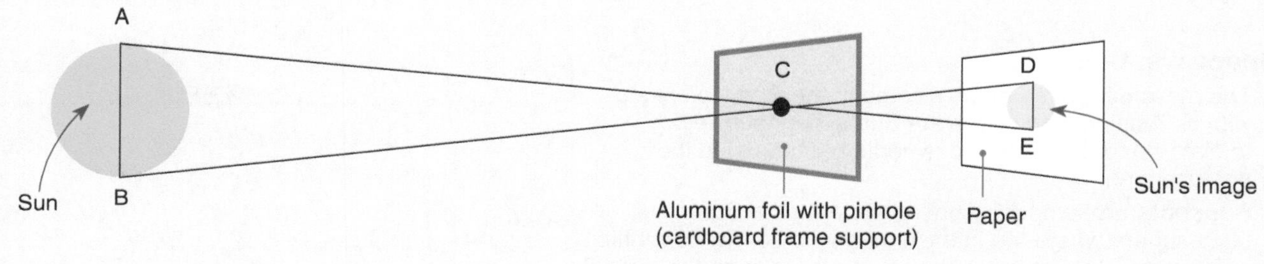

The two triangles in the diagram above are geometrically similar, therefore all corresponding sides are in the same ratio. This means that **AB÷AC is equal to DE÷EC**. The distance AC is 150 million km. Therefore:

$$\frac{\text{AB km}}{\text{150,000,000 km}} = \frac{\text{DE cm}}{\text{EC cm}} \quad \text{or} \quad \frac{\text{Diameter of Sun (km)}}{\text{150,000,000 km}} = \frac{\text{Diameter of image (cm)}}{\text{Distance from pinhole to image (cm)}}$$

4. Record your measurements in the space below:

   (a) Distance between pinhole and image: ______

   (b) Diameter of the image: ______

   (c) Calculate the diameter of the Sun, using your measurements: ______

   (d) Compare your result to others in your class. How close are theirs to yours? ______

   (e) Pool your class results and find the average diameter of the Sun. Compare this to the known diameter of the Sun. How close was the class's average result?

ISBN: 978-1-98-856693-1

Radiating light

- The nuclear reactions inside the core of the Sun produce photons of light that move outwards to the surface and then into space. Photons can take tens, to hundreds of thousands of years to reach the Sun's surface.
- Above the core is the **radiation zone** – an area of ionized gas (plasma), where energy is transported out by radiation and conduction. The temperature varies from 15 million K near the interior of the zone, to 1 million K near the edge. The radiation zone is very dense, so photons travelling through it are subject to many collisions. As a photon travels through the radiation zone, it is absorbed and remitted by nuclei at random. As a result, photons can take 170,000 years to leave the radiation zone.
- Above the radiation zone is the **convection zone**, where energy is transported by convection. This motion creates the Sun's magnetic field. The image of the surface of the Sun (far right) taken by NASA, shows the surface to be granulated. Each of the granulations is the top of a convection cell. The brighter, inner part of each granulation is where hot plasma is rising to the surface. The dark edges are where cooler plasma is descending. The darker spots are small sunspots.
- Above the convection zone is the **photosphere**. Here, the heat and light that have been radiated and convected from the Sun's interior are released into space as electromagnetic waves (radiation).

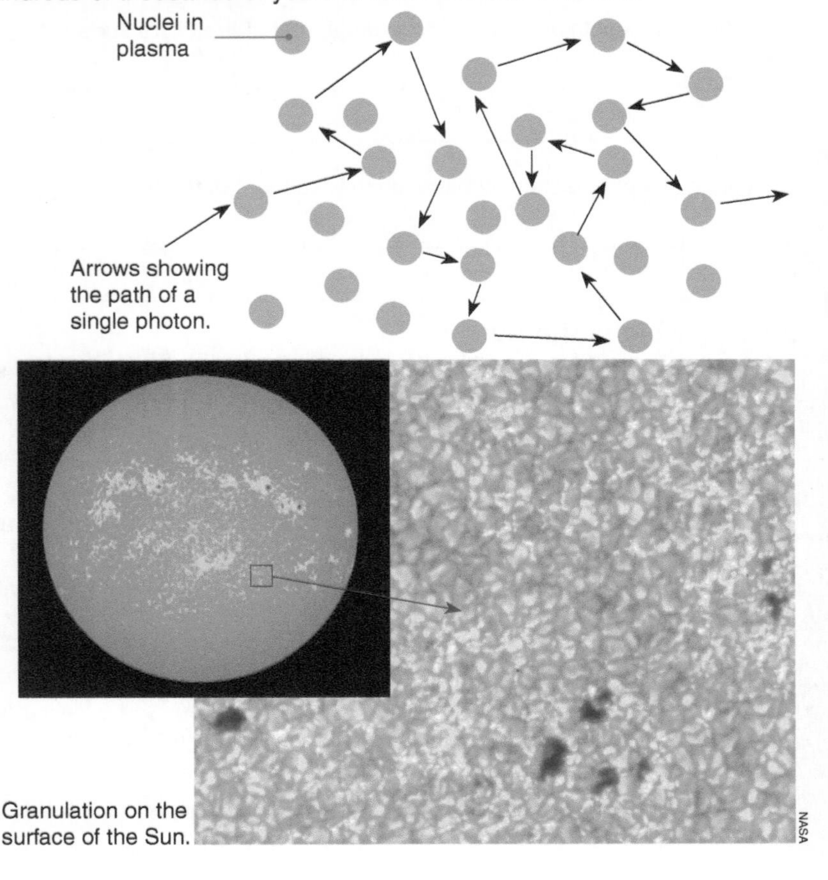

Granulation on the surface of the Sun.

Space weather!

- The movement of so much plasma in the Sun, combined with its rotation, can cause the Sun's magnetic field to distort and affect the movements of material in the photosphere.
- **Sunspots** are temporary phenomena on the Sun's photosphere where the intense magnetic activity can inhibit convection. This causes a darker, cooler spot on the surface as hot material is prevented from rising up.
- The magnetic field lines near sunspots often tangle and reorganize, causing explosions of energy associated with secondary phenomena such as solar flares, solar prominences, and coronal mass ejections. These add to the material constantly streaming from the Sun (the solar wind), sometimes disrupting the Earth's own magnetic field.

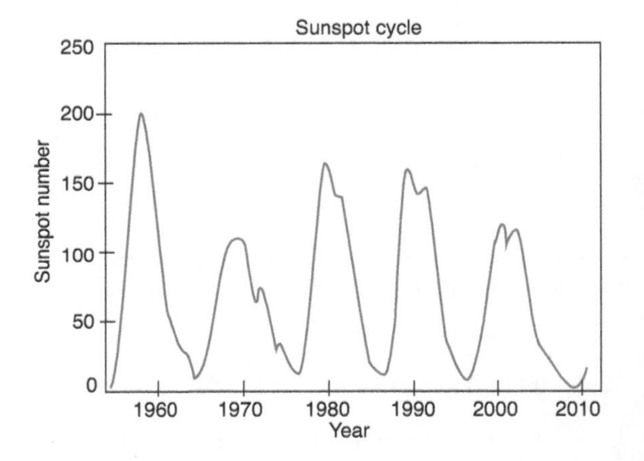

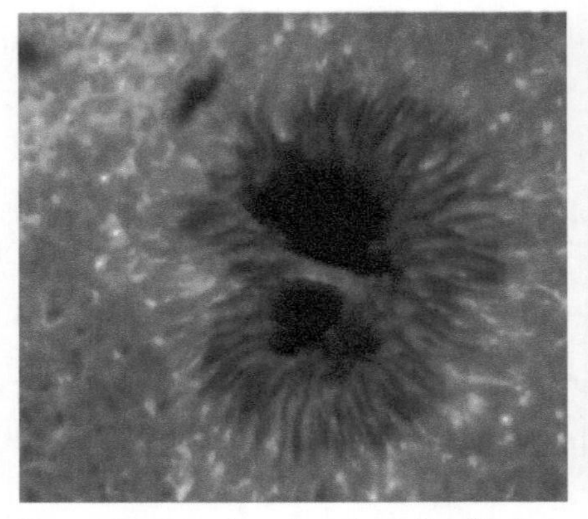

Sunspots come in pairs where the Sun's magnetic field punches through the surface, loops and plunges back through.

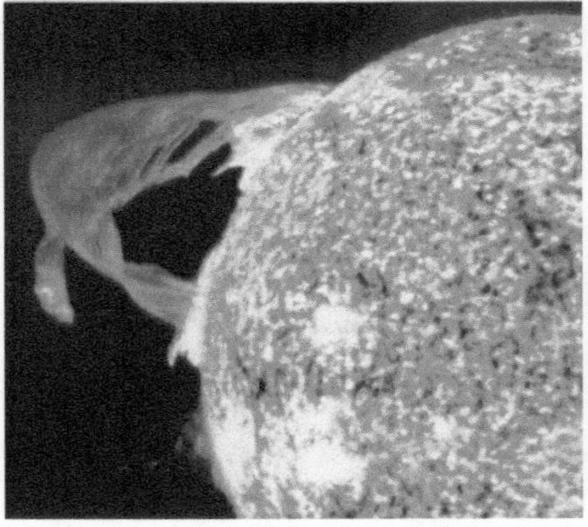

Solar prominences are loop shaped outbursts. They follow along the magnetic field lines of the Sun.

Solar flares are sudden releases of electromagnetic energy that can extend thousands of kilometers into space.

ISBN: 978-1-98-856693-1

5. (a) How do the photons emitted by the Sun originate?

(b) Why do the photons take so long to reach the surface of the Sun?

6. Why does the surface of the Sun look granulated?

7. What is the approximate length of the sunspot cycle?

8. What is a solar prominence?

For how long will the Sun shine?

- For a long time, one of the biggest mysteries in physics and astronomy was why did the Sun not burn out? By the 1850s, evidence was building that Earth and the life on it had been around for hundreds of millions, if not billions, of years. Life clearly needed the Sun, yet no one could explain how the Sun could have lasted for so long.
- Following Cecilia Payne-Gaposchkin's discovery in 1925, we realized that the Sun was mostly made of hydrogen.
- Knowing now, that the Sun is powered by the nuclear fusion of hydrogen into helium, we can calculate the age of the Sun. The Sun has a power output of 3.8×10^{26} J/s (joules per second (watts)).

9. The mass of a hydrogen proton is 1.673×10^{-27} kg. The mass of a helium atom is 6.644×10^{-27} kg. During fusion, 4 protons form the 2 neutrons and 2 protons in a helium nuclei. Calculate the mass missing from the hydrogen to helium fusion reaction:

10. The missing mass is turned into energy. We can use Einstein's equation $E = mc^2$ to calculate the energy produced when one atom of helium is produced. Use E (joules) m (missing mass in kg) and c (speed of light, 300,000,000 m/s):

11. If the Sun emits 3.8×10^{26} J/s, calculate the number of hydrogen to helium reactions that occur every second:

12. Calculate the mass the Sun converts into energy every second:

13. Nuclear fusion only occurs in the core of stars, such as the Sun. Estimates put the mass of the Sun's core at 10% of the Sun's total mass. When this mass of hydrogen is used up the Sun will begin to "die":

(a) Calculate the mass of the Sun's core:

(b) What mass of hydrogen is reacted every second?

(c) Calculate how may seconds it will take for the Sun to use up the mass of hydrogen fuel in its core:

(d) Convert this to years:

(e) Given that we know the age of the Earth to be about 4.5 billion years old (and therefore that is also presumably the age of the Sun) how many more years will the Sun shine for?

ISBN: 978-1-98-856693-1

19 Life Cycle of Stars

Key Question: How do stars form and change over their life cycle, and how does mass affect the life cycle of stars?

- Nuclear fusion in the core of a **star** produces a continuous stream of high energy photons, causing pressure that pushes the matter of a star outwards. However, gravity, produced by the mass of the star, is always pulling the matter of the star inwards towards the core. These two opposing forces determine the size of a star and keep its size static for most of its life cycle.
- You have calculated the age of our **Sun** and how long it will burn for. From this, you can conclude that the Sun is a star in middle age. But what was it like when it was younger? What will it look like when it is older? To answer this, we must look at other stars (below).

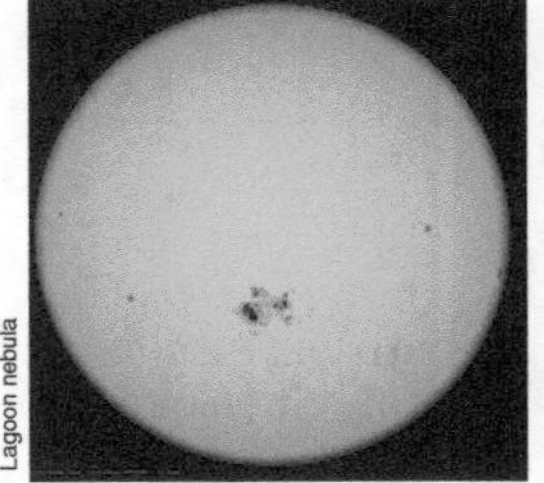

All images NASA except Lagoon nebula

A. The Sun

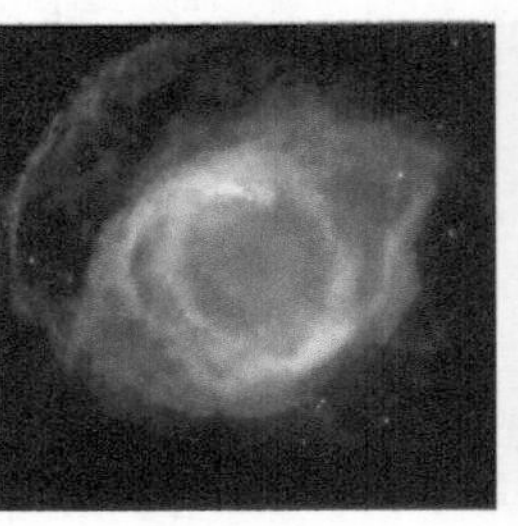

B. Helix Nebula (planetary nebula)

C. Mira, a red giant

D. White dwarf (arrowed)

E. Lagoon Nebula. An area of star formation.

ESO CC 4.0 https://www.eso.org/public/images/eso1403a/

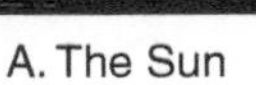

1. (a) The images above show stars that were similar to our Sun at different parts of their life cycle. Place the images in the order that you think would show the life cycle of our Sun, from young to old:

   (b) Which of these structures do you think is the largest?

   (c) What would happen if the temperature in a star's core increased?

   (d) What would happen if the temperature in a star's core decreased?

Forming a star

- We have seen that the Sun burns hydrogen nuclei in its core to form helium nuclei. But before this happens, two questions must be answered: where does the hydrogen come from, and how do the fusion reactions begin?
- Hydrogen is the most common **element** in the universe. Hydrogen and helium (and trace amounts of other elements) are found as nebulae, huge clouds of dust and gas that may be light years across.
- A disturbance near the nebula, e.g. the shockwave from a supernova, may cause it to begin to collapse, as gas atoms are pushed closer to each other and are attracted by gravity to others.
- Given that the gas will eventually collapse to a central point (the eventual star), the majority of the atoms will have a very large amount of gravitational potential energy (think of something suspended a light year off the ground). This is the energy that can spark the nuclear reactions in a new star.

NASA/ESA

The Carina Nebula, an area of star formation, as imaged by the James Webb Space Telescope

2. (a) What happens to the speed of the atoms in the nebula as they fall inwards towards its center?

   (b) Explain how this change can ignite nuclear reactions in the center of the newly forming star:

ISBN: 978-1-98-856693-1

Ages and sizes

- Just looking up at the night sky is enough to tell us that there are many different types of stars. Some appear blue, others are red. Some are very bright, some seem much larger in the sky than others.
- Some of this, of course, is because of the different distances to the stars. But some of the differences are due to the size and age of the stars.
- Consider the different examples of stars below:

Canopus is the second brightest star in the sky (after Sirius). It is a white star, 8 times more massive than the Sun. Some estimates put its age at a few tens of million of years old.

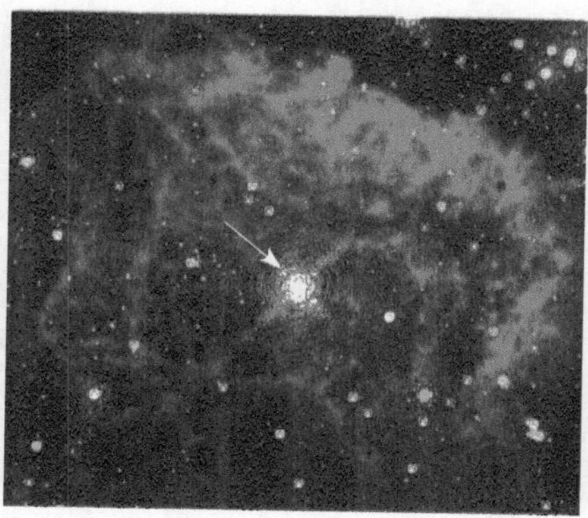

The Pistol star (bright star center) is a blue hypergiant star and one of the most luminous stars in the Milky Way. It has a mass 27.5 times the Sun. Its age is estimated at just 4 million years.

All images: NASA

Proxima Centauri is a red dwarf star and the closest star to the Sun. It is just 0.12 solar masses and has a luminosity of 0.0017 times that of the Sun. It is estimated to be 4.5 billion years old.

NASA

Cygnus X-1 is an X-ray source, accepted to be a black hole about 6000 light years from Earth. It is thought the original star may have been over 40 solar masses.

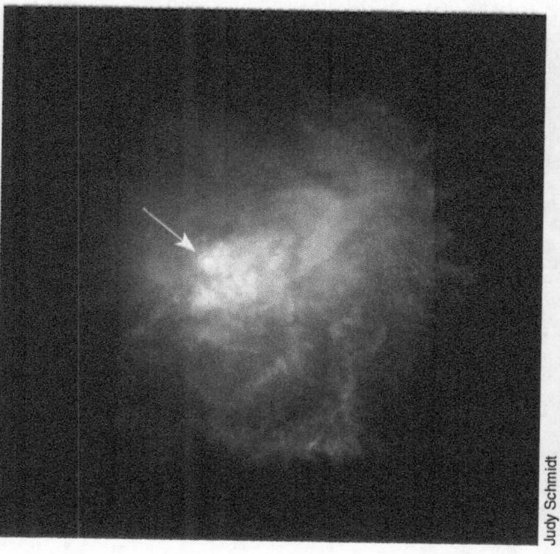

Judy Schmidt

VY Canis Majoris is a red hypergiant star and one of the largest stars known. It is thought to be 17 solar masses and to have a radius 1420 times that of the Sun. Its age is estimated at 10 million years.

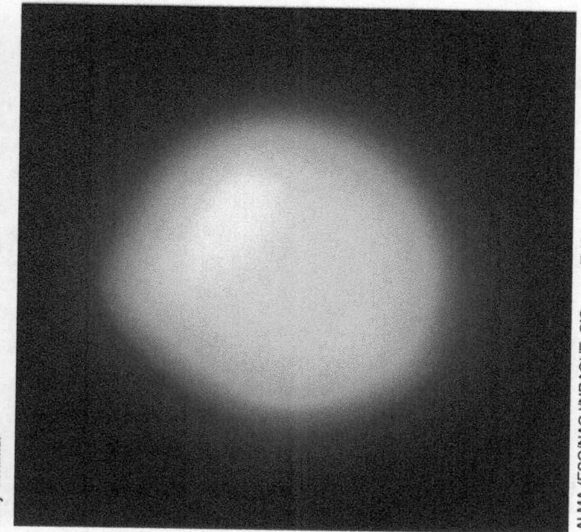

ALMA (ESO/NAOJ/NRAO)/E. O'Gorman/P. Kervella

Betelgeuse is a red supergiant star and the second brightest star in the constellation of Orion. It has a mass 11.6 times the Sun, and is thought to be about 8 million years old.

3. (a) Put the stars above in order, from the most massive to the least massive: __________

   (b) VY Canis Majoris has entered the final stages of its life cycle. It could explode in as little as 100,000 years. It is thought the Pistol star might explode in as little as 1 million years. Proxima Centauri is likely to shine for another trillion years. What can be said about the life time of a star and its mass?

   (c) Suggest why this relationship occurs: __________

   (d) What color do old, dying stars appear? __________

ISBN: 978-1-98-856693-1

▶ A star forms from a cloud of dust and gas called a **nebula** (*pl.* nebulae) which may be many light years across. The nebula may begin to collapse due to a nearby shockwave and continue to shrink under gravity, releasing heat as it gets smaller. The heat eventually reaches temperatures hot enough to start nuclear reactions and ignite the star.

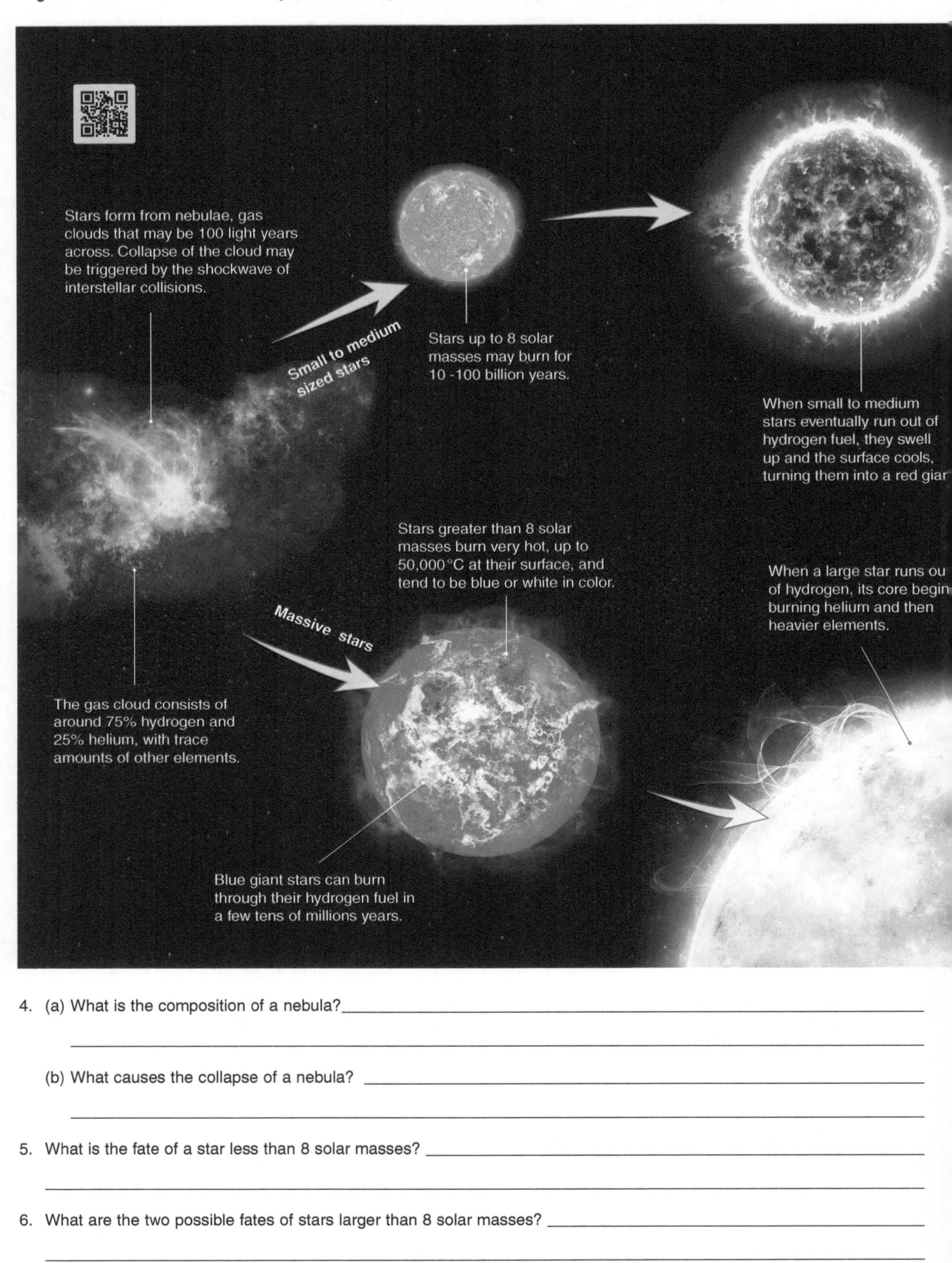

4. (a) What is the composition of a nebula? ______________________

   (b) What causes the collapse of a nebula? ______________________

5. What is the fate of a star less than 8 solar masses? ______________________

6. What are the two possible fates of stars larger than 8 solar masses? ______________________

ISBN: 978-1-98-856693-1

- The path of a star's life cycle depends on its mass. A very large star burns its fuel very quickly and may eventually end its life in a **supernova**. Stars similar to the Sun burn their fuel far more slowly and end as **white dwarf** stars.

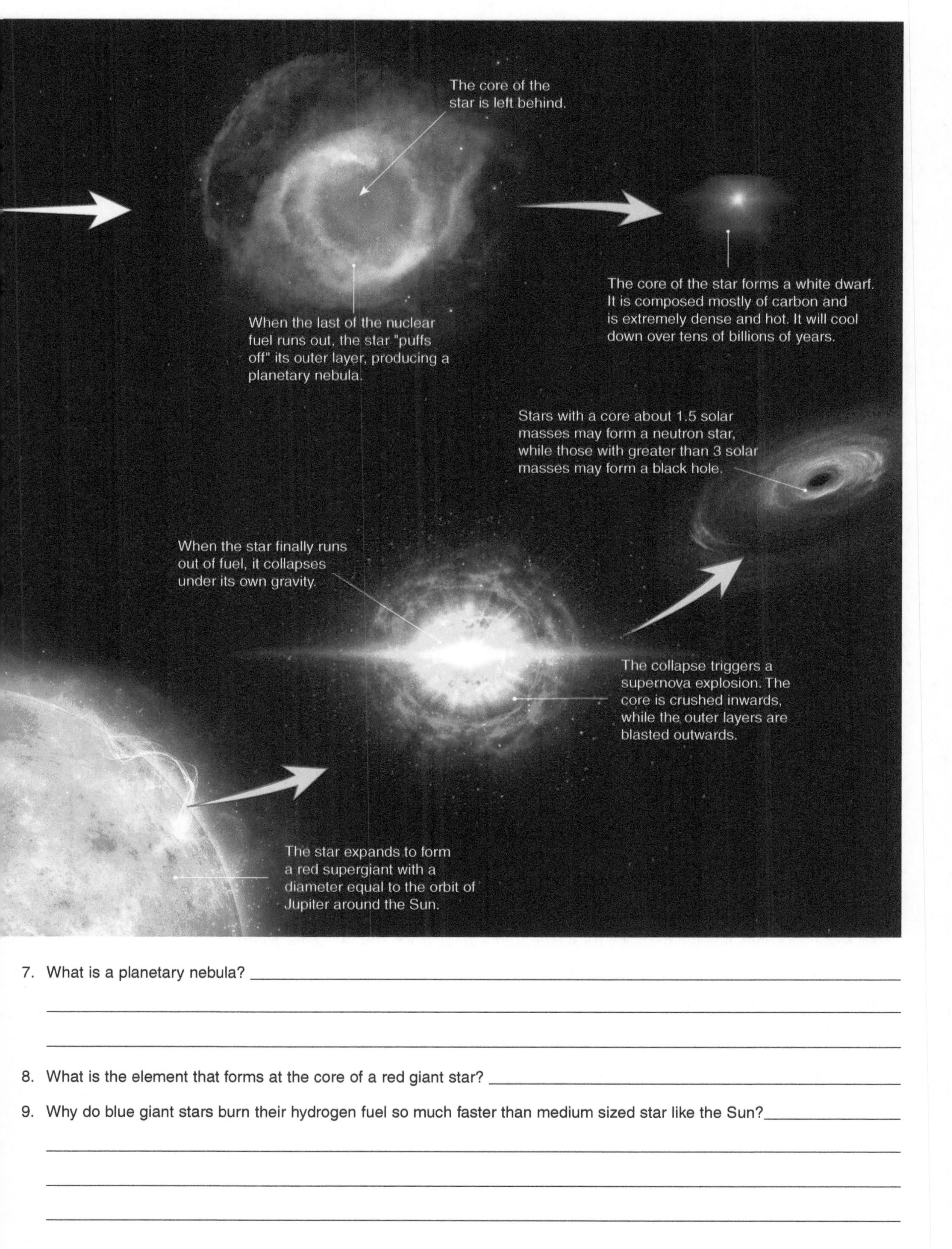

7. What is a planetary nebula? ______________________________

8. What is the element that forms at the core of a red giant star? ______________________________

9. Why do blue giant stars burn their hydrogen fuel so much faster than medium sized star like the Sun? ______________________________

ISBN: 978-1-98-856693-1

20 Interpreting Hertzsprung-Russell Diagrams

Key Question: How can we classify stars, and can we determine any relationships between their characteristics?

Hertzsprung-Russell diagram

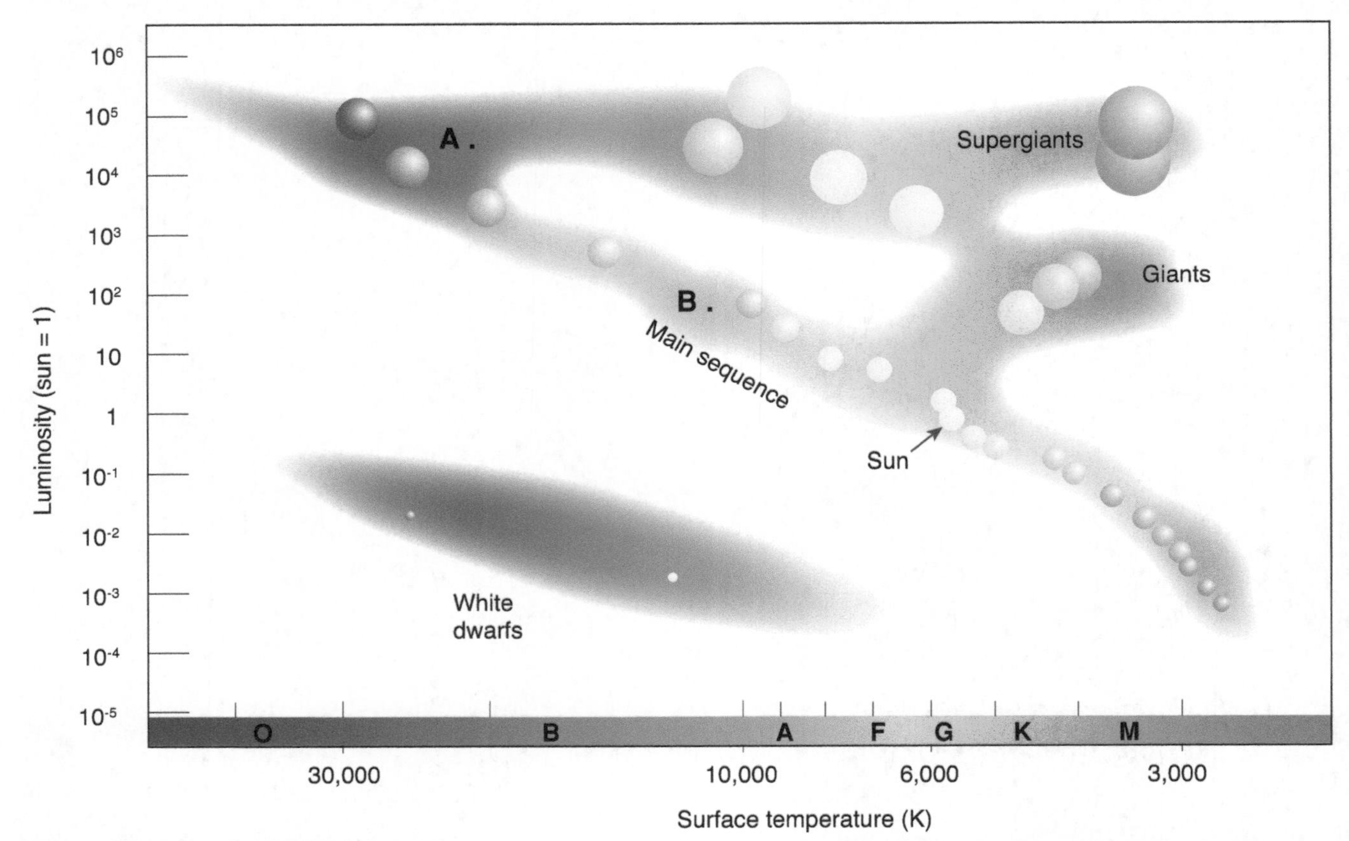

- The **Hertzsprung-Russell diagram** plots the temperature of a **star** against its luminosity. The position of the star on the graph tells us about its present stage in its life cycle, and its mass. For most of their life, stars are found in the main sequence and are called **main sequence stars**. White dwarfs are found near the bottom left, while giant stars are found in the top right. As a star progresses through its life cycle, it will move off the main sequence. A star like the **Sun** will move to the upper right (red giants), before moving down to the lower left (white dwarfs).
- The diagram may list surface temperature or spectral classification along the horizontal axis. The diagram can also be used to estimate the distance to a star using the star's apparent magnitude and the absolute magnitude of a similar star with a known distance. The observed star is shifted vertically on the graph to overlap the reference star. The difference in magnitude shift to match the stars relates directly to the distance of the observed star.

Star spectral classes

- Originally, stars were classified on the strength of the hydrogen lines in their absorption spectrum. These classifications were eventually rearranged to reflect the temperature of the star. Type O stars are the hottest, with surfaces of tens of thousands of degrees, and shine in the blue part of the spectrum. M type stars are cool and are dull red. Each class has ten divisions (0-9). The Sun is a G2 class star (a yellow dwarf).

1. Use the Hertzsprung-Russell diagram to determine the following:

   (a) The surface temperature of the Sun: ______________________________

   (b) The temperature and luminosity of the star at the point labeled A: ______________________________

   (c) The temperature and luminosity of the star at the point labeled B: ______________________________

2. Why are most stars found in the main sequence part of the diagram? ______________________________

____

____

____

ISBN: 978-1-98-856693-1

21 Red Giants

Key Question: What happens when a Sun-like star uses up its supply of hydrogen and enters the final stage of its life cycle?

Running out of hydrogen

- When the core of a **star** similar to the **Sun** (up to eight solar masses) begins to run out of hydrogen (after about 10 billion years), the core contracts due to gravity, increasing the pressure and temperature. This causes hydrogen fusion to begin in a shell around the core, while helium fuses to carbon in the core. The extra heat and light produced expands the star's outer layers. Because of the extra surface area, the surface temperature drops, but luminosity increases up to 1000 times because of the extra size.
- Stars with masses 0-8 times that of the Sun do not produce enough gravitational pressure in the core to progress fusion beyond carbon and oxygen. As the last of the helium is converted to carbon, fusion stops and the outer layers are lost as a planetary **nebula** (nothing to do with planets). The core will shine as a white hot, extremely dense, white dwarf star.

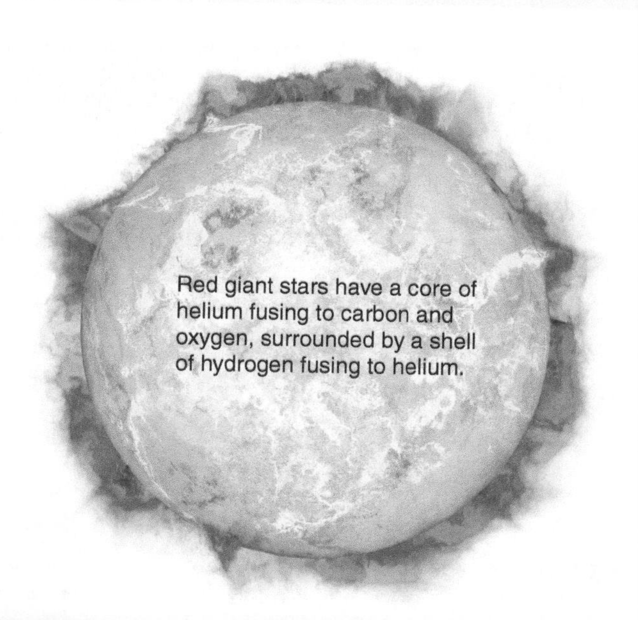
Red giant stars have a core of helium fusing to carbon and oxygen, surrounded by a shell of hydrogen fusing to helium.

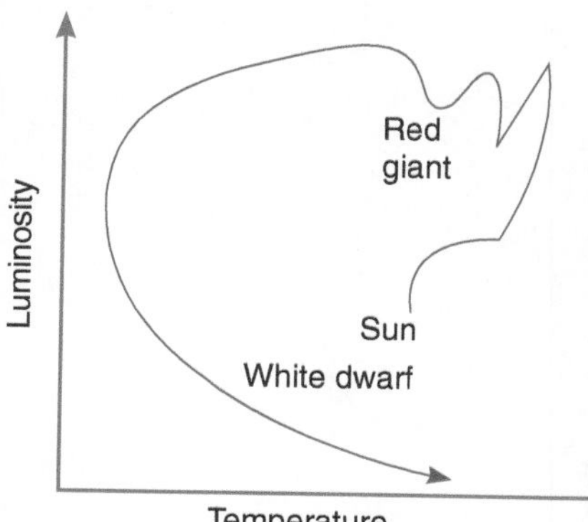

As a Sun-like star nears the end of its life, it moves off the main sequence as a red giant. Over the final two billion years, the star may move back and forth about the Hertzsprung-Russell diagram, as its core progressively burns hydrogen and helium in different layers.

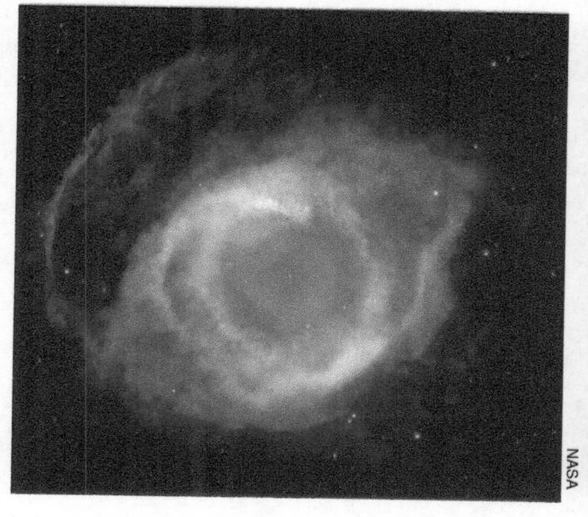

Eventually, the star runs out of hydrogen and helium. The core temperature and pressure are too low to continue fusion and a core of carbon and oxygen forms. The hot outer layers are shed into space as a planetary nebula, leaving behind a dense, white hot core.

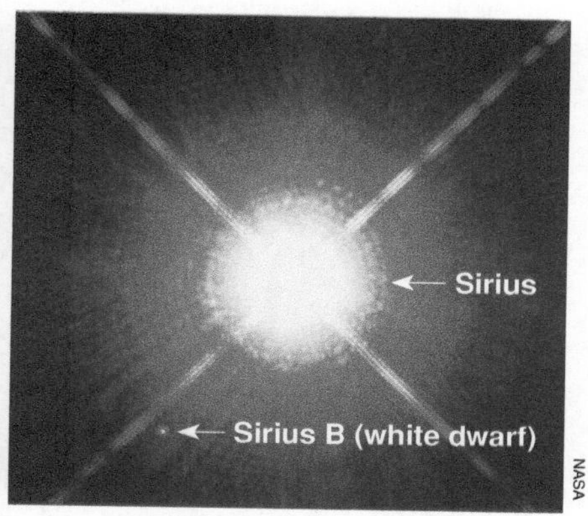

White dwarfs are the leftover cores of a Sun-like star. They can be a million times more dense than the original star's average density, with a density of 10^6 g/cm^3. No longer supporting nuclear fusion, the white dwarf slowly cools to a black dwarf over about a quadrillion years.

1. Give a brief description of why a sun-like star swells to a red giant near the end of its life:

2. Explain why red giants have very high luminosity even though they have very low surface temperatures:

3. What is the cause of a planetary nebula?

4. What is the composition of a white dwarf?

5. Why is it highly unlikely that there are any black dwarfs in the universe?

ISBN: 978-1-98-856693-1

22 Supernovae

Key Question: What causes a supernova, and what results from it?

- Supernovae are some of the most violent events in the universe. They produce so much energy in one monumental explosion that they can outshine a whole galaxy. The luminosity of such an explosion may be five trillion times more than the Sun. Depending on the size of the original star, a neutron star or black hole may form immediately after the explosion.

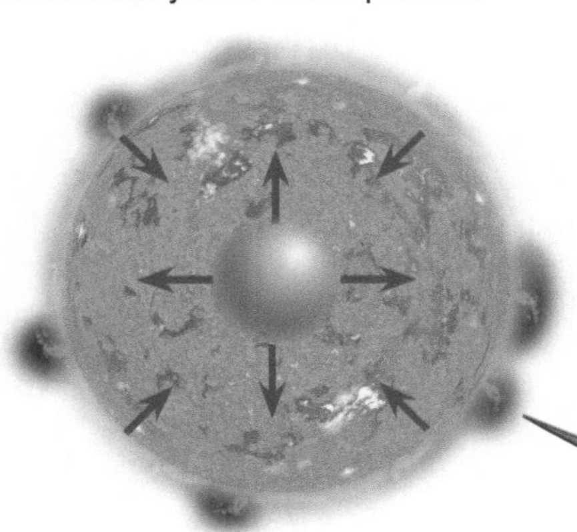

2. In the core, hydrogen fuses into helium. Eventually, the hydrogen in the core begins to be used up. The core contracts under gravity, forming a core of helium surrounded by a shell of hydrogen. As the core contracts and temperature and pressure rise, the helium core gains sufficient energy to begin fusing into heavier elements such as carbon and oxygen. The outer layers are pushed further outwards and the star forms a red supergiant.

1. Stars greater than eight times the mass of the Sun produce enormously high temperatures in their core. The heat and light from their nuclear reactions pushes the gases out, away from the core. However, their immense gravity pulls them back in. For the majority of its life, the giant star is at equilibrium between these opposing forces.

The heavy **elements** sink to the core where they ignite and fuse to form heavier elements. The star may form onion like layers of heavier and heavier elements undergoing fusion.

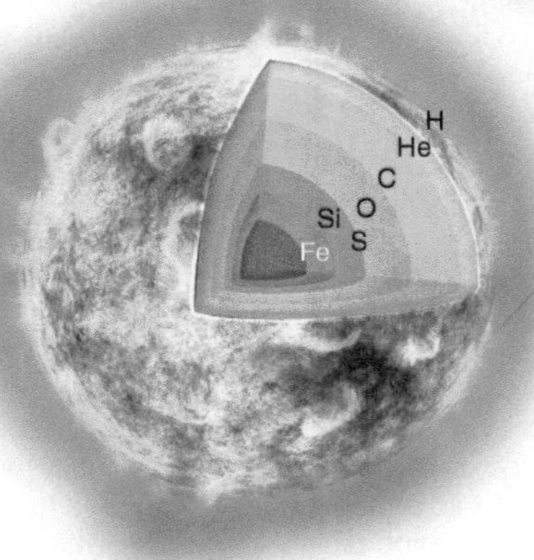

3. Eventually, fusion in the core produces iron. The nucleus of an iron atom is extremely stable. More energy is required to fuse iron atoms with other atoms (or break them apart) than is produced from their fusion. Therefore, when iron forms inside a star's core, the process of **stellar nucleosynthesis** stops. The core no longer produces the outward pressure to support the outer layers. The inward force of the star's gravity takes over so the star, and its core, collapse.

1. (a) What is a supernova? ______________________________

   (b) What size of stars can undergo a supernova? ______________________________

2. During the life of a massive star, what keeps the star from collapsing under its own gravity? ______________________________

3. Why does a massive star form onion-like layers of elements near the end of its life? ______________________________

4. What event triggers the collapse of a massive star? ______________________________

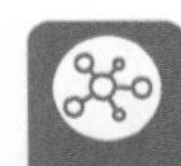

ESS1.A SPQ EM

ISBN: 978-1-98-856693-1

4 The collapse of the star is cataclysmic and rapid. It has been calculated that the speed of the collapsing layers may reach 23% of the speed of light and the core reaches 100 billion K. Protons and electrons are crushed together to form neutrons. Neutrons are forced together and the core becomes so dense that the falling layers rebound outwards in a titanic explosion called a **supernova**. The pressures produced are high enough to cause the iron and other elements in the core to fuse into even heavier elements such as gold. This is called **supernova nucleosynthesis**.

5a The core of the star is smashed inwards. Stars with cores between 1.5 and 3 solar masses form neutron stars, i.e. stars composed entirely of neutrons. They may have a diameter of just 20 km and a mass twice that of the Sun. A pea-sized piece of neutron star would have a mass of about 25,000,000 tonnes.

5b In stars with cores greater than 3 solar masses, nothing is strong enough to withstand the force of gravity pulling the core inwards and it collapses to a black hole, a point with no dimensions and gravity so great that not even light can escape.

As material falls into the black hole, it heats up and emits huge jets of x-rays that may reach millions of kilometers into space.

Event horizon – the point at which nothing, not even light, can escape from the black hole's gravity.

Accretion disk – material swirling around the black hole forms a disk.

NASA/ESA

Supernova 1994D (arrowed left) in galaxy NGC 4526, taken by the Hubble Space Telescope. Notice how the bright supernova easily matches the brightness of the entire galaxy beside it.

Cygnus X-1 (right) was the first black hole discovered. It has a mass of about 15 times that of the Sun and an event horizon of just 44 km. As the black hole cannot be seen, the image is of the x-rays emitted by superheated gas surrounding it.

NASA

5. How does a neutron star form? ______________________________

____

____

6. (a) What is a black hole? ______________________________

____

(b) How does a black hole form? ______________________________

____

____

(c) What is the event horizon of a black hole? ______________________________

____

ISBN: 978-1-98-856693-1

23 Black Holes

Key Question: How can we study black holes, when they release no information?

- Black holes are areas of space-time where gravity is so strong that nothing can escape from it. Not even light waves travel fast enough to escape the gravity of a black hole. As a result, they are indeed totally black, but the material around them may become hot enough to glow in various parts of the EM spectrum.

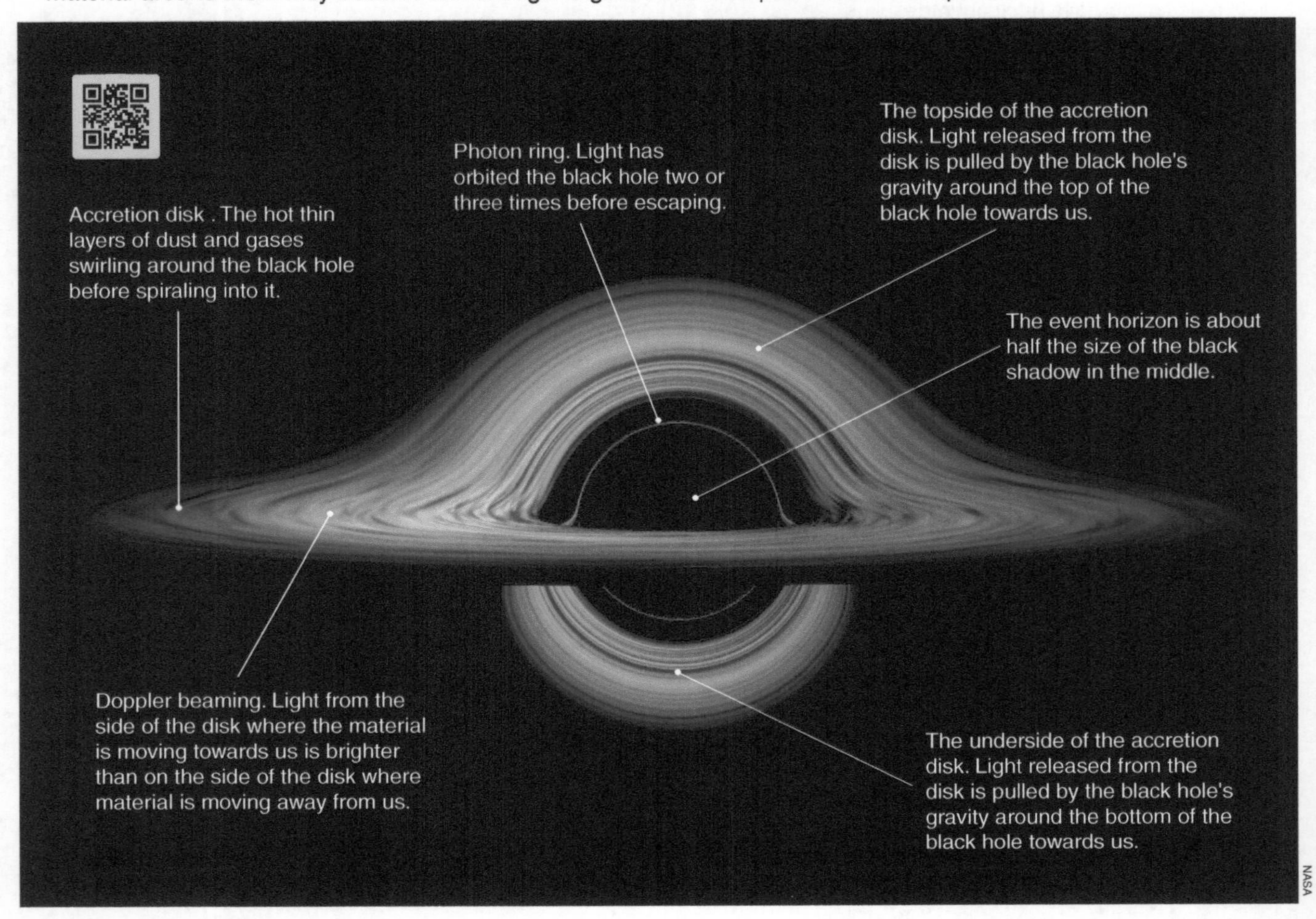

Explaining the image

- The image above, produced by NASA, is a simulation of a black hole as it would appear from nearby space. Because of the intense gravity around the black hole, light rays from the accretion disk are bent in multiple ways. Viewed from the "front" the disk appears to rotate in opposite directions at the top and bottom, i.e the top part of the disk appears to rotate counter clockwise, while the bottom part of the disk appears to rotate clockwise.
- The intense gravity field of the black hole distorts the path of light rays leaving the accretion disk so that they are bent around the black hole, allowing us to see parts of the disk we would never normally see from such an angle.

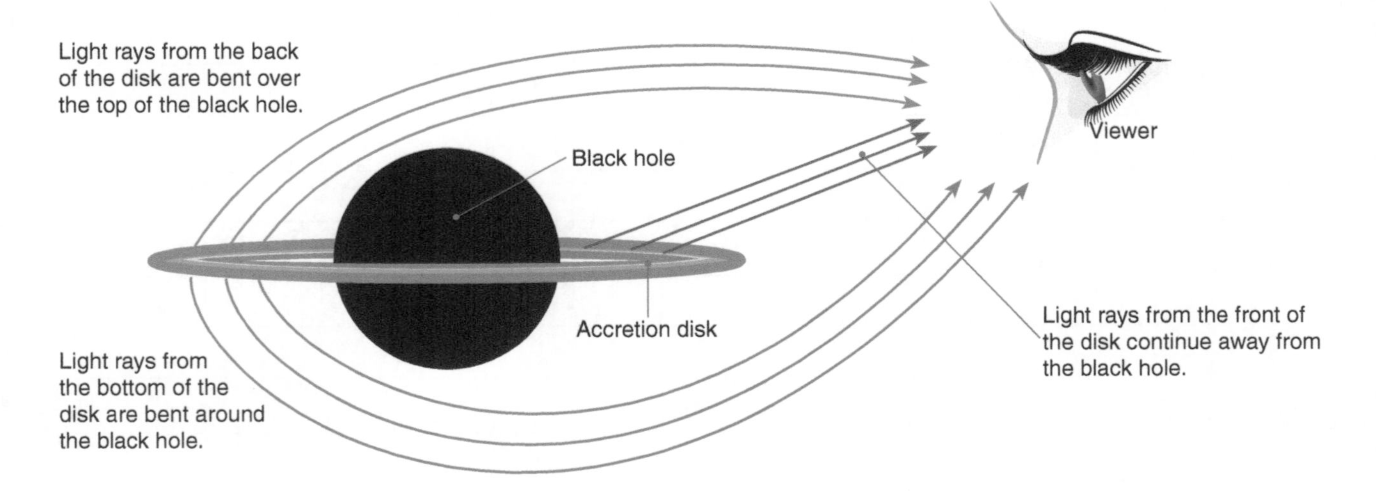

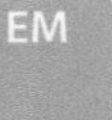

ISBN: 978-1-98-856693-1

Imaging a black hole

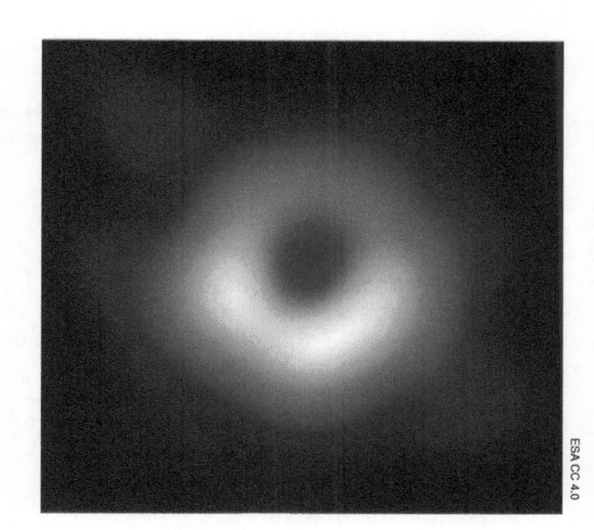

- The image on the right is of the super massive black hole (SMBH) at the centre of the galaxy Messier 87 and is the first ever direct imaging of the accretion disk around a black hole, and the black hole beyond.
- It was produced by data gathered by the Event Horizon Telescope, a network of eight radio telescopes situated around the world (this is not a photograph).
- From our perspective, the **event horizon** (with a diameter just half the black circle in the middle) covers just 40 microarcseconds of sky (about 1.1×10^{-8} of a degree of the sky, 1 arcsecond = 1/3600th of a degree). In real distance, it measures 40 billion km across.
- The mass of this SMBH is calculated at 6.5 billion of times that of our Sun. The disk around it measures 3.7 trillion kilometers across.

Inside a black hole

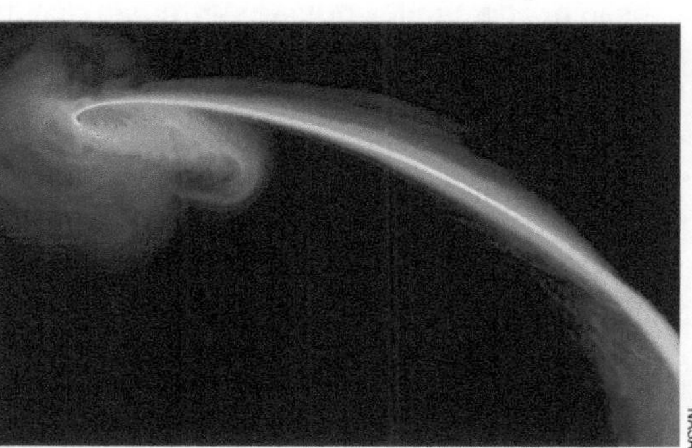

- As no information can leave a black hole, to determine what happens beyond the event horizon we can only use mathematics, such as Einstien's equations on relativity and gravity.
- Because of the massive gravity of a black hole, to an outside viewer an object falling into a black hole appears to slow down and takes an infinite time to reach the event horizon. At the same time its image becomes **red-shifted** and fades away (usually within a second).
- A person or object falling into a black hole would experience an extreme gravitational gradient. Falling feet first, the feet would experience far greater gravity than the head and so be pulled faster toward the black hole. This results in spaghettification, or the stretching, of the person. Eventually, the person or object would be pulled into a stream of atoms by the intense gravity.

1. Explain why the accretion disk around a black hole appears so distorted to an outside viewer: ______________________

2. (a) How was the data from Messier 87 gathered? ______________________

   (b) Explain why this method works better than using just one telescope: ______________________

3. The super massive black holes at the center of galaxies are orders of magnitude greater than the mass of our Sun. How might these SMBH have become so big?

____

ISBN: 978-1-98-856693-1

24 Nucleosynthesis

Key Question: How do elements form inside stars, and what is the limit of this formation?

Nucleosynthesis

- **Nucleosynthesis** is the production of new **atomic nuclei** from pre-existing ones. Nucleosynthesis most commonly occurs in nature by nuclear fusion in the core of **stars**. Nuclear fusion requires enormous energy as the nuclei must be accelerated to extremely high speeds in order to overcome the repulsive forces that normally keep them apart.
- **Elements** up to iron (26 protons) are formed in the core of stars. Elements heavier than iron are formed during supernovae, the explosion of giant stars. Very heavy elements may be formed in the collisions of neutron stars.

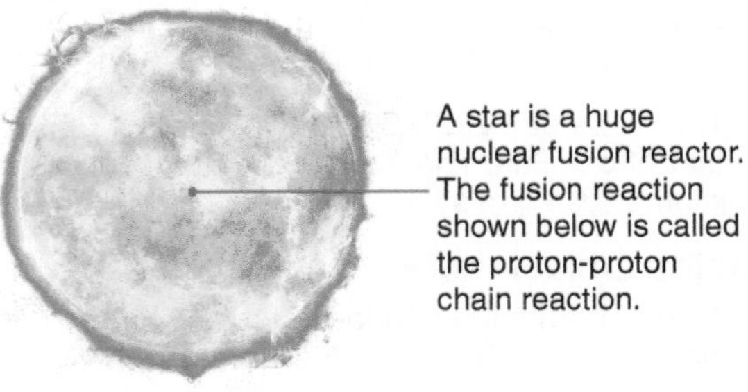

Nucleosynthesis of helium

- A star spends most of its existence converting hydrogen into helium. This **stellar nucleosynthesis** occurs in the core of a star where extremely high temperatures and pressures are found.

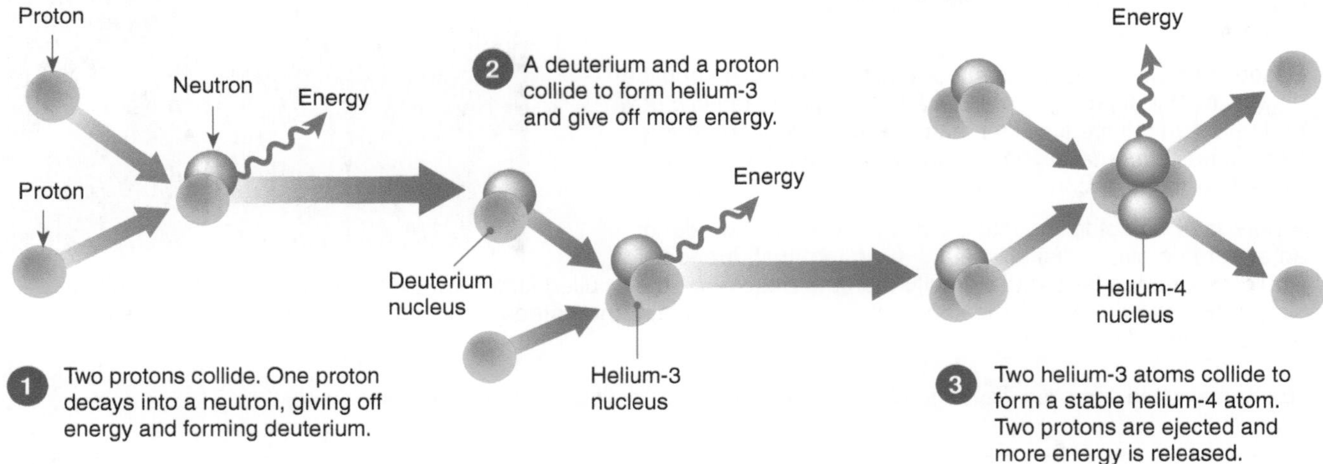

Formation of heavy elements

- Fusion of iron atoms with other atoms to form heavy atoms requires energy. The energy comes from a supernova. **Supernova nucleosynthesis** occurs during the explosion of a massive star. Atoms, protons, and neutrons are smashed together and produce heavy atoms such as uranium, lead, and gold.

The nucleus of an iron atom is extraordinarily stable (right). More energy is required to fuse iron atoms with other atoms than is produced from their fusion. Thus, when iron forms inside a star the process of nucleosynthesis stops and the star collapses.

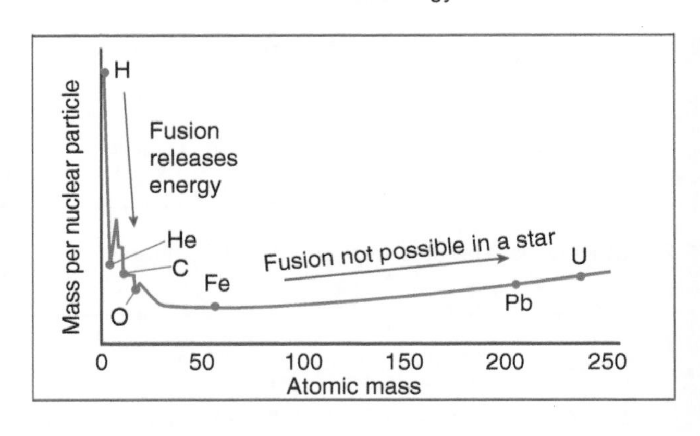

1. Define nucleosynthesis: ______________________________

2. Why does the formation of iron lead to the collapse of a star? ______________________________

3. Using the information on this page, and your own research, produce a poster or computer slide show to show how elements are formed by stellar nucleosynthesis and supernova nucleosynthesis. Present your poster to the class or your group or produce a voice over for your computer slide display.

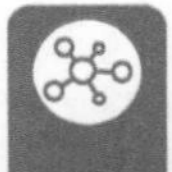

ESS1.A SPQ EM

ISBN: 978-1-98-856693-1

25 Review Your Understanding

Key Question: What caused the Crab Nebula, and what is hidden at its center?

▶ At the beginning of this chapter, you were shown the Crab Nebula, the object at the center of it, and given some history of its recorded observations. You should now be able to explain what caused the nebula and describe the object in the middle of it.

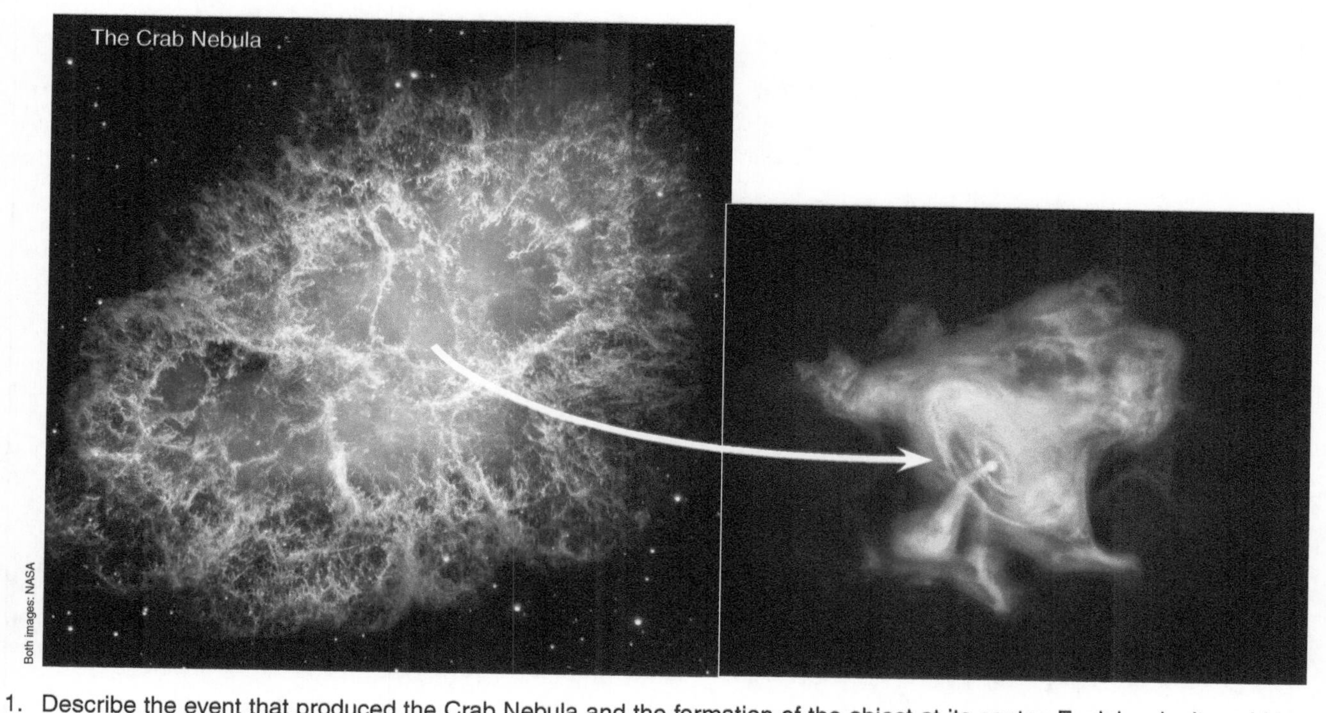

1. Describe the event that produced the Crab Nebula and the formation of the object at its center. Explain why it could be seen clearly in the night sky in 1054 but can now only be seen with a telescope. Include an explanation of why the object in the center can only be seen clearly with x-ray telescopes

ISBN: 978-1-98-856693-1

26 Summing Up

1. Use the list below to draw and label a star's potential life cycle. Include a brief description of each stage. Identify the pathway that represents our Sun.

   protostar, small-medium star, large-star, white dwarf, black hole, neutron star, supernova, red giant, red super-giant, planetary nebula, nebula:

2. The Big Bang occurred 13.7 billion years ago. Describe the evidence for the Big Bang, and include how the evidence was gathered:

ESS1.A SPQ EM

ISBN: 978-1-98-856693-1

Questions 3-5 require you to use the online resource **Star in a Box.** Follow the link at the **BIOZONE Resource Hub** or go to starinabox.lco.global.

3. On the home screen, click **Open the lid**. You will see a Hertzsprung-Russell diagram showing the main sequence band of stars. The program shows a default star of 1 solar mass. You will see a dotted pathway going from the star around the HR diagram. This is the path a 1 solar mass star will take around the HR diagram as it progresses through its life cycle. Click the **play** button in the bottom right-hand corner to see the star move along the pathway and the time it takes to do so (timer at the bottom of the screen). You can control the speed in the drop down box next to the play button.

   (a) According to the timer, how long does a 1 solar mass star spend in the main sequence? ______________________

   (b) What is the lowest surface temperature this star will reach? ______________________

   (c) When will this happen according to the timer? ______________________

   (d) What will the luminosity (brightness) be, compared to the Sun? ______________________

   (e) On the Hertzsprung-Russell diagram below, draw the star and the pathway it will take around the HR diagram.

4. Set the star's mass to six solar masses and click play.

   (a) How long does this star stay on the main sequence? ______________________

   (b) What is the maximum luminosity this star reaches? ______________________

   (c) On the Hertzsprung-Russell diagram below, draw the star and the pathway it will take around the HR diagram.

5. Set the star's mass to 20 solar masses.

   (a) How long does this size star live before it ends in a supernova? ______________________

   (b) On the Hertzsprung-Russell diagram below,s draw the star and the pathway it will take around the HR diagram.

6. You will have noticed that on some of the pathways you drew, the star loops back on itself while in the red giant stage. What might be causing these loops in its pathway?

____

____

____

____

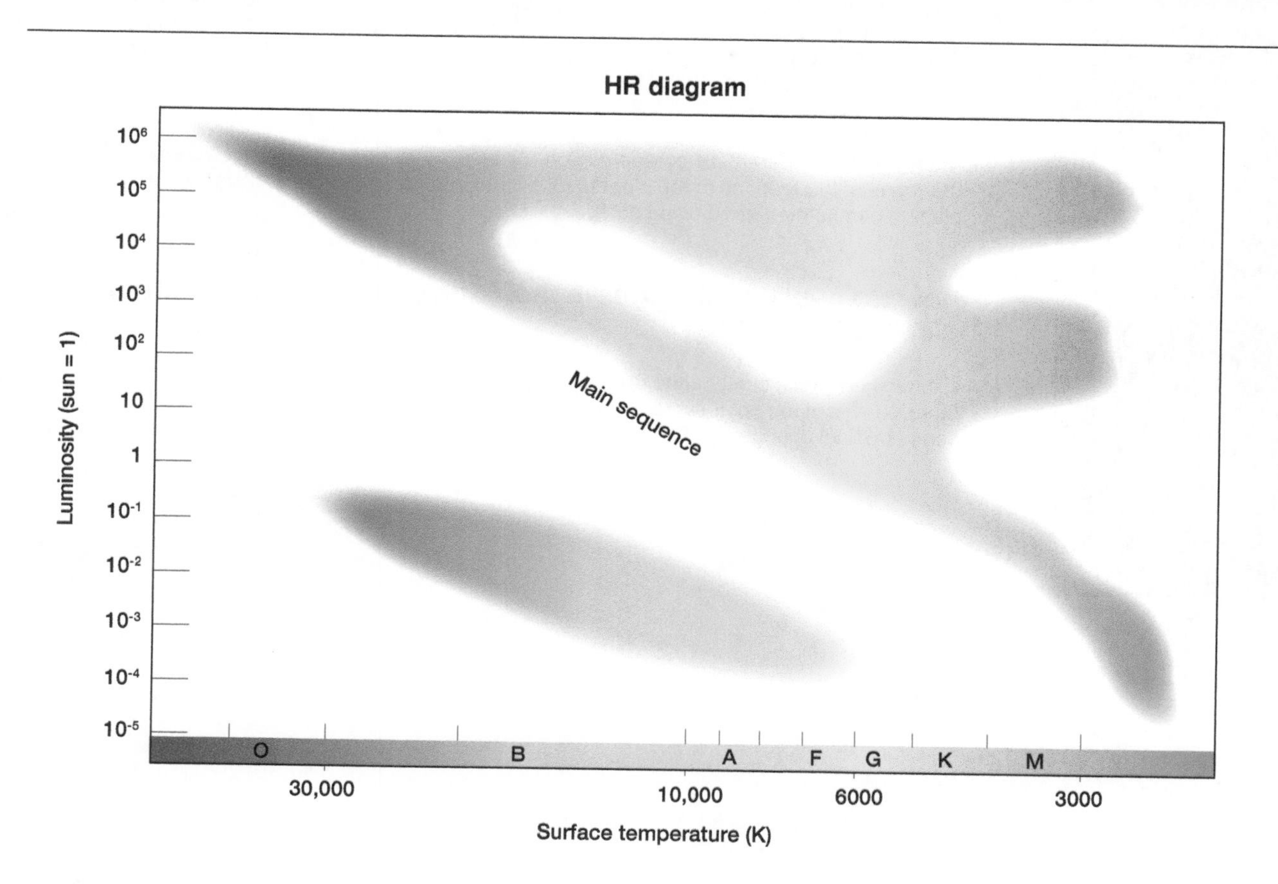

ISBN: 978-1-98-856693-1

Chapter 3

Earth and the Solar System

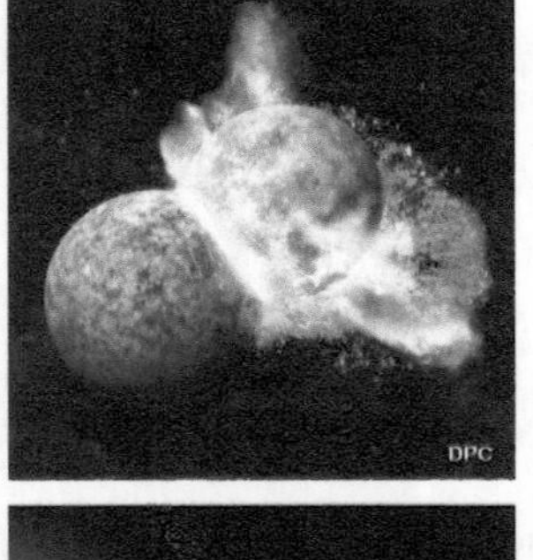

Activity number

Anchoring Phenomenon

Solar System Relationships: What's the relationship between the Sun, the planets that orbit it, and the time they take to complete an orbit? — 27 41

What common features do orbiting objects have in common?

- ☐ 1 Examine and describe different technologies for exploring the solar system. Describe how some of those technologies are guided to their target and how they land. Explain the importance of the information they send back. — 28
- ☐ 2 Understand the origins of our solar system. Know that features of the planetary orbits and the composition of the gas planets provide evidence for how the solar system formed. — 29
- ☐ 3 Describe the composition of our solar system. Understand that the Sun is the overwhelming source of gravity in our solar system, and its mass causes the planets to form elliptical orbits around it. — 30
- ☐ 4 Know that planets orbit in ellipses. Using appropriate equipment, show how the distance between foci affects the shape of an ellipse. Model the warping of space by mass, and show how this affects the orbits of the planets around such a mass, i.e. the Sun. — 31
- ☐ 5 Understand that orbits of planets follow Kepler's laws, which are mathematical rules describing common features of the motions of orbiting objects. Use Kepler's laws to show the relationship between the orbital period of a planet and its distance from a Sun. — 32
- ☐ 6 Understand Kepler's laws can be modified to apply to all masses and that they are a simplification of Newton's Law of Universal Gravitation. Use Kepler's and Newton's laws to calculate the mass of stars and period of planets orbiting them, and the periods and distance of satellites orbiting planets. Apply mathematical models of ellipses and orbital mechanics to model the orbit of Halley's Comet. — 33 34 - 36 42
- ☐ 7 Know that the apparent retrograde motion of planets viewed from a point on Earth is the result of the motions of the planets relative to each other, and that distances to the planets can be measured using parallax. — 37

How do cyclical changes in the Earth's long term orbit affect climate?

- ☐ 8 Explain how orbits can change due to the gravitational effects from, or collisions with, other objects in the solar system, and that changes in Earth's orbit, tilt, and rotation cause cyclical changes on Earth. — 38-39

27 Solar System Relationships

Key Question: What's the relationship between the Sun, the planets that orbit it, and the time they take to complete an orbit?

- Looking up at the night sky, you can often see four planets, clearly.
  - Venus appears as a bright star near the eastern or western horizon just after sunset or just before sunrise.
  - Mars is a distinctive red star above the horizon, that often wanders across the sky over a month or so.
  - Jupiter is one of the brighter objects in the night sky and appears as a slightly yellow star often high in the sky.
  - Saturn appears as a dimmer yellow star, again often high in the sky.
- All of these planets change position over time, and where they appear depends on many factors.
- You may be aware that the planets take different times to **orbit** (go around) the Sun. An obvious question is: why? What is the pattern around the orbital period (the time it takes for a planet to orbit the Sun) and a planet's distance from the Sun?
- What about comets and asteroids? How do we explain their orbital behavior? Why do comets suddenly appear very bright in the sky for weeks at a time then, just as suddenly, disappear, sometimes never to be seen again?
- Why do planets change position in the sky, night after night? Why does Venus sometimes appear as the evening star in the west, and sometimes the morning star in the east, but never seen high in the sky at midnight?

1. The solar system is shown in the image above. Name the planets in order, from left to right:

___

2. (a) Which planet orbits the Sun most slowly? ___

(b) Which planet orbits the Sun most quickly? ___

(c) In small groups, discuss what might cause this difference in orbital speed. Write down your ideas: ___

___

___

___

___

3. Comets have orbits that, at times, bring them in close to the Sun and at other times have them far away, past the orbit of the outer planets. Suggest why they orbit like this. Are they always orbiting at the same speed? Why, or why not?

___

___

___

___

4. Use the information on pages 76-77 to make a scale model of the distances of the planets from the Sun. You could do this in groups using people as planets, or make a paper model. What scale works best to give a good impression of distances to the outer planets?

ISBN: 978-1-98-856693-1

28 Exploring the Solar System

Key Question: How have we come to know so much about the solar system?

Orbiters and probes

- Although telescopes of various types can provide a large amount of data about the **planets**, various orbiter and flyby missions over the decades of space flight have provided the detailed images and information we now have about the planets, and the distant planets in particular.
- The inner planets (Mercury, Venus, Earth, and Mars) have been the objects of many orbiter and flyby missions because they are reasonably close to Earth. The outer planets (Jupiter, Saturn, Uranus, and Neptune) have had far fewer orbiter and flyby missions, partly because they are so far away.

The Mars Odyssey orbiter has orbited Mars since 2001

Voyager 2 flew past Saturn in 1981

All images NASA

Orbiters

Orbiter missions, as the name suggests, enter orbit around the target planet and gather information. Orbiters may have equatorial or polar orbits. They tend to be long duration missions. Orbiters have been sent to all the planets except Uranus and Neptune.

Flybys

Flyby missions fly past a planet or asteroid. Once the flyby is complete, little useful data will be gathered again. Flybys are normally used when achieving orbit is too difficult, or multiple planets are to be visited. Flybys have been the only missions to Uranus and Neptune.

Gravity assist

- One of the most useful procedures for altering the path taken by a space probe is the gravity assist. The **gravity** of a planet can bend the path of the probe and can also accelerate or decelerate it, depending on the course taken. It is useful for accelerating probes into deep space, e.g. Voyager 1 and 2, or New Horizons, or causing probes to settle into particular orbits.

The Mariner 10 mission in 1974 was the first space probe to use a gravitational assist (from Venus) to change its pathway. It orbited the Sun once for every two times Mercury orbited, meeting the planet two more times, making it the first probe to return to a planet. Mercury's proximity to the Sun makes it difficult to insert a probe into orbit around it.

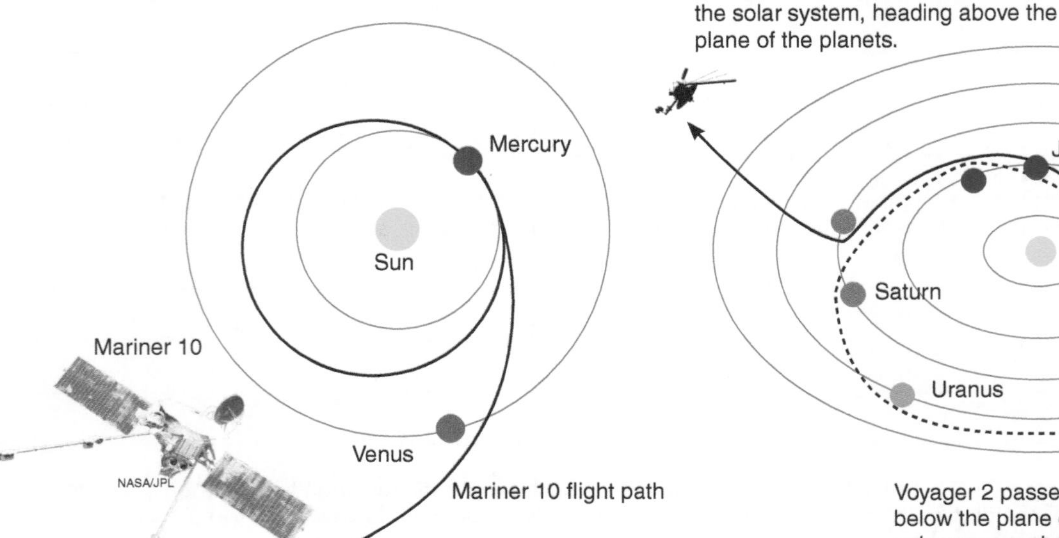

As a probe approaches (effectively falling towards) a planet, it picks up speed. The probe swings around the planet but instead of continuing in an orbit around the planet, the probe is moving fast enough to break free, effectively being thrown out and away, like a rock from a slingshot.

Voyager 1 swung around Saturn and left the solar system, heading above the plane of the planets.

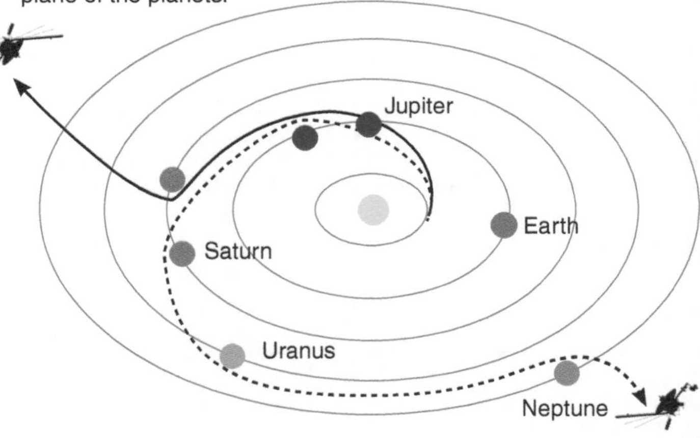

Voyager 2 passed by Neptune then down below the plane of the solar system. It is the only space probe to visit Uranus or Neptune.

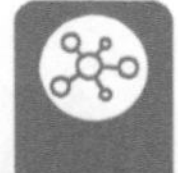

ISBN: 978-1-98-856693-1

New Horizons

- One of the more recent and extremely successful flyby missions was the New Horizons mission to Pluto. Until 2015, Pluto and the Kuiper belt objects (KBOs) were unexplored. Even the best Hubble images showed Pluto as little more than a fuzzy disk. It was thought that Pluto was just a ball of frozen nitrogen and methane.
- The July 2015 flyby by the New Horizons spacecraft showed it as an apparently active world, with high mountains and multicolored plains.

The New Horizons spacecraft took nine years to reach Pluto and took close-up images for the first time, flying 12,500 km above the surface. It flew past the Kuiper belt object, 486958 Arrokoth, in 2019.

Close-up images of Pluto showed young, high ice mountains and deep canyons that suggest recent geological activity. Some of the mountains are 3400 meters high.

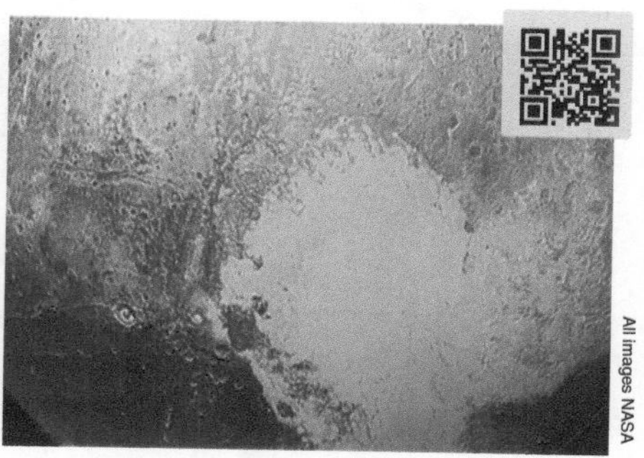

Pluto has one of the most contrasting surfaces in the solar system. Above, is Tombaugh Regio, nicknamed "The Heart" because of its shape. It is a thousand kilometer wide plain of nitrogen ice.

Juno

- The Juno space probe entered orbit around Jupiter in 2016. It has been specially built to deal with the extreme radiation given off by Jupiter.
- During its mission, Juno flew past several of Jupiter's moons.

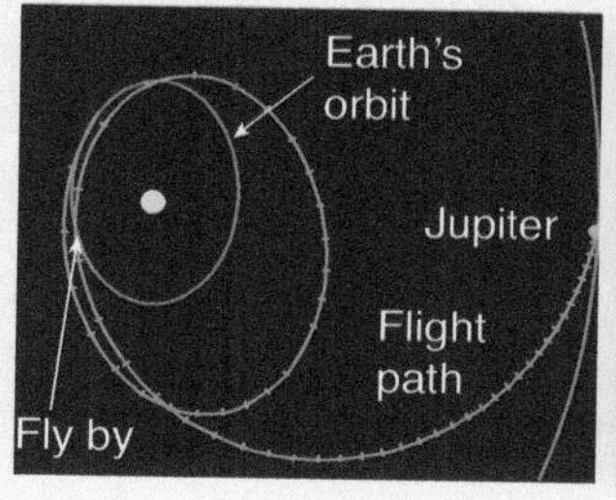

During Juno's journey, Earth provided a gravity assist speed boost. It orbits in a polar orbit.

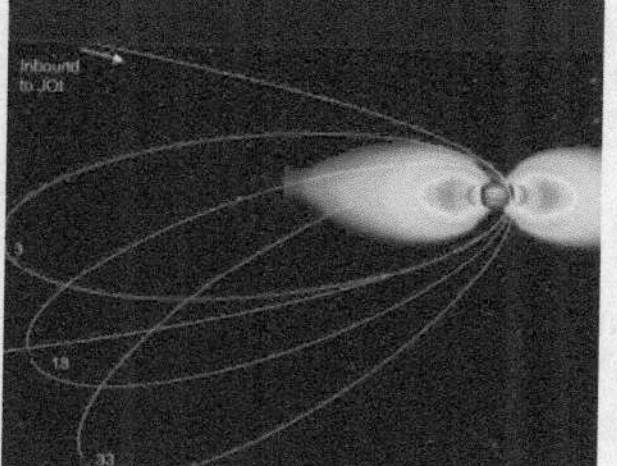

Juno orbits in an exaggerated ellipse, allowing it to fly extremely close to Jupiter's cloud tops.

Cassini

- Cassini was the orbiter for the Cassini-Huygens mission to Saturn. It orbited Saturn from 2004 to 2017.
- Cassini ended its mission by flying through Saturn's rings several times before being deliberately crashed into the giant planet.

Cassini discovered a hexagonal pattern of clouds around Saturn's north pole, for which there are no conclusive explanations.

Cassini flew past Saturn's giant moon, Titan, and used radar to look below the planet's atmosphere. It discovered lakes of methane on Titan's surface.

1. Describe the differences between orbiters and flybys: ______________________________

____

____

2. Explain the use of gravitational assists: ______________________________

____

____

____

3. Why have the outer planets undergone fewer orbiters and flybys than the inner planets? ______________________________

____

____

4. It is very difficult for a space probe to enter orbit around Mercury. Suggest why this might be: ______________________________

____

ISBN: 978-1-98-856693-1

Landers and rovers

- Although orbiters can gather a lot of data about a planet from orbit, landers and rovers are currently the only way to see various features of the surface close-up, or test its composition.
- Landers and rovers have been sent to many parts of the solar system, including the planets, the Moon, and asteroids.

Exploring Mars

More than ten lander or rover missions have now successfully landed on Mars; more than any other planet. An enormous amount of data has been gathered about the planet as a result. This data is useful for comparing to geological processes here on Earth, and in paving the way for a future manned mission to the red planet.

Curiosity

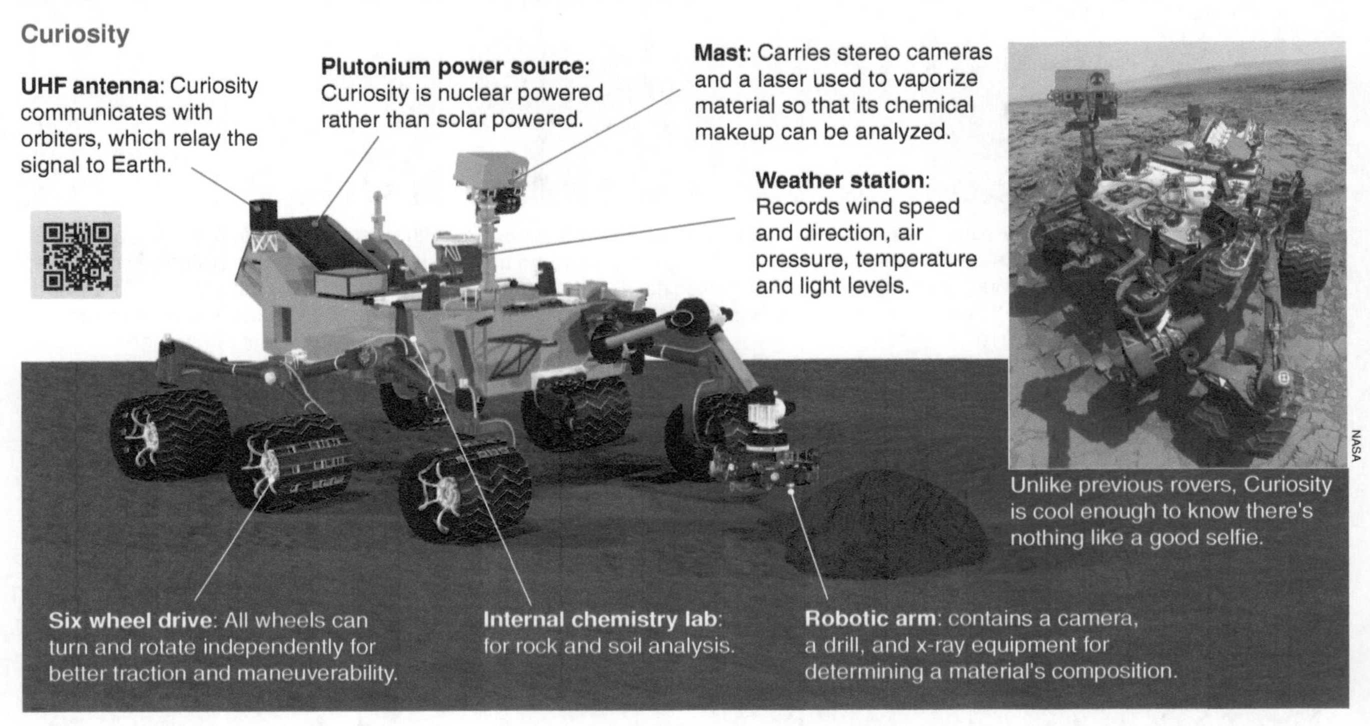

Unlike previous rovers, Curiosity is cool enough to know there's nothing like a good selfie.

The Curiosity rover (above) landed on Mars in 2012 and is still operational. It is about the size of a small car and has a mass of 899 kg. Its mission is to investigate the Martian climate and geology. It will assess whether the target site inside Gale Crater has ever offered environmental conditions favorable for life, e.g. water, and carry out studies relevant for any future human exploration. A more advanced version of this rover, Perseverance, landed in 2021.

Curiosity and Perseverance are so large that parachutes were not enough to slow their descent to Mars' surface. Instead, both used a "sky-crane" to slow the descent and lower the rovers to the ground.

Curiosity and Perseverance are the largest rovers to land on Mars. NASA's original Sojourner is tiny in comparison. Twin rovers, Spirit and Opportunity, operated between 2004 and 2010 (Spirit) and 2018 (Opportunity).

The Perseverance rover also carried the mini helicopter, Ingenuity. After completing the first powered flight on another planet, it now scouts out routes for Perseverance.

5. Describe the differences between landers and rovers, and their ability to gather information: ______________________

____

____

____

____

____

ISBN: 978-1-98-856693-1

Landers

Unlike rovers, landers aren't mobile. This reduces their cost, but also the amount of information that they can gather.

The Viking landers (1 and 2) were the first landers to not only land, but use rockets to soft land on Mars. They tested the soil for life but the results were negative. The landers produced the first images from the surface of Mars and studied the atmosphere and soil. The landers operated for about six years.

During its mission to Saturn, the Cassini space probe dropped the Huygens lander into the clouds of Titan. As the lander parachuted down, it took images of lakes and rivers of liquid methane. Huygens landed on a river delta. Rocks rubbed smooth by flowing liquid methane indicate erosion happens on other planets in the same way that it does on Earth.

The Russian Venera landers are the only landers to have reached the surface of Venus. They returned images from the surface, showing basalt-like rock and volcanic plains. Despite later versions of the landers being built to withstand the extreme conditions on Venus, the landers never lasted longer than a few hours on the surface before failing.

The Apollo landers are the only landers to have carried humans to another celestial object: the Moon. Each lander carried two astronauts to the surface. The second part of the mission, the upper ascent stage, carried them back to the command module, in orbit around the Moon.

Mars Pathfinder consisted of both a lander, that acted as a base station, and the first rover (Sojourner) to land on Mars. While the lander was able to take images and record atmospheric data, the rover was able to travel just over 100 meters before communication to it was lost.

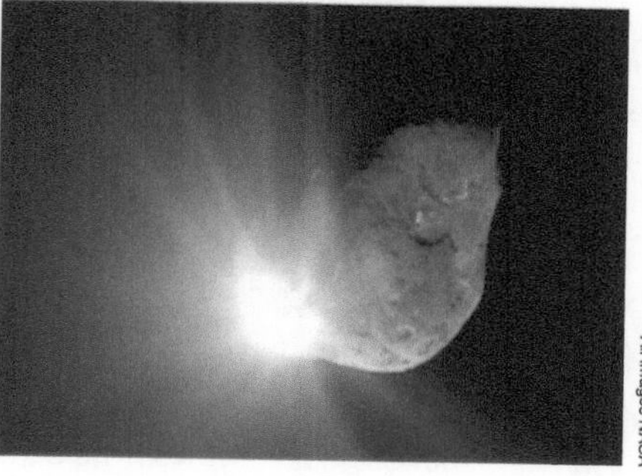

Impactors are a type of lander that deliberately crashes into the surface of a planet. By doing this, the impactor can expose layers below the surface, for study. Shock waves from the impactor can be used to study the interior of small celestial bodies.

All images NASA

6. Why were parachutes not used to slow Curiosity and Perseverance on their final descents? ______________________

____

7. How do these rovers communicate with Earth? ______________________

____

8. Ingenuity is the first helicopter to fly on another planet. Explain why such a device could be very useful in planetary exploration:

____

____

9. Explain why rovers and landers are sent to explore the surface of distant worlds instead of astronauts:

____

____

____

____

____

____

ISBN: 978-1-98-856693-1

29 Formation of the Solar System

Key Question: How did the solar system form and how has it changed over the last 4.5 billion years?

1. How does a large slowly spinning cloud of gas become a fast spinning disk? ______

______

______

______

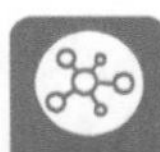

ISBN: 978-1-98-856693-1

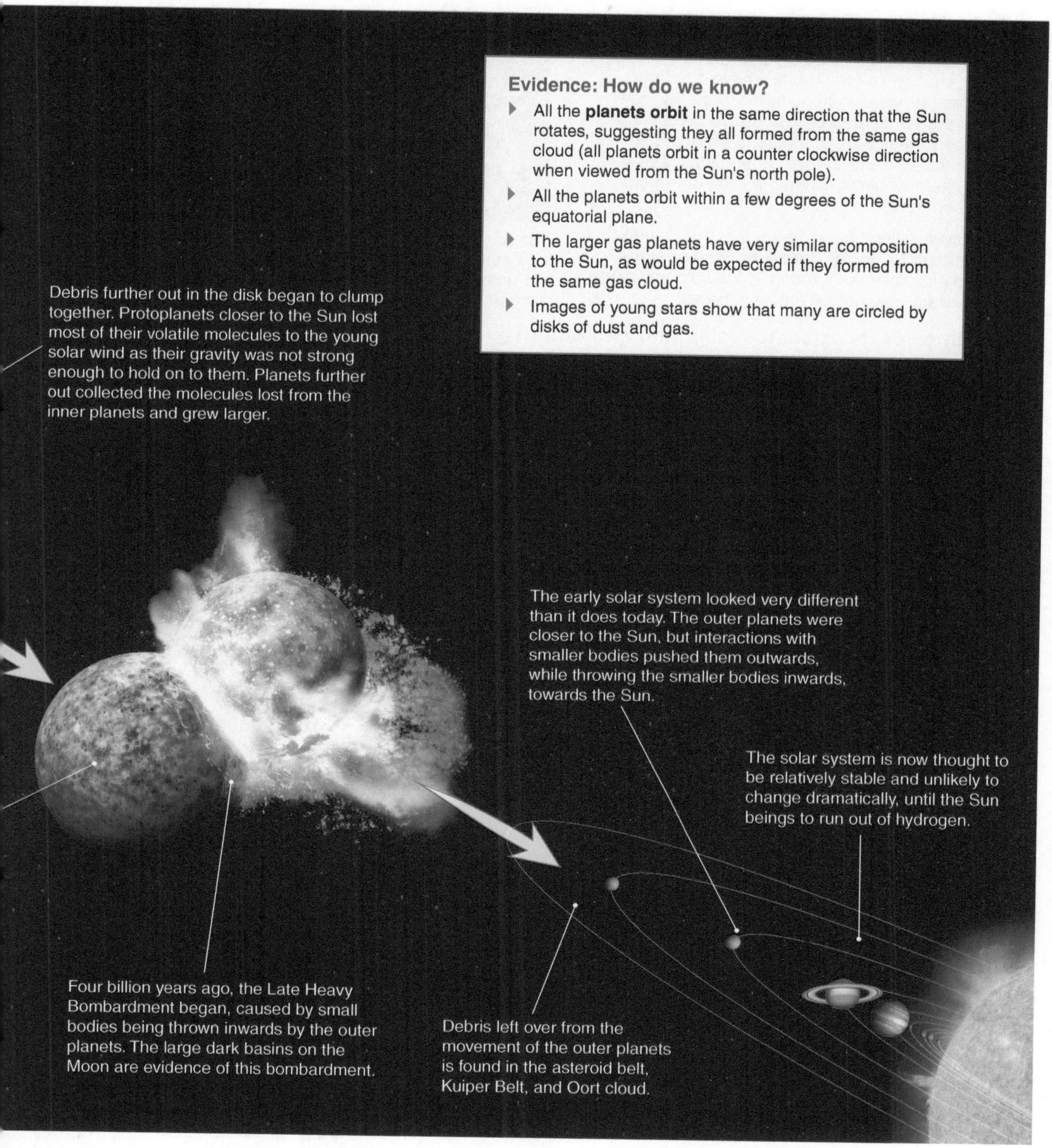

Evidence: How do we know?

- All the **planets orbit** in the same direction that the Sun rotates, suggesting they all formed from the same gas cloud (all planets orbit in a counter clockwise direction when viewed from the Sun's north pole).
- All the planets orbit within a few degrees of the Sun's equatorial plane.
- The larger gas planets have very similar composition to the Sun, as would be expected if they formed from the same gas cloud.
- Images of young stars show that many are circled by disks of dust and gas.

Debris further out in the disk began to clump together. Protoplanets closer to the Sun lost most of their volatile molecules to the young solar wind as their gravity was not strong enough to hold on to them. Planets further out collected the molecules lost from the inner planets and grew larger.

The early solar system looked very different than it does today. The outer planets were closer to the Sun, but interactions with smaller bodies pushed them outwards, while throwing the smaller bodies inwards, towards the Sun.

The solar system is now thought to be relatively stable and unlikely to change dramatically, until the Sun beings to run out of hydrogen.

Four billion years ago, the Late Heavy Bombardment began, caused by small bodies being thrown inwards by the outer planets. The large dark basins on the Moon are evidence of this bombardment.

Debris left over from the movement of the outer planets is found in the asteroid belt, Kuiper Belt, and Oort cloud.

2. Describe three pieces of evidence for the current theory of the formation of the solar system: ______

______

______

______

ISBN: 978-1-98-856693-1

Are all planetary systems the same?

- The standard theory of the formation of the solar system is that the planets formed from the vast disk of ice, dust, and gas that surrounded the early Sun. While this is true, the details of how the solar system arrived at its current configuration are still debated.
- Evidence from studies of extra-solar planets and planetary systems suggests that our solar system is quite unusual. Of the three thousand or so planetary systems studied so far, very few have as many planets as our solar system. In many cases, solar systems are dominated by one or two giant planets very close to their star. In others, several small planets orbit so close to their, often small, star the entire system would fit within the orbit of Mercury around our Sun.
- These observations have meant that the standard theory, of smaller rocky planets forming near the star, and giant planets forming in the colder regions of the system may not be entirely correct.

The star, Kepler-11 (104% the mass of the Sun) has 6 planets, all larger than the Earth but smaller than Neptune (except possibly the largest and outermost planet). All the planets orbit well within the distance of Venus to the Sun.

The Earth owes its existence to Jupiter and Saturn

The Grand Tack hypothesis suggests that Jupiter began formation before the other planets. It is thought that Jupiter formed about 3 AU from the young Sun. Because the Sun was cooler then, this was beyond a point known as the frost line, when it is cold enough for ice crystals to form.

Jupiter grew larger, sweeping up and clearing the material in its orbit. Its growing mass caused its orbit to shift. It began to migrate in towards the inner solar system and moved through the regions of the asteroid belt and where Mars was forming.

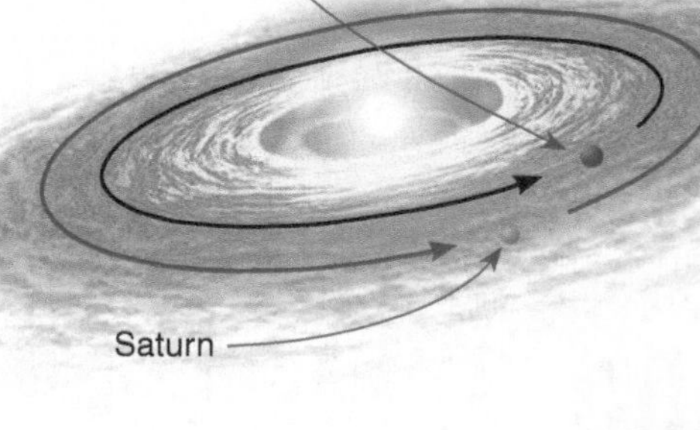

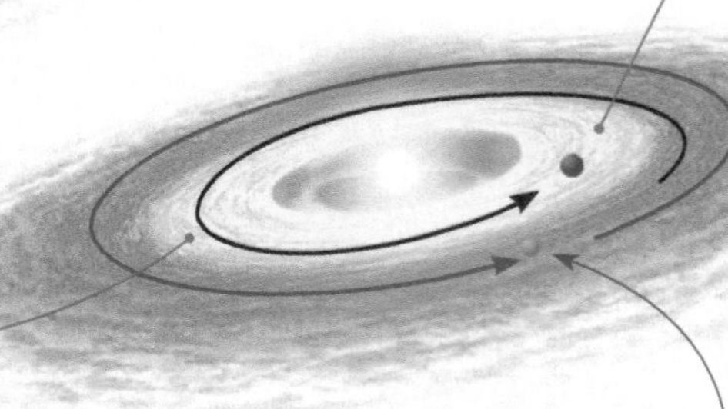

Jupiter's powerful gravity scattered most of the material in this region, both towards the inner planets and outwards to the far parts of the solar system

Saturn has also been growing larger and also migrating into the inner solar system.

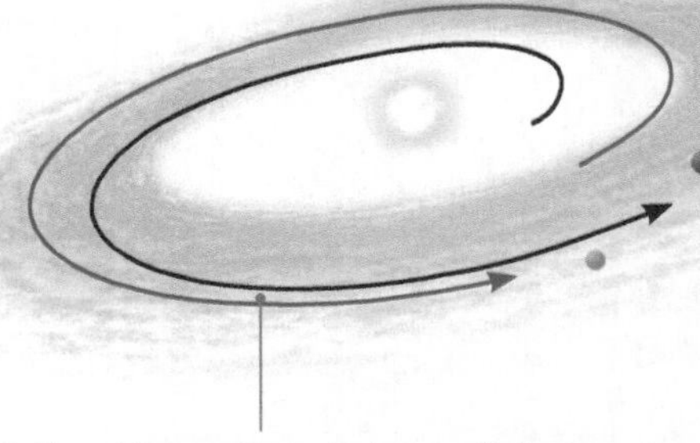

The gravitational interactions between Saturn and Jupiter caused the two giant planets to migrate back out to the outer solar system. As the Sun has grown hotter, the frost line has moved out beyond the asteroid belt.

The movement of Jupiter and Saturn cleared much of the material from the inner solar system, limiting the size of the inner planets, especially Mars. However, as the giant planets migrated back to the outer solar system, they caused a large number of comets carrying water to be thrown inwards, towards the inner planets. Earth, as a result, has a large amount of water on its surface.

ISBN: 978-1-98-856693-1

3. What are some observations that suggest our solar system is unusual, compared to other planetary systems?

4. Why did having two giant planets form close to each other have such a significant effect on the solar system?

5. (a) Jupiter has a radius of 69,911 km. The radius of Earth is 6371 km. Using the formula: volume = $(4/3)\ \pi \times \text{radius}^3$, how many times would Earth fit into Jupiter?

(b) Jupiter has a mass 318 times that of Earth. What does this, combined with the answer from 5(a), tell us about the density of Jupiter?

6. Table 1 shows the fraction of exoplanets (planets outside the solar system) of various sizes discovered so far:

(a) Is the data a normal distribution or skewed?

(b) What does the data tell us about planet formation?

Table 1

Planets per star	Number of stars
8	2
7	1
6	8
5	22
4	62
3	157
At least 2	22

7. Table 2 shows the frequency of planets in planetary systems:

(a) Is the data a normal distribution or skewed?

(b) What does the data tell us about the formation of planetary systems?

Table 2

Percent of stars with at least one planet	Planetary size (radius relative to Earth)
20.7 %	Earth (up to 1.25)
31.7%	Super earth (1.25 - 2)
39.6%	Neptune size (2-6)
6.7%	Jupiter size (6-15)
1.3%	Larger (15+)

ISBN: 978-1-98-856693-1

30 The Solar System

Key Question: What is the structure of the solar system, and what are the significant parts of it?

* **1 AU** = the distance from the Earth to the Sun = 150 million km.

The asteroid belt between Mars and Jupiter denotes the separation between the inner and outer solar system.

Jupiter
Distance from Sun: 5.20 AU

Sun
Diameter: 1.4 million km

The Moon

Mars
Distance from Sun: 1.52 AU

Earth
Distance from Sun: 1 AU

Venus
Distance from Sun: 0.72 AU

Mercury
Distance from Sun: 0.39 AU

The inner planets all have rocky surfaces so that they are also called the terrestrial planets.

DID YOU KNOW?
Erratic movements of icy worlds in the outer solar system provide some evidence for an undiscovered and very distant ninth planet.

Diagram not to scale

1. How many planets are there in the solar system? ______________________________

2. What is the main difference between the inner planets and the outer planets? ______________________________

____

3. What feature separates the inner planets from the outer planets: ______________________________

____

ESS1.B

ISBN: 978-1-98-856693-1

- The **solar system** consists of the Sun, eight planets, a number of dwarf planets, and other smaller objects such as comets and asteroids. Planets **orbit** the Sun, have enough **gravity** to form a sphere, and sweep their orbit clear of debris. The dwarf planets are not large enough to sweep their orbits clear of debris.
- The four inner planets all have rocky surfaces, while the four outer planets are mainly gas. The inner planets are separated from the outer planets by the asteroid belt.

4. Name the three areas in the solar system where small frozen, rocky debris is found: ______________________

____

5. (a) Which planet is nearest the Sun? ______________________

(b) Which planet is furthest from the Sun? ______________________

(c) Recall the definition of one AU (p10). Calculate the distance of Uranus from the Sun, in km: ______________

ISBN: 978-1-98-856693-1

- Of the seven planets in the night sky, only five (Mercury, Venus, Mars, Jupiter, and Saturn) were known to the ancient astronomers, and it was not until 1781 that Uranus was recorded as possibly a planet or comet, and then not until 1783 that it was officially a new planet.
- In 1821, tables of Uranus' calculated orbit were produced and soon after, astronomers noted that the observed orbit deviated from the calculated orbit. It suggested to astronomers that another planet was affecting Uranus' orbit. Calculations for the new planet's position were made in 1845, and in 1846 Neptune was discovered, just 1° from where the calculations suggested it should be.

The pull of gravity shows the way

Differences between the calculated and observed orbit of Uranus suggested another planet beyond it. Neptune was discovered within a year of its suspected position being calculated.

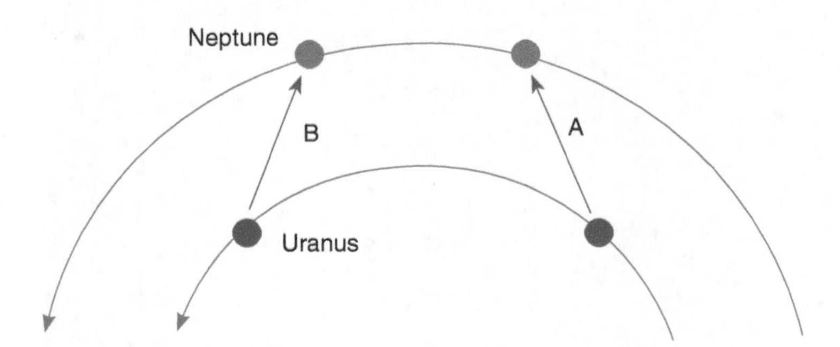

At position A, Uranus is attracted to Neptune and is accelerated along its orbit. At position B, Uranus is slowed by its attraction to Neptune.

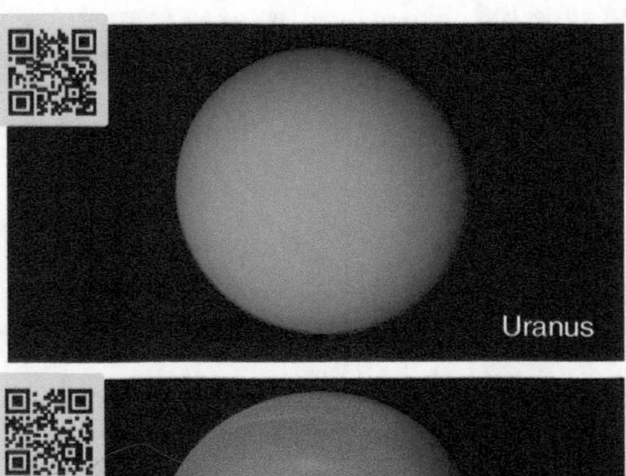

- When Pluto was discovered in 1930, it was classified as the ninth planet. However, by 2006, nearly a dozen Pluto sized objects had been discovered orbiting the Sun. This caused a problem. If Pluto was a planet, then surely all these near Pluto-sized objects should also be planets. The issue was resolved in 2006, when the International Astronomical Union adopted three rules for defining a planet. Pluto, and all objects like it, were now called dwarf planets, as they did not follow all three rules.

How to be a planet

1. The object must orbit a star, e.g. the Sun, but not anything else otherwise it is a moon.
2. The object must have enough gravity to form itself into a sphere, i.e. it's round, like the Earth.
3. The object must clear its neighborhood of other objects, i.e. other objects along its orbit are captured or flung out of its orbit.

Dwarf planets

There are five recognized dwarf planets. However, there are many other dwarf planet-like objects discovered but yet to be recognized, or named officially. Many of the dwarf planets are part of what are collectively called Kuiper belt objects. The Kuiper belt is an area beyond the orbit of Neptune that contains the icy-rocky remnants from the formation of the solar system. Pluto, once a planet, is now recognized as one of these.

NASA

Ironically, the New Horizons spacecraft, which took this picture of Pluto, was launched the same year Pluto was demoted from planetary status.

6. Explain the importance of observation and calculations for predictions in finding Neptune: ______________________

7. Uranus orbits 19.19 AU from the Sun. Neptune orbits 30.07 AU from the Sun. At their closest approach to each other what is the distance between Uranus and Neptune?

8. Which rule applying to planets do the dwarf planets not follow? ______________________

ISBN: 978-1-98-856693-1

The dust between the planets

The New Horizons spacecraft (Activity 28) was occupied while flying the billions of kilometers to Pluto. In 2007 it flew past Jupiter, using the planet for a gravitational assist and took images of the planet and its moons. Attached to the spacecraft, facing the direction of travel, is the Student Dust Counter (below), built by students at the University of Colorado Boulder. This counted the number and density of the dust particles in space as it travelled to Pluto.

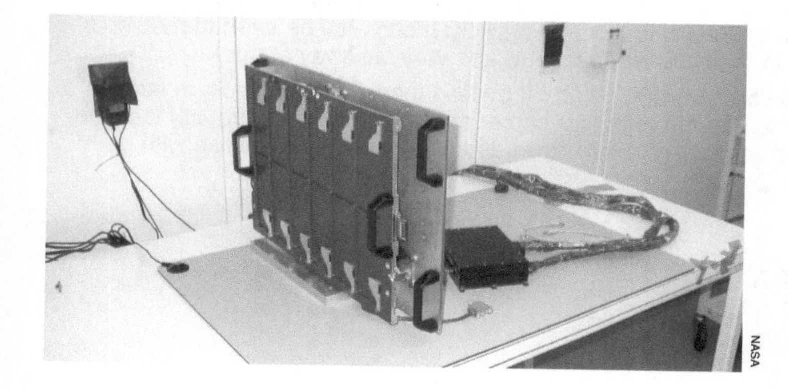
NASA

The table below shows the number of dust particle "hits" per AU travelled from Earth by the New Horizons.

Distance (AU)	No. of hits*	Particles/km^3**
1-2	404	21.5
2-3	227	12.11
3-4	662	35.31
4-5	1143	60.96
5-6	291	15.52
6-7	1270	67.73
7-8	708	37.76
8-9	274	14.61
9-10	1687	89.97

* These are minimum numbers as the counter was periodically switched on and off.
** This is a minimum amount as the spacecraft is actually travelling in a curve rather than a straight line.

9. (a) Draw a histogram of the particle density of space from 1 AU to 10 AU.

   (b) Which distances have the greatest particle density? ______________________

10. Pluto has a very elliptical orbit compared to the planets. At its closest approach, Pluto is 30 AU from the Sun. At its furthest, it is 49 AU from the Sun.

   (a) What is the difference in kilometers between Pluto's distance from the Sun from its closest and furthest positions?

   ____

   (b) What is unusual about Pluto's position relative to other planets at its closest approach? ______________________

   ____

ISBN: 978-1-98-856693-1

31 The Motion of Celestial Objects

Key Question: How do planets, moons, comets, and asteroids move, when orbiting a larger mass.

Orbits

- In a perfect situation, a **planet** might orbit a star in a circular orbit, but due to gravitational interactions with other objects, e.g. moons, asteroids, and other planets, a circular orbit is most unlikely. It can also be seen that objects such as comets travel in orbits that are very close to their star at one point, and very far away at another.
- The planet Venus has the most circular orbit in the solar system, being off by less than 1%. A circle is, in fact, a special occurrence of a shape called an ellipse. Whereas the path of a circle "orbits" around a central point called the focus, the path of an ellipse "orbits" around two separate points known as foci. A circle is an ellipse with both foci in the same place.

Investigation 3.1 Elliptical orbits

See appendix for equipment list.

1. In the box below, draw a series of ellipses using each bracketed pair of dots as focal points (foci). You will need a piece of string 15 cm long, two thumbtacks, and a pencil.
2. Tie the string into a loop. Press the thumb tacks into the dots as focal points (put corkboard or thick card behind the page to protect your book).
3. Loop the string around the thumbtacks and your pencil. Keep the loop tight by gently pushing outwards with your pencil as you draw the curve.

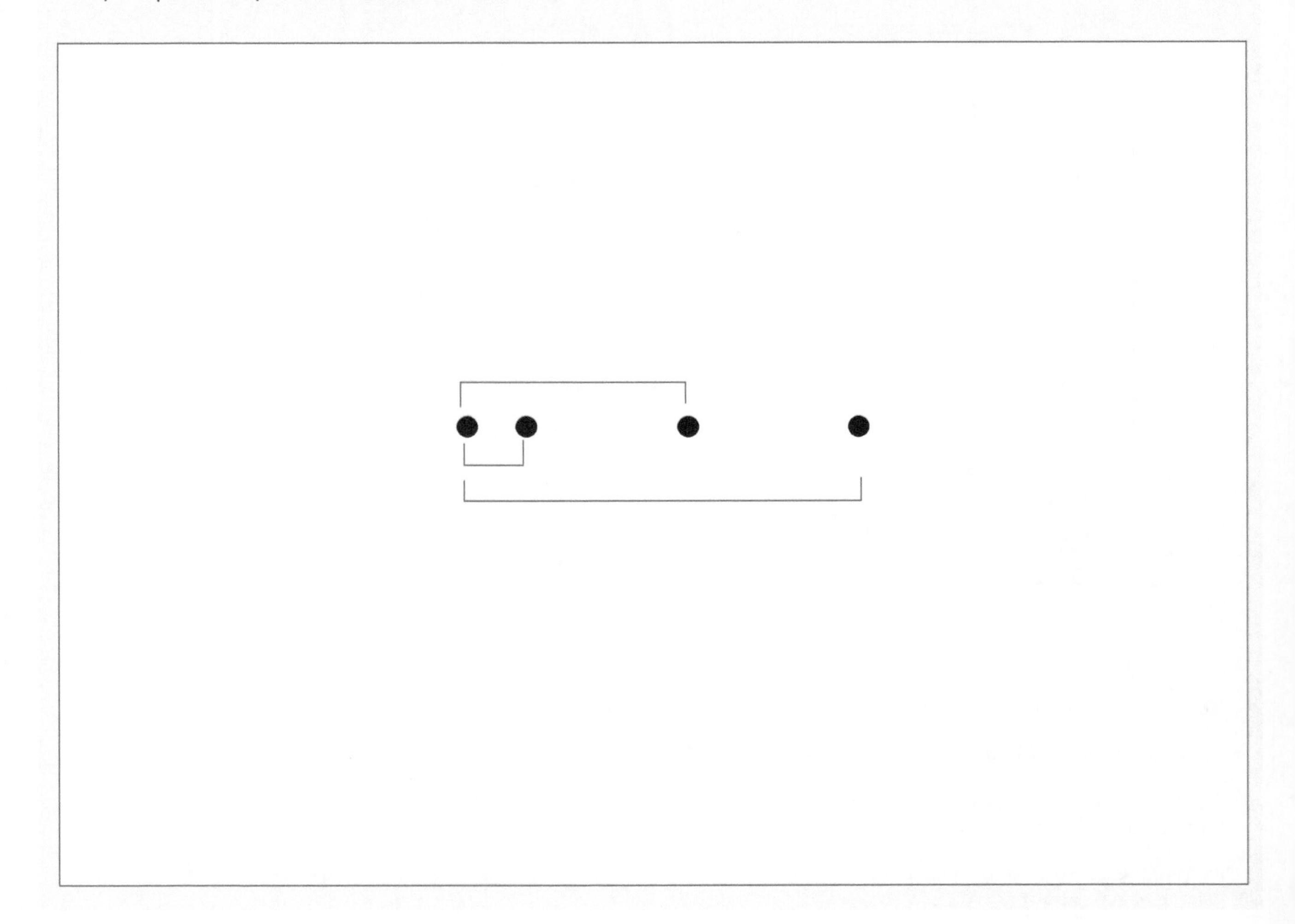

1. How does the distance between foci affect the shape of an ellipse? ______________________

____

ISBN: 978-1-98-856693-1

Orbits and escape velocity

- Our **solar system** consists of the Sun, eight planets, numerous dwarf planets, and almost uncountable numbers of comets and asteroids. Many of these objects orbit the Sun in elliptical orbits that are roughly circular, with the Sun near the center of the circle. However, many do not. The most well known of these are comets, but many of the dwarf planets, especially those in the outer solar system, also orbit with highly elongated orbits.
- How an object orbits, depends on many things. These include how it formed, where it formed, the gravitational force from nearby objects, and its velocity during an encounter with any other object.

- Escape velocity is the velocity required to escape the gravitational pull of an object at a particular distance from it.
- The diagram on the right shows the orbit of a planet (P) around a star. Its possible orbits could vary, depending on its actual velocity (v) compared to its escape velocity (v_E) and the velocity needed for the planet to orbit in a perfect circle (v_C).
- Resident planet: circle, ellipse 1 and ellipse 2 on the diagram show planet P staying in orbit around the star.
- Visiting planet: parabola and hyperbola on the diagram show planet P escaping orbit.

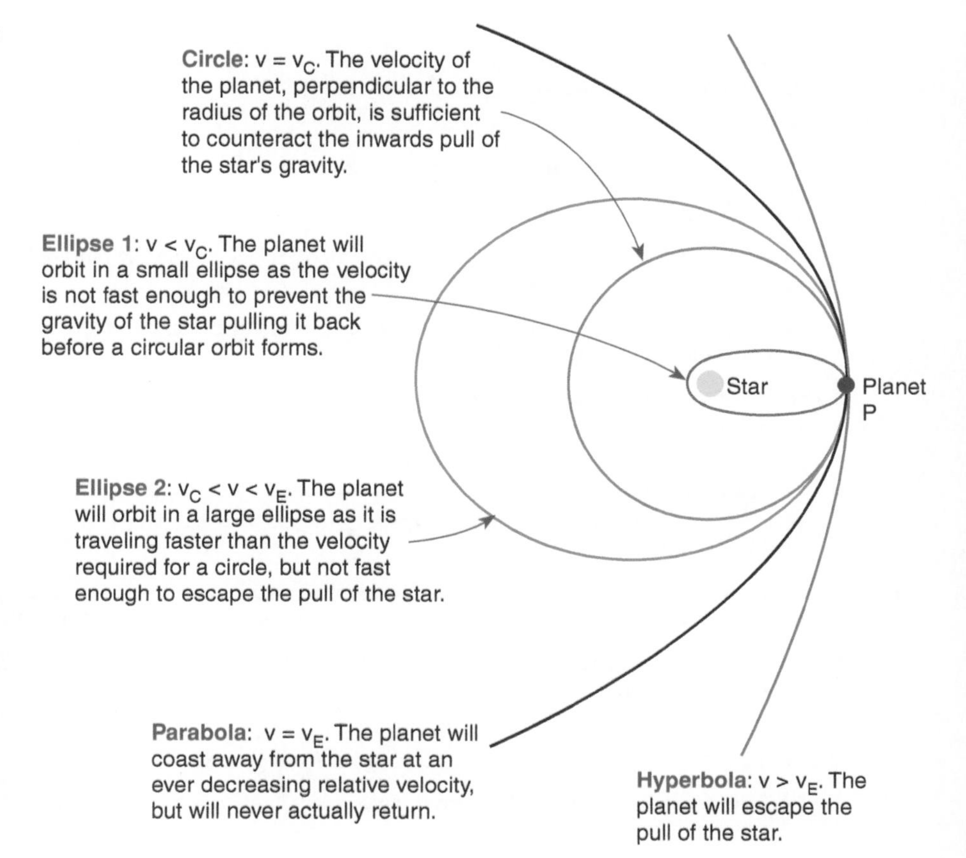

Scott McDougall
Comets have a highly elliptical orbit

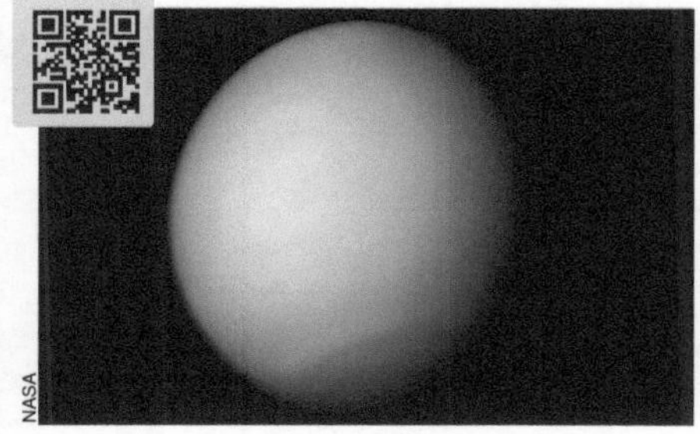
NASA

Venus has the most circular orbit in the solar system, being less than 1% off a perfect circle. At its closest approach to the Sun, Venus is 0.716 AU away from the Sun, while at its furthest, it is 0.726 AU from the Sun. One AU (astronomical unit) is the average distance from the Sun to the Earth, about 150 million km.

NASA

Sedna is one of the most distant dwarf planets. It has a dramatically elongated orbit compared to the planets of the solar system. At its closest approach to the Sun, Sedna closes to 72 AU, but then swings back out to 936 AU from the Sun. Its orbit takes over 11,400 years to complete.

NASA

In 2017, the interstellar object "Oumuamua" entered the solar system. Its trajectory brought it close to the orbit of Mars. Oumuamua was traveling at such a high speed that, although the Sun's gravity bent its path, it was not captured. It has since travelled back out past the outer planets on its way out of the solar system.

2. (a) Of the five orbits shown in the diagram top right, which most likely matches the orbit of Oumuamua?

____

(b) What would happen to the shape of Venus's orbit if it gained velocity as it moved along its orbit? ____________________

____

(c) How would the size of the escape velocity be affected if a planet orbits closer to a star? ____________________

____

ISBN: 978-1-98-856693-1

Modeling orbits

- What causes an orbit? That depends on how complicated you want the answer. A simple answer is **gravity**. A more complex answer is the bending or warping of space around an object with mass.
- All objects have mass. The more mass they have, the greater they bend or warp space around them. An orbiting object is simply following the curves in space around a massive object.
- Space is, obviously, three dimensional, so it is difficult to model bending three dimensions into a curve. Bending two dimensions, e.g. a sheet of paper, into a curve is somewhat more simple. By doing so you can model how planets orbit stars.

Investigation 3.2 Modeling orbits 1

See appendix for equipment list.

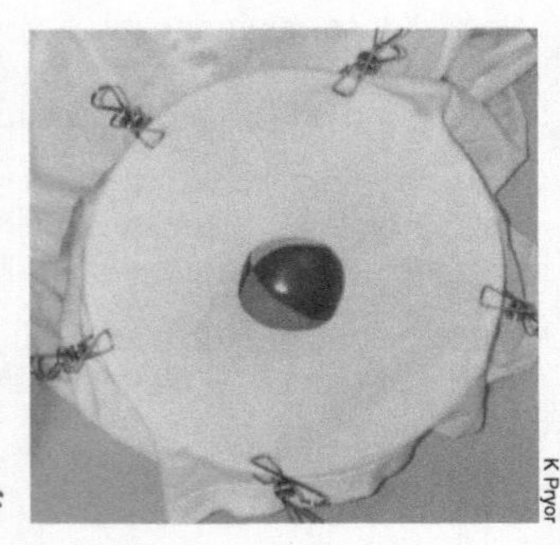
K Pryor

1. Obtain a large bowl; the wider and deeper the better.
2. Over the large bowl, place a large sheet of material or plastic, so that it covers the entire opening of the bowl.
3. Secure the material in place using clips, e.g. bulldog or binder clips, or pegs around the lip of the bowl (right above).
4. Obtain five balls or other spherical objects. Examples that work well are: a tennis ball, a large marble, a small marble, a large ball bearing, and a rubber bouncing ball.
5. The small marble will act as the planet. The other four balls will act as stars of various sizes and masses. You may wish to measure their diameter and mass for better accuracy of answers.
6. Place one of the "stars" in the center of the sheet, over the bowl, and wait for a moment until it has stopped moving, or rolling if it was off center.
7. Roll the marble around the lip of the bowl and observe the path the marble takes (right below). Do this two more times. Try rolling the marble at higher and lower speeds.
8. Replace the first "star" with a second star. Repeat step 7.
9. Repeat steps 7 and 8 for the other two "stars".

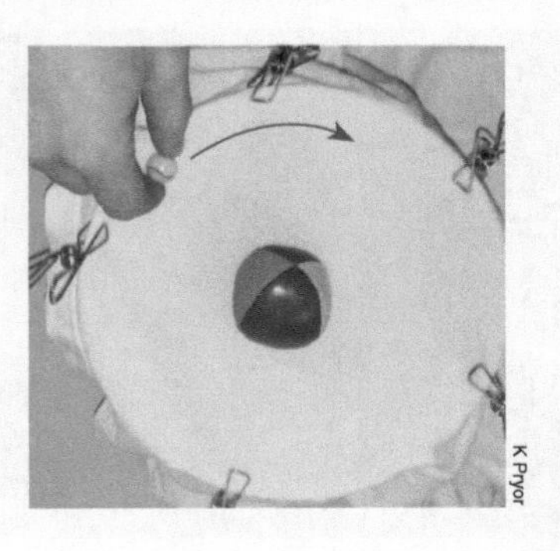
K Pryor

3. Describe the path of the marble around the first "star" at slow, medium, and high speeds: ______________________________

4. Describe the effect of changing the mass of the star on the "orbit" of the "planet": ______________________________

5. What are the limitations of this model? ______________________________

6. What might happen to the orbits if no friction occurred between the marble and the material? ______________________________

ISBN: 978-1-98-856693-1

32 Kepler's Laws and Orbits

Key Question: How do Kepler's laws describe the motion of the planets?

Kepler and planetary motion

- The orbits of **planets** are often thought of as circular, but in fact they are ellipses. The orbits of the planets follow some simple mathematical rules worked out by Johannes Kepler, in 1609. The laws, however, are not entirely perfect, as planets are affected by the gravitational pull of other planets, especially Jupiter.

1. Each planet moves in an elliptical orbit with the Sun at one focus. An ellipse is a curve around two focal points (f_1 and f_2). It has a semimajor (a) and a semiminor axis (b), shown below in red. The further apart the foci are, the more elongated the ellipse is.

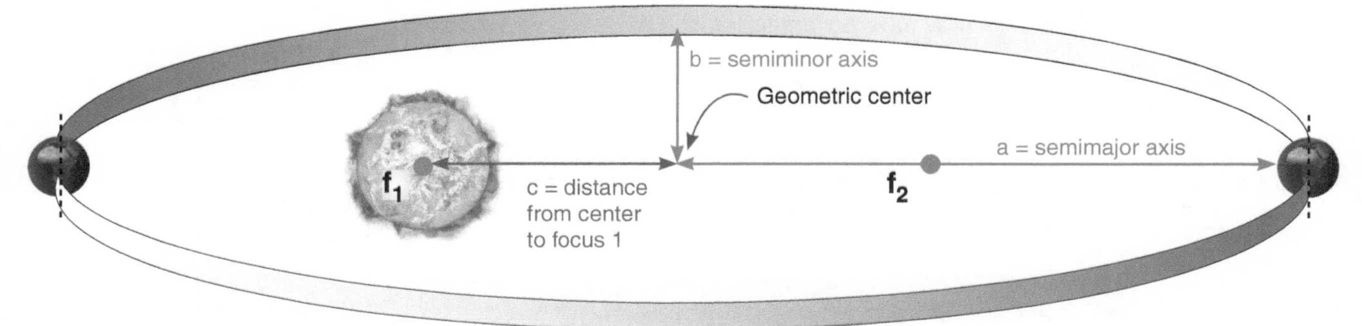

2. A line between the Sun and a planet sweeps over equal areas during equal time periods. The further a planet is from the Sun, the slower it orbits. As it comes closer, the speed at which the planet orbits increases. However, over a set time, a line drawn from the Sun to the planet will still sweep over an area of space equal to when it was moving slowly.

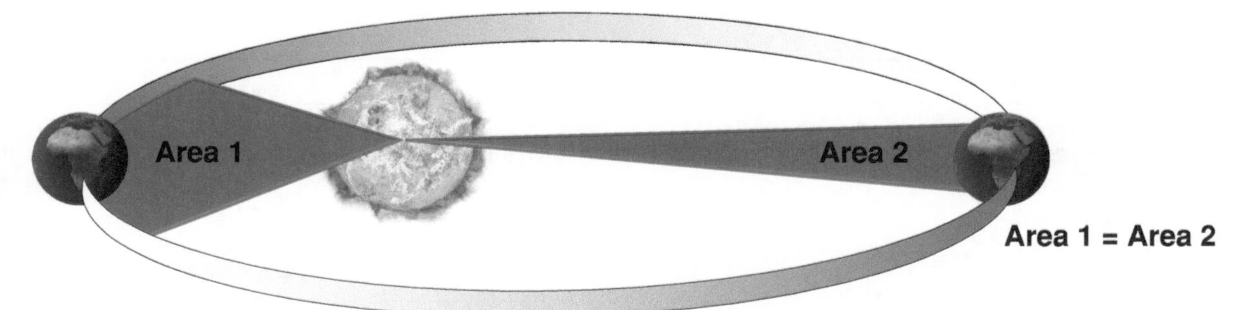

3. The square of any planet's orbital period (**T**) (the time it takes for one orbit) is proportional to the cube of its semi-major axis (**a**); therefore:

$$T^2 = \text{constant} \times a^3$$

If a is measured in AU, and T is measured in Earth Years, then this combination of units makes the value of the constant = 1. The result is the simple equation $\mathbf{T^2 = a^3}$

A further consequence of T^2 being proportional to a^3 is that the ratio is the same for all planets (see the dark blue box).

$$\frac{T_1^2}{a_1^3} = \frac{T_2^2}{a_2^3}$$

* **1 AU** = the distance from the Earth to the Sun = 150 million km.

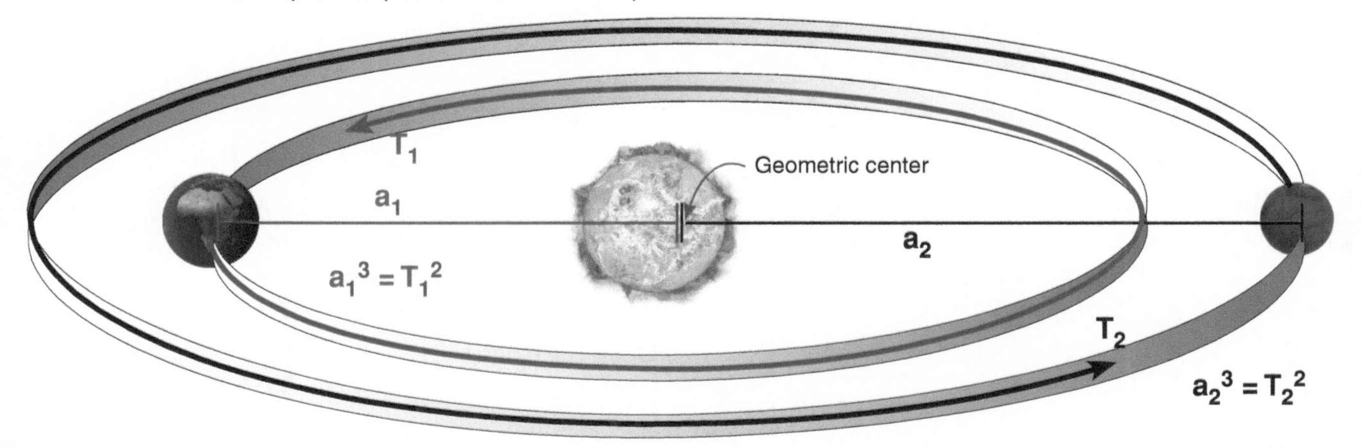

ISBN: 978-1-98-856693-1

Aphelion and perihelion

- The elliptical shape of a planet's orbit means that, at some point, the planet will make its closest approach to the Sun (called perihelion) and at another point it will be at its most distant (called aphelion).
- Because Earth's orbit is almost circular, there is very little difference between aphelion and perihelion. The Northern Hemisphere's winter occurs in perihelion and the Northern Hemisphere's summer occurs during aphelion.
- The deviation of an ellipse from being circular is called its **eccentricity**, which is given a value between 0 and 1. The closer the value to 0, the closer the ellipse is to a perfect circle. The eccentricity of Earth's orbit is 0.0167 (nearly circular), whereas comets may have eccentricities of 0.9.

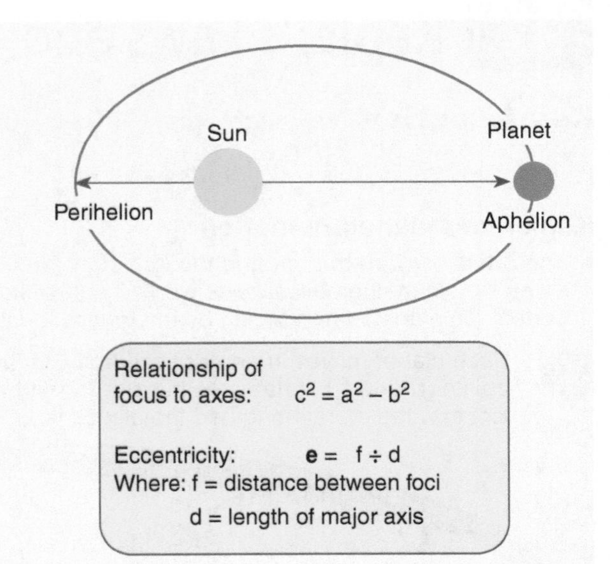

Relationship of focus to axes: $c^2 = a^2 - b^2$

Eccentricity: **e** = $f \div d$
Where: f = distance between foci
d = length of major axis

1. Complete the table below using $a^3 = T^2$. Use the worked example below as a guide:
   Calculating the orbital period (T) of the dwarf planet Ceres from its distance from the sun in AU:
   a = 2.77 AU. $a^3 = 2.77^3 = 21.25 = T^2$ $T^2 = 21.25$ $\sqrt{21.25} = T$ **T= 4.61 years**

	Planet	a (AU)	a^3	T^2	T (Earth Years)
(a)	Mercury				0.24
(b)	Earth	1.00		1.00	
(c)	Venus	0.72			
(d)	Jupiter			140.85	
(e)	Saturn		867.43		
(f)	Neptune				164.79

2. Use your answers to question 1 to plot the planet's orbital period vs the planet's average distance from the Sun on the graph below:

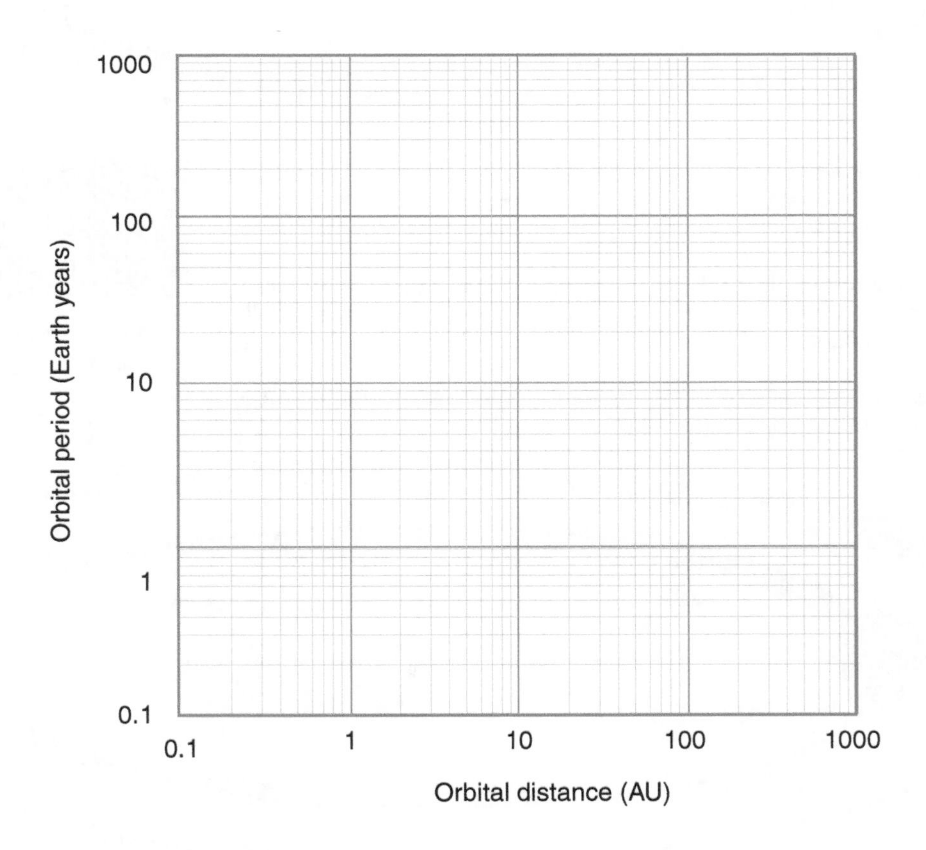

ISBN: 978-1-98-856693-1

(b) Use the internet or other research to add Mars, Uranus, and Pluto to your plot. Do they fit the trend?

3. For each elliptical orbit shown below, rule in the major and minor axes; measure '**a**' (semimajor) and '**b**' (semiminor); then calculate **T** and **e** and **c** (NOTE scale: 1 cm = 10 AU. x marks the position of the star, o is the orbiting object. The first one has been done for you.

(i)

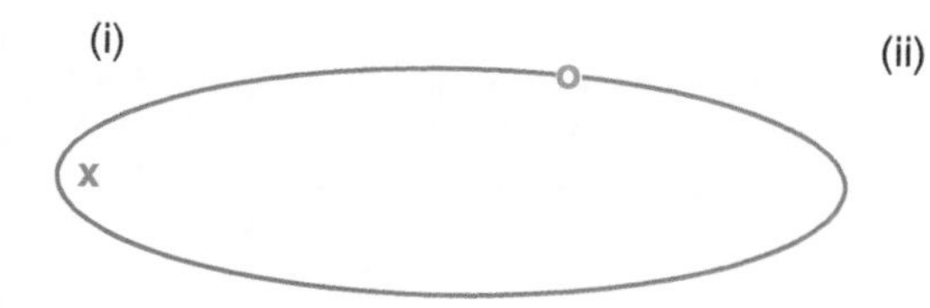

(ii)

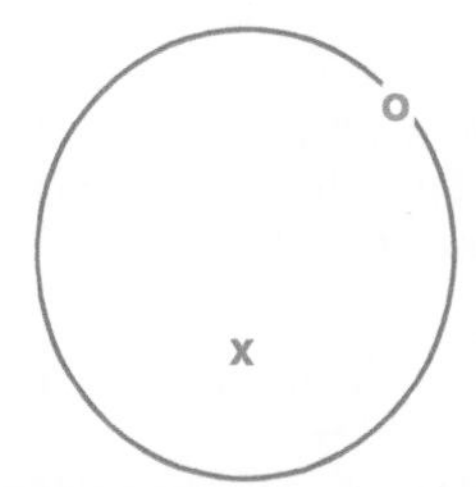

(iii)

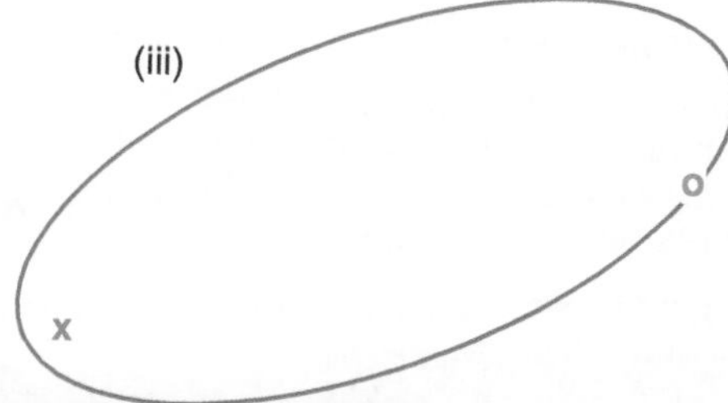

	a	b	c	T (Earth Years)	e
(i)	30 AU	9 AU	29 AU	164	0.95
(ii)					
(iii)					

4. Why does a line between a planet and the Sun sweep out equal areas during equal time periods, no matter the planet's distance from the Sun during its orbit?

5. Calculate the following:

(a) The semimajor axis of the orbit of the dwarf planet Eris from the Sun is 67.8 AU. What is its orbital period?

(b) Makemake has an orbital period of 307.5 years around the Sun. What is the semimajor axis of its orbit?

(c) Convert your answer for (b) into kilometers:

6. Explain why a comet with a semimajor axis of 10.33 AU and an eccentricity of 0.906 is most unlikely to actually be found 10.33 AU from the Sun:

7. (a) Use $T_1^2/a_1^3 = T_2^2/a_2^3$ to solve the following: Jupiter's moon Ganymede, takes 7.15 Earth days to orbit Jupiter. Ganymede is measured to be 1,070,000 km from Jupiter's center. A second moon of Jupiter, Callisto, takes 16.69 Earth days to orbit Jupiter. How far away is Callisto from the center of Jupiter?

(b) It was also noted that Jupiter's moon Io takes just 1.77 days to orbit the planet. How far away from Jupiter is Io?

ISBN: 978-1-98-856693-1

33 Gravity and Newton's Laws

Key Question: What is gravity and how can it be described mathematically?

What is gravity?

- **Gravity** is a property of mass. All mass has gravity and the greater the mass, the greater the gravity. Gravity is an attractive force (F) and it pulls objects together. The effect of gravity decreases, the further apart the objects are (see inverse square law, Activity 4, p11); even so, large structures like galaxies can exert gravitational effects over millions of light years.
- Isaac Newton published his law of gravitation in 1687 and included the equation:

$$F = G \frac{M_1 M_2}{r^2}$$

F: gravitational force (N)
M_2 is the mass of object 2 (kg)
M_1 is the mass of object 1 (kg)
G: gravitational constant = **6.673×10^{-11} Nm^2/kg^2**
r is distance between centers of objects (meters)

- The equation allows the force of gravity acting between two objects to be calculated. We can see that the force of gravity is proportional to the product of the masses and inversely proportional to the square of their distance apart.

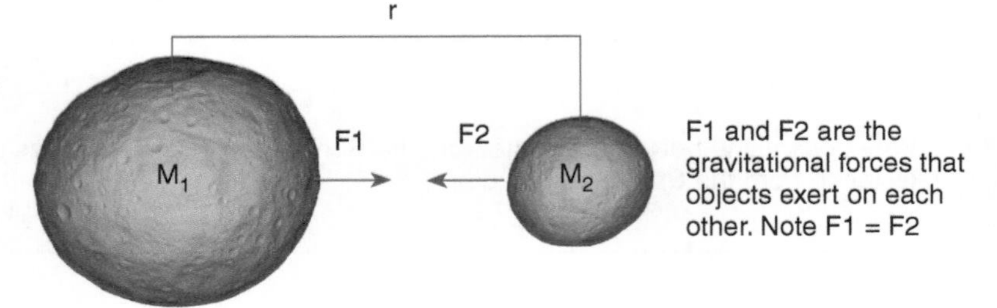

What is an orbit?

- The Sun is the overwhelming source of gravity in our **solar system**. Its gravity reaches far into space and all the objects in the solar system **orbit** around it.
- But what is an orbit? The **planets** are all falling towards the Sun. However, they are also moving sideways, relative to the Sun. The effect is that they trace elliptical orbits through space.
- It is important to remember the gravitational pull the planets exert on the Sun is equal to the Sun's gravitational pull on the planets, but because the Sun is so much bigger, it barely moves, instead it wobbles around its axis on a tiny orbit of its own.
- The closer the match between the mass of the orbiting objects the more pronounced this wobble is. The center of the Earth-Moon system, for example, is 4670 km from the center of the Earth, i.e. within the radius of the Earth.

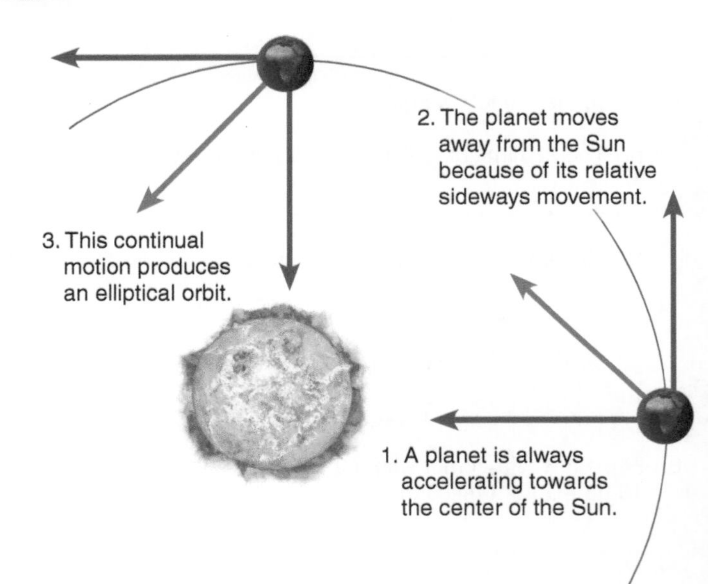

1. What is gravity? ______________________________

____

2. Using Newton's equation for the universal law of gravitation, what would be the effect on the force between the Earth and Moon of changing the following:

   (a) Doubling the distance between the Earth and Moon: F would (increase / decrease / remain the same) (circle one).

   (b) Doubling the mass of the Moon: F would (increase / decrease / remain the same) (circle one).

   (c) Halving the mass of the Earth: F would (increase / decrease / remain the same) (circle one).

3. The Earth exerts the same gravitational pull on the Sun as the Sun does on the Earth. Explain why the Earth orbits the Sun in a wide orbit, while the Sun only wobbles on its axis:

____

____

ISBN: 978-1-98-856693-1

Investigation 3.3 Modeling orbits 2

See appendix for equipment list.

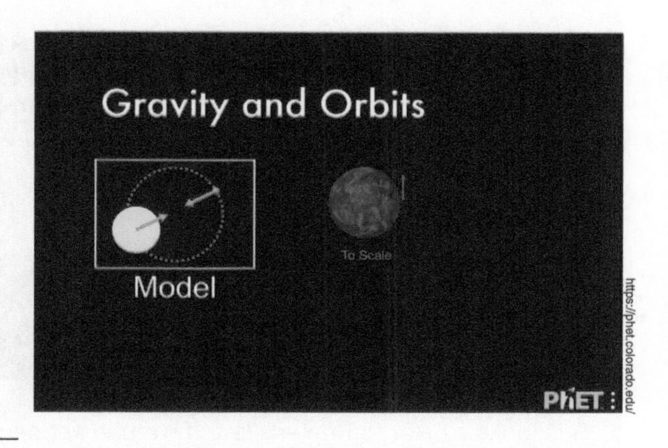

1. The online simulation PhET Gravity and Orbits (see the BIOZONE **Resource Hub** for the link) is a simple program that models the orbits of the Earth-Moon-Sun system and can vary the size of the star and planet.
2. Open the program and choose the Model option. You can view the vectors for velocity and gravity by clicking on the check boxes. You can adjust the length of the arrows by clicking and dragging them with the mouse.
3. Select the Earth-Sun system if it is not already selected. View the velocity and gravity vectors. Click play. While the simulation is going, increase the mass of the Earth to 2.0. What happens?

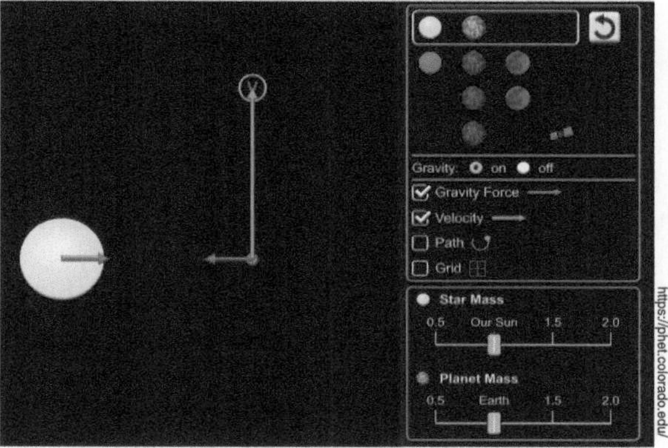

4. Now set the Earth's mass to 0.5. What happens?
5. Reset the Earth's mass to 1. Set the Sun's mass to 2.0. What happens now?
6. Explain the result of (3) and (4), and (5):
7. Set the system to show the Earth-Moon-Sun system. Click the path check box, then click play. Observe how the Moon orbits the Earth and the paths they take. There is something not quite right with this simulation. Can you describe what it is?
8. Click on the velocity check box to see the vectors for velocity. Explore the effect of increasing the Moon's velocity and position. Try changing the parameters of the orbit and speed. Can you set up another stable system? Run the system for many years to see what happens in the long term.
9. Set the system to show the Earth-Moon system. Click the path check box, then click play. Observe how the Moon orbits the Earth and the paths they take. What do you notice now? Set the mass of the Moon to 2.0. Now what do you notice?

ISBN: 978-1-98-856693-1

34 Applying Newton's Law to Kepler's Laws

Key Question: By comparing Kepler's and Newton's equations, what new information or insight can we gain?

Isaac Newton realized that the orbital period of a **planet** was related to the mass of the star and the mass of the planet. He was able to derive all of **Kepler's laws** from his law of universal gravitation, producing simple formulae that could be used to calculate the mass of any orbiting body, based on the orbital period and the distance of the body orbiting it.

- This can be simplified as:

$$M = \frac{a^3}{T^2}$$

M = mass in solar masses
a = distance in AU
T = orbital period in Earth Years

- This looks similar to Kepler's law. If we use astronomical units (AU) for **a** and Earth years for **T** (as we have earlier), then using Newton's realization that T is related to the mass of the star, **M** must be in solar masses, where 1 solar mass is equal to the mass of the Sun (1.99×10^{30} kg).
- Using these equations, we can calculate the mass of any central body based on the orbital period and distance of the orbiting body. An example of how to rearrange the equation, step by step, is in Appendix 3, p324.

Using the equation

Example 1: (a) A star has a mass of 4 solar masses and has a planet orbiting 5 AU from it. What is the period of the planet's orbit in years?
(b) What is the mass of the star in kg?
(c) What is the distance between the star and the planet?

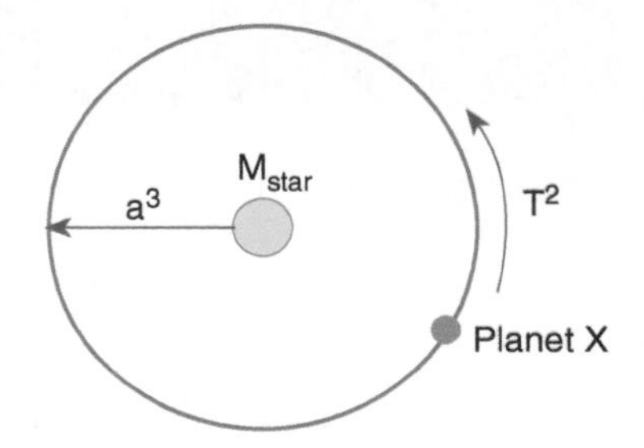

(a) $T^2 = a^3/M_{star} = 5^3/4 = 125/4 = 31.25$.

T = 5.6 years

(b) $M_{star} = 1.99 \times 10^{30} \times 4 = 47.96 \times 10^{30}$ kg

(c) $a = 1.5 \times 10^{11} \times 5 = 7.5 \times 10^{11}$ m

Example 2: Planet X orbits star 1 and planet Z orbits star 2. Both planets take 2 Earth years to orbit their respective stars. However, planet X is 2 AU from its star, while planet Z is 1 AU from its star.

(a) What is mass of each star, in solar masses?
(b) How many times bigger is one star than the other?

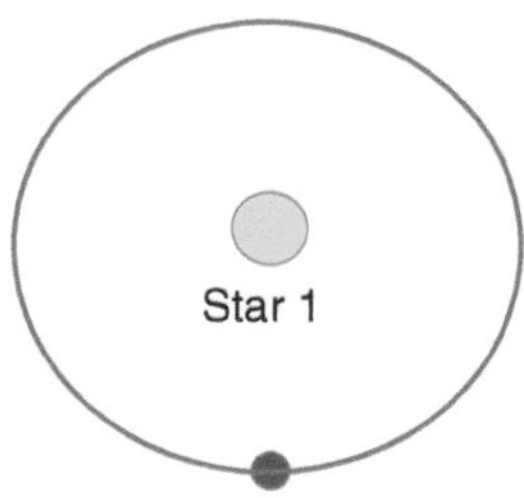

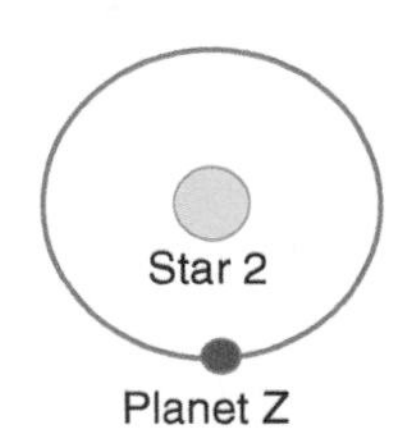

(a) $M\ star\ 1 = \frac{a^3}{T^2} = \frac{2^3}{2^2} = \frac{8}{4} =$ **2 solar masses**

$M\ star\ 2 = \frac{a^3}{T^2} = \frac{1^3}{2^2} = \frac{1}{4} =$ **0.25 solar masses**

(b) **2 solar masses ÷ 0.25 solar masses = 8.**
Star 1 is 8 times more massive than star 2.

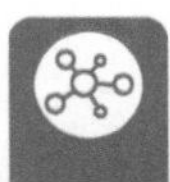

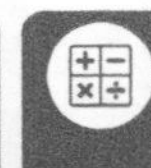
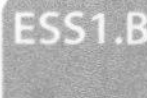

ISBN: 978-1-98-856693-1

1. Calculate the distance (in AU) of a planet from its star's center for a planet with an orbit of 145 years and a star 2.5 times the mass of the Sun.

2. Calculate the orbital period of a planet that is 35 AU from its star's center if the mass of the star is 1.5 times the mass of the Sun.

3. Trappist-1 is a small star about 40 light years from Earth. It is orbited by seven planets. The orbits of these planets have been calculated from data collected by Earth-orbiting observatories. The planet labeled Trappist-1g takes 12.35 days to orbit the star and is about 6.75 million km from the star. How big is Trappist-1 compared to our Sun? (Hint: Convert days to years, and km to AU, to give the answer in solar masses.)

4. (a) The largest star so far observed is estimated to be 315 times as massive as the Sun. Assuming it was possible for a planet to orbit this star at the same distance as the Earth is from the Sun, calculate the planet's orbital period in days. (Hint: 'a' is 1AU; M is already given to you, in solar masses):

   (b) At what distance (in AU) from the star's center would the planet need to be in order to orbit it in one Earth year?

5. (a) Observations of a star 30 light years away showed it was being orbited by a planet once every 1.5 Earth years. It was also calculated the planet was 1.75 AU from the star. What is the mass of the star in solar masses?

   (b) Observations of a second star showed that its planet orbited it in 0.5 years and was 0.9 AU distant. Calculate the difference in solar masses between the two stars and state which star is larger:

6. A group of astronomers claim to have found a new planet orbiting the Sun at 3 AU and taking 1.5 years to orbit the Sun. Is the astronomer correct in their findings? Justify your answer:

7. (a) The star S2 orbits the supermassive black hole Sagittarius A* at a distance of about 970 AU. It takes 16.05 years to complete one orbit. What is the mass of Sagittarius A* in solar masses?

   (b) A recent estimate of the mass of Sagittarius A* put its mass at 4.31 million solar masses. Does your answer from 11 (a) match this? What could be the cause of the difference (if any).

ISBN: 978-1-98-856693-1

Using the gravitational constant

- You may have noticed that using $M = a^3 \div T^2$ is useful when the distance in AU is known or the mass of a star is in solar units. Using AU and solar units gives a good idea of scale, and $M = a^3 \div T^2$ is easy to compute, but it does not produce the best answer in terms of mass and distance.
- It is also not the best equation to use when trying to compute the mass of a planet around which a moon or satellite orbits, or if the known units are already in kilograms and meters. Planets are many orders of magnitude less than the mass of the Sun, e.g. Earth is 0.000003 solar masses and, if the units of mass are already in kilograms and meters, then it makes little sense in converting into solar mass and AUs if the answer needs to be in kilograms and meters.
- In cases such as this, a more universal equation is required. It is a more accurate equation of Kepler's third law produced by Newton.

$$M = \frac{4\pi^2 a^3}{G T^2}$$

M = mass in kilograms
a = distance in meters
T = orbital period in seconds
G: the gravitational constant = **6.673×10^{-11} Nm^2/kg^2**

Example: A moon orbits a planet at a distance of 3.5×10^8 m from its planet's center (most moons and planets have almost circular orbits, so the semimajor axis is almost equal to the semiminor axis). It takes the moon 20 days to orbit the planet. What is the mass of the planet (in kg)? Note that $4\pi^2$ and G are always the same numbers.

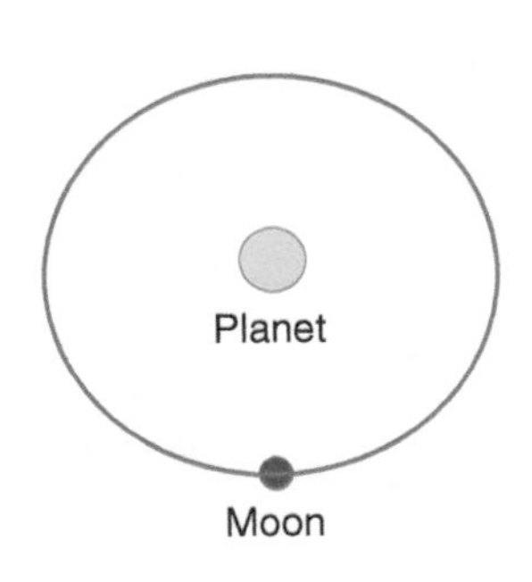

Days need to converted to seconds. Seconds in a day = $60 \times 60 \times 24 = 86400$
Seconds in 20 days = $20 \times 86400 =$ **1728000**

Mass of planet $= 4\pi^2 a^3 / GT^2$

$$= \frac{(4 \times 3.142^{2)} \times (3.5 \times 10^8)^3}{6.673 \times 10^{-11} \times (20 \times 24 \times 60 \times 60)^2}$$

$$= \frac{39.478 \times 2.7 \times 10^{25}}{6.673 \times 10^{-11} \times 1728000^2} \qquad = \frac{39.478 \times 2.7 \times 10^{25}}{6.673 \times 10^{-11} \times 2.99 \times 10^{12}}$$

$$= \frac{1.066 \times 10^{27}}{199.25}$$

$$= \mathbf{5.35 \times 10^{24}\ kg}$$

The equation is essentially the same as $M = a^3 \div T^2$ except for the modifiers $4\pi^2$ and G and the modification of units. The following question will test your ability to use this new equation. Note that rearranging this equation to find a and T can be tricky. Students who wish to take up the challenge of solving the equation for a and T are invited to do so. However, for ease of use the equations for finding a^3 and T^2 are below (see also Appendix 3, p324):

$$T^2 = \frac{4\pi^2 a^3}{GM} \qquad a^3 = \frac{MGT^2}{4\pi^2}$$

8. Mars' moon Phobos orbits Mars with an average distance of about 9380 km from the center of the planet and has an orbital period of about 7 hr 39 min. Use this information to estimate the mass of Mars in kg.
(Hint: $M = 4\pi^2 a^3 \div GT^2$. Convert T to seconds, and 'a' from km to meters.)

9. Saturn's moon, Hyperion, orbits at a mean radius of 1.48×10^9 m from Saturn. Saturn has a mass of 5.657×10^{26} kg What is the orbital period of Hyperion?

ISBN: 978-1-98-856693-1

35 Satellites

Key Question: How do satellites orbit, and can we apply Newton's and Kepler's laws to them?

There are hundreds of **satellites** orbiting the Earth. The majority are used in communications, e.g. carrying television signals, but others are used in monitoring weather or surveying the Earth's surface. Satellites **orbit** the Earth at different altitudes and at different inclinations: some orbit around the Earth's equator, others have a polar orbit.

Orbiting the Earth

There are three basic orbital heights in which satellites are placed:

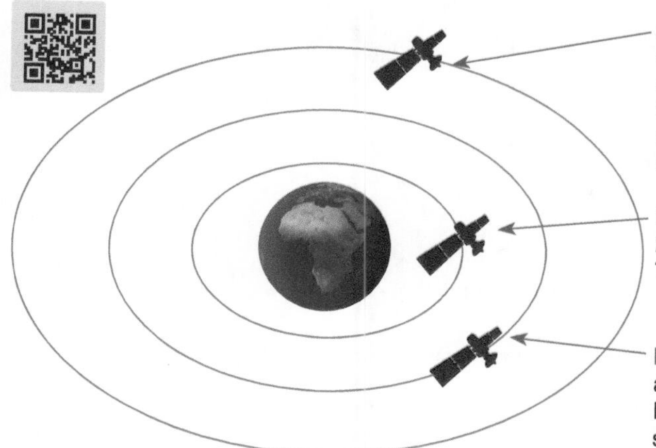

Geostationary orbit (GEO) is at an altitude of about 36,000 km. At this distance, the satellite takes the same time to orbit the Earth as the Earth takes to complete one rotation, keeping the satellite above the same point on the Earth.

Low Earth orbit (LEO) is around 200 km to 3000 km above the surface. The International Space Station is in LEO.

Medium Earth orbit (MEO) is at an altitude of about 3000 km to 30,000 km. It is used for communications and GPS satellites.

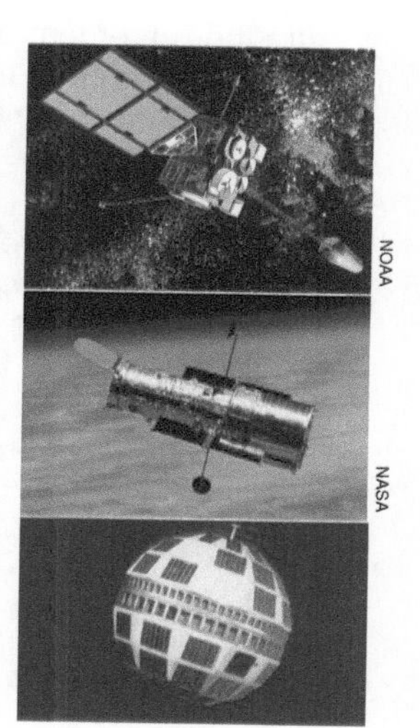
NOAA
NASA

Orbital speed

- The closer a satellite is to the Earth, the faster is has to move in order to stay in orbit. Satellites that orbit too close to the Earth encounter drag from the Earth's atmosphere and slow down, falling to a lower orbit. Occasionally these need to be manoeuvred to maintain their altitude. We can use **Kepler's laws** to estimate the speed and orbital period of a satellite.

Calculating orbital speed and period

The International Space Station (ISS) orbits at about 400 km above the Earth. How long does it take to complete one orbit, and at what speed is it moving?

- First, we must add the Earth's radius to the altitude of the ISS to determine the distance of the ISS from the center of the Earth: 6.371×10^6 m + 4×10^5 m = 6.771×10^6 m. The mass of the Earth is 5.972×10^{24} kg. Applying Kepler's third law we find that T^2 = 30,752,275 and T = 5,545 s = 92 minutes, or about 1.5 hours.
- The ISS orbit is almost circular, so calculating the circumference of a circle the size of its orbit using $c = 2\pi r$ = 42,543,448 m. Dividing distance by time = 42,543,448 m / 5545 seconds = 7672 m/s

NASA

We can also use the equation $v = \sqrt{(GMe/r)}$ to calculate orbital speed:
Where v is the velocity (orbital speed) in m/s, G is the gravitational constant, Me is the mass of the Earth (kg), and r is the radius of the orbit (m).

1. Explain why a geostationary satellite is useful for carrying a continuous television signal from one side of the planet to the other.

____

____

____

2. (a) The Hubble Space Telescope orbits 559 kilometers above the surface of the Earth. Calculate the time (in hours) it takes to orbit the Earth:

____

____

(b) Calculate the HST's orbital speed: _______________

____

ISBN: 978-1-98-856693-1

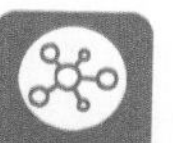

Maintaining the ISS orbit

- The orbit of the International Space Station (ISS) varies over time, sometimes dropping to an altitude of 330 km or rising to an altitude of 410 km (right). It orbits at an angle of 51.6° compared to the Earth's equator.
- At times, the ISS is deliberately raised and lowered in its orbit. This would occur especially for scheduled launches of the space shuttles so that the orbiter wouldn't have to fly quite so far.
- After the retirement of the space shuttles in 2011, the nominal orbit of the ISS was raised. Modern supply rockets are much lighter than the shuttle, so the extra distance is not as critical.
- Because the ISS is in LEO, its orbit is affected by friction with the remnants of the upper atmosphere. This reduces its velocity and causes its altitude to reduce over time. The ISS requires about 7.5 tonnes of fuel per year to maintain orbit.

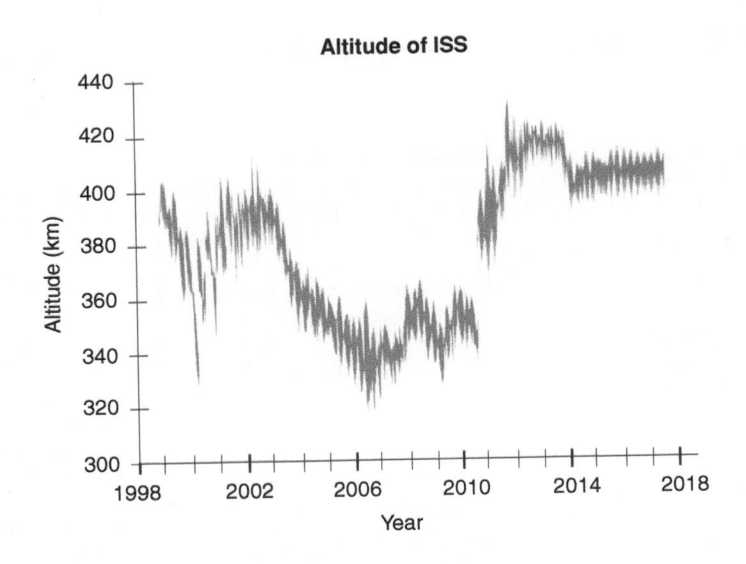

3. Why would NASA engineers want to reduce the flight distance of the space shuttle?

4. Mars has a mass of 6.39×10^{23} kg and a radius of 3.3895×10^6 m. It takes 24 hours and 37 minutes to complete one rotation. If scientists studying Mars wanted to put a satellite in a geostationary orbit around Mars' equator, what would the altitude of the satellite have to be?

5. (a) Another groups of Mars scientists want to put a satellite in a polar orbit around Mars so that they can use cameras to photograph the surface. The cameras on the proposed satellite can photograph an area of Mars 1640 km wide. The scientists want their satellite to ascend over the equator enough times each day so that the camera can view the entire planet as it ascends over the equator in one Mars day's rotation. The part of the planet being photographed will always be facing the Sun, i.e. the satellite will pass over the equator about local noon each day. Calculate the altitude the satellite will need to orbit at to achieve this:

(b) Why is a polar orbit a particularly useful orbit when surveying a planet?

ISBN: 978-1-98-856693-1

36 Case Study: The Orbit of Halley's Comet

Key Question: From observations, can we calculate the shape of the orbit of Halley's Comet?

- Halley's Comet is probably the most famous comet in the solar system. Its short period and close approach to the Sun means that it is the only comet visible to the naked eye that can be seen more than once in a person's lifetime.
- The comet has been recorded throughout history, with the first noted recording going back to about 240 BC. However, it was not until 1705 that Edmond Halley published a commentary on comets in which he showed that the similarity of comets sighted in 1531, 1607, and 1682 was because they were, in fact, the same comet.
- He was able to use Newton's ideas of planetary motion to show that the difference in appearance time between 1531 and 1607, and 1607 and 1682 were due to the gravity of Jupiter. He also predicted that the comet would appear again in 1758. Dutifully, the comet did appear again, on Christmas eve 1758, reaching perihelion on March 13 1759.

Halley's Comet, 1986

NASA

1. Halley's Comet is a short period comet. From the sightings mentioned above, determine the average period (T) of the comet in years:

2. Use your answer from above to calculate the semimajor (a) axis for the comet:

3. Observation of Halley's Comet in 1986 showed its closet approach to the Sun was 0.586 AU. What is significant about this distance (given that the comet orbits in an ellipse)?

4. Recall that the distance from the center of the orbit to the focus is related to the semimajor and semiminor axis by the equation $c^2 = a^2 - b^2$. Use this equation to calculate the length of the semiminor axis of Halley's comet:

5. Recall that the eccentricity of an orbit can be calculated using the equation $e = f \div d$. Calculate the eccentricity of Halley's comet

6. You now have all the points required to sketch a plot of Halley's Comet. Use the grid below to show its orbit around the Sun, including its closest and furthest distances from the Sun:

ISBN: 978-1-98-856693-1

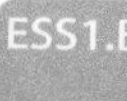
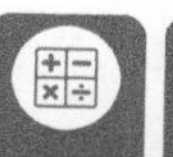

37 Moving Planets

Key Question: Why are the movements of planets in the sky different from the stars, and can we use these movements to calculate a planet's distance from Earth?

- When a **planet** is observed in the night sky, night after night, and at the same time each night, the planet is seen to move across the sky (the term "planet" from Greek means "wandering star").
- Planets may be inferior, being between Earth and the Sun, or superior, being beyond the Earth. The superior planets move across the sky from west to east, as seen at the same time, night after night.
- However, at times, they reverse this movement, often for weeks, before resuming their initial direction. This reversal of movement is called **apparent retrograde motion**.
- The retrograde motion of Mars is shown below:

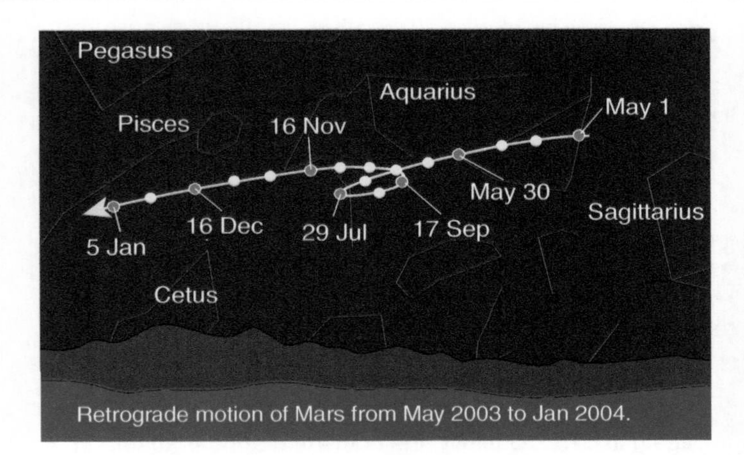

Retrograde motion of Mars from May 2003 to Jan 2004.

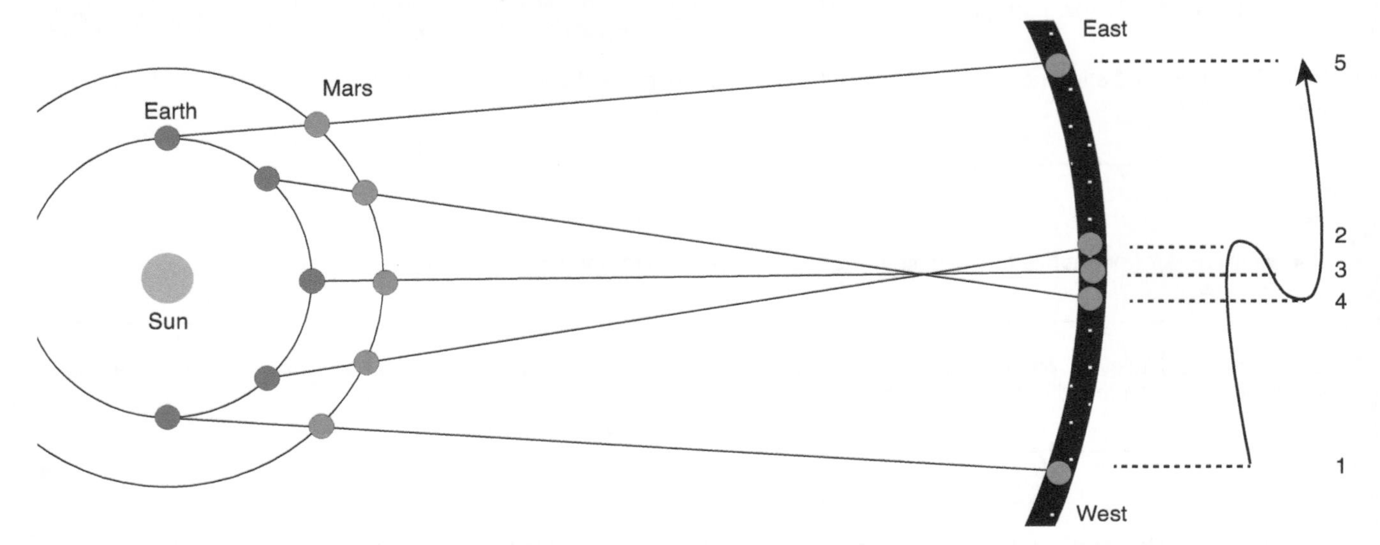

- Earth **orbits** the Sun faster than planets further away from the Sun, e.g. Mars. It is constantly catching up with, then overtaking Mars. From our point of view, Mars appears as a red point of light against the background stars that moves across the night sky from west to east as the Earth approaches it. Then, as the Earth begins to catch up with Mars, the planet begins to move backwards across the sky to the west. The Earth then passes Mars and it appears to start moving east once more.
- A similar apparent motion occurs with the inner planets Venus and Mercury from our viewpoint, except that it is the inner planets that are catching up with and passing the Earth.
- Depending on the orientation of the planets as they pass each other, the retrograde motion may take the form of a loop or a zig zag in the sky.

1. Complete the model below of the retrograde motion of Venus (use the diagram above as a guide):

2. Use this model to explain why Venus usually can't be seen at position 3.

3. Explain why the retrograde motion of planets in the sky is an illusion:

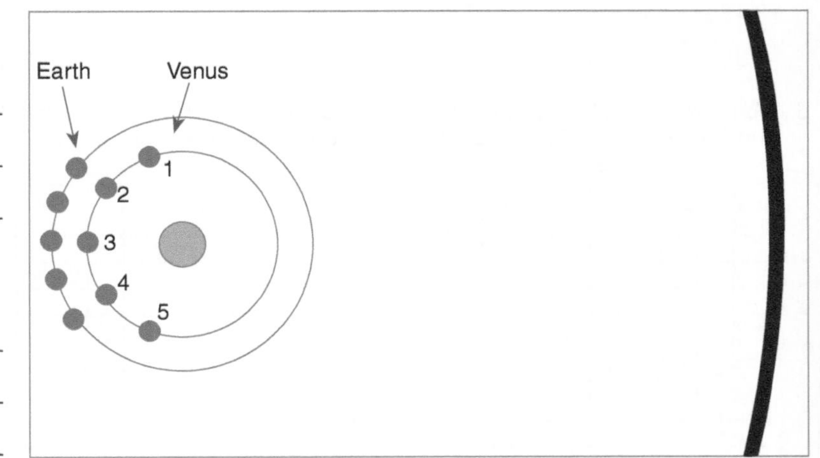

ESS1.B SPQ

ISBN: 978-1-98-856693-1

Measuring the distance to planets (parallax)

- Obtaining a reasonably accurate distance measurement to at least one planet became important for astronomers, since this would provide a "yardstick" to compute the distance to other planets. But how do we do this?
- Astronomers use an effect called parallax to measure the distances to faraway objects, such as stars and planets. Parallax is the apparent displacement of an object due to a change in the observer's point of view.
- The effect can be seen by holding your thumb in front of you and looking at it with your left eye closed. Then look at it with your right eye closed. Your thumb hasn't moved, but it will appear to move against the background.
- This effect can be used to measure distance to far away objects.

Astronomers can measure a planet's position at widely spaced positions on Earth and, from the apparent change in position, calculate the planet's distance from Earth.

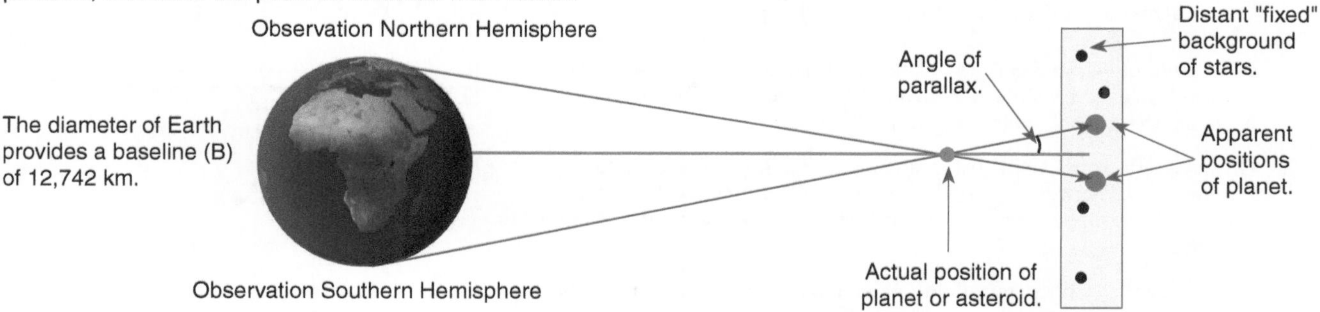

- As the Earth orbits the Sun, a distant planet or nearby star will appear to move against the more distant background stars. Astronomers can measure a star's position once, and then again 6 months later, giving a baseline of 2 AU.
- Measuring the distance to the stars by parallax is possible only to about 1000 parsecs. However, the distances to stars measured by parsecs act as a calibration for other, less direct, ways of measuring distance to stars further away.

The transit of Venus

- Observing the passage of Venus across the face of the Sun (its transit) was one of the most important astronomical tasks of the late 1700s. In 1716, Edmund Halley had proposed a method of using parallax to measure the distance to Venus, based on observing its transit across the Sun from two different positions on Earth (below):

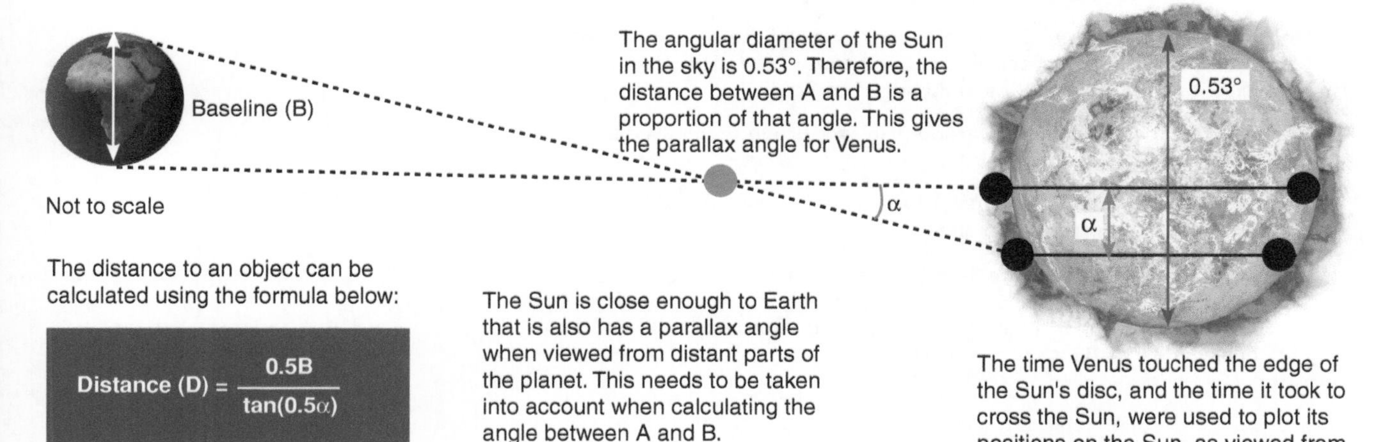

The distance to an object can be calculated using the formula below:

$$\text{Distance (D)} = \frac{0.5B}{\tan(0.5\alpha)}$$

The Sun is close enough to Earth that is also has a parallax angle when viewed from distant parts of the planet. This needs to be taken into account when calculating the angle between A and B.

The time Venus touched the edge of the Sun's disc, and the time it took to cross the Sun, were used to plot its positions on the Sun, as viewed from two positions on Earth.

4. (a) A transit of Venus was observed in 2012. Measurements were taken from the US cities of Anchorage and Honolulu, which are 4482 km apart. The measured angle (α) between the two transits (after taking the Sun's parallax into account) was 0.0056 degrees. Use the formula to calculate the distance from Earth to Venus:

___

___

(b) Explain why providing an absolute distance between Earth and Venus can help find the distances of other planets from the Sun:

___

___

___

ISBN: 978-1-98-856693-1

Investigation 3.4 Parallax

See appendix for equipment list.

1. Creating a parallax angle measuring tool (diagram right):
   1. Place a protractor on a corkboard or thick cardboard and tape it in place.
   2. Push a pin completely through one end of the straw.
   3. Place the straw on the protractor and push the pin through the hole in the protractor into the board. The straw should be able to pivot on the pin.

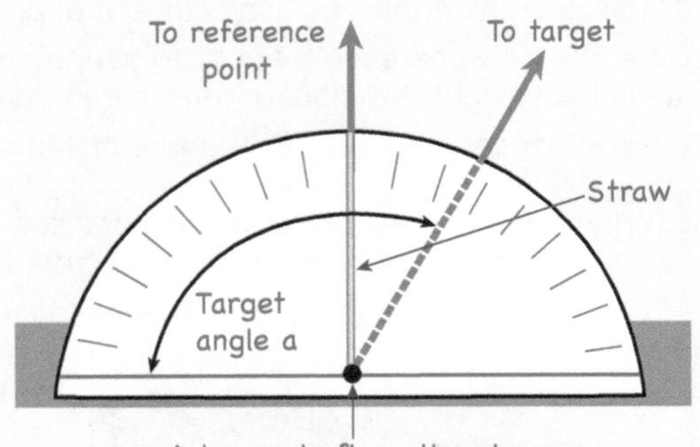

2. In groups of 4 head out to the school's field. Face in a direction where there is a visible background with variation to observe, such as the school building, goalposts, etc.
3. One student from each group should stand somewhere distant between the background and the rest of the group of students. This student represents the distant planet you are trying to find the distance to.
4. The student in the group doing the measuring should pick a distant reference point somewhere behind the student in the field.
5. Lay down a measuring tape to act as your group's baseline. It should be roughly perpendicular to the direction of your target object and the reference point. Record the length of your baseline (e.g. 2 m) in the table below.
6. At the start of the baseline, turn the straw of the parallax measuring tool to 90°and sight down the straw so that the distant reference point is lined up.
7. Still at the start of your baseline, and keeping the parallax measuring tool still, turn the straw so that it is lined up with the target student. Record the target angle shown by the straw on the parallax measuring tool (reading degrees L→R on the protractor) .
8. Move to the other end of the baseline. Keeping the parallax measuring tool parallel with the baseline, turn the straw, and sight the target student. Record the angle as shown by the straw.
9. Repeat the process for each student in the group (each student should be a different distant planet).
10. Find the parallax angle for each student planet by subtracting the larger target angle from the smaller.
11. You now need to use a little trigonometry to calculate the distance to the planets in your group. The distance to your object (D) is related to the parallax angle (α) and the baseline length (B) by the trigonometric relationship (tangent):

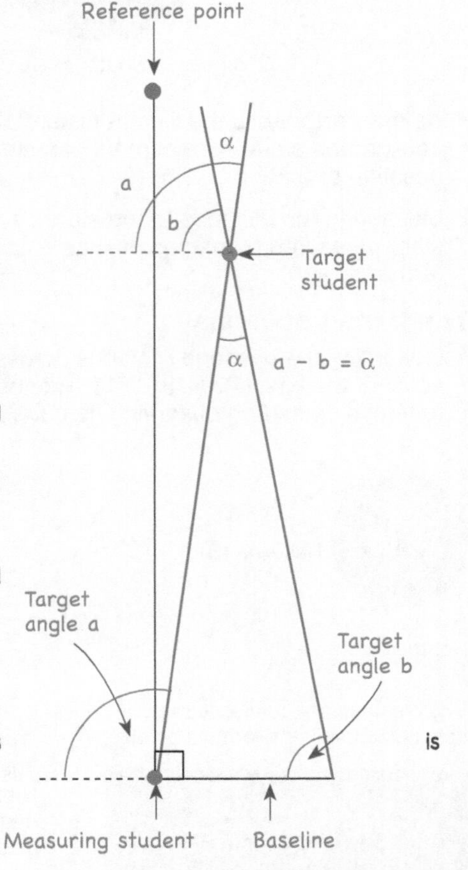

is

$$D = \frac{0.5B}{\tan(0.5\alpha)}$$

	Target angle a	Target angle b	Parallax angle (α) (subtract the larger target angle from the smaller)	Baseline (B) length (m)	Distance (D) to target (m) D = 0.5B ÷ tan(0.5α).
Student 1					
Student 2					
Student 3					
Student 4					

An alternative set up for this investigation, which is a little more involved but provides a somewhat more accurate simulation, is provided on BIOZONE's Resource Hub.

ISBN: 978-1-98-856693-1

38 The Earth and The Moon

Key Question: How do the Earth and Moon influence each other?

Formation of the Moon

- The Moon is the Earth's only natural **satellite**. It formed about 4.5 billion years ago, just a few million years after the **solar system** condensed into a swirling disk. A Mars-sized proto-planet, commonly called Theia, smashed into the Earth. The debris that was flung off eventually condensed as the Moon. Evidence for this hypothesis includes:

- The Moon has a lower density than the Earth, consistent with the density of the upper layers of the Earth.
- The Earth and Moon have similar isotope ratios of their elements, suggesting they formed at the same time.
- The Moon's angle of orbit (5°) is different to the Earth's tilt (23.4°); the Earth was tilted over due to the collision.

The Moon's orbit

- The Moon is 384,400 km from the Earth. It completes an orbit of the Earth once every 27.3 days, the same time it takes to complete one rotation. This means the same side of the Moon always faces the Earth. It is a phenomenon called tidal locking. The Earth's **gravity** pulls on the Moon's crust as the Moon rotates. This causes friction that slows the Moon's rotation and keeps one side of the moon facing the Earth.
- The Moon is the largest natural satellite in comparison to its planet in the solar system. Its mass is large enough to move the center of the Earth-Moon orbit (the barycenter) 4670 km from the center of the Earth.

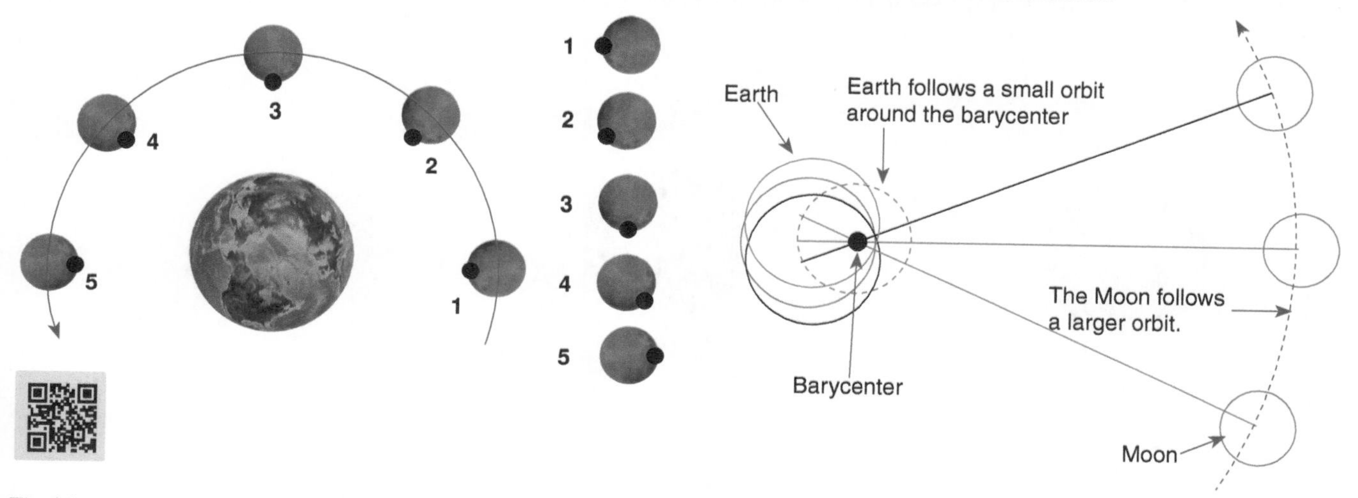

The Moon may appear to not rotate from our point of view but this diagram shows how a point on the moon does rotate.

The Earth and Moon orbit a common center called the barycenter. This is inside the radius of the Earth.

1. Use the mass of Earth (5.972×10^{24} kg) and the distance of the Moon from Earth to show that the Moon takes 27.3 days to orbit the Earth, and not 29 days as it appears to by the phases of the Moon:

2. Explain why, even though the Moon rotates once every 27.3 days, only one side of the Moon ever faces the Earth.

ISBN: 978-1-98-856693-1

39 Cyclical Changes

Key Question: What effect do the long term changes in the Earth's orbit have on the Earth's long term climate?

- Earth is not stable in space. It is affected by the **gravity** of the Sun, the planets, and the Moon. These influences affect the tilt of the Earth's axis and the shape of its orbit. The changes in orbit and tilt can combine to cause extreme changes in the Earth's climate, e.g. producing ice ages. The Earth experiences three main orbital and rotational cycles:

Axial tilt (obliquity)

Relative to its orbital axis, the Earth's rotational axis is at an angle of about 23.4°. This angle is responsible for seasonal changes. The angle is not constant and changes between 22.1° and 24.5° over a period of about 41,000 years. The greater the degree of tilting, the greater the difference between the summer and winter seasons.

Planet	Axial tilt	Planet	Axial tilt
Mercury	0.1°	Jupiter	3°
Venus	177°	Saturn	27°
Earth	23.4°	Uranus	98°
Mars	25°	Neptune	30°

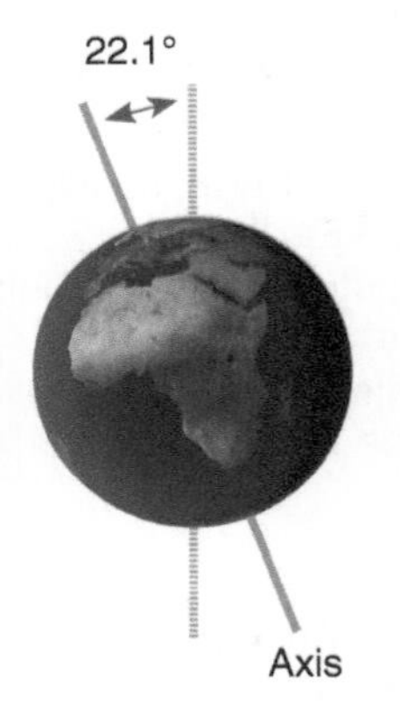

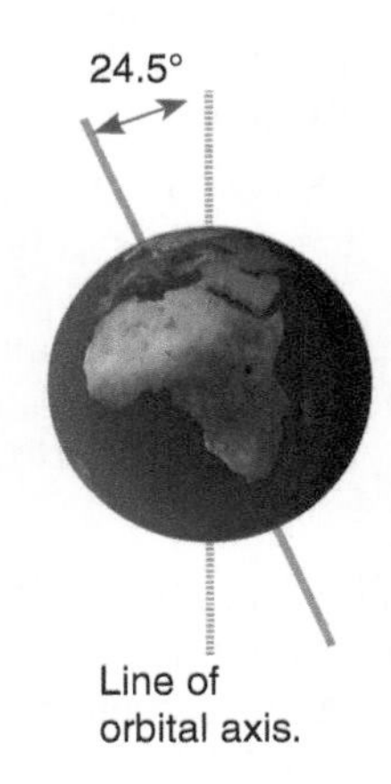

Precession

Like a spinning top, Earth wobbles about on its axis. This causes the Earth's axis to describe a cone in space. An entire cycle takes about 26,000 years. Precession alters the direction the Earth's axis is pointing. For example, during June, the Northern Hemisphere is pointed towards the Sun. However, 13,000 years ago the occurrence of the seasons was opposite to what they are today.

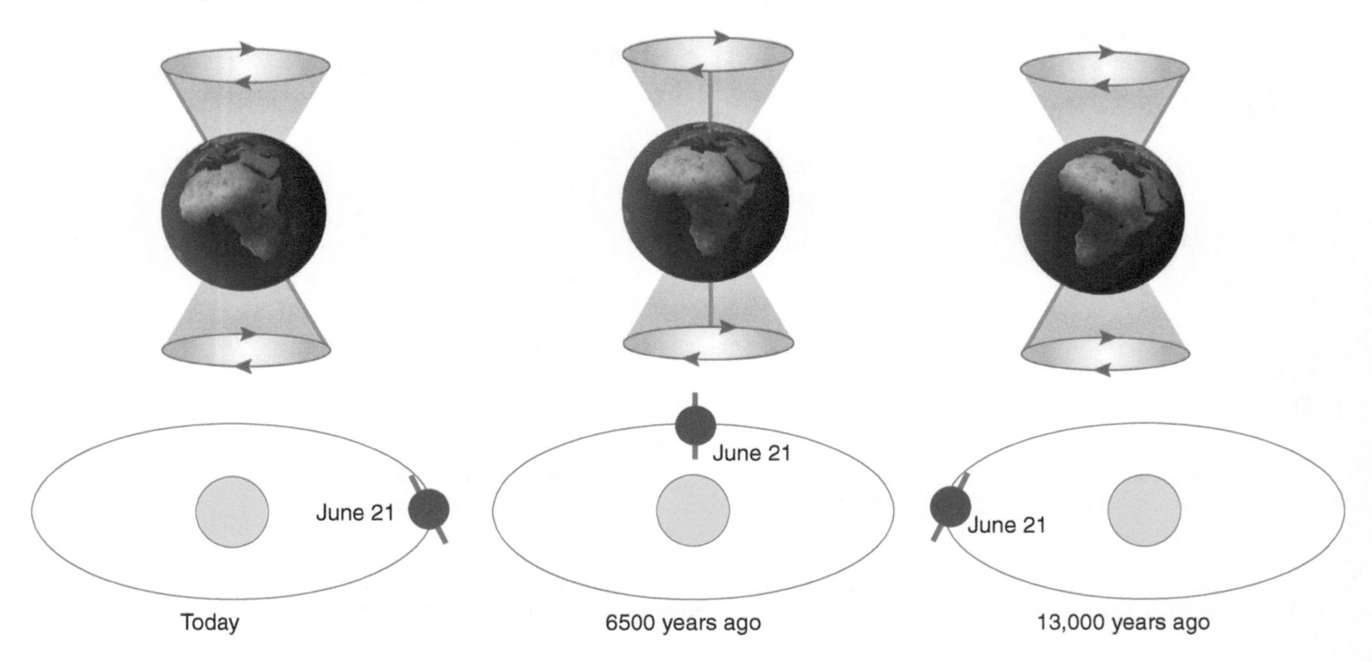

Orbital eccentricity

The Earth's elliptical orbit changes its **eccentricity** from very nearly circular (eccentricity of 0.000055) to slightly elliptical (eccentricity 0.0679). Circular orbits tend to make the differences between the seasons rather mild, while more elliptical orbits exacerbate the difference. The changes in eccentricity have a cycle of about 100,000 years.

Of the planets in our solar system, Mercury has the most eccentric orbit, while Venus has the least eccentric orbit.

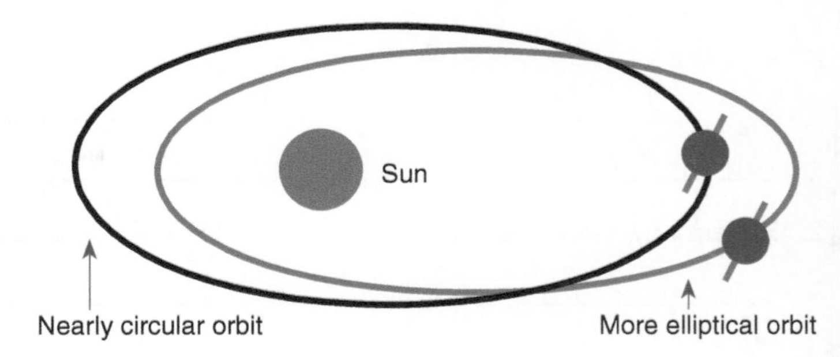

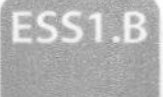

ISBN: 978-1-98-856693-1

Effect of cycles

- The combination of obliquity, precession, and eccentricity change (called Milankovitch cycles) have major effects on the Earth's climate, especially if the extremes of each coincide.
- Obliquity, precession, and eccentricity change can all be calculated for hundreds of thousands of years in the past and future (lines 1,2,3, below). Their effects can then be combined to produce a graph showing the maximum solar radiation received by Earth (line 4 below). Ice cores can then be compared to see if there are any correlations (line 5).

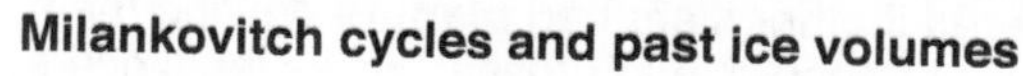

Milankovitch cycles and past ice volumes

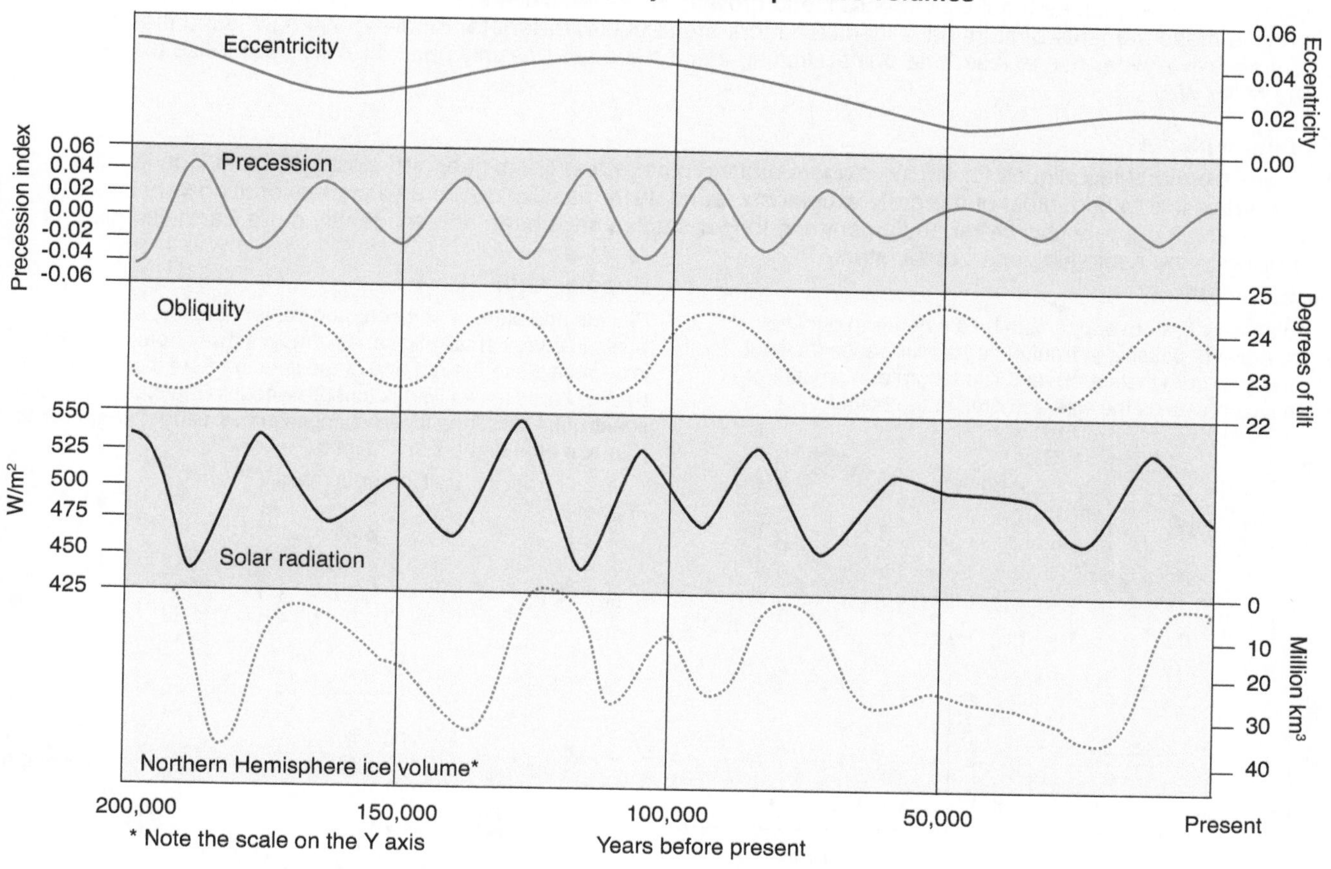

1. Describe the relationship between axial tilt and the difference in seasons: ______________________

2. Venus has an axial tilt of 177°. Describe the effect of this on the rotation of the planet compared to other planets:

3. Describe how the timing of the Northern Hemisphere's seasons would have changed over the last 26,000 years due to the Earth's precession:

4. Describe how orbital eccentricity affects the difference between seasons: ______________________

5. Describe the relationship between Milankovitch cycles and Earth's climate: ______________________

ISBN: 978-1-98-856693-1

40 Studying Exoplanets

Key Question: How can astronomers tell if planets are orbiting other stars?

- For many years, people wondered if other stars had **planets** orbiting them. It was generally assumed that other stars must have planets but it was impossible to prove it. However, since the 1990s, new techniques and more precise measurements of stars have identified more than 2000 **exoplanets**. Studies have now found that, on average, every star has at least one planet orbiting it and there are possibly up to 11 billion Earth-like planets in the Milky Way.

Finding a planet

- There are many techniques for finding planets orbiting other stars. The bigger and closer a planet is to its star, the easier it is to find. Most of the early exoplanets found were massive Jupiter-like planets orbiting very close to their stars. More recently, better equipment and longer studies have been able to identify more Earth-like planets orbiting in the habitable zone of their star.

Transit method

If a planetary system happens to be aligned with our line of sight, a planet passing in front of its star will cause the light reaching us from the star to dim. The length and amount of dimming can tell us the size and orbit of the planet.

Star
Planet
Light intensity
Time
Light intensity
Time

Doppler shift

Planets and stars orbit a common center of mass, so the star orbits in a very small ellipse. As it moves away from us, its light is stretched into the red end of the spectrum. As the star moves back towards us, its light is compressed into the blue end of the spectrum. Measuring these changes allows us to determine the size and orbit of the star's planets.

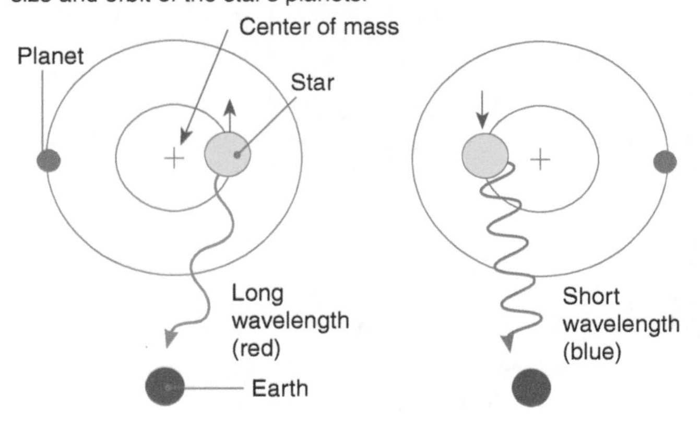

Exoplanets and our solar system

The most common theory for the formation of our solar system is the **nebula** theory. This theorizes that solar systems generally form with rocky planets near the star and larger gas planets further away. However, this is not what we see when we look at other planetary systems. Instead, most of the planetary systems we see have large gas planets orbiting close to their stars. Explanations for this vary, but it seems that the formation of Jupiter and Saturn close together stabilized their orbits and kept them from spiraling in towards the Sun, unlike most other systems seen so far. Also, the study of other systems has found that there can be many different configurations of planets, including orbiting binary stars (Kepler 16 and 34) and planets orbiting on wildly different planes from each other , e.g. Kepler 56.

NASA

Kepler 186f is the most Earth-sized planet found in a star's habitable zone. It is 500 light years from Earth.

1. (a) Explain how the transit method is used to find planetary systems: ______________________

   (b) Explain how measuring Doppler shift can be used to find planets: ______________________

   (c) In what situation might these methods be unable to find planets? ______________________

ISBN: 978-1-98-856693-1

41 Review Your Understanding

Key Question: What's the relationship between the Sun, the planets that orbit it, and the time they take to complete an orbit?

▶ At the beginning of this chapter, you were asked to discuss your thoughts on various relationships between the planets and the Sun. You should now be able to provide a more precise discussion on those relationships.

1. (a) What is the relationship between a planet's orbital period and its distance from the Sun?

   (b) Why does this relationship occur?

2. The Earth orbits the Sun at 1AU. What might happen to the Earth's orbit if the Sun:

   (a) Suddenly doubled in mass:

   (b) Suddenly halved in mass:

3. Comets have very eccentric orbits. At which points in their orbits are they moving the fastest and the slowest?

4. Use your knowledge of orbital mechanics to calculate the orbital period, in hours, of the space probe placed into orbit 45,000 km from the center of Neptune. (Note: Neptune has a mass of 1.024×10^{26} kg):

ISBN: 978-1-98-856693-1

42 Summing Up

1. Below, is a model of a distant solar system. The star in the center is one solar mass (it is the same size as our Sun). The distances from the center of the star to the orbits shown is to scale. It has been determined that the innermost planet takes 123 Earth days to orbit the star. Use this data to calculate the distance from the star to the other four planets and the comet along their semimajor axis, and the time they take to orbit the star. Write the answer to your calculations next to the appropriate planet.

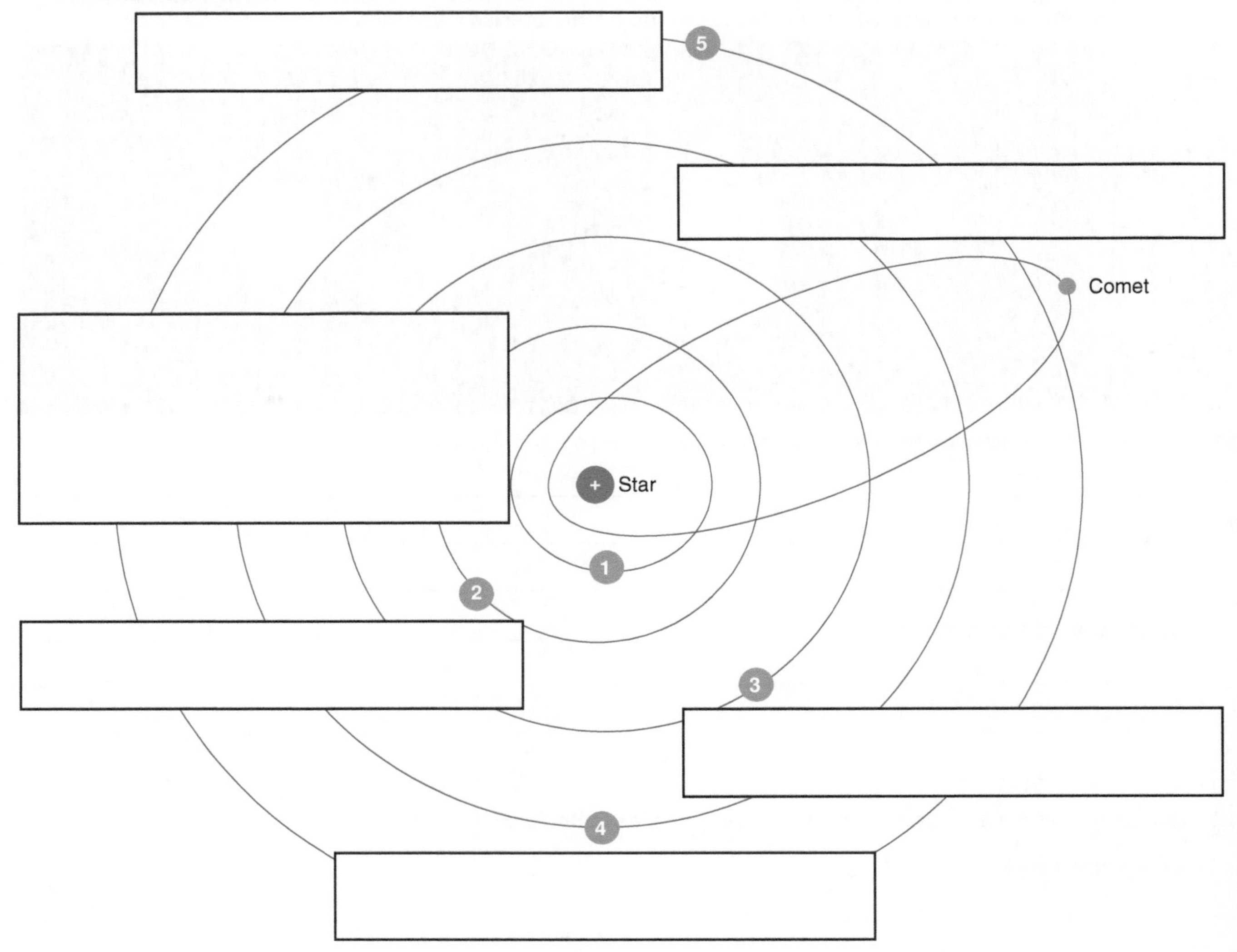

2. The diagram below shows the path of a comet with an eccentric orbit about a star. Use the diagram to explain the motion of the comet as it moves around its orbit:

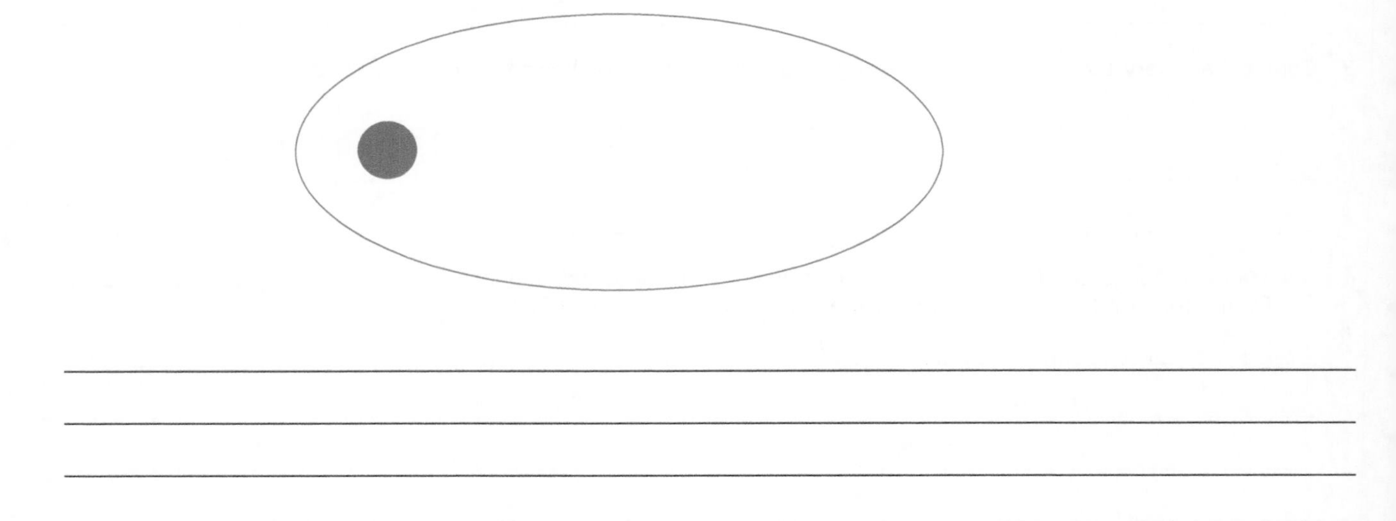

ISBN: 978-1-98-856693-1

CHAPTER 4

The History of Planet Earth

Meteorite Recon cc 3.0

Anchoring Phenomenon

An age old puzzle: How do you estimate how old something is? — 43 52

What are the rocks in the Earth's crust?

- ☐ 1 Describe some features of the Earth, including the crust. Identify features of the crust, including the main types of rocks that are found on the surface. Identify those parts of the Earth most useful for dating purposes. — 44

- ☐ 2 Explain the difference between the continental crust and the oceanic crust. Explain why the rocks of the continental crust are much older than the rocks of the oceanic crust. — 44-45 53

- ☐ 3 Describe methods and models used for dating the Earth. Explain why early methods for dating the Earth provided answers that were often many billions of years short. Describe the importance of radioactive decay in dating the Earth. Explain the difference between relative dating and absolute (radiometric) dating. — 46

How do extraterrestrial objects help date the Earth?

- ☐ 4 Explain why dating the Earth's formation using terrestrial rocks is difficult. Describe the techniques of radiometric dating, including the use of uranium in zircon crystals from Earth and minerals from meteorites. Model half-lives using M&M's® — 47

- ☐ 5 Explain the use of extraterrestrial objects in dating the formation of the Earth. Describe evidence from Moon rocks, craters, and meteorites. Explain evidence for the age of the Earth using radiometric dating, crater counters, oxygen ratios, and zinc ratios. Explain why using multiple dating methods provides a more accurate age range than one method alone. — 47

- ☐ 6 Explain how studies of Earth's neighboring planet, Mars, have potential to shed light on Earth's early history. Explain how studies of asteroids and comets help us understand how Earth got its water. — 48 49

- ☐ 7 Describe the history of the Earth from its formation to present day, using second hand data. — 49 50

- ☐ 8 Explore the conditions needed for life to appear and be maintained on Earth. Explain why the conditions for life are rare, and may not exist on planets around other stars. — 51

43 An Age Old Puzzle

Key Question: How do you estimate how old something is?

- There are two options for the existence of the Earth. Either it has been here forever or it had a beginning.
- If it has existed forever, we must ask how the structures within it, and the processes that shape its surface, have been maintained over an infinite amount of time.
- If it has a beginning, we must ask how long ago that beginning was, and what the evidence is.
- How do we go about finding the age of something? Objects can have a definitive age, which is how old they actually are. They can also have a relative date, which is how old they are compared to something else.
- The photo on the right shows a box filled with various objects. How could you go about dating these objects so that you distinguish the ages of the objects and space them out on a timeline of production?

1. If someone gave you any object at all, e.g. a toy car, a ball, a split piece of wood, how would go about estimating the age of that object?

2. If you wanted a precise answer for the age of the object, what might you do?

3. Geology can give a good estimate of the Earth's age but nuclear physics can precisely date the Earth. In groups, discuss what you know about how these areas of science date objects and events:

4. How old is the oldest object you own? How do you know it's that old? What evidence do you have to justify your claim?

ISBN: 978-1-98-856693-1

44 The Earth

Key Question: How has the Earth's geological activity reshaped its surface?

The Earth formed around 4.5 billion years ago along with the rest of the solar system. The interior is still molten, reaching up to 5700°C in the core. This heat drives crustal movements that have produced the surface we see today.

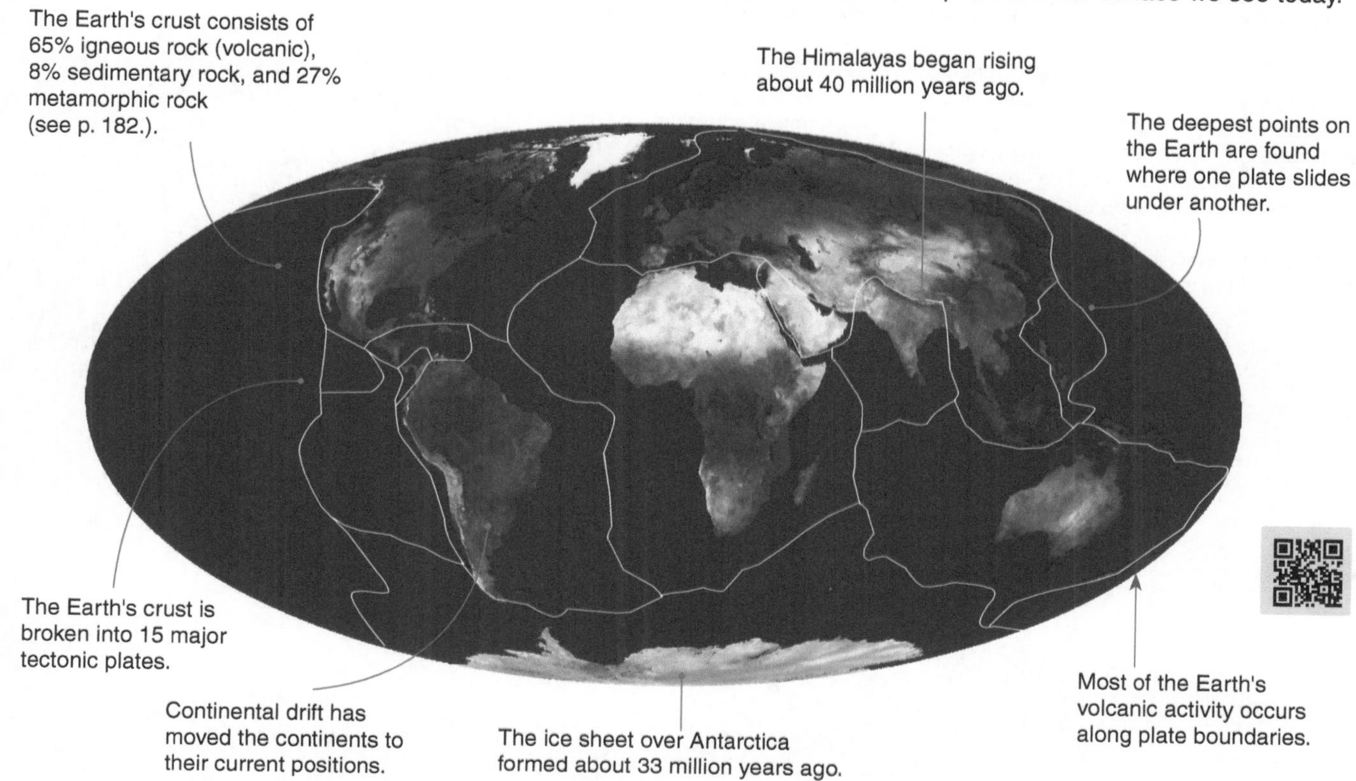

The Earth is geologically active. Convection currents in the mantle below the crust drive continuous continental drift and help form volcanoes and mountains.

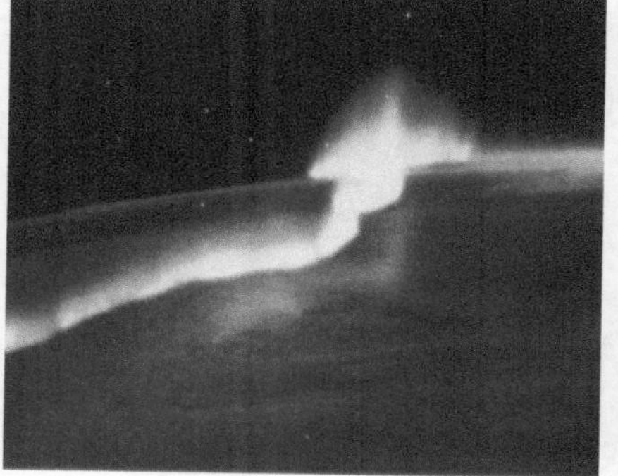

Earth's liquid outer core surrounds a solid, iron inner core. The movement of the liquid metal produces electric currents which generate a magnetic field. The field's polarity has reversed many times.

Earth's atmosphere is 78% nitrogen, 20.9 % oxygen. The oxygen was produced by photosynthetic cyanobacteria about 2.3 billion years ago.

1. What process moves the continents across the surface of the Earth? ______________________

2. What is a consequence of the convection currents in the mantle? ______________________

3. What causes the Earth's magnetic field? ______________________

4. Where did the Earth's atmospheric oxygen come from? ______________________

ISBN: 978-1-98-856693-1

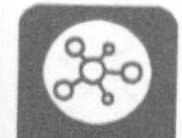

45 The Earth's Crust

Key Question: What are the different properties of continental and oceanic crust?

- The Earth's crust is thin compared to the bulk of the Earth, averaging just 25-70 km thick below the continents, and about 10 km thick below the oceans. The crust can be divided into **continental crust** and **oceanic crust**. Continental crust is less dense than oceanic crust and is a lot older.

The continental crust is made up of igneous, metamorphic, and sedimentary rocks. It is not recycled within the Earth to the same extent as oceanic crust, so some continental rocks are up to 4 billion years old. The crust "floats" in the mantle at a level determined by its thickness and density. The more mass there is above sea-level, the deeper the crust must extend down to support it.

The Earth's oceans, made of liquid water, cycle moisture through the atmosphere to the land and back again.

Water precipitated from the atmosphere forms rivers and lakes, which flow back to the ocean, eroding the landscape in the process.

Continental slope

Abyssal plain

Soil and vegetation

Crust

Mantle

The oceanic crust makes up more than two thirds of the Earth's surface and is composed of relatively dense basalt-rich rocks covered by a thin layer of sediment. The oceanic crust is relatively young; even the oldest parts of the ocean floor are no more than 200 million years old.

Sedimentary rocks
Sediments eroded from continents and compressed into rock can be later lifted and exposed in mountains and other formations.

Igneous rocks, such as basalt (above), form a major component of the crust and are essentially unchanged since their formation.

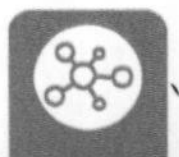

ESS1.C ESS2.B P SC

ISBN: 978-1-98-856693-1

Oldest and newest rocks

- Earth is dynamic. The surface is always changing. Although rocks on the surface are constantly being eroded, buried, melted, and regenerated, some parts of the continental crust are relatively stable and have survived repeated cycles of rifting and collision. These areas contain the oldest rocks on Earth. On the ocean floor, new rock is constantly being formed at the mid ocean ridges.

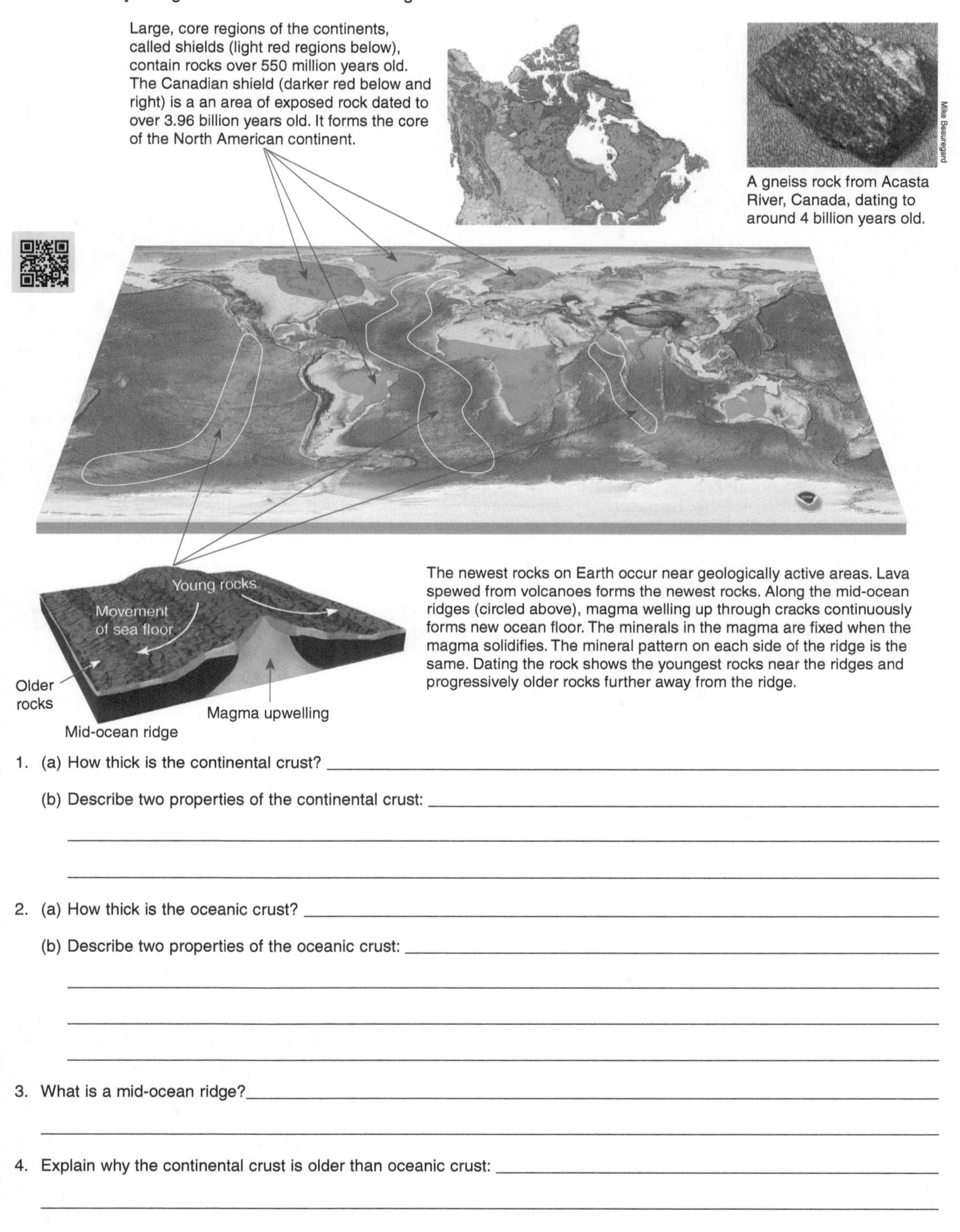

Large, core regions of the continents, called shields (light red regions below), contain rocks over 550 million years old. The Canadian shield (darker red below and right) is a an area of exposed rock dated to over 3.96 billion years old. It forms the core of the North American continent.

A gneiss rock from Acasta River, Canada, dating to around 4 billion years old.

The newest rocks on Earth occur near geologically active areas. Lava spewed from volcanoes forms the newest rocks. Along the mid-ocean ridges (circled above), magma welling up through cracks continuously forms new ocean floor. The minerals in the magma are fixed when the magma solidifies. The mineral pattern on each side of the ridge is the same. Dating the rock shows the youngest rocks near the ridges and progressively older rocks further away from the ridge.

1. (a) How thick is the continental crust? ____________________

   (b) Describe two properties of the continental crust: ____________________

2. (a) How thick is the oceanic crust? ____________________

   (b) Describe two properties of the oceanic crust: ____________________

3. What is a mid-ocean ridge? ____________________

4. Explain why the continental crust is older than oceanic crust: ____________________

ISBN: 978-1-98-856693-1

46 Dating the Earth

Key Question: How do scientists model the age of the Earth?

Mt Etna with Monti Rossi in middle ground.

- The age of the Earth is currently accepted as around 4.5 billion years old. This was not always the way. Until the Renaissance period, starting around 500 years ago, the Earth was accepted as being quite young (anywhere between 7500 years old to 6000 years old). However, discoveries over the last 500 years, and especially in the last 200 years, have produced evidence that the Earth, all of the other planets, and the Sun are very old.
- Charles Lyell was a Scottish geologist who helped demonstrate how natural events could be used to explain Earth's history. In the summer of 1828, Lyell travelled through France and Italy studying volcanoes. When Lyell reached Mount Etna, in Sicily, he observed numerous phenomena that could only be explained if the Earth was much older than people thought. Firstly, he noticed that Mt Etna was built up from many small cones formed by past eruptions, but only one of these cones, Monti Rossi (46 m high), had actually newly appeared in the last two hundred or so years. Given that Mt. Etna was more than 3000 m high this meant Mt Etna must have been tens, if not hundreds, of thousands of years old.
- Lyell also discovered that shellfish sold in the fish markets of nearby towns were identical to fossil shellfish he found in limestone beds at the base of Mt. Etna. Importantly, Mt Etna appeared to be *on top of* the limestone beds. So if Mt Etna was hundreds of thousands of years old, the fossil shellfish must have been much older than that.
- This suggested to Lyell that geological events happened very slowly. If the building of volcanoes and fossilization of shells happened so slowly, then the Earth must have been at least tens of millions to hundreds of millions of years old. Much older than was currently accepted.

1. Lyell reasoned the age of the Earth partially using a method called relative dating. Describe how this method works:

2. Explain why relative dating cannot produce a definitive age for the Earth:

3. What would be needed in order to produce a definitive age for the Earth?

4. Which of the layers shown on the right is the oldest layer?

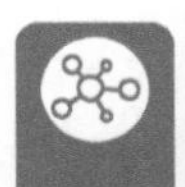  
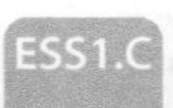  
ESS1.C PS1.C P SC

ISBN: 978-1-98-856693-1

Early models and estimates for the age of the Earth

- Before the discovery of radioactive decay, calculating the age of the Earth was difficult. Most models focused on the cooling of the Earth from a molten ball of rock, as there was no knowledge of radioactive decay.
- Georges Louis Leclerc developed one of the earliest models for dating the Earth. In 1778, he used the cooling rate of iron spheres to model the cooling of the Earth from a ball of molten rock. Extrapolating his data, he proposed the Earth was 70,000 years old, far older than the age of a few thousand years that many people believed at the time.
- In 1862, William Thomson (Lord Kelvin) also reasoned that the Earth had cooled from a molten ball of rock that he estimated must have been about 4000°C and, using the latest geothermal gradients, calculated possible ages of between 20 million and 400 million years old.
- In 1895, John Perry argued that Lord Kelvin had not included convection currents in a molten mantle. He included convection currents in his calculations and arrived at an age of 2 to 3 billion years.
- In 1900, John Joly calculated the rate that the seas should have accumulated salt to reach their current level of salinity. He used this to calculate the age of the Earth at 100 million years old.

Radioactivity offers another solution

- The discovery of radioactivity and, more importantly, that radioactive decay provides an absolute way of measuring time, provided a way of providing definitive dates for the rocks of the Earth.
- Early attempts to use radioactive decay as a way of dating the Earth were filled with errors due to the many unknowns of the new science, but they did begin to show that the Earth had to be at least hundreds of millions of years old.
- Using the theory that uranium decays to lead following a precise decay chain, Arthur Holmes published calculations in 1927 that the Earth was between 1.6 to 3.0 billion years old.
- Refinements of the decay series for various radioactive isotopes and ways of measuring isotope ratios have helped date the age of the Earth to 4.54 billion years, plus or minus a few tens of millions of years.

Radioactive decay of potassium into calcium and argon

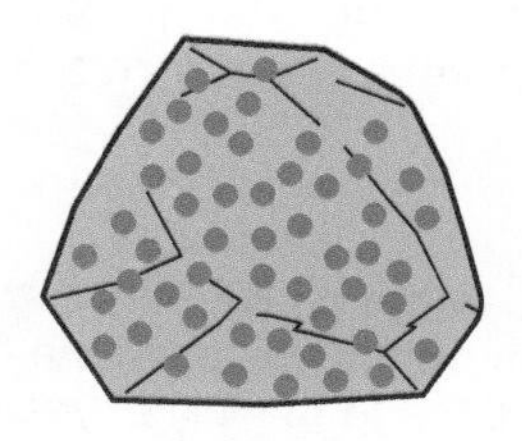

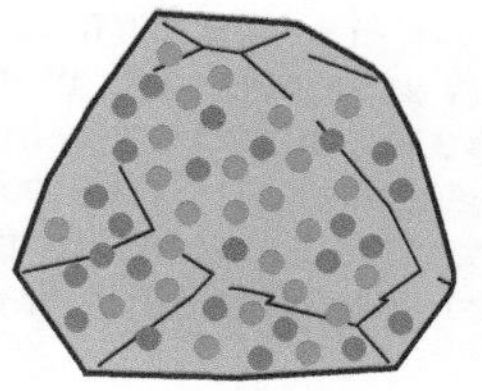

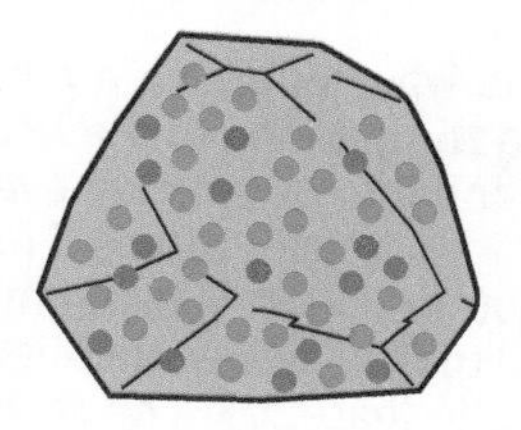

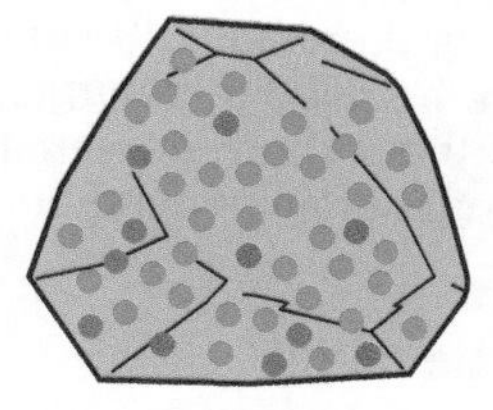

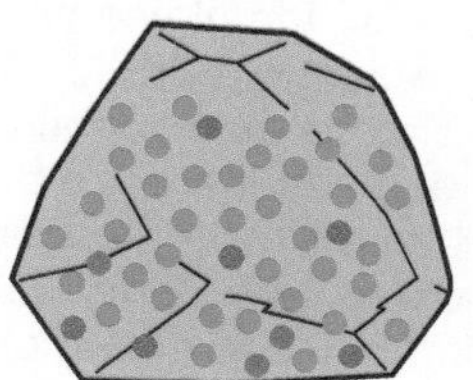

Potassium-argon dating is a commonly used radiometric dating technique. Potassium decays into calcium 89% of the time and argon about 11% of the time. Argon is inert and so is not contained in most minerals. Its mass in minerals is therefore related to the decay of potassium.

5. What assumption did many of the early models for dating the Earth make about the cooling of the Earth? ____________

6. What important process did these assumptions leave out, and how did it affect estimates of the Earth's age? ____________

7. Explain why using the decay series of several different radioactive isotopes to date the Earth will provide a more robust, accurate answer to the Earth's age:

8. How does the presence of argon atoms in a rock provide a way of dating the rock? ____________

ISBN: 978-1-98-856693-1

47 Evidence for the Age of the Earth

Key Question: How does comparing minerals on Earth and extraterrestrial bodies help us understand the formation and age of the Earth and Moon?

Dating the Earth

- The very oldest material dated on Earth is a **zircon** crystal found in a metamorphosed sandstone from Western Australia. It is dated to 4.4 billion years old, just a hundred million years after the Earth formed. Due to Earth's dynamic history, minerals older than this are unlikely to be found. However, other bodies in the solar system have remained essentially unchanged since its formation. Dating them can therefore tell us the age of the solar system, and how long ago Earth first formed.

Radiometric dating

- One of the most accurate ways of dating a mineral sample is **radiometric dating**. Many of the heavier elements, e.g. uranium and thorium, decay over time; their atoms break apart into smaller atoms. The rate of decay depends only on the original element's isotope. Uranium-238 ultimately decays into lead-206, and uranium-235 decays to lead-207. The ratios of uranium-238 to lead-206 and uranium-235 to lead-207 in a sample can therefore be used to determine the time since the sample formed. There are other ways of using radiometric dating, but all depend on decay of radioactive elements.

Zircons- the oldest crystals found

- Zircons are crystals containing the elements zirconium, silicon and oxygen, with the formula $ZrSiO_4$. They form when molten rock cools. Zircons also contain traces of uranium when they form and can therefore be dated radiometrically. Uranium has a similar electron structure to zirconium and so sometime gets incorporated into the zircon crystal structure, but lead does not. The uranium decays over time to lead. Therefore the ratio of U-238 to Pb-206 and U-235 to Pb-207 can tell us how long ago the crystal formed (far right).

Evidence from meteorites

- **Meteorites** are solid pieces of debris, e.g. from an asteroid, that have fallen to Earth and survived the impact. Meteorites originate from material that formed when the solar system formed, so they can be used to estimate the age of the solar system and therefore Earth. Most meteorites are small, only a few centimeters in diameter. The largest known meteorite is the Hoba meteorite in Namibia, which is 2.7 meters across and weighs 60 tonnes.
- Meteorites can be dated using the ratios of lead-206, 207, and 208, to lead-204. Lead 206, 207, and 208 are all formed from the radioactive decay of uranium or thorium. Lead 204 is primordial (existing since the beginning of time); it is not formed from radioactive decay. The ratio of lead-206, 207, or 208 to lead 204 can tell us how long ago the meteorite formed: the ratio of lead-206 to lead-204 increases with time.
- Because the decay rates of the parent uranium isotopes and the radioactive lead isotopes are known, the age corresponding to each ratio of lead isotopes can be determined. These techniques have dated the oldest meteorites at 4567 million years ± 0.01%.

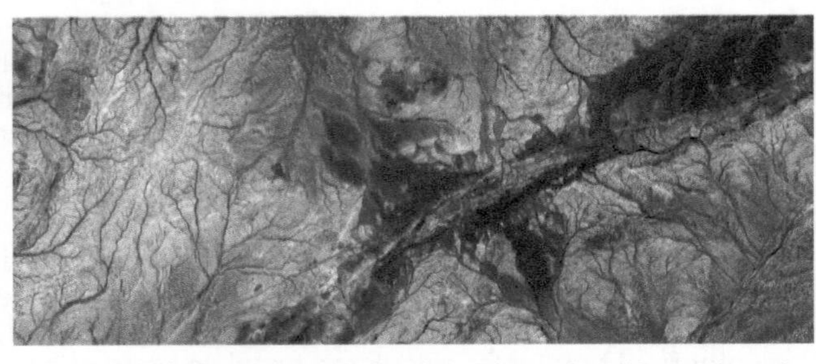

The Jack Hills formation (Australia), where the oldest minerals on Earth have been found.

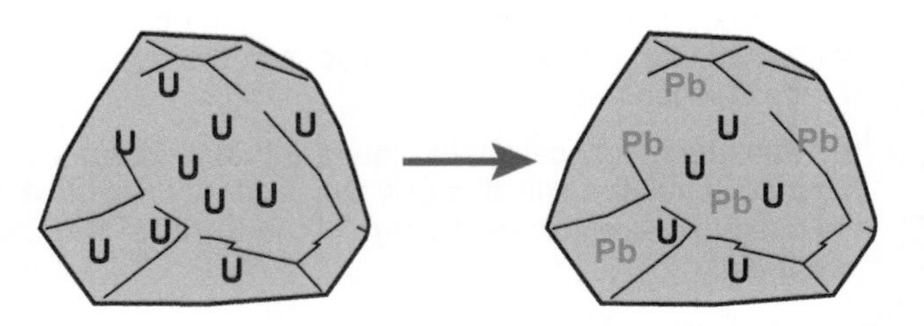

Unstable atoms, e.g. uranium, change into stable atoms, e.g. lead, following a long but predictable decay series involving many radioactive elements.

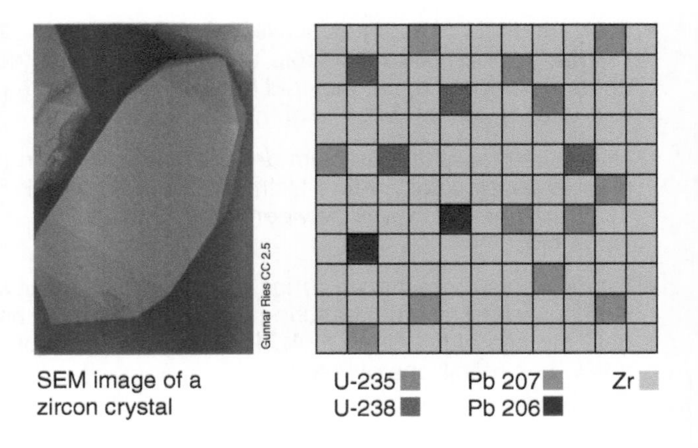

SEM image of a zircon crystal

The Hoba meteorite

ESS1.C PS1.C P SC

ISBN: 978-1-98-856693-1

Half-lives

- Every radioactive material has a specific half-life. This is the time taken for half the parent material to decay into daughter material. For example, the radioactive material carbon-14 decays into nitrogen-14 and has a half-life of 5730 years. If a mass of carbon-14 was measured at 5 grams, in 5730 years (one half-life) there would be 2.5 grams left. In another 5730 years there would be 1.25 grams of carbon-14 left.

Investigation 4.1 Modeling half-lives

See appendix for equipment list.

1. Work in pairs for this investigation. Place 100 M&M's® in a lidded container and shake them up.
2. Pour them out onto a plate and remove the M&M's® with the M facing up. These represent decayed atoms. Record the number of M&M's® left (M facing down) in the table below.
3. Put the remaining M&M's® back into the container and repeat the procedure. Repeat this until there are no more M&M's®.

Round number											
M&M's® left											

1. (a) Plot a line graph of the decay of M&M's®. Plot the number of M&M's® remaining on the y axis, and the number of half-lives (rounds) on the x axis. Join the points to form an approximate decay curve.

   (b) Compare your decay curve with those of your classmates.
   Is it the same or different? Why?

   ____

   ____

   ____

   ____

   ____

   ____

NEED HELP?
See activity 6

2. How old is the oldest dated mineral on Earth? ___________________________________

3. Explain why it is difficult to find rocks older that about 4 billion years old on Earth: ___________________________________

   ____

   ____

   ____

4. Why are objects such as meteorites useful for dating the age of the Earth? ___________________________________

   ____

   ____

   ____

   ____

5. The half life of uranium-235 is 700 million years. Analysis of a rock sample showed that the uranium had undergone three half lives. How old was the rock sample?

   ____

ISBN: 978-1-98-856693-1

Evidence from moon rocks

- Moon rocks here on Earth come from lunar meteorites and samples collected by the manned American Apollo and unmanned Soviet Luna missions. The Apollo missions brought a total of 380.96 kg of moon rock back from the various landing sites on the Moon.
- The Moon has little active geology so most of the surface rocks are almost as old as the Moon. It is generally accepted that the Moon was formed when a protoplanet (named **Theia**) smashed into the Earth early in the development of the solar system.
- The Moon has also suffered major impacts, some so large they exposed the lunar mantle. This means the **lunar rocks** taken from the lowlands (the darker areas seen from Earth) are younger than those of the highlands (the brighter areas). Also, the lunar highlands are more heavily cratered than the lowlands, indicating they are older (see "Crater counting").

Crater counting

- The amount of impact cratering created by meteorites can be used to date a surface. At its very simplest, a young surface has very few craters, an old surface has more. Different sized craters form at different rates and there are more small craters than large craters. We can therefore conclude that ancient surfaces not only have a larger number of craters, but larger sized craters compared to young surfaces.
- Generally, craters around 1 km in diameter are used as a reference point when using this method. Using the rocks brought back from the Moon, the number of craters at the sample site and the age of the surface can be compared.
- On a planet such as Earth, only large or very recent craters are visible on the surface. Smaller and more ancient craters have been eroded away by geological processes.

Oxygen isotope ratios

- Oxygen has three stable natural isotopes, ^{16}O, ^{17}O, and ^{18}O. It has been found that the ratios of ^{18}O:^{16}O and ^{17}O:^{16}O are unique to a planet or asteroid. However, the more closely related planetary bodies are, the closer the ^{18}O:^{16}O and ^{17}O:^{16}O ratios. The ratios are measured in terms of the deviation from the Standard Mean Ocean Water (SMOW) in parts per thousand (denoted δ). When the deviations are plotted on a graph ($\delta^{17}O$ versus $\delta^{18}O$) all the measurements from one planet or asteroid fall on their own unique line.

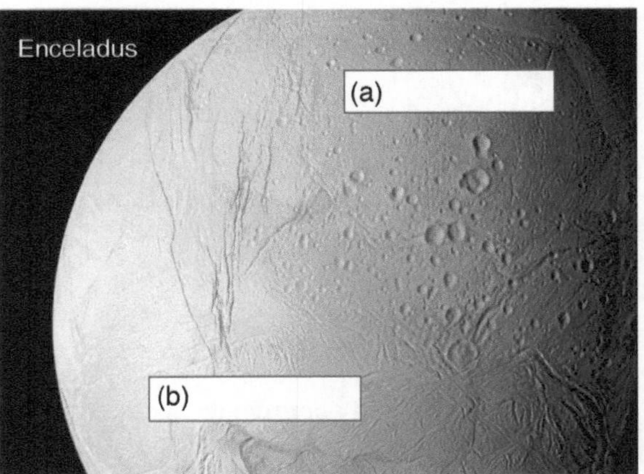

Mars rocks have their own unique oxygen isotope ratios

6. What is the purpose of dating Moon rocks? ______

7. Why are Moon rocks younger than Earth rocks? ______

8. Why would we expect older surfaces to have more and larger craters than a younger surface? ______

9. The photo, middle above, shows the surface of Saturn's moon Enceladus. On the photo, use labels to identify the youngest and oldest parts of the surface:

ISBN: 978-1-98-856693-1

Craters on the Earth

- Looking at other planetary bodies in the solar system (below), you may notice numerous craters all over the surfaces, especially on planets and bodies with little or no atmosphere and geologic activity:

Far side of the Moon

Mars

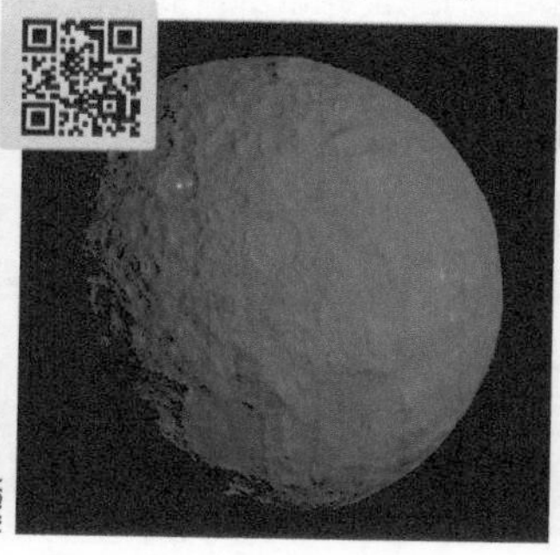
Ceres

Mercury

- Craters are found on all the rocky planetary bodies (planets, dwarf planets, moons, and asteroids) in the solar system but are apparently absent when looking at images of the Earth. It is reasonable to assume the Earth has undergone the same amount of bombardment as other bodies in the solar system over its history. Why then can we not see any craters?
- In fact, the Earth has undergone the same kind of bombardment as other bodies in the solar system. Scientists have uncovered evidence for numerous impact sites all over the Earth, as shown in the image below:

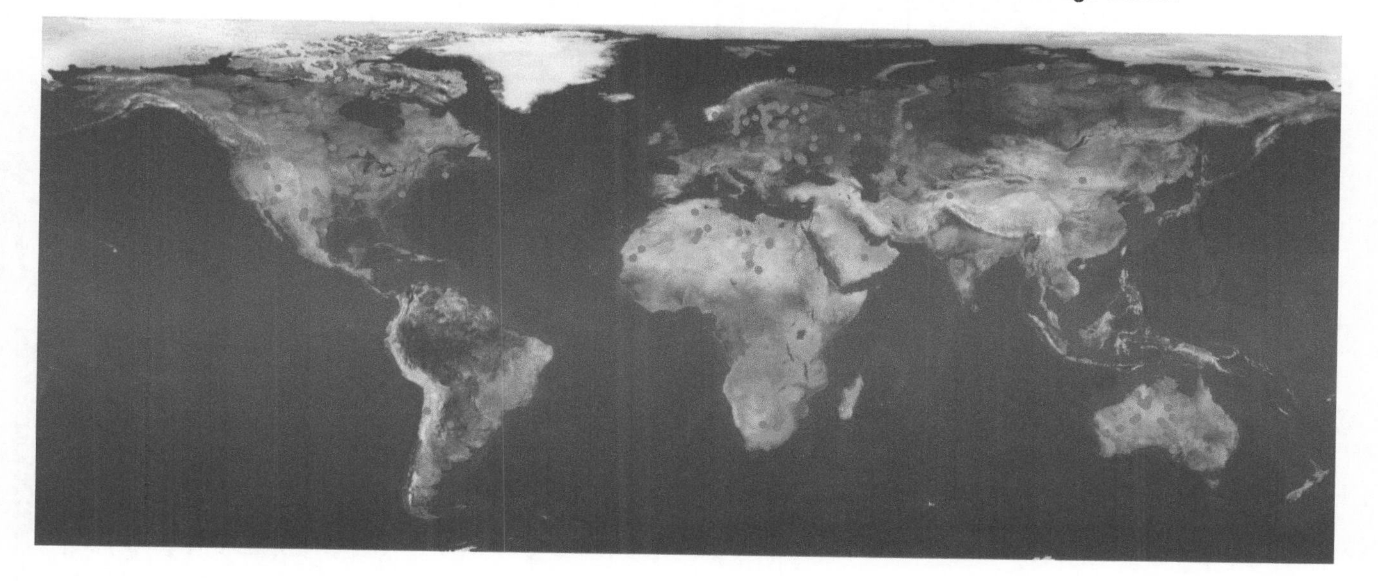

10. Compare the images below. The one on the left is from the Moon, the central image is of Mars (which has a thin atmosphere and evidence of ancient water flows), and the image on the right is from Earth:

Moon crater

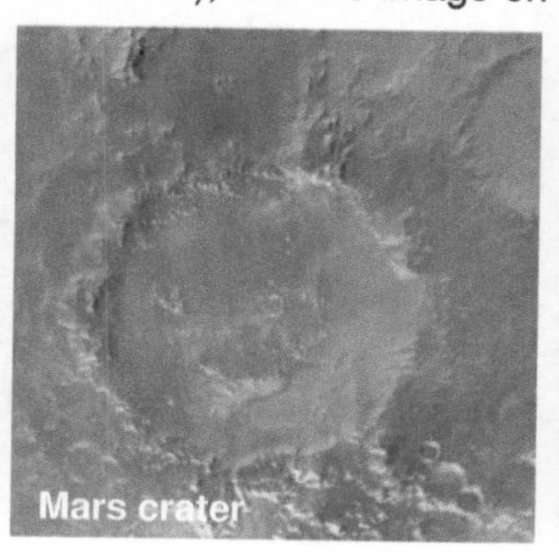
Mars crater

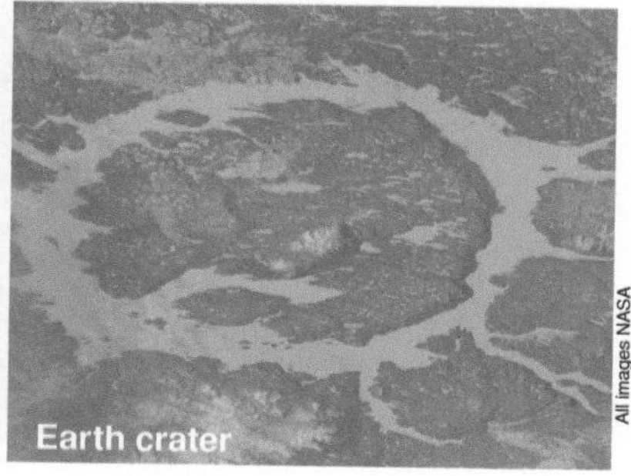

Earth crater

(a) Why might craters on Earth be less common than on other terrestrial bodies in the solar system? ______________

____

____

(b) How might this affect the use of craters as a tool to date the Earth? ______________

____

____

ISBN: 978-1-98-856693-1

Dating the formation of the Earth

Absolute ages of rocks

- You have been given explanations of various different techniques that can be used to date the Earth and stages of its history. The data in the next series of topics provide evidence for a history of the formation of the Earth.

11. The data in the table below shows the age of various rocks and materials from the Earth and other bodies of the solar system. The material was dated using radiometric dating:

Material	Age (millions of years)	Error (+/-) (millions of years)	Dating method
Chondrite meteorite	4568	0.3	Pb-Pb
Chondrite meteorite	4566	0.7	Pb-Pb
Chondrite meteorite	4565	0.9	Pb-Pb
Mars meteorite	4428	25	U-Pb
Mars meteorite	4070	40	Ar-Ar
Mars meteorite	4040	100	U-Pb
Mars meteorite	3920	100	Ar-Ar
Moon rock highland	4426	65	U-Pb
Moon rock highland	4339	5	U-Pb
Moon rock lowland	3800	20	Ar-Ar
Moon rock lowland	3770	70	Ar-Ar
Earth - Australia	4404	68	Pb-Pb
Earth - Australia	4363	8	Pb-Pb
Earth - Australia	4341	6	Pb-Pb
Earth - Canada	3939	31	Pb-Pb
Earth - Greenland	3809	7	U-Pb
Earth - Canada	3737	23	Pb-Pb

(a) Plot the data above on the graph below using dot points:

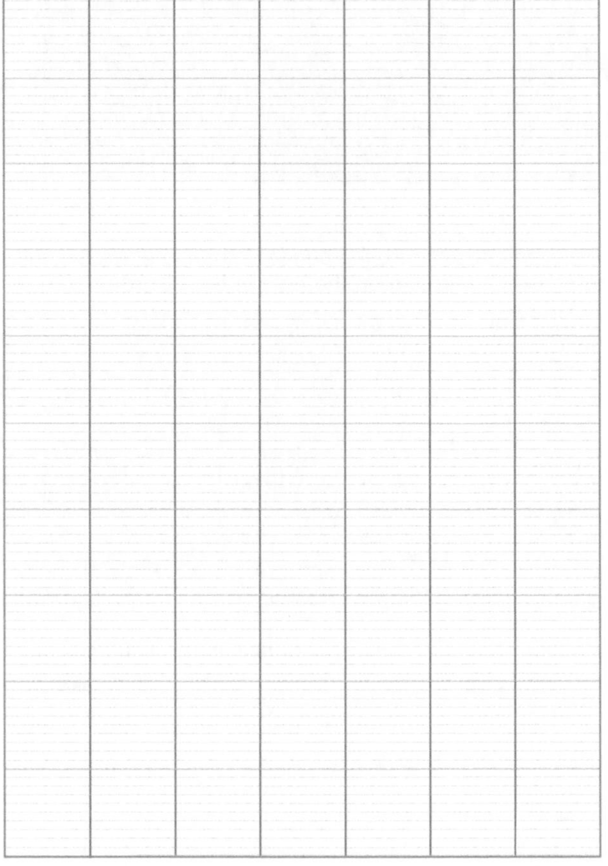

Collecting moon rocks (Apollo 17)

NASA

Moon rock (Apollo 15)

NASA

Chondrite meteorite

H. Raab CC 3.0

ISBN: 978-1-98-856693-1

(b) How old is the oldest rock type? ______________________________

(c) How much older than the oldest Earth rocks is this rock type? ______________________________

(d) Where might this type of rock have come from? ______________________________

Oxygen isotope ratios

12. The data in the table below shows the deviations in oxygen isotope ratios ($^{17}O:^{16}O$ and $^{18}O:^{16}O$) from SMOW for different rocks and materials from the Earth and other bodies of the solar system:

Material	$\delta^{17}O$	$\delta^{18}O$
Chondrite meteorite	–3.61	1.19
Chondrite meteorite	–2.73	1.51
Chondrite meteorite	–0.91	3.52
Chondrite meteorite	0.4	5.86
Mars meteorite	2.64	4.45
Mars meteorite	2.60	4.38
Mars meteorite	2.87	4.87
Mars meteorite	2.99	5.09
Moon rock highland	3.14	5.99
Moon rock highland	3.02	5.77
Moon rock lowland	2.92	5.56
Moon rock lowland	2.81	5.43
Earth rock	4.82	9.25
Earth rock	2.81	5.44
Earth rock	3.33	6.43
Earth rock	2.98	5.72

(a) Plot the data above on the graph below using dot points. Plot each group of rocks in its own color and include a key:

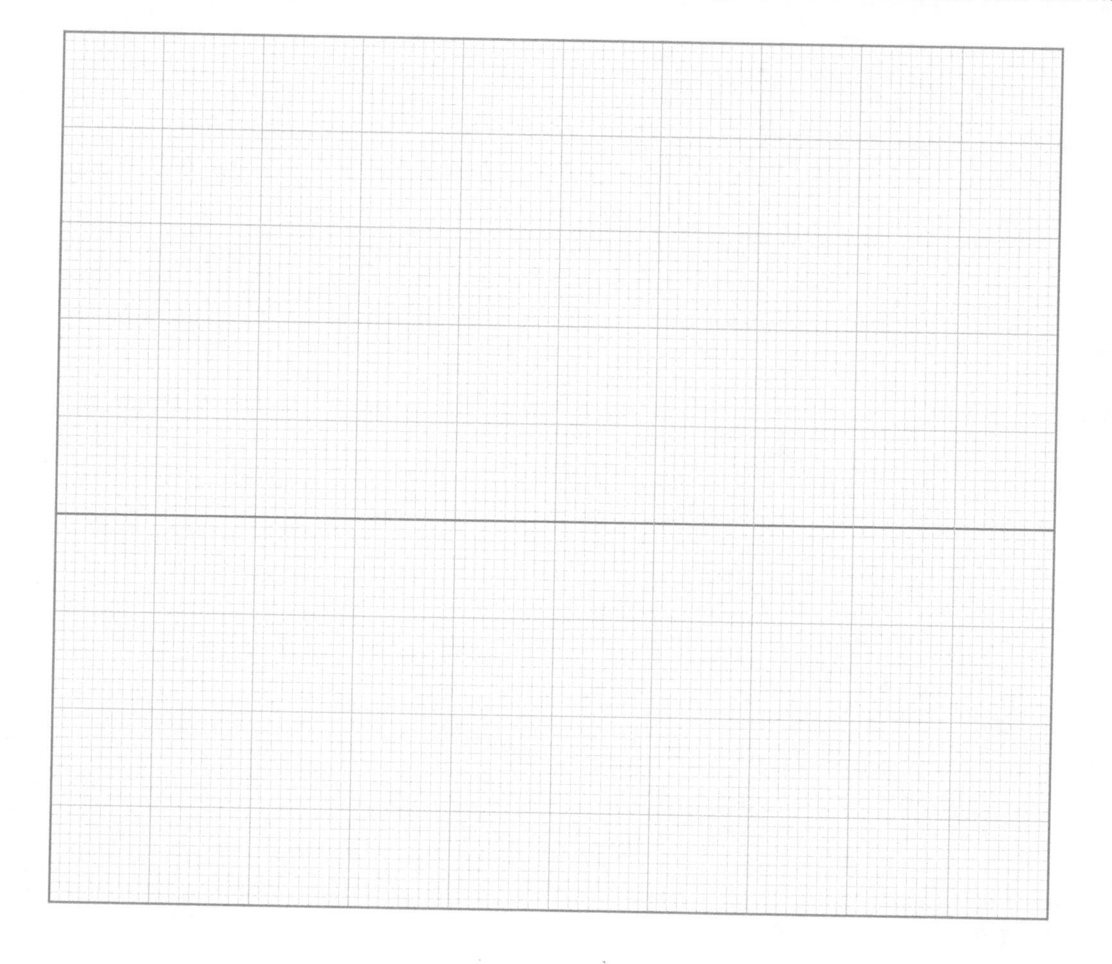

ISBN: 978-1-98-856693-1

(b) Describe the shape of the plots:

(c) What do you notice about the Earth and Moon plots?

(d) What does this mean?

Crater counting

13. The data (right) shows the age of lunar rocks and the number of craters of diameter >1 km per km^2 at the sample site:

(a) Plot the data on the grid below. Try placing a curve of best fit through the points. A spreadsheet may help you.

(b) Describe the shape of the graph:

(c) When was crater formation most frequent?

(d) What do you think was happening around this time?

Site	Number of craters with diameter >1 km per km^2 at sample site	Age (billions of years)
Terrae	0.35	4.35
Apollo 16	0.12	4.1
Apollo 14	0.03	3.9
Apollo 15	0.025	3.85
Apollo 16	0.025	3.85
Apollo 17	0.010	3.7
Apollo 11	0.0065	3.45
Luna 16	0.003	3.4
Apollo 12	0.004	3.2
Apollo 15	0.003	3.3
Copernicus	0.0015	0.85
Tycho A	0.00009	0.1
North Ray	0.00005	0.05
Cone crater	0.00002	0.01

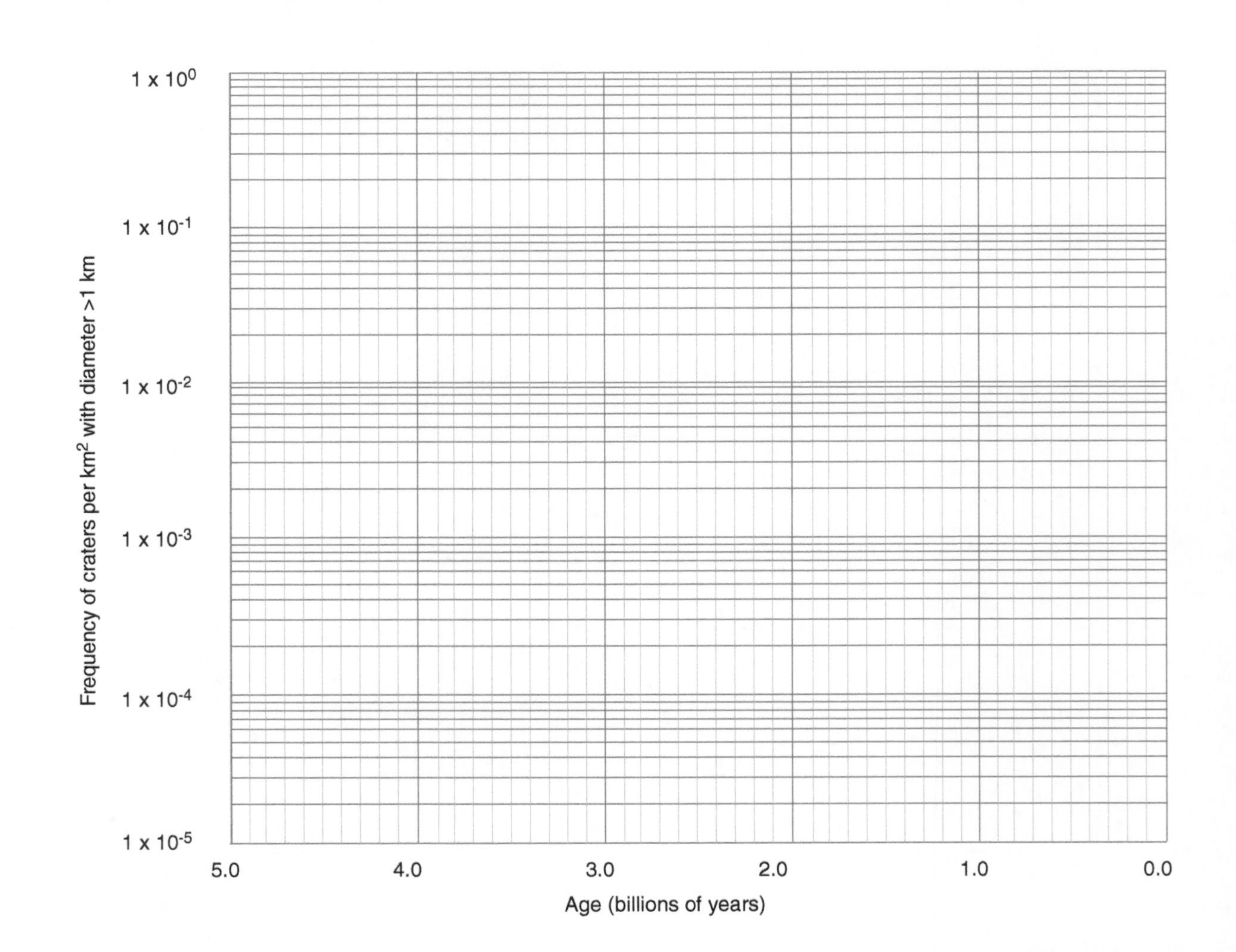

ISBN: 978-1-98-856693-1

Comparing zinc isotopes

14. The graph below shows the difference in zinc isotope ratio between various terrestrial bodies, including the Earth and Moon. Zinc is strongly fractionated (separated by mass) when in a gaseous form but not under normal processes in the mantle. When in a gaseous state, lighter isotopes are more likely to be lost by evaporation.

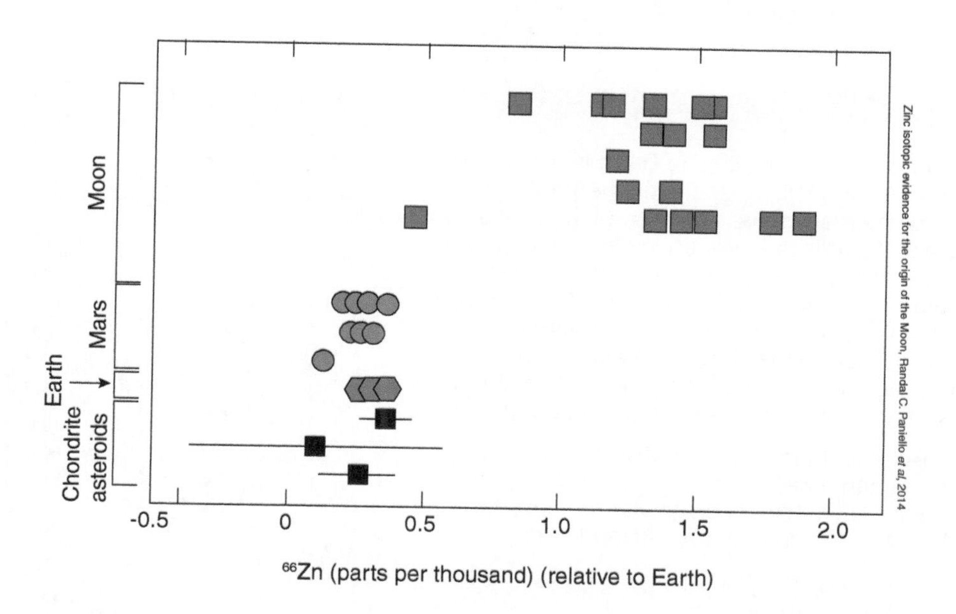

(a) What does the graph show about the Zn isotope ratio between the Moon and other terrestrial bodies, e.g. the Earth?

(b) What does this suggest about the formation of Earth, and even Mars, in comparison to the Moon?

15. Summarize the information in this activity about the age and formation the Earth and Moon:

ISBN: 978-1-98-856693-1

48 What Can Mars Tell Us?

Key Question: How has robotic exploration of Mars helped us understand why it is different from Earth?

- Mars has some similarities to Earth in inclination, structure, composition, and even the presence of water on their surfaces. However, Mars is also very different. Its surface is dry and cold and its gravity is only a third of Earth's. Yet Mars is the most explored of all the planets except Earth because it is the most hospitable of the other planets. Mercury is far too close to the Sun, and Venus is far too hot and its atmosphere too dense. Mars offers the best possibility of all the planets for human colonization.
- Exploration of Mars in preparation for possible future human missions has shown that, although Mars may once have been similar to an early Earth, it has followed a very different history.

Earth is loaded with organic molecules (molecules that contain both carbon and hydrogen). Most of these are related to biological activity. Mars has few organic materials. Using Curiosity's Sample Analysis at Mars (SAM) laboratory, simple organic molecules were detected in significant, but still small amounts. However these molecules could have formed by simple reactions in the rocks.

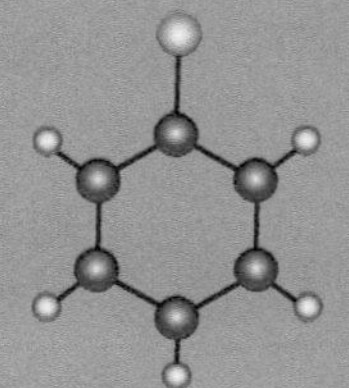

Chlorobenzene is one of the simple organic molecules found on Mars.

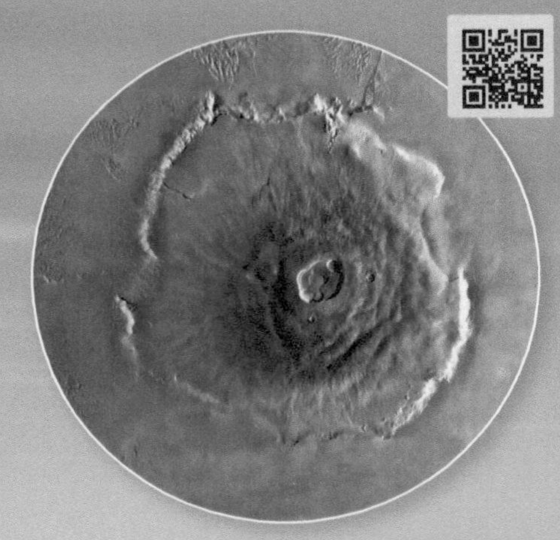

Olympus Mons is the largest volcano in the solar system. It is a basalt shield volcano that formed over tens of thousands of years. Olympus Mons and Mars' other volcanoes formed from hot spots under the crust. Unlike Earth, Mars has no **plate tectonics**, so the crust remained above the hot spot, allowing enormous volcanoes to form.

Both the Curiosity and Perseverance rovers carry an extensive range of tools for the analysis of rocks and chemicals they encounter on the surface of Mars.

All images NASA

1. What is the significance of plate tectonics to volcano size on Earth? ______________________________

____

____

2. Explain why Mars has few organic molecules in its surface soils: ______________________________

____

____

____

ISBN: 978-1-98-856693-1

The ChemCam on board Curiosity and SuperCam on Perserverance are used for spectroscopy. They fire high intensity laser pulses at a target rock and the resulting spark at the rock surface is analyzed by spectrometers. The different wavelengths of light indicate different types of elements and molecules in the rock.

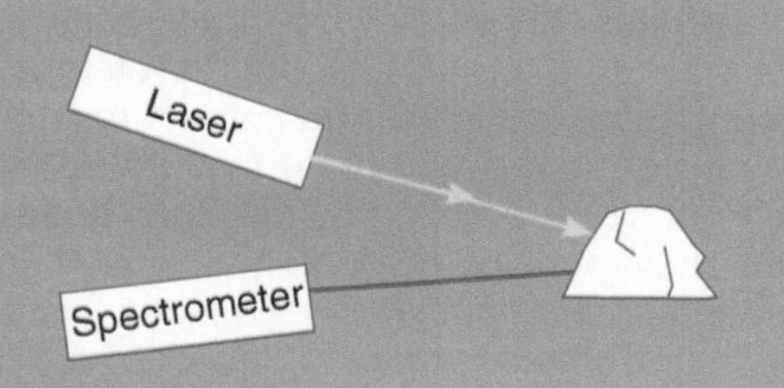

These devices have confirmed that much of the dust and soil on Mars is hydrated (it has water bonded to it). Other analysis has shown that most of the hydrogen in Mar's water is deuterium (hydrogen with a neutron). The water containing lighter hydrogen (protium) has evaporated into space.

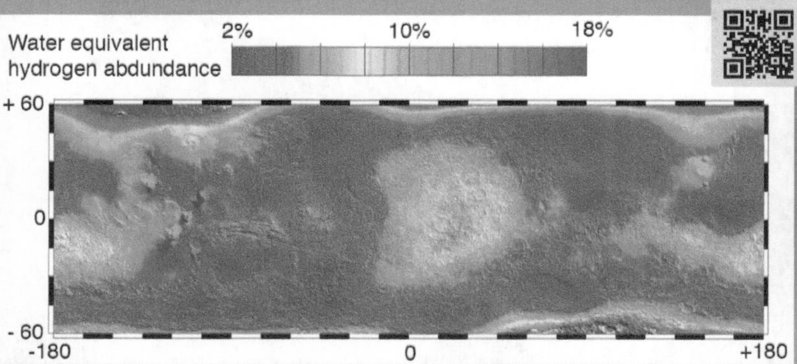

This map shows the distribution of Mars' subsurface water. Water is present in the highest concentrations near the poles and on the highlands.

Images of dry river beds, canyons, and grooves on sedimentary rock (above) indicate that Mars had plentiful running water at some time in the distant past. The grooves on the rock are caused by water currents.

The confirmation that Mars had plentiful water in the past, and probably a fairly hospitable climate, and possibly subsurface water today leads us to the ultimate question: If Mars was hospitable, did life evolve there and, if so, is it still there today? We have yet to answer this question. It has been tested many times but the answers so far have been negative or ambiguous. One clue for life on Mars is the detection of methane in the atmosphere. On Earth, methane is produced predominantly through biological processes. Methane seems to be being continuously made on Mars, but is just as quickly being removed. Methane's origin could be biological or geological.

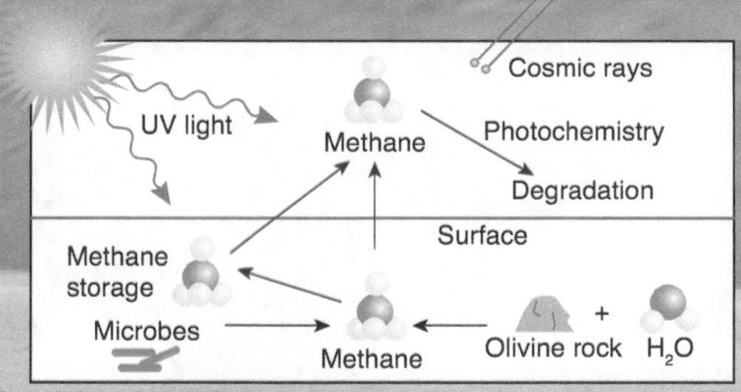

Possible schematic for methane production and loss on Mars

3. What evidence is there that Mars once had large amounts of flowing water? ______

4. What happened to Mars' water? ______

5. Why does the detection of methane not necessarily indicate life on Mars? ______

ISBN: 978-1-98-856693-1

49 Information from Probe Missions

Key Question: How has the information from space probes helped us understand the earliest history of Earth?

Comets

Comets are chunks of frozen rock, dust, water, and gas that move through the solar system in highly eccentric orbits. Short term comets originate in the Kuiper belt, whereas long term comets originate in the Oort cloud. Passing by the Sun causes them to heat up, vaporizing the water, dust, and gas, and creating a long tail that always faces away from the Sun. Comets represent material from the early solar system. Eight space probes have carried out missions to nearby comets.

Comet McNaught (also known as the Great Comet of 2007) as seen from New Zealand just after sunset.

Rosetta

The **Rosetta** space probe was launched by the ESA in 2004. It made a gravity assist flyby of Mars, and flybys of the comets 2867 Šteins and 21 Lutetia. Rosetta then entered hibernation for 31 months before reawakening in January 2014. In August 2014, the Rosetta space probe reached comet 67P and entered orbit around it.

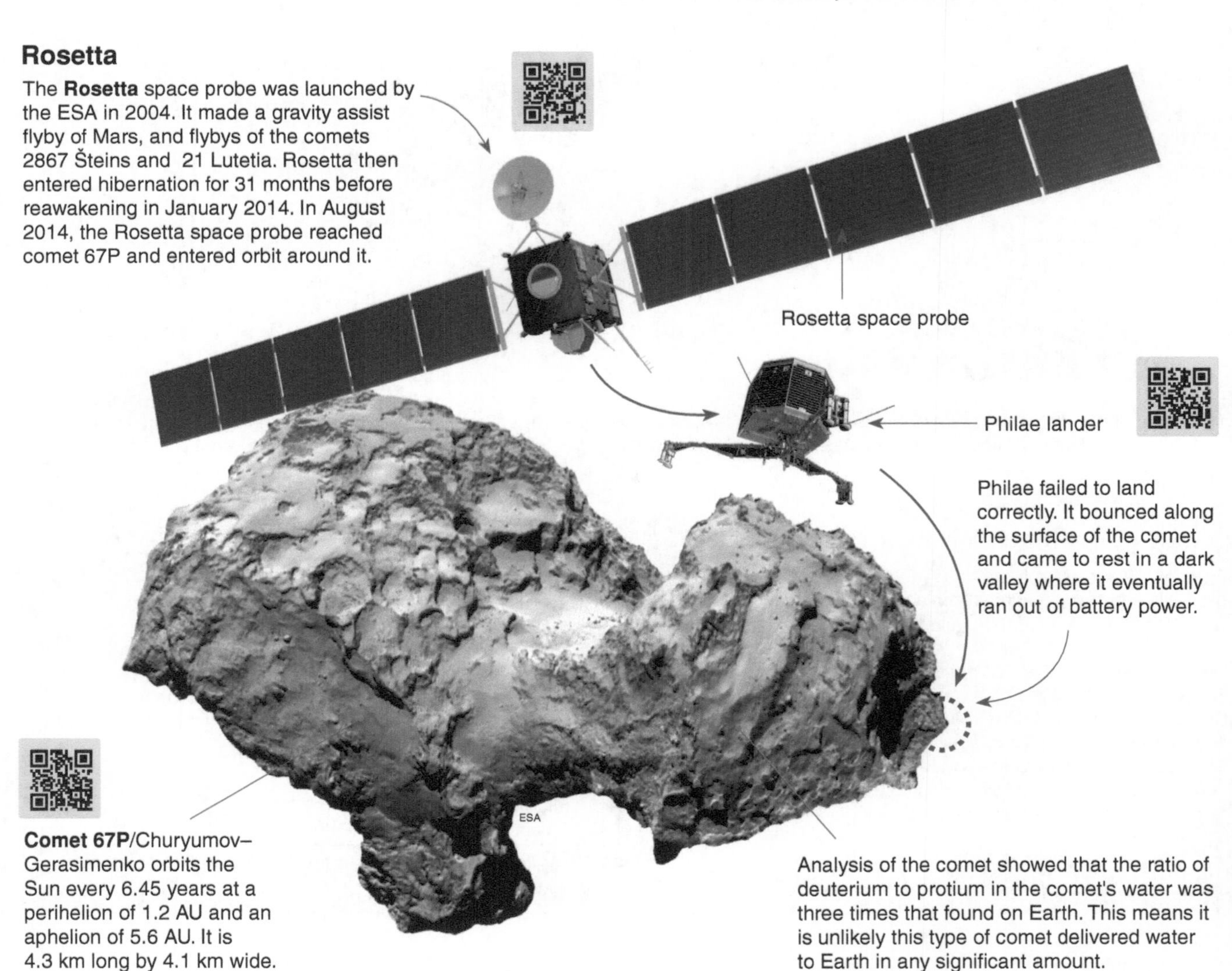

Philae failed to land correctly. It bounced along the surface of the comet and came to rest in a dark valley where it eventually ran out of battery power.

Comet 67P/Churyumov–Gerasimenko orbits the Sun every 6.45 years at a perihelion of 1.2 AU and an aphelion of 5.6 AU. It is 4.3 km long by 4.1 km wide.

Analysis of the comet showed that the ratio of deuterium to protium in the comet's water was three times that found on Earth. This means it is unlikely this type of comet delivered water to Earth in any significant amount.

Detecting water

Hydrogen atoms can be found as both a single proton with an electron (protium) or as a proton and neutron with an electron (deuterium). Deuterium is heavier than protium and is very rare (0.0156% of all hydrogen). In Earth's oceans, there is about one atom of deuterium in 6420 atoms of hydrogen. Changes in this ratio in water molecules in comets or asteroids can be used to help answer questions about the origin of Earth's water.

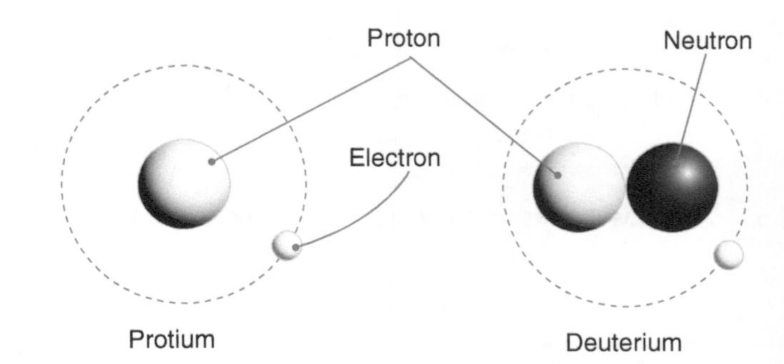

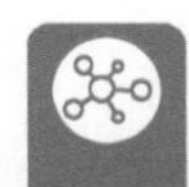

ESS1.C P SC

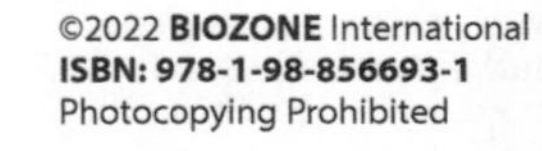

ISBN: 978-1-98-856693-1

Stardust

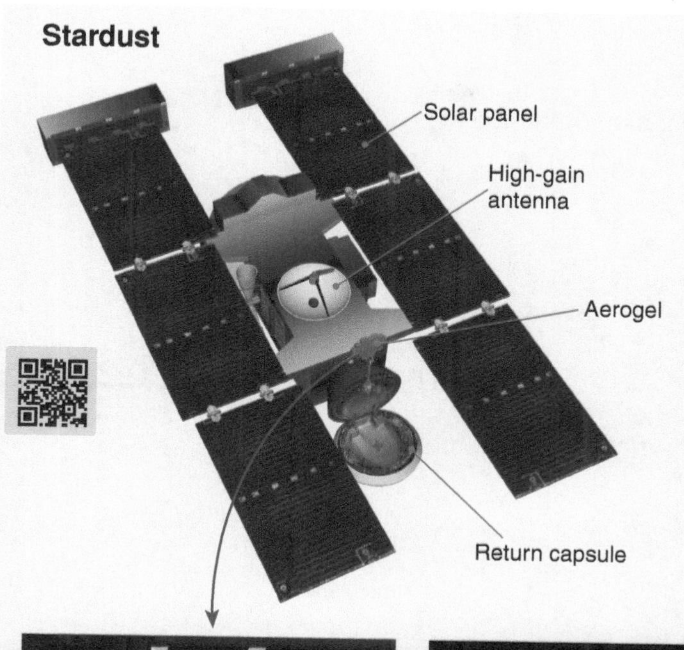

- **Stardust** was a space probe launched by NASA in 1999. Its primary mission was to rendezvous with comet **Wild-2**, collect dust samples from the coma (the dust cloud surrounding the comet nucleus), and return them to Earth. It was the first time samples from a comet were returned to Earth.
- As the probe neared the comet, a capsule opened and deployed a tennis racket sized collector holding blocks of aerogel. The dust particles streaming from the comet buried themselves into the gel.
- The capsule was then released as the probe passed by Earth in 2006.
- Analysis of the dust particles gathered by the probe suggested that material from the inner solar system was transferred to the outer solar system after its formation.
- The amino acid glycine was also detected in the material ejected from the coma, adding weight to the idea that comets brought at least some of the building blocks of life to Earth.

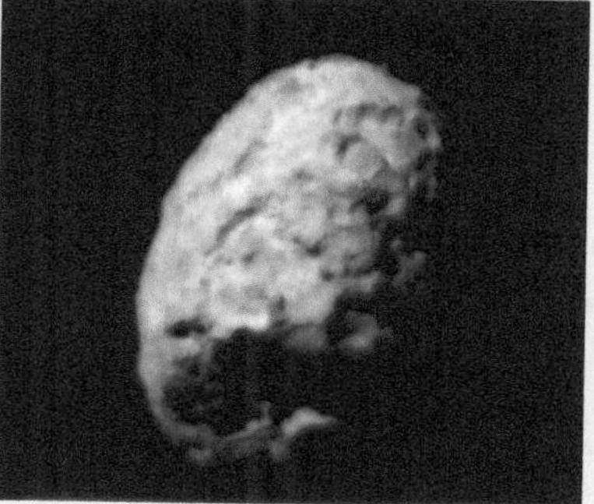

Comet Wild-2 (left) has a diameter of about 5 km. Until 1974, it orbited in the outer solar system, taking about 43 years per orbit. In September 1974, it passed within 1 million km of Jupiter. Jupiter's massive gravity pulled the comet into the inner solar system and changed its orbit to about 6 years.

Andrzej Mireck

The space probe **Giotto** flew past **Halley's Comet** in 1986, becoming the first space probe to study a comet. It found the comet to be 4.5 billion years old and 80% water.

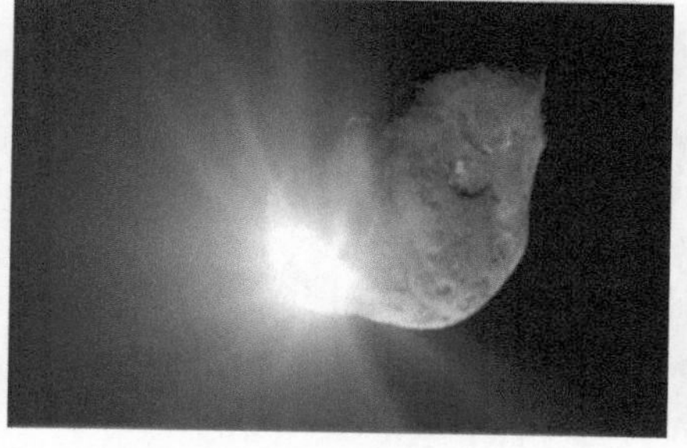

The **Deep Impact** space probe visited comet Tempel-1 in July 2005. It released a copper impactor that created a 100 m wide crater (above) so that cameras could photograph the interior of the comet.

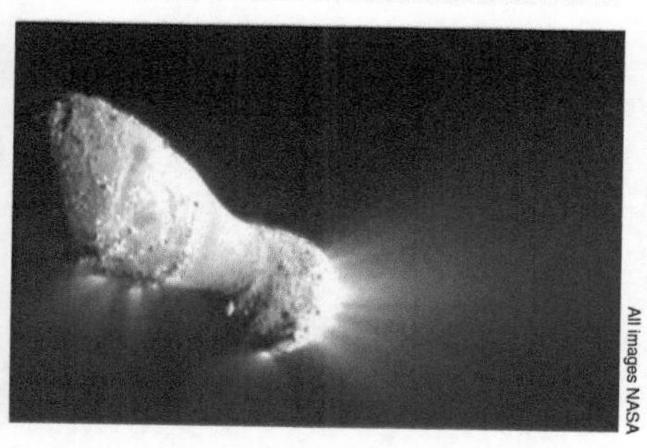

All images NASA

Deep Impact also visited Comet **Hartley 2**. In 2011, it was found that the comet contained water very much like Earth's, supporting the argument that comets brought at least some water to Earth.

1. (a) What evidence is there that comets may have delivered water to Earth early in its history? ______

   (b) What evidence is there that only certain types of comet delivered the water? ______

2. What is the evidence that the building blocks of life were carried to Earth on comets? ______

3. Why was an impactor deployed by Deep Impact at Tempel-1 and what might it help discover? ______

ISBN: 978-1-98-856693-1

50 The Earth's History

Key Question: What were the events in the formation of the Earth?

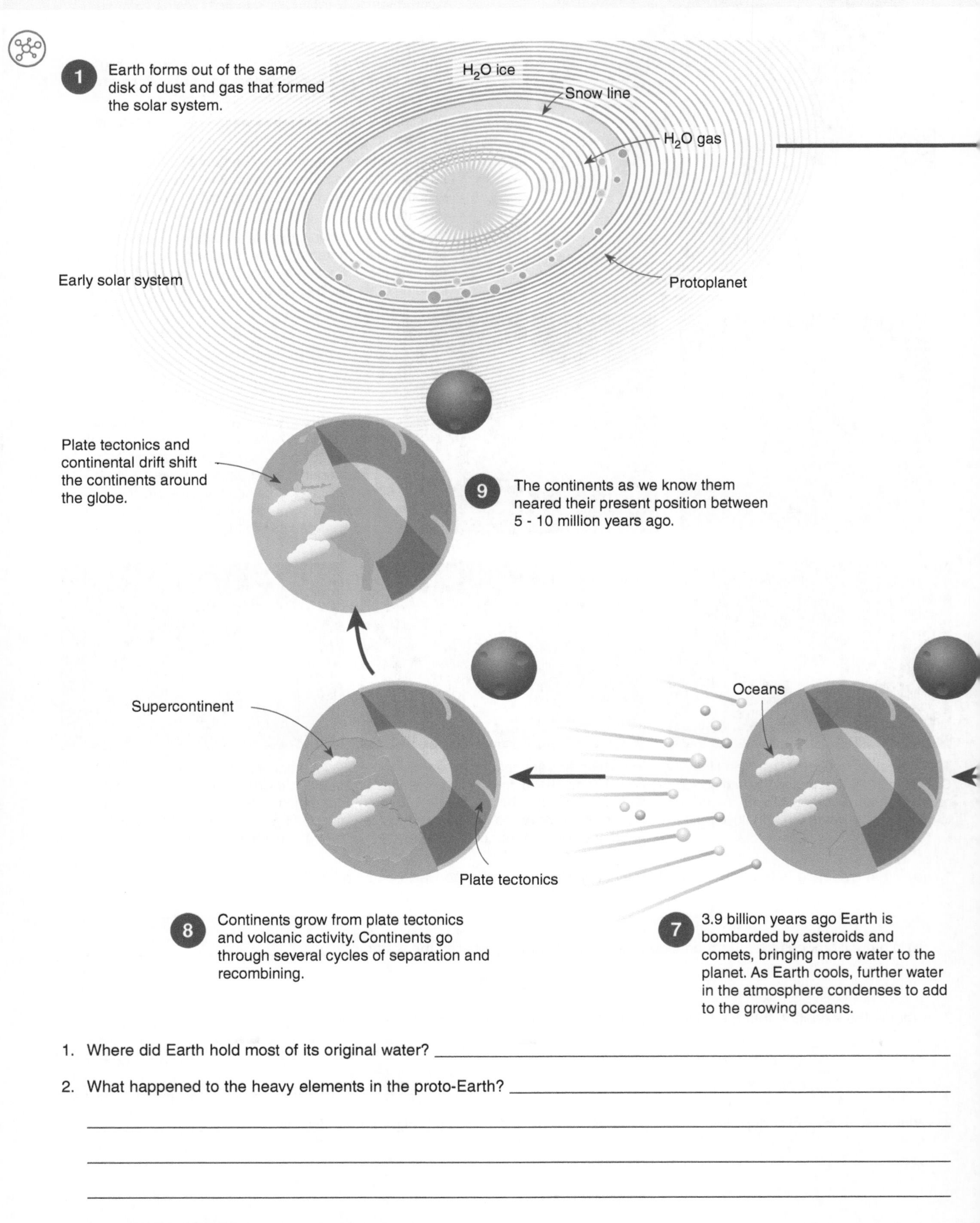

1. Where did Earth hold most of its original water? ______________________

2. What happened to the heavy elements in the proto-Earth? ______________________

____

____

____

ISBN: 978-1-98-856693-1

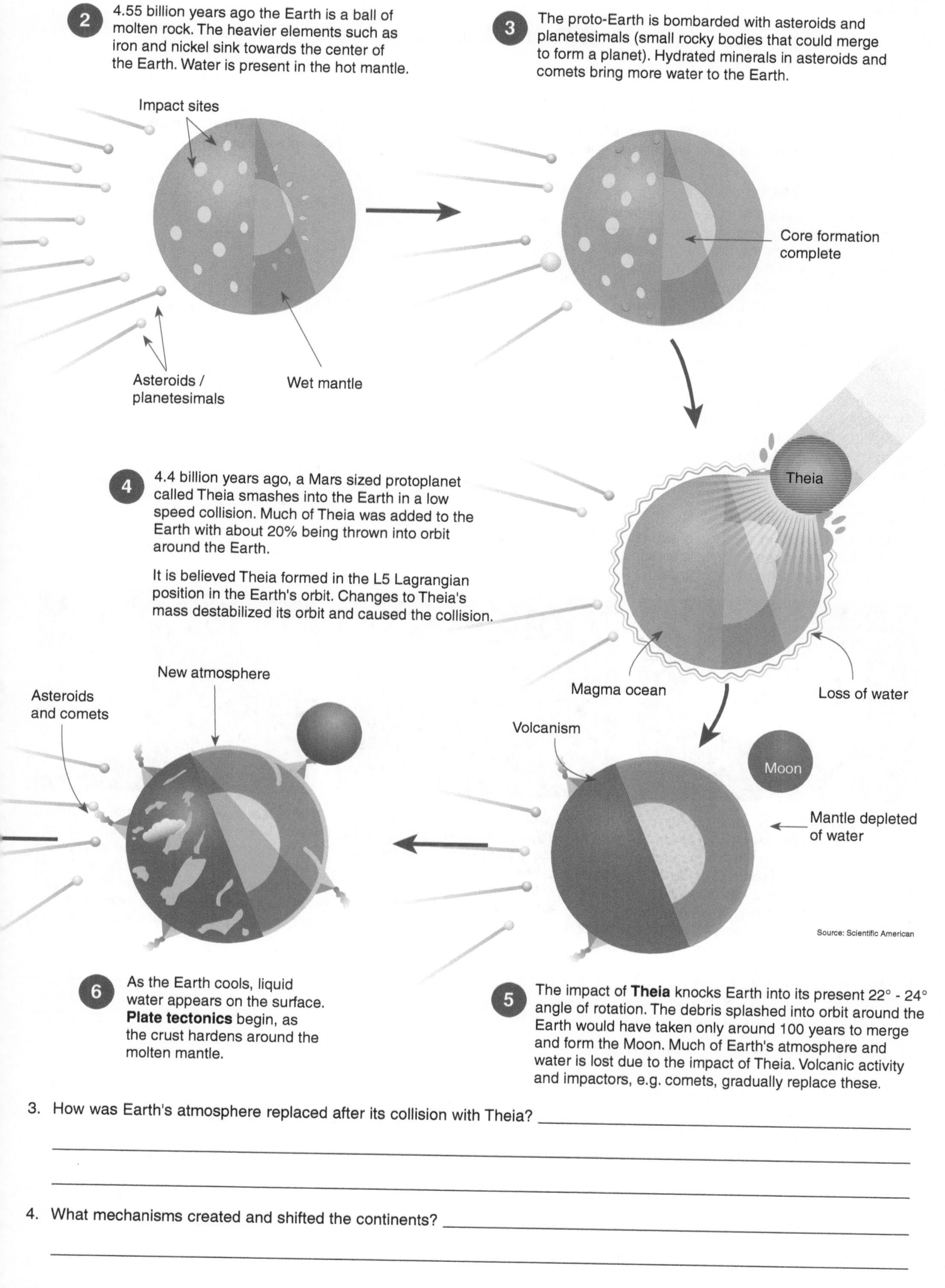

3. How was Earth's atmosphere replaced after its collision with Theia? ______________________

____

____

4. What mechanisms created and shifted the continents? ______________________

____

ISBN: 978-1-98-856693-1

51 The Goldilocks Planet

Key Question: What are the conditions that have allowed Earth to be a habitable planet?

There is one thing that life absolutely must have to survive: liquid water. Water is important as a medium for dissolved molecules and ions to carry out the reactions of life. There are numerous places in the solar system where liquid water probably exists, but other conditions make life (certainly complex life) in those places unlikely.

The habitable zone

- At a certain distance from a star there is a zone where the conditions are just right for liquid water. Not too hot that the water boils, not too cold that it is permanently frozen. Earth sits just inside the inner edge of the habitable zone of our Sun. If the Sun was smaller or dimmer, this zone would be closer to the Sun and Earth would be too cold. If the Sun was bigger or brighter, the zone would be further from the Sun and Earth would be too hot. The habitable zone could be extended by the conditions on a planet or moon, such as hydrothermal vents in oceans covered by ice, e.g. Saturn's moon Enceladus.

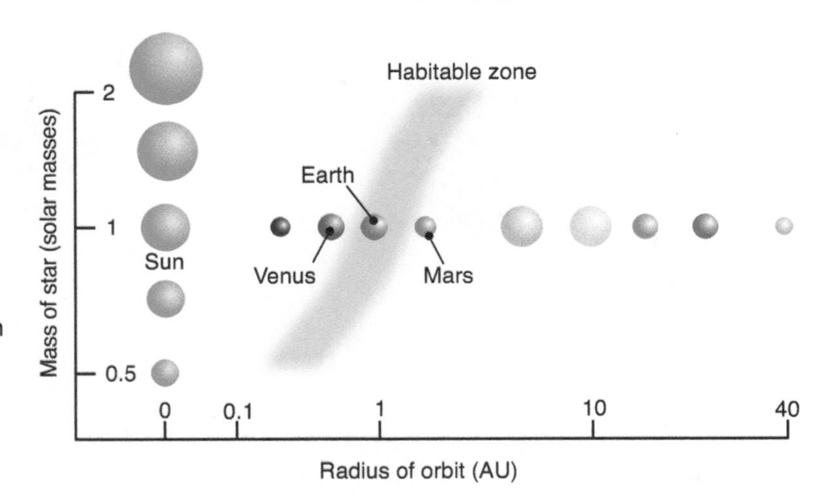

Other conditions

- Not only is Earth in the Sun's habitable zone but it has several other properties that make it suitable for life. Some of the important requirements for life are shown below. For the development of complex life, it is likely that there is an even longer list of requirements.

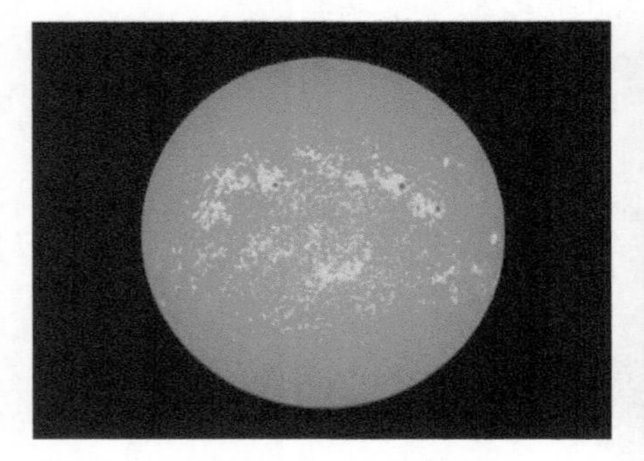

All images NASA

A long lived star: Large stars can burn out and explode after less than a billion years. Given that life on Earth appeared less than half a billion years after Earth formed, a large star might allow life to form but wouldn't exist long enough for life to evolve beyond the very simplest forms.

A stable orbit: A planet that moves in and out of the habitable zone would either be periodically far too cold or far too hot for life to evolve. Life may start while the planet is in the habitable zone, but would likely be extinguished as a planet moved out of the habitable zone.

Sufficient mass: If there is not enough mass, water and important gases cannot be retained and would escape into space, such as occurred on Mars. A planet that is too massive, generates too much gravity. This can have the effect of increasing atmospheric pressure, e.g. the gas planets.

1. Why is water needed for life? ______________________________

____

2. What are some factors that help maintain liquid water on Earth's surface? Explain: ______________________________

____

____

3. Why is a long lived star necessary for life to arise and evolve? ______________________________

____

____

____

ISBN: 978-1-98-856693-1

52 Review Your Understanding

Key Question: How do you estimate how old something is?

- There are many techniques for working out how old something is. Relative dating might put objects in order based on where they were found in rock layers. Absolute dating uses radioactivity to date rocks.
- At the start of this chapter you were asked about how you might date an object.
- What about the objects in the box? To date them, you would have to develop a set of rules about the materials they were made of, the style they are made in etc. For example, we know plastics were not fully developed until the early 1900s, therefore plastic objects are likely to be younger than non-plastic objects. But we also know that not all objects are made from plastic, so other things must be considered, such as the presence and type of electronics, styling, and function.

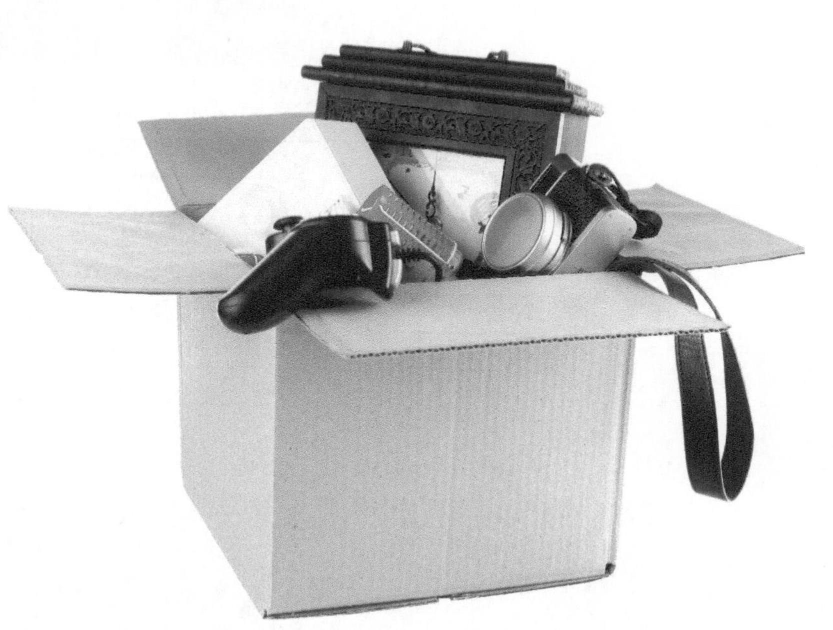

1. When using relative dating to date layers of rock, what rule must we follow or assume to be correct, in order for the dating to make sense?

2. When dating rocks using radioactivity for absolute dating, what rule do we follow or assume to be correct, in order for the dating to make sense?

3. Give a brief description of how radiometric dating works:

4. For any number of half-lives (t), the proportion of radioactive atoms left (r) is equal to 0.5t, i.e. $r = 0.5t$. This can be rearranged for t so that $t = ln(r) \div -0.6931$. The half-life of uranium-238 is 4.5 billion years. The half live of uranium-235 is 700 million years. Use this information to calculate the age of the zircon crystal represented on the opposite page. Note that *ln* refers to natural logarithms.

U-235 | Pb 207 | Zr
U-238 | Pb 206

ISBN: 978-1-98-856693-1

53 Summing Up

1. The diagram below shows the South Atlantic ocean. Samples taken from the seabed were dated using radiometric dating. The positions of the sample and their age are shown in the table below:

Sample number	Latitude	Longitude	Age of rock (millions of years)
1	14° S	23° W	62
2	35° S	43 W	100
3	25° S	7° E	80
4	41° S	6° W	40
5	11° S	11° W	20
6	26° S	15° W	10
7	24° S	23° W	55
8	25°S	13°W	10
9	50°S	19°W	40

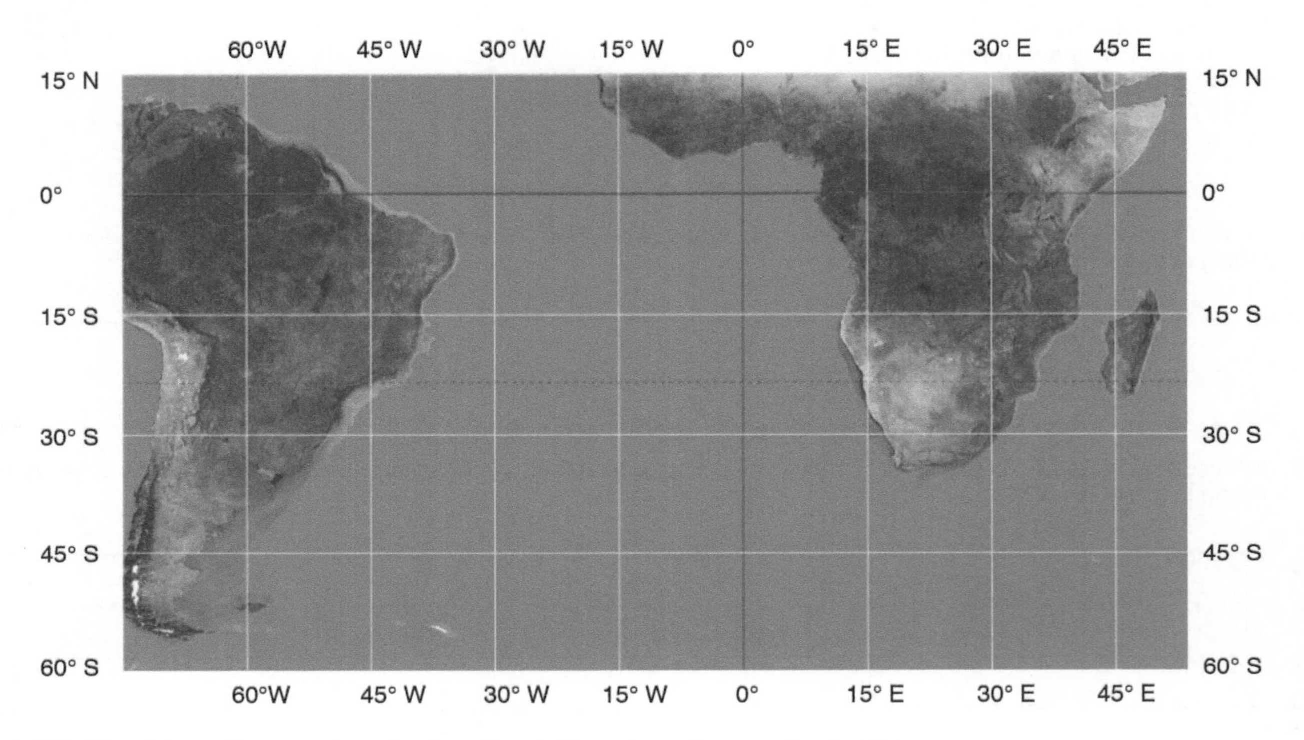

(a) Plot the data on the map above to show the position where the sample was taken:

(b) What happens to the age of the rock as you move from west to east across the South Atlantic?

____

____

(c) Draw a line on the map to indicate where rocks of the age 0 million years would be found:

(d) Explain what causes the production of new rocks on the seabed: _______________________

____

____

2. Explain why rocks in the continental crust are older than rocks in the oceanic crust: _______________

____

____

____

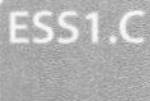

ISBN: 978-1-98-856693-1

3. Explain why the rocks from the lunar lowlands are younger than the rocks from the lunar highlands:

4. The image (right) shows Uranus' moon Miranda. Note that some parts are cratered and other parts have long streaks across them which may have formed from tidal stretching (being stretched by Uranus' gravity). Study the area in the white box. Which event occurred first, the tidal stretching or the crater impacts? Explain your answer:

NASA

5. When studying other planets and extraterrestrial objects, e.g. comets, identifying the ratio of hydrogen isotopes in any water found is an important task. Describe the information the hydrogen isotope ratio can tell us about an object's water in relation to Earth:

6. Discuss the development of models for dating the Earth and how these models changed as techniques developed and new information was discovered.

ISBN: 978-1-98-856693-1

Earth's Systems

Concepts and connections
Use arrows to make connections between related concepts in this section of the book

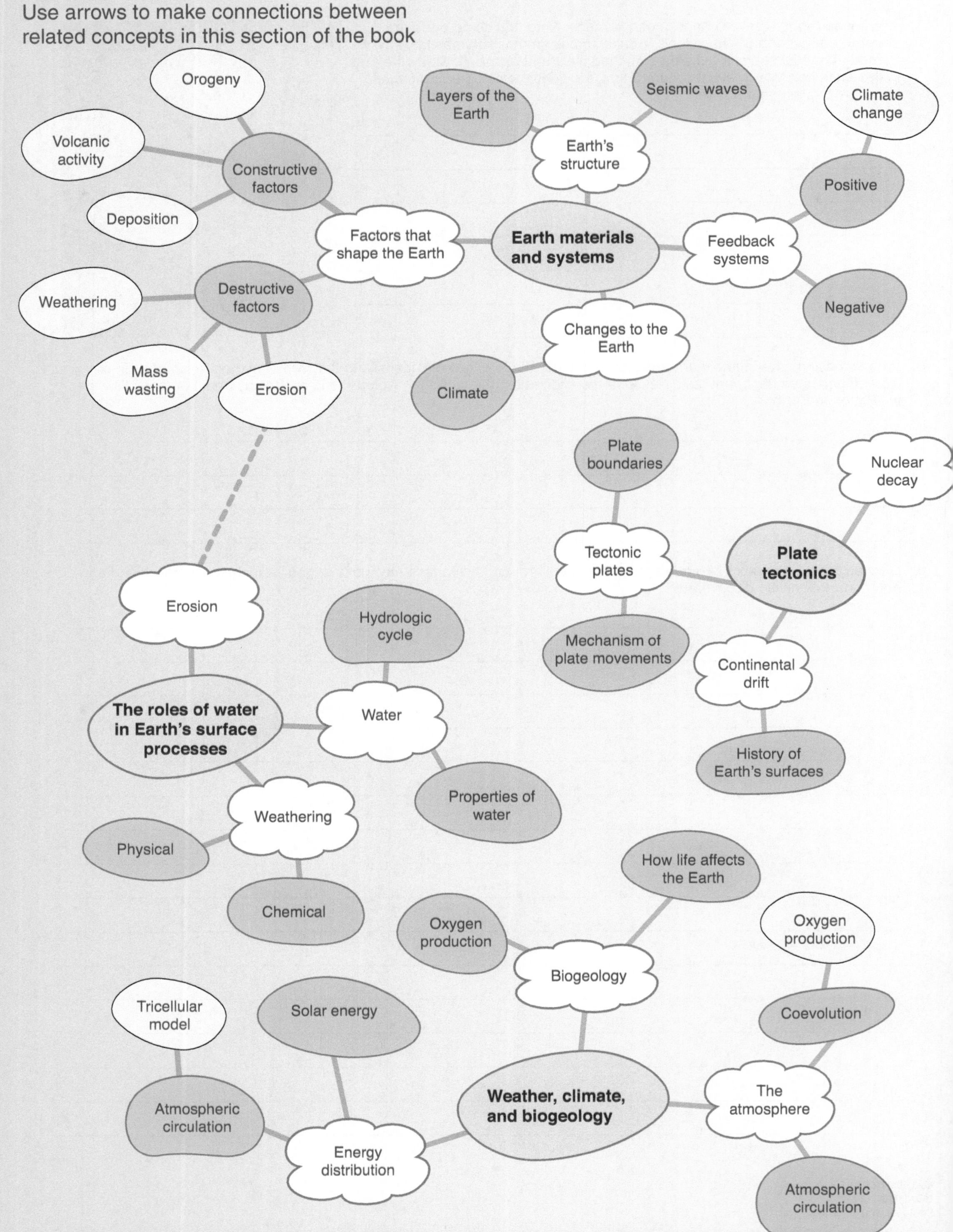

CHAPTER 5

Earth's Materials and Systems

Anchoring Phenomenon

Constant changes: What processes continually shape the Earth's surface? 54 66

What is the evidence for the current model of the Earth's structure?

☐ 1 Examine a model of the Earth's structure and identify the solid inner core, liquid outer core, and solid mantle and crust, including the lithosphere and asthenosphere. **55 57**

☐ 2 Use data from seismographs to plot travel times for seismic waves from an earthquake. Use this data to identify structural changes in the Earth. Use various lines of evidence to justify the current model of the Earth's internal structure. **56**

☐ 3 Examine and describe parts of the Earth's crust, including the differences between the lithosphere and asthenosphere. Explain how scientists can determine the nature of the material separating these layers. **57**

How are feedback effects involved in changes to the Earth?

☐ 4 Understand that the Earth's surface is shaped by both constructive forces, such as volcanism and tectonic uplift, and destructive mechanisms, such as mass wasting, weathering, and erosion. **58**

☐ 5 Examine how the Earth's systems are dynamic and interact with one another. Explain how constantly changing interactions between these different systems cause feedback effects. Identify feedback as negative, which stabilizes systems against changes, or positive, which amplifies changes. **59**

☐ 6 Explore feedback systems leading to an escalating loss of sea ice in the Arctic. Carry out an investigation to examine the effect of albedo on ice melting. **59 60**

☐ 7 Describe how human activities can cause escalating effects on water and soil systems using the examples of dams and overgrazing. Explain how over-exploitation can set up a positive feedback that can quickly strip a landscape of its resources, e.g. soil. **61 62**

☐ 8 Understand that the geological record shows changes to global and regional climate can be caused by interactions between the changing energy output of the Sun or the orbit of the Earth, tectonic events, ocean circulation, volcanism, vegetation, glaciers, and human activity. These changes can occur on a variety of time scales. **39 63-65 67**

NOAA

54 Constant Changes

Key Question: What processes continually shape the Earth's surface?

NASA

- The surface of the Earth is constantly changing. Processes on the surface build and breakdown structures such as mountains and valleys and produce the varied environments we see today.

1. In groups of three or four, discuss the processes that build and break down features of the Earth's surface. Make a list of the types you can think of and include a brief description of each:

2. The Earth is known to have several distinct internal layers. How do we know this? What processes listed in question 1 might help us understand the structure of the Earth and how? Discuss this in your groups and describe your ideas below:

3. Climate change is currently an important issue for the Earth. It is a phenomenon that, once started, becomes increasingly difficult to stop, due to natural processes. What might these be, and why might they cause runaway changes to the Earth's climate?

ISBN: 978-1-98-856693-1

55 Structure of the Earth

Key Question: What do we know about the structure of the Earth?

▸ The Earth is layered due to the density of different materials in it. The Earth's **crust** has a density of about 3 g/cm^3 and the core has a density of about 12 g/cm^3. Movement of **convection** currents in the **mantle** shifts the plates of the Earth's crust, while movement of the **outer core** produces the Earth's magnetic field.

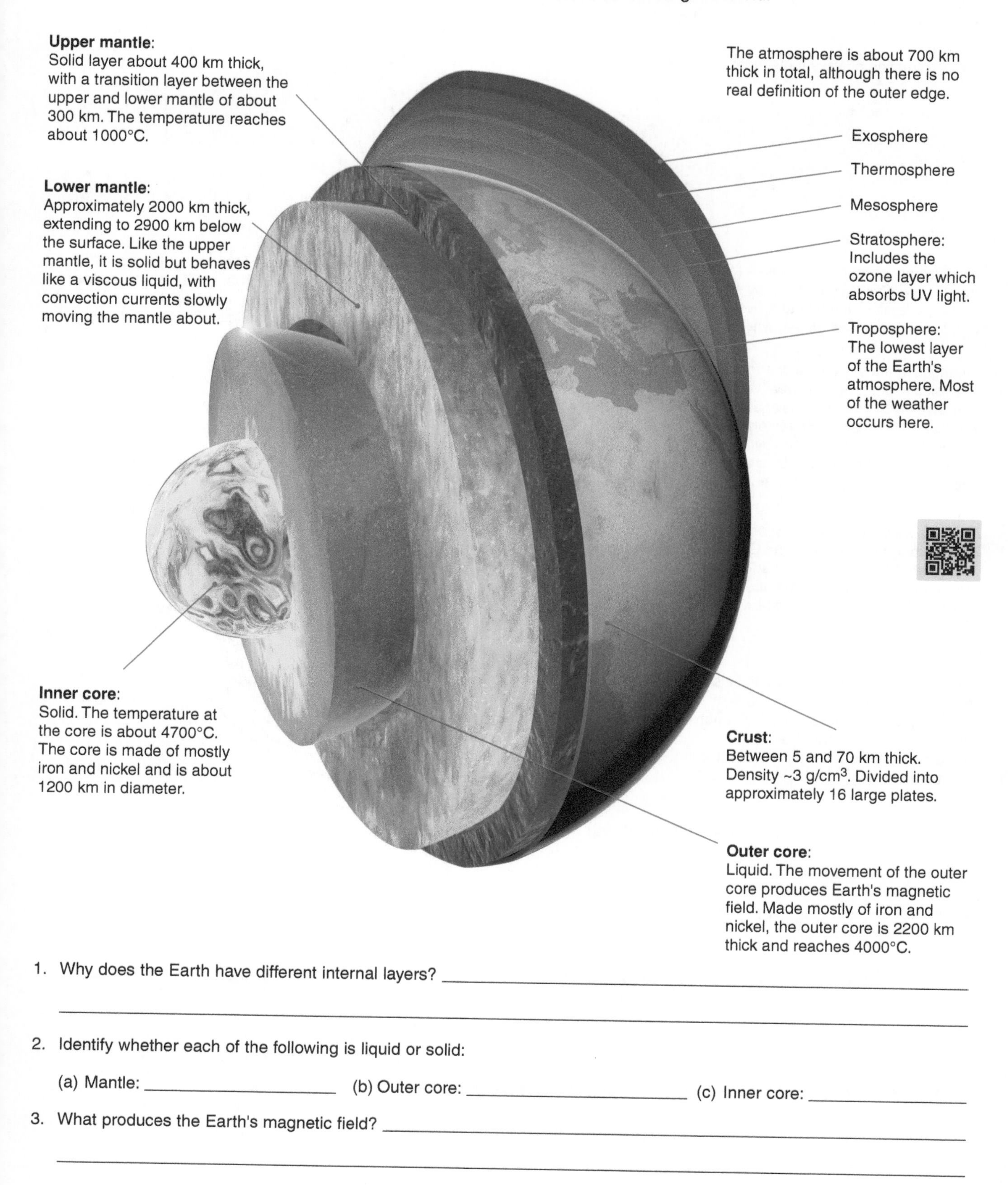

1. Why does the Earth have different internal layers? ______________________________

____

2. Identify whether each of the following is liquid or solid:

(a) Mantle: ______________ (b) Outer core: ______________ (c) Inner core: ______________

3. What produces the Earth's magnetic field? ______________________________

____

ISBN: 978-1-98-856693-1

56 Evidence for Earth's Structure

Key Question: What does seismic evidence and measurement of magnetic changes in rocks tell us about the structure of the Earth?

Seismic waves

Movement of the ground along fault lines in the Earth's **crust** causes earthquakes. During an earthquake, two types of ground wave are produced; compressional, or **P-waves** and shear, or **S-waves**. Seismographs are instruments that record ground motion during an earthquake.

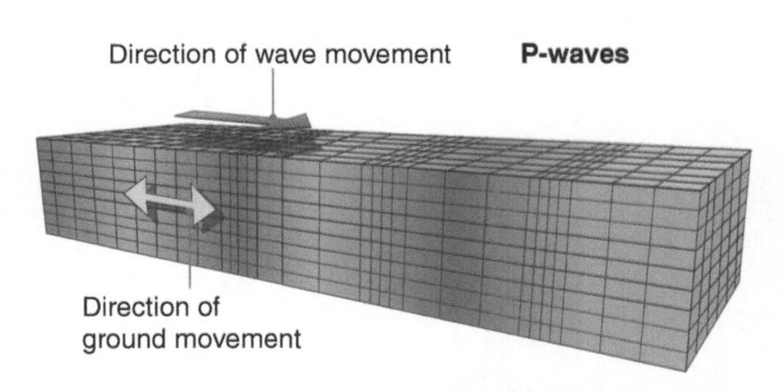

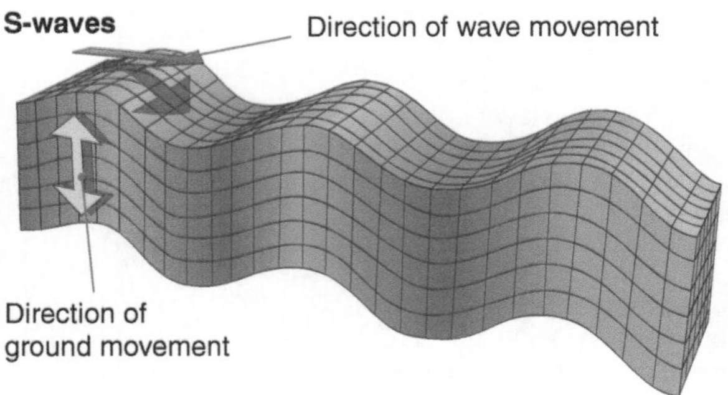

P-waves are compression waves (similar to sound waves in air). P-waves are the fastest moving wave from an earthquake and are therefore the first to arrive at a seismograph. P-waves can travel through all media, whether liquid or solid.

S-waves are transverse waves. They move the ground perpendicular to their direction of travel. They are unable to travel through liquids. They move more slowly than P waves, arriving at a seismograph some time after the P wave.

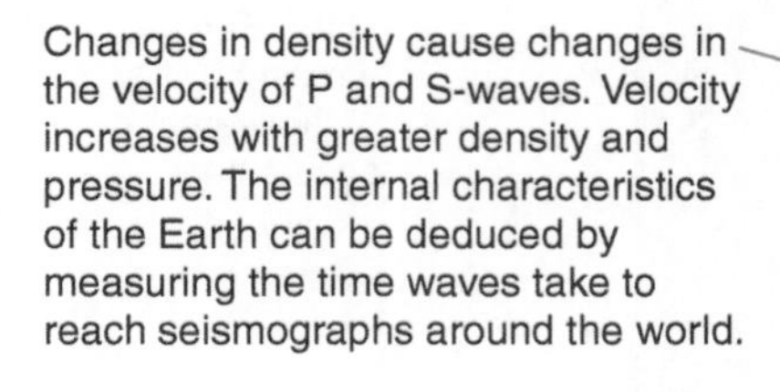

Changes in density cause changes in the velocity of P and S-waves. Velocity increases with greater density and pressure. The internal characteristics of the Earth can be deduced by measuring the time waves take to reach seismographs around the world.

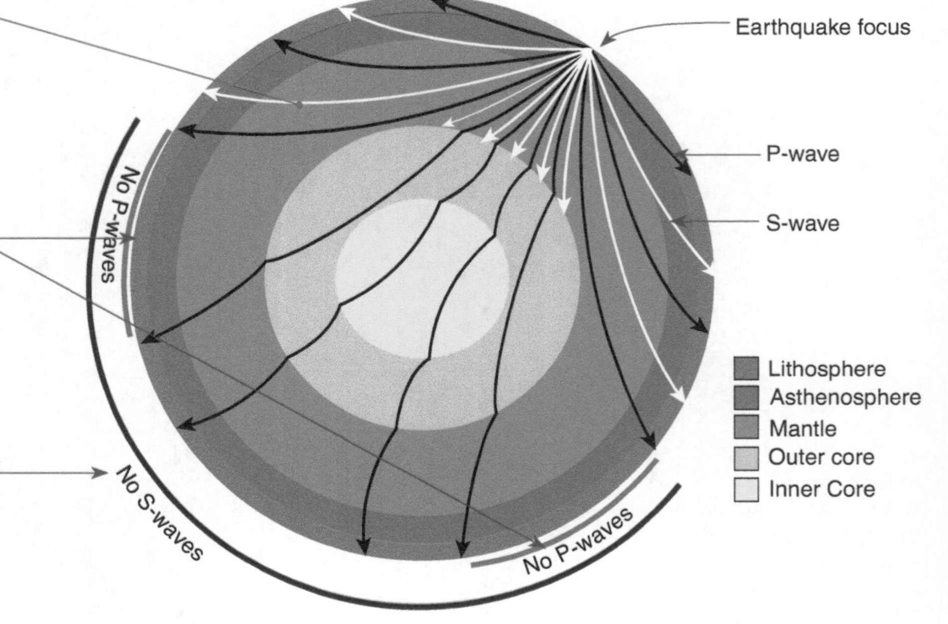

Seismic waves refract (bend) as they pass through the layers of the Earth. Because of this, there is a shadow between 103° and 142° from the earthquake's focus (origin) where no P-waves are detected.

S-waves do not travel through liquids. No S-waves are detected opposite where they would have to pass through the Earth's **outer core**. We can therefore conclude that the outer core must be liquid.

1. Describe two differences between P-waves and S-waves: ______________________

____

____

____

2. What causes the P-wave shadow between 103° and 142° from an earthquake's focus? ______________________

____

____

3. How do we know that the mantle is a solid that behaves like a viscous fluid rather than liquid? ______________________

____

____

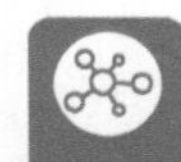

ESS2.A

ISBN: 978-1-98-856693-1

The deep structure of the Earth

- Seismographs record the magnitude of earthquakes. The difference in time it takes for earthquake waves to reach different seismographs can be used to determine the structure of the Earth.
- The table (right) shows the time taken for the first P-waves from a 7.2 magnitude earthquake in Baja California (04 November 2010) to reach seismometers around the world, as determined by a sudden change in the background data.
- The locations of the seismographs are given by the degrees from the Earth's center below the origin of the earthquake (the epicenter). There are 360° in a circle, so 180° would be on the other side of the planet from the epicenter (see following page).

Location (degrees)	Time to reach station (minutes)
2	0.7
15	3.5
25	6.0
38	7.4
50	9.1
65	10.6
77	11.9
89	13.0
101	13.8
113	19.5
122	19.8
140	19.7
151	19.7

4. Graph the data on the grid below as a scatter graph (don't join the points):

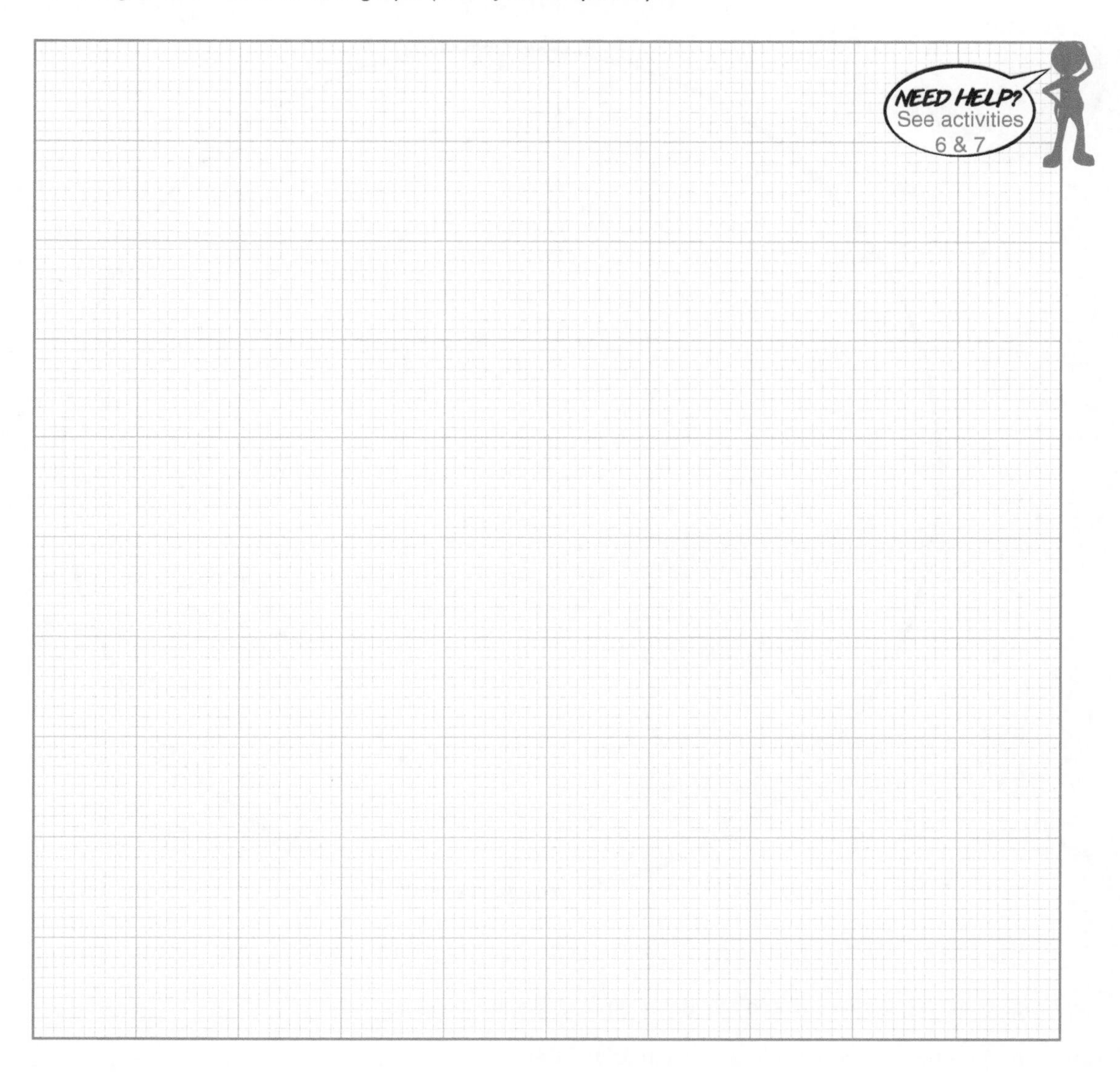

5. There is an anomaly in this data where there appears to be a sudden increase in the time of travel. At what location (in degrees) does this anomaly appear?

____

ISBN: 978-1-98-856693-1

6. (a) If the interior of the Earth was uniform (all the same), what effect would this have on the travel times of seismic waves as they passed through the Earth?

____

____

(b) What does the anomaly we see in the graph tell us? ____

____

7. (a) The circle below represents a cross section through the interior of the Earth. From the line from the center to the point marked A, use a protractor to measure the angle you wrote in question 5. Mark along the circle's edge where this angle cuts the circle. Do this in both directions from point A.

(b) Draw 2 straight lines from point A to the marks you have made on the circle.

(c) Now rotate point A by 30° along the edge of the circle (shown below for you). Repeat (a) and (b) above, measuring and drawing lines from 30°.

(d) Rotate point A another 30°. Repeat this and repeat (a) and (b). Repeat this process until you return to the original point A.

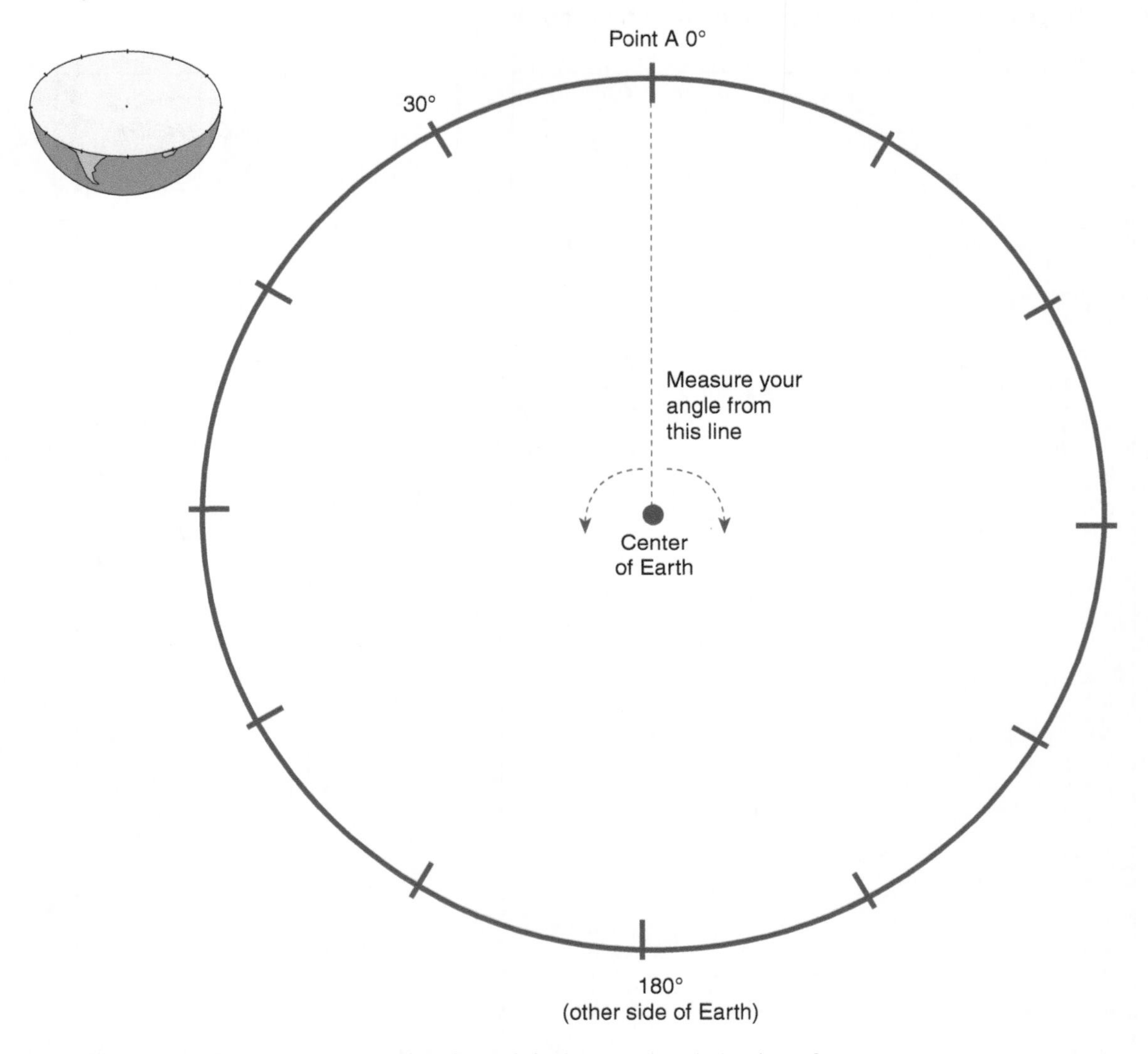

8. (a) What general pattern or shape has been left clear on the circle above? ____

(b) What does this tell us above the structure of the Earth? ____

____

____

____

____

ISBN: 978-1-98-856693-1

9. (a) Measure the radius (in mm) of the circle representing the Earth on the previous page: ____________________

(b) Measure the radius of the inner shape you mapped (in mm): ____________________

(c) Given that the radius of the Earth is 6371 km, at what depth (in km) does the structure appear to be?

____

____

10. The diagram (right) shows the velocity of P-wave and S-waves at different depths in the Earth.

(a) What happens to the velocity of the P-wave at 3000 km depth?

____

(b) What happens to the S-wave at 3000 km depth?

____

(c) Relate the diagram (right) to the diagram of the Earth you mapped on the previous page. In what state (of matter) is the material in the center of the Earth revealed by your mapping? How do you know?

____

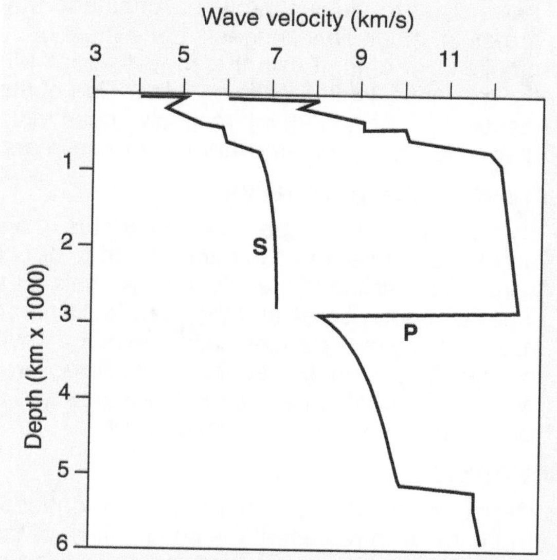

____

____

____

____

____

____

____

The outer structure of the Earth - discovering the Moho

- In 1909, Andrija Mohorovicic was studying seismic waves from an earthquake near Zagreb, Croatia. He plotted a scatter graph of the travel times of P-waves and S-waves from the earthquake epicenter to various seismometers. The fitted trend lines are shown (right). Note $\overline{P}$ and P_n are primary waves. The notation reflects the models Mohorovicic used to calculate the lines. $\overline{S}$ and S_n are secondary waves.
- Mohorovicic noticed 2 distinct sets of P and S waves and a difference in the travel time of the waves.
- His work resulted in the discovery of the Mohorovicic discontinuity.

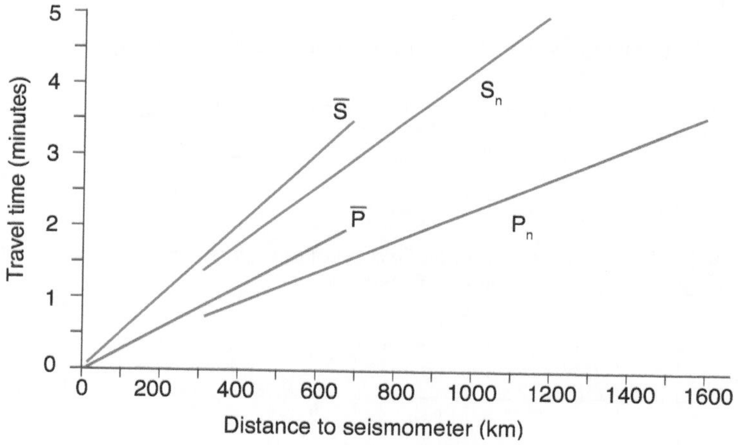

11. (a) At approximately what distance from the epicenter do the wave travel times of the P waves start to diverge from each other, and the S waves start to diverge from each other?

____

(b) Are the waves slowing down or speeding up after this point (compare $\overline{P}$ to P_n and $\overline{S}$ to S_n)? ____________________

(c) What do you think this change in travel time (= change in velocity) might represent? ____________________

____

____

____

ISBN: 978-1-98-856693-1

Magnetic evidence

- The fact that the Earth has a layered structure can be deduced by measuring the direction of the magnetic field in rocks from different locations. Indeed, the simple fact that the Earth has a strong magnetic field is evidence to suggest there must be a liquid **outer core** surrounding an iron **inner core**. This produces a dynamo effect, in which electrical currents in the liquid outer core generate a magnetic field.

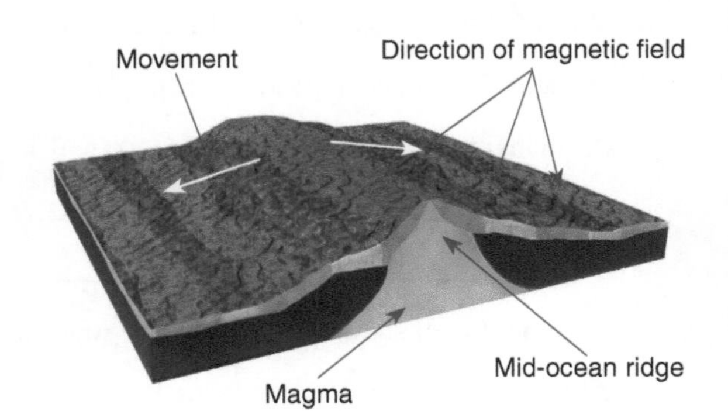

Mid ocean ridges

- The magnetic field aligns magnetic minerals in rocks when they form. The best example of this is along the Mid-Atlantic Ridge. Radiometric dating of rocks on either side of the ridge shows that the youngest rocks are close to the ridge, while those close to the continents of Africa and South America are much older. This suggests there must be an upper, mobile layer of the Earth that moves about. Measurements of the magnetic field of rocks on either side of the ridge show identical patterns and, interestingly, these indicate that the magnetic field reverses every few million years.

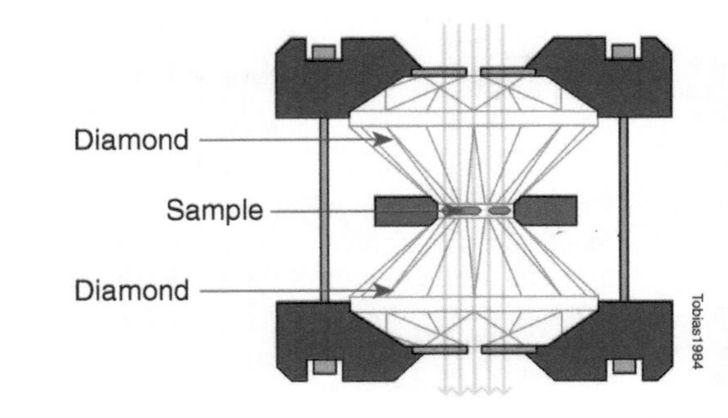

Laboratory experiments

- By measuring the properties of materials under high pressure and temperature and comparing them to data on the Earth's core, it is possible to identify the materials that make up the inner and outer cores and the **mantle**. Experiments like this are done in small devices called diamond anvil cells (right, middle). The sample is squeezed between two diamond anvils while being heated by a laser. Pressures and temperatures can match those of the Earth's core.

H. Raab

Meteorites

- Certain types of meteorites called carbonaceous chondrites (right, bottom) represent the composition of the early Earth. Their composition shows that more nickel and iron should be present in the Earth than we see on the surface or in magma welling up from the mantle. The speed of seismic waves in the mantle do not match what would be expected if more iron and nickel was present. The missing material must therefore be in the core.

12. What evidence is there that the Earth's outer core is liquid? ____________________

13. Explain how the magnetic field orientation in rocks around the Mid-Atlantic Ridge provides evidence that the outer layer of the Earth is a crust of mobile rock:

14. How do laboratory experiments help us understand the structure of the Earth? ____________________

15. How does evidence from meteorites help our understanding of the Earth's composition and structure? ____________________

ISBN: 978-1-98-856693-1

57 Lithosphere and Asthenosphere

Key Question: What are the properties of the layers of the crust and upper mantle, and how are they able to move about?

The lithosphere

- The **lithosphere** (*lithos* = "stone") is made up of the **crust** and the uppermost part of the upper **mantle**. It is both rigid and solid, and broken up into sections called tectonic plates.
- The lithosphere can be divided into continental lithosphere, which contains relatively light minerals, and oceanic lithosphere, which contains much denser minerals. The lithosphere ranges from 400 km thick over the continents to 70 km thick in the oceans.

The asthenosphere

- The **asthenosphere** (*asthenes* = "weak") lies below the lithosphere. This layer of rock is viscous and plastic (semi-fluid) in its behavior. It changes through plastic deformation, slowly moving about and so allowing for movement of the tectonic plates above.
- The asthenosphere is relatively thin, around 100 km thick. The boundary between the lithosphere and asthenosphere is thermal. The lithosphere conducts heat out to the surface, whereas the asthenosphere retains its heat.

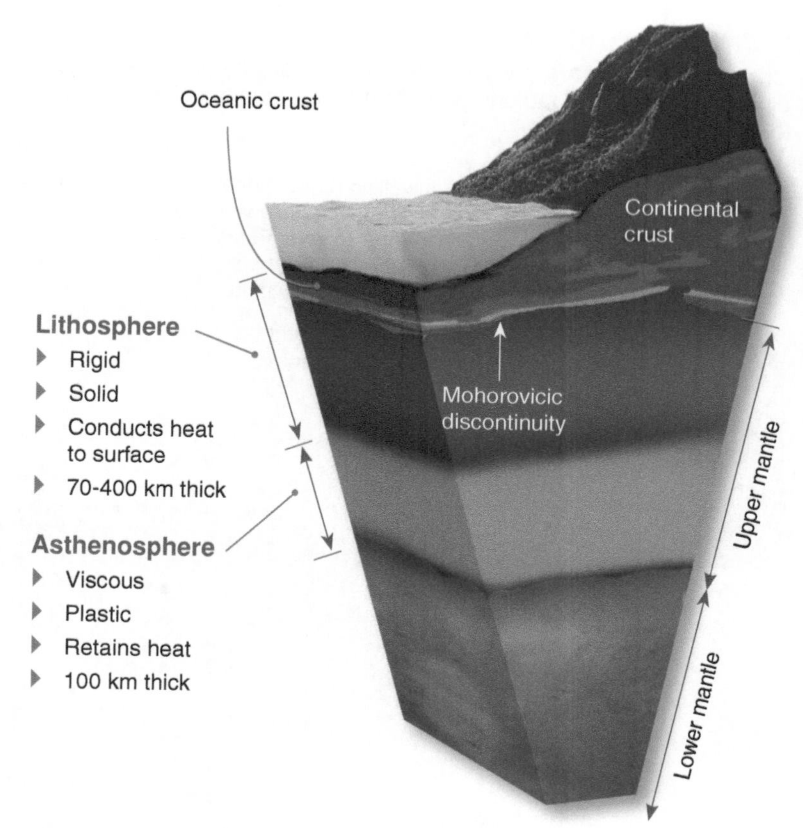

Experiments reveal more detail about the upper layers of the Earth

- In an experiment in New Zealand, geologists exploded charges of TNT to produce seismic waves and recorded their echoes from layers of rock in the Earth. The echoes revealed a jelly-like layer of rock just 10 km thick between the rigid upper layer of the Earth (lithosphere) and the more plastic lower layer (asthenosphere). This research solved the problem of how the lithosphere could move about on the surface of the asthenosphere.

1. (a) Describe the structure of the lithosphere: ______________________

   (b) Describe the structure of the asthenosphere: ______________________

2. Describe the general method that scientists use to study the interior of the Earth: ______________________

3. Why would exploding charges of TNT be a useful (and convenient) way of exploring the internal structure of the Earth?

ISBN: 978-1-98-856693-1

EM

ESS2.A

58 Factors That Shape the Earth

Key Question: How do the interactions between constructive and destructive factors shape the Earth's surface?

Constructive factors

Constructive factors are those that build features on the surface of the Earth. They include deposition of sediments, uplifting, folding and faulting of the land by tectonic activity, and volcanic activity.

Volcanic activity

Volcanic activity builds land. Magma welling up from deep below the **crust** bursts out of cracks in the crust as a volcano. When magma reaches the surface it is called **lava**. Pulverized rock and lava thrown into the air by the eruption of a volcano is called ash. Together, lava and ash can build new land.

Orogeny

Large scale tectonic uplifts are called orogenies and may occur over millions of years. Orogenies are capable of lifting vast areas the Earth's crust above the surface. The Laramide Orogeny in North America, ending about 35 million years ago, formed the Rocky Mountains due to oceanic tectonic plates driving under the western edge of the North American Plate.

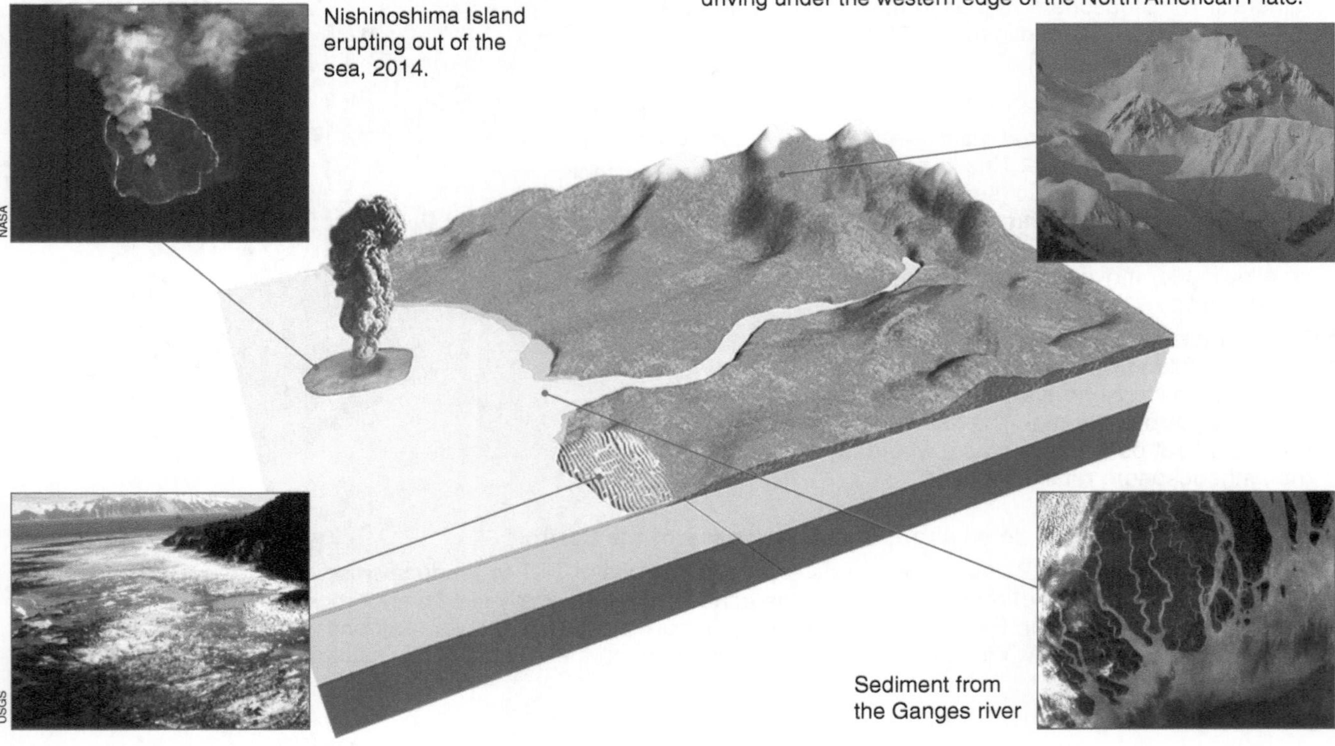

Nishinoshima Island erupting out of the sea, 2014.

Sediment from the Ganges river

Tectonic activity

New land can be formed by uplift during earthquakes. The seabed rising out of the sea extends the beach and adds to the land. The photo above shows Cape Cleare, Montague Island, Prince William Sound, Alaska, after a large earthquake in 1964. The sea originally extended to the base of the cliffs. However the earthquake lifted the seabed by an estimated 10 m, creating a new beach (white area).

Sediment deposition

Deposition is the process of sediments being added to a land mass. Sediments, such as sand, may be carried by streams or rivers, blown by the wind, carried in ice, or slide down hills as landslides. New land can be formed when sediments are deposited in river deltas or near the shore. If the sediments are held in place by tree roots, e.g. mangroves, then the land may become permanent and be slowly extended out to sea.

1. Describe three constructive factors that shape the Earth's surface: ____________________

____

____

____

____

2. Describe three destructive factors that shape the Earth's surface (see next page): ____________________

____

____

____

ESS2.A CE SC

ISBN: 978-1-98-856693-1

Destructive factors

Destructive factors are those that remove features on the Earth's surface. They include mechanisms such as weathering, mass wasting, and erosion.

Weathering

Weathering is caused by physical, chemical, and biological processes. Together, they break down rocks into finer particles. Physical weathering includes factors such as heat and pressure changes. Chemical weathering involves chemical reactions that may dissolve minerals in the rock. Biological weathering occurs when rocks are exposed to the actions of living organisms, such as the organic acids and enzymes produced by microorganisms.

Mass wasting

Mass wasting, or mass movement, is the sudden movement of large volumes of rock and material, as in landslides. All rocks have a finite strength and will fail beyond this. The pull of gravity, combined with weathering and erosion, will eventually cause a hillside to collapse. High cliffs and steep slopes are particularly susceptible to mass wasting. A high cliff undercut by a river or wave action can quickly collapse, causing the edge of the cliff to retreat.

Erosion

Erosion is the loosening and removal of weathered material. A key part of erosion is the transport of materials away from their origin, lowering the mean level of the land. Erosion may occur through the action of water, wind, or glaciers. It is often linked to deposition, as materials are transported and deposited elsewhere, e.g. river deltas.

3. Use the information presented in this activity to draw and label a model of land formation and destruction:

ISBN: 978-1-98-856693-1

59 Feedback in Earth's Systems

Key Question: What feedback systems operate on Earth, and how do they affect the climate?

Feedback on Earth

Feedback occurs when the output of a system is used as input in that system. On Earth, there are many feedback systems, both negative and positive, operating at the same time. **Negative feedback** systems tend to stabilize a system around a mean (average condition), whereas **positive feedback** tends to increase a departure from the mean.

Negative feedback in nature

Feedback systems can be complex and the result of many interacting factors. The diagram below illustrates a simplified negative feedback system involving the production of clouds. Clouds reflect incoming sunlight back into space so have the effect of lowering the Earth's surface temperature.

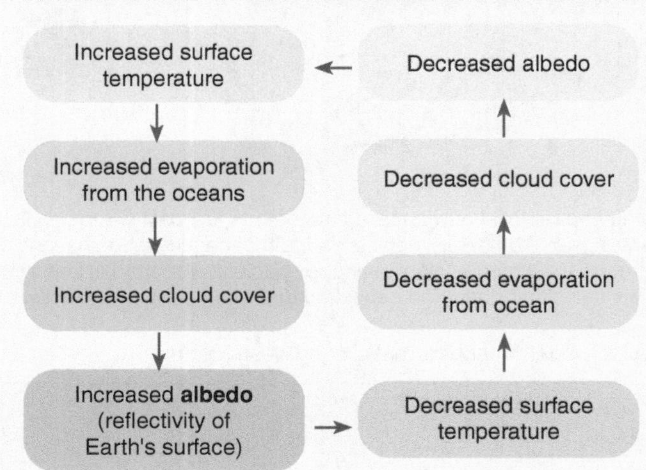

Negative feedback systems help to stabilize the Earth's climate. The evaporation of water from the oceans is affected by temperature, which may be influenced by an increase in solar output or carbon dioxide. The negative feedback of cloud production keeps the cloud cover of the Earth relatively constant.

Positive feedback in nature

Positive feedback systems on Earth tend to drive large scale changes to environments and the climate. The current increase in CO_2 in the atmosphere is driving numerous positive feedback systems. The diagram below illustrates the effect of methane (a greenhouse gas) release from permafrost. As the Earth warms, the permafrost melts, releasing methane which in turn causes the Earth to warm further.

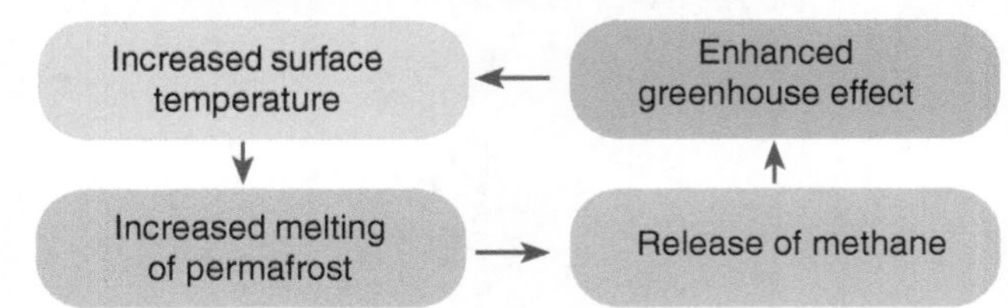

Increased surface temperatures also increase the amount of ice melting and so decreases the Earth's **albedo**:

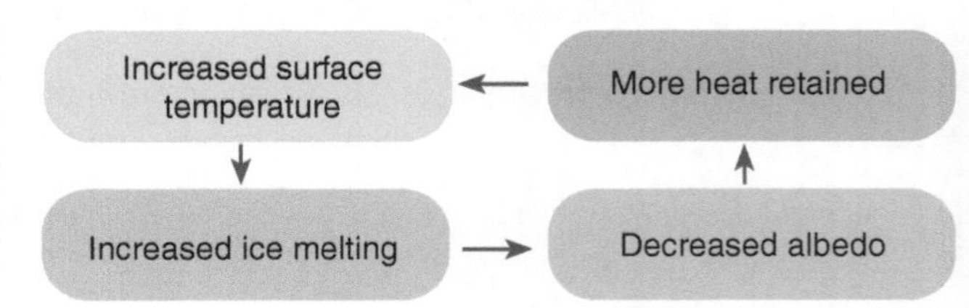

Several positive feedback systems acting at the same time can cause large changes to the climate. Although these are balanced to some extent by negative feedback systems, it is likely there will eventually be a "tipping point" at which a runaway climate change event will occur.

1. What is the difference between positive feedback and negative feedback? ______________________

____

____

____

2. On Earth, negative feedback systems tend to have what effect on the climate? ______________________

____

3. What effect do positive feedback systems have on Earth's climate? ______________________

____

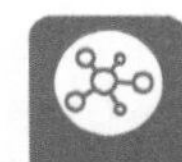

ESS2.A CE SC

ISBN: 978-1-98-856693-1

60 Ice Sheet Melting

Key Question: How can the melting of sea ice cause a positive feedback loop that exposes more heat absorbing surfaces and increases ice sheet melting?

Changes in polar sea ice

- The surface temperature of the Earth is partly regulated by the amount of ice on its surface, which reflects a large amount of heat into space. However, the area and thickness of the polar sea-ice is rapidly decreasing. From 1980 to 2008 the Arctic summer sea-ice minimum almost halved, decreasing by more than 3 million km^2. The 2012 summer saw the greatest reduction in sea-ice since the beginning of satellite recordings.
- This melting of sea ice can trigger a cycle where less heat is reflected into space during summer, warming seawater and reducing the area and thickness of ice forming in the winter. At the current rate of reduction, it is estimated that there may be no summer sea-ice left in the Arctic by 2050.

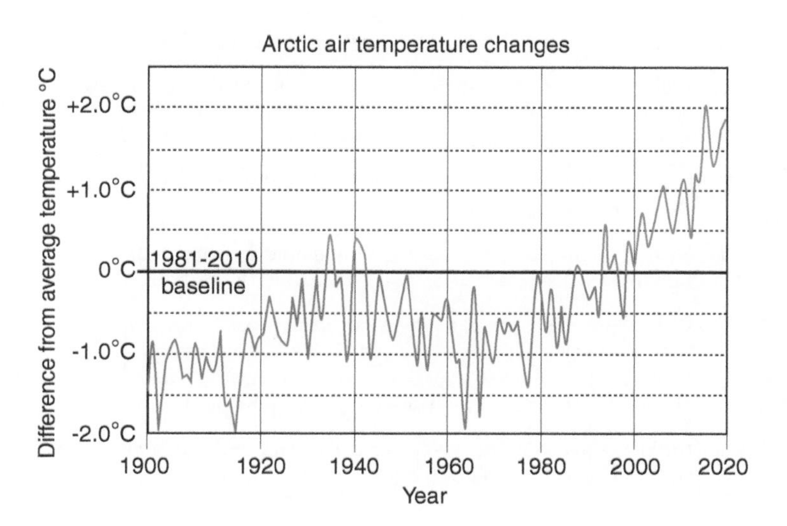

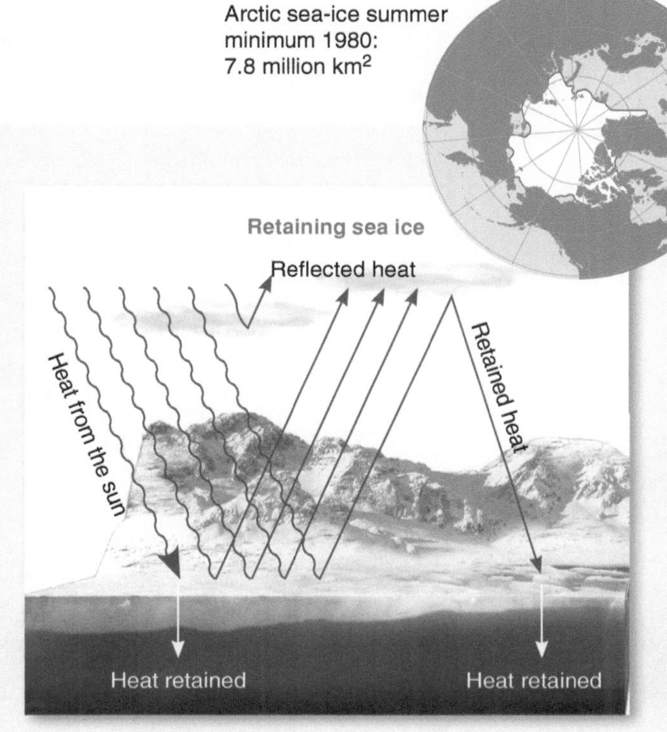

The high **albedo** (reflectivity) of sea-ice helps to maintain its presence. Thin sea-ice has a lower albedo than thick sea-ice. More heat is reflected when sea-ice is thick and covers a greater area. This helps to reduce the sea's temperature.

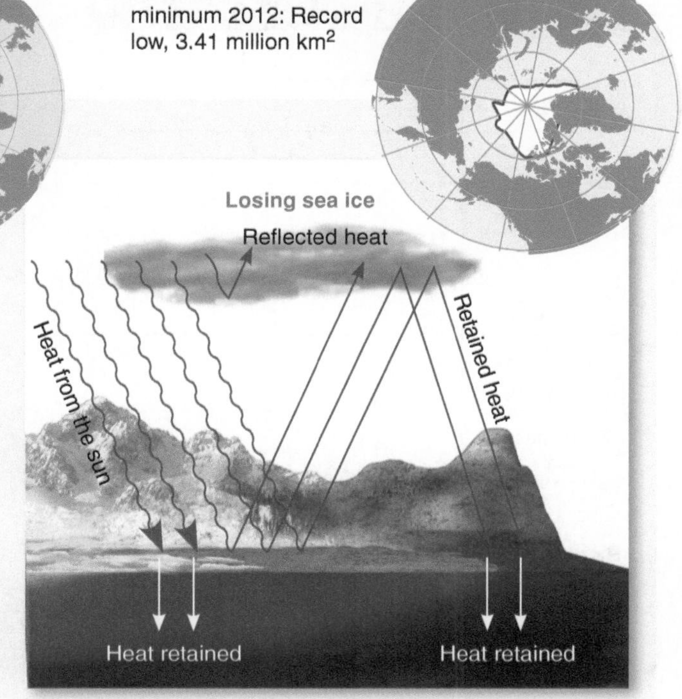

As sea-ice retreats, more, non-reflective surface is exposed. Heat is absorbed instead of reflected, warming the air and water and causing sea-ice to form later in the fall than usual. Thinner and less reflective ice forms, perpetuating the cycle.

1. Calculate the difference in summer sea-ice area between 1980 and 2012: ______________________________

2. How does low sea-ice albedo and volume affect the next year's sea-ice cover? ______________________________

____

____

____

3. What type of feedback system is operating here? ______________________________

ISBN: 978-1-98-856693-1

SC EM ESS2.A

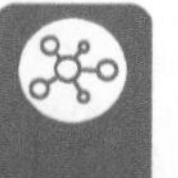

Investigation 5.1 Modeling ice sheet melting

See appendix for equipment list.

1. Work in pairs or groups of three. Collect two 500 mL Florence or Erlenmeyer flasks. Paint one of the flasks black and wrap the second flask in aluminum foil.
2. Weigh out six ice cubes (~60-90 g). Record the weight on the table below. Weigh out a second lot of ice cubes; these must have the same mass as the first.
3. To each flask, add 200 mL of 20°C water and the weighed ice cubes.
4. Seal the flasks and insert a thermometer into each. Record the temperature (time zero) on the table.
5. Place the flasks in a sunny spot and record the temperature every two minutes for 10 minutes. If it is not a sunny day, use a 60W tungsten lamp placed 15 cm from the flasks as the heat source.
6. After 10 minutes, remove the ice cubes and reweigh them. Record the values on the table below.

Thermometer
Aluminum foil
500 mL flask painted black
200 mL of water + 6 ice cubes

Time (minutes)	Temperature - black flask (°C)	Temperature - foil coated flask (°C)
0		
2		
4		
6		
8		
10		
Initial mass of ice (g)		
Final mass of ice (g)		

4. Plot the temperature changes on the grid:
5. Which flask has the greatest albedo?
6. Calculate the change in mass of the ice cubes for both the black and foil covered flasks:
7. Why is it important to start with the same total mass of ice in each flask?
8. What would you change if you wanted to show the effect of more or less sea ice on albedo?
9. Write a conclusion for the investigation:

ISBN: 978-1-98-856693-1

61 Dams and Erosion

Key Question: What is the effect of dams on the wider environment?

Effects of dams on natural systems

Sediment transport

Sediment carried from the upper part of the river is released when the river reaches a lake behind a dam. In the absence of a dam, this sediment may have been laid down on the river bed further downstream, or it may have been carried to the sea and added to the estuary and surrounding beaches.

Fish populations

Dams prevent migratory fish from moving up or down river, either to spawning areas as adults or out to sea as fry (juveniles). Some dams may have built-in fish ladders to allow fish to bypass the dam, but many do not and therefore disrupt life cycles of migratory fish, such as salmon.

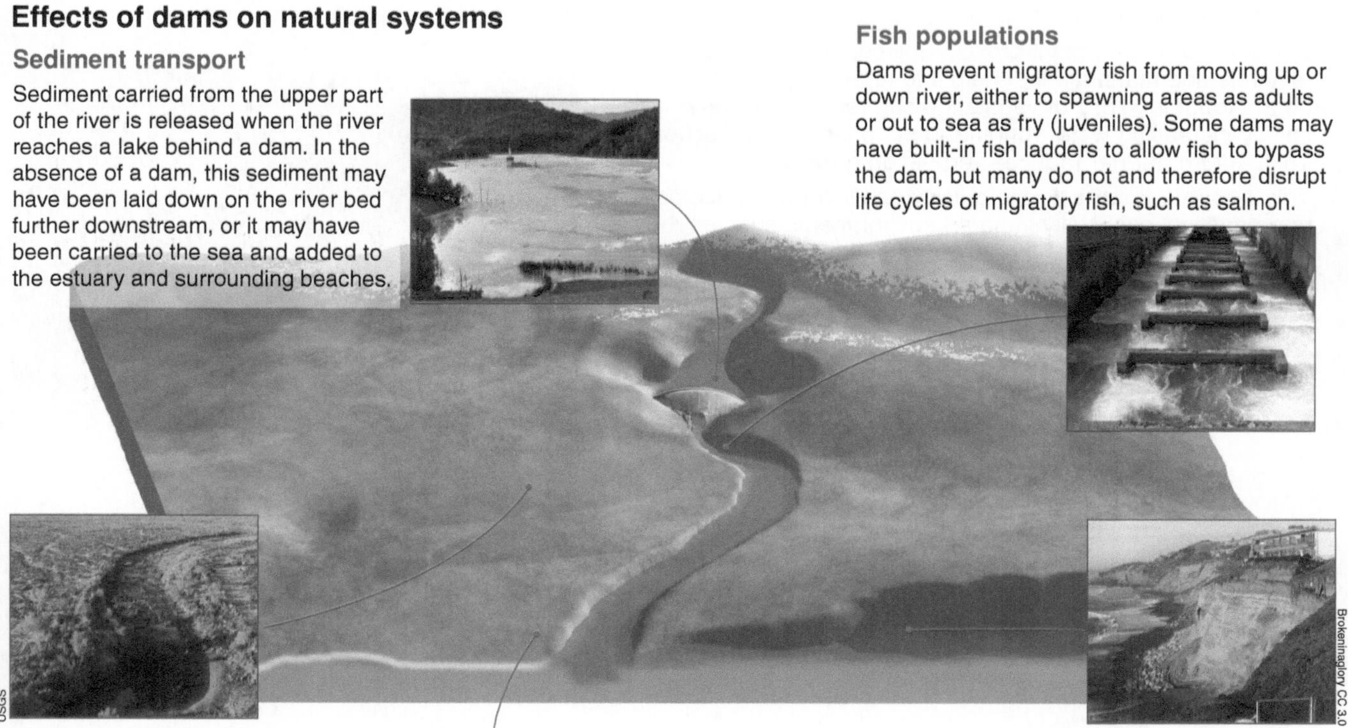

Flood plain fertility

Natural rivers flood and deposit nutrient-rich sediment over the floodplain, as well as modifying the floodplain and river channel, e.g. changing direction or producing layered terraces. The natural flood cycle is disrupted by dams, which are often used for flood control.

Salinity

Reduced water discharge from the river allows seawater to intrude into the delta or estuary. This causes levels of salt in the surrounding soil to rise. In some river deltas, e.g. the Nile delta, once fertile soil can no longer be used due to high salt levels.

Erosion

Without the sediment load, waters down-river of the dam tend to pick up more sediment, eroding the riverbed instead of building it with sediment transported from upstream. Without sediment depositing at the estuary, the sea can quickly erode the foreshore. Sediment is often carried by the sea and deposited on beaches. Without the sediment, the beaches are also quickly eroded.

1. Explain how damming a river to produce a reservoir for irrigation or hydroelectric power can have several unintended "knock-on effects" down-river from the dam:

2. Use the following list to complete the diagram of the downstream effects of damming a river: *reduced sediment, reduced flooding, coastal erosion, ecosystem deterioration, dam, saltwater intrusion, reduced nutrients*:

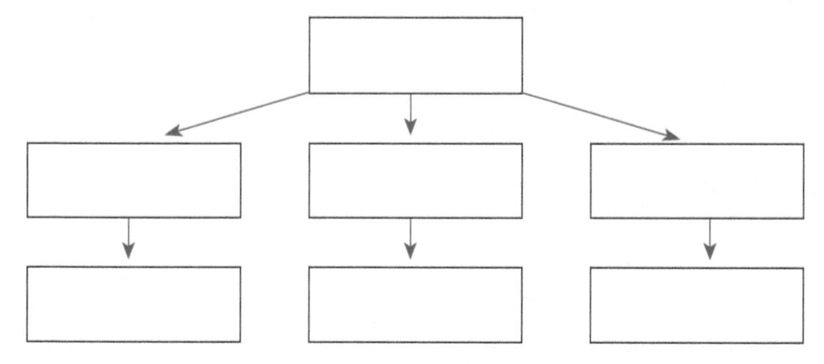

ISBN: 978-1-98-856693-1

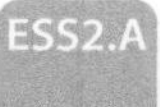

62 Soil Erosion and Feedback

Key Question: How does overexploitation of Earth's natural systems cause the disruption of those systems?

Soil and water loss

- Soil is important for plant growth. Soil contains various minerals and materials that help it to retain water and remain bound together. Loss of vegetation can reduce the water in soil by increasing water runoff and the effect of wind action. This, in turn, further reduces vegetation growth.
- This **positive feedback** can quickly cause land to become unproductive, especially in harsh environments such as the semi-arid rangelands of the south and mid-western United States. Here, overgrazing by livestock removes plant cover and increases evaporation from exposed soils. Rangelands can quickly be turned into dry, sandy deserts as the soils dry out and plant growth is reduced.

USDA

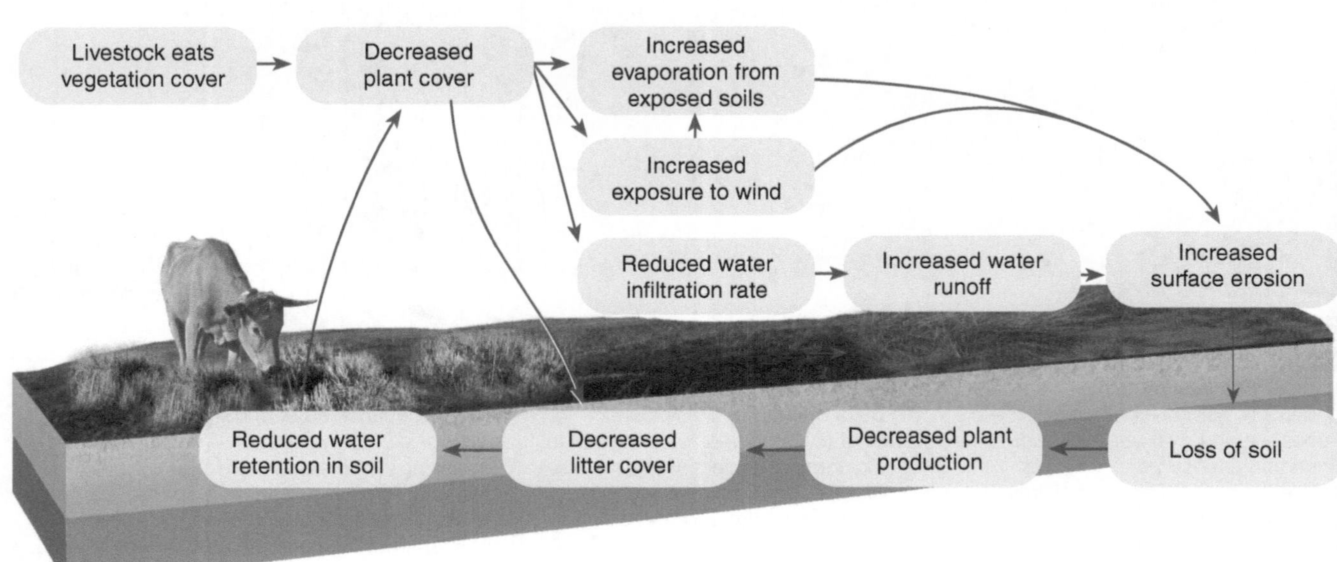

USDA

The Dust Bowl in the 1930s was a result of drought and the removal of vegetation. Soils lying fallow (without crop cover) dried out and blew away, ruining over 14 million hectares of farmland.

Overgrazing has detrimental effects on grasslands, opening space for invasion by weeds and increasing susceptibility to erosion by removing grass cover and trampling seedlings.

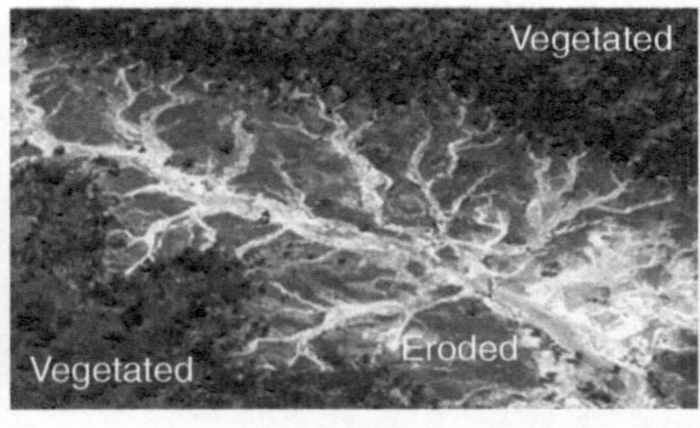

Erosion of soil in forests can result from deforestation. The tree roots maintain soil structure. Without them, the soil washes away, leaving bare earth and unstable ground, as in the catchment pictured above.

1. List three effects of decreased plant cover on soil: ______________________________

____

2. Describe how each of these three effects contributes to soil erosion:

(a) ______________________________

(b) ______________________________

(c) ______________________________

ESS2.A CE SC

ISBN: 978-1-98-856693-1

63 Short and Long Term Changes

Key Question: What changes does the dynamic nature of the Earth cause, over both the short and long term?

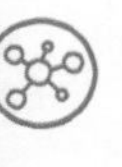

Environmental changes come from three sources: the biosphere, geological forces (crustal movements and plate tectonics), and cosmic forces (the movement of the Moon around the Earth and the Earth and planets around the Sun).

- All three forces can cause cycles, steady states, and trends (directional changes) in the environment. Environmental trends, such as climate cooling, cause long term changes in communities.
- Some short term cycles, such as tides, or day and night, may influence local environmental patterns. Others, e.g. seasons, can cause large scale environmental changes, such as the advance and retreat of the polar sea-ice every winter and summer.

Every winter, the freezing of the sea around Antarctica almost doubles the continent's effective size.

Time scale and geographic extent of environmental change

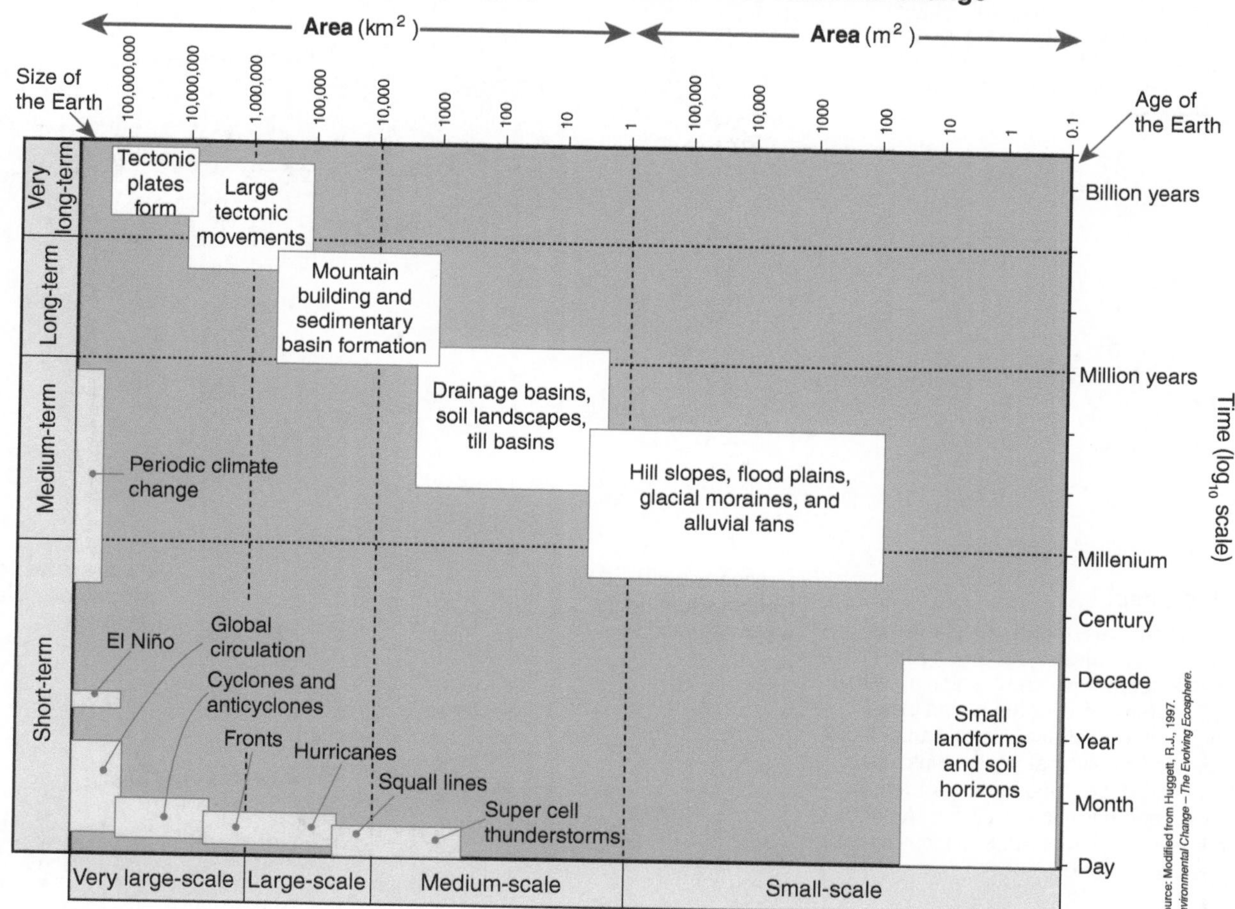

1. Identify the geologic event that is the largest, and takes the longest amount of time: ____________________

____

2. Identify two very large scale events that take a relatively short amount of time to occur: ____________________

____

3. How long does it take for a soil landscape to form? ____________________

____

ISBN: 978-1-98-856693-1

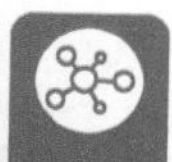

64 Short-Term Changes to the Earth

Key Question: How do cyclic, and periodic sporadic changes, such as volcanic eruptions, affect the Earth in the short term?

The Earth is constantly changing. Some of these changes occur in short term cycles, such as the El Niño Southern Oscillation and seasonal changes over the year. Others are sudden but short lived events that cause immediate but non-cyclic changes, such as volcanic eruptions.

El Niño Southern Oscillation

- Interactions between atmospheric and the oceanic circulation are at the core of most global climate patterns. The El Niño-Southern Oscillation cycle (ENSO) is the most prominent of these global oscillations, causing weather patterns involving increased rain in specific places but not in others. It is one of the many causes of drought.

Normal climatic conditions

In non-El Niño conditions (right), a low pressure system over Australia draws the southeast trade winds across the eastern Pacific from a high pressure system over South America. These winds drive the warm South Equatorial Current towards Australia's coast. Off the coast of South America, upwelling of cold water brings nutrients to the surface.

Rising warm moist air associated with heavy rainfall and low pressure.

Descending warm air associated with high pressure and dry conditions.

Southeast trade winds

South Equatorial Current

Thermocline

Accumulation of warm water

Upwelling of cold, nutrient-rich waters into shallow warm surface waters.

El Niño effect

In an El Niño event (right), the pressure systems over Australia and South America are weakened or reversed, beginning with a rise in air pressure over the Indian Ocean, Indonesia, and Australia. Warm waters block the nutrient upwelling along the west coast of the Americas. El Niño brings drought to Indonesia and northeastern South America, while heavy rain over Peru and Chile causes the deserts to bloom.

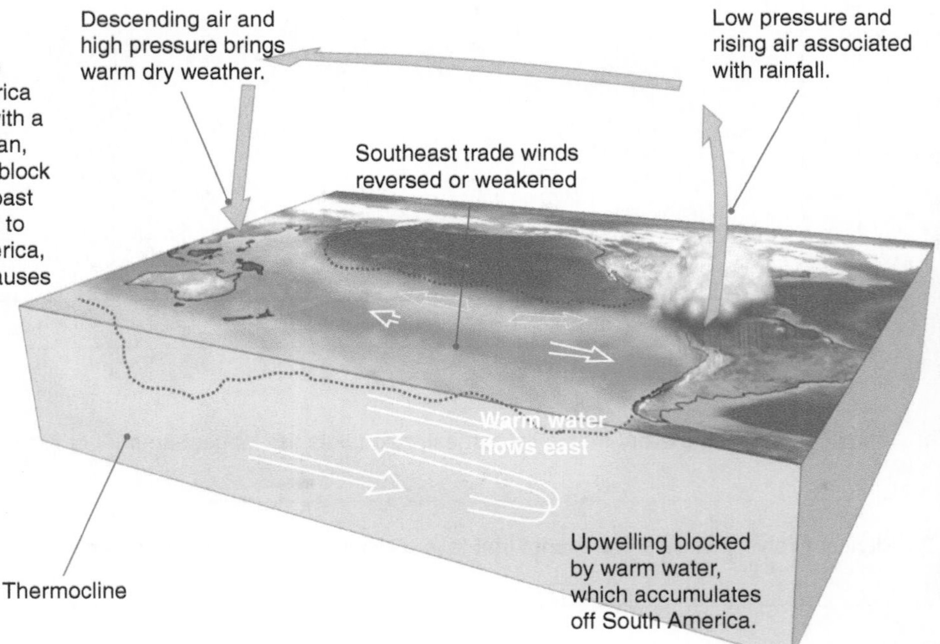

ISBN: 978-1-98-856693-1

Volcanic eruptions and climate

- Large volcanic eruptions can affect the global climate by blasting ash and aerosols into the atmosphere.
- A well documented example of this is the eruption of Mount Pinatubo, located on the island of Luzon in the Philippines. Eruptions began on June 3 1991, after almost 500 years of virtual inactivity. On June 15, after many large explosions, Mount Pinatubo entered its final eruptive phase, blasting 10 km^3 of ash, 34 km into the atmosphere. The Earth's climate was severely affected by Pinatubo's eruption. Over the course of the eruption, some 17 million tonnes of SO_2 and 10 km^3 of ash were released into the atmosphere. The ash caused an almost 10% reduction in sunlight reaching the Earth's surface over the following year, and global temperatures dropped by 0.5°C over the following 2-3 years. Ozone levels reached some of their lowest recorded levels.
- Similarly, the eruption of El Chichon in Mexico, 1982, lowered the global temperature by 0.5°C over two years, emitting about half the SO_2 volume of Pinatubo.
- In the 1800s, the eruptions of Tambora and Krakatoa in Indonesia caused severe climate effects in places as far away as Europe and North America. Effects included early snow falls and such cold wet weather that 1816, the year after the eruption of Tambora, was called the year without a summer.

Mount Pinatubo eruption, 1991

1. Describe two ways in which volcanic eruptions can affect the Earth's climate: ______

2. What caused the "year without a summer"? ______

3. (a) What year did Mt Pinatubo erupt?: ______

   (b) What volume of ash and SO_2 were ejected from the volcano? ______

   (c) What effect did this have on the Earth's climate? ______

4. (a) Describe the events that cause El Niño conditions: ______

   (b) What is the effect of El Niño on the climate of the western coast of South America? ______

   (c) What is the effect of El Niño on the climate of Indonesia and Australia? ______

ISBN: 978-1-98-856693-1

- Recall that the orbit of the Earth changes over long periods of time, from a mostly circular to a more elliptical orbit, that the axial tilt changes from between 24.5° and 22° relative to the Sun, and that the precession of the Earth (see p.98) causes changes to the timing of the seasons.
- These are very long term cycles that last tens of thousands of years, and when certain parts of the cycles line up, e.g. maximum axis tilt and eccentricity, they affect the amount of solar radiation the Earth receives and have the ability to trigger **ice ages** or **glaciations.**
- These cycles are independent of the Sun's energy output. However, there are shorter cycles of solar activity and energy output that may last hundreds of years that appear to affect the Earth's climate. Even so, the difference in energy output from the Sun over these cycles is minimal (about 0.1%).

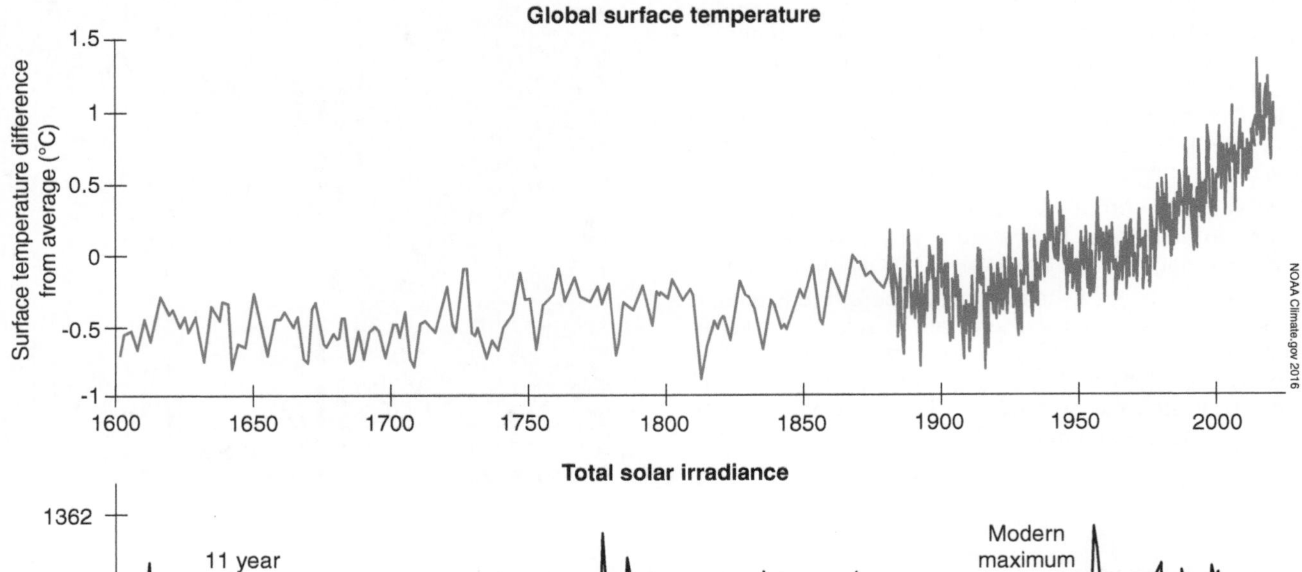

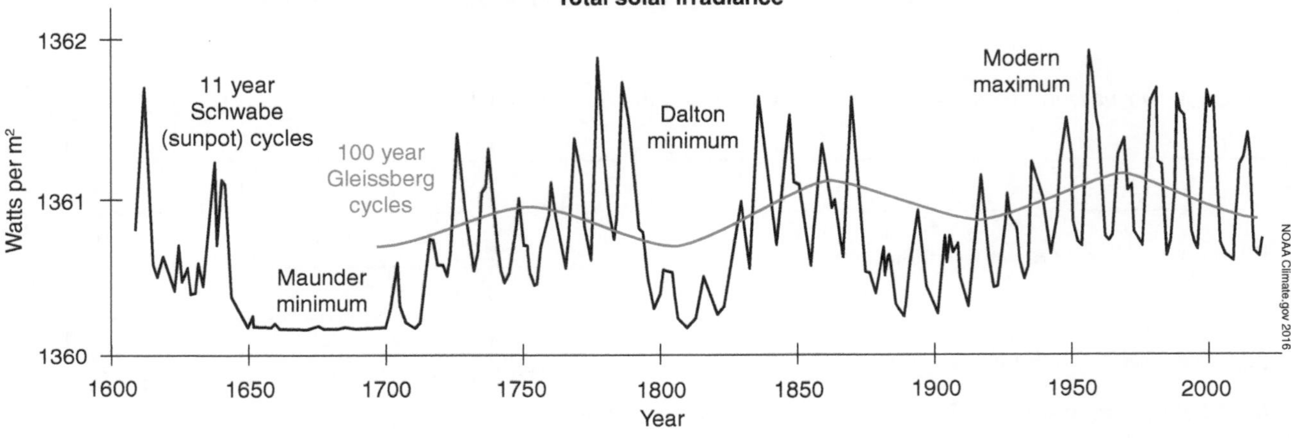

5. What would the effect of Earth having a more elliptical orbit have on the climate?

6. Does there appear to be any correlation between the energy output of the Sun (solar irradiance) and the Earth's temperature between 1600 and 1900? Explain:

7. How can we (almost) definitively say that the current increase in the Earth's surface temperature is not linked to solar activity?

ISBN: 978-1-98-856693-1

65 Long-Term Changes to the Earth

Key Question: What changes occur to the Earth's environment over hundreds, to millions of years?

Some changes to the Earth happen on such vast time scales that they are not perceivable to humans. Changes may take place over thousands to million of years. Some changes appear to be cyclical, such as the advance and retreat of **ice ages** and **glaciations**, while others are continuous, such as continental drift.

Ice ages and glaciations

The Earth has gone through five ice ages, i.e. long periods of time when massive ice sheets covered large parts of the globe. The latest ice age began about 2.7 million years ago and is still ongoing. Within an ice age, there are periods of warmer climate conditions called **interglacials**, such as the present. The cooler periods of time are called glacials. These tend to last longer than the interglacials. The current interglacial began about 12,000 years ago. Ice cores (right) confirm the advance and recession of glacials.

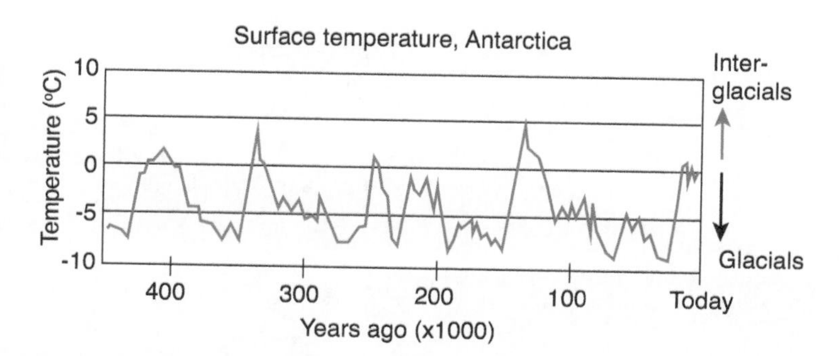

Within ice ages, there can be several periods of warming and cooling. What causes these changes is not fully understood, but they may be due to changes in carbon dioxide and methane in the atmosphere, changes in solar output, and changes in the Earth's orbit.

The glaciers that spread across much of the Northern Hemisphere during the last glaciation began to retreat about 20,000 years ago. As they melted, the flood of fresh water into the oceans shut down ocean currents, which caused warming in the Southern Hemisphere, releasing CO_2 from the seas and warming the planet.

In North America during the last glaciation, ice covered all of Canada and extended south as far as the Upper Midwest, Idaho, Montana, and Washington. Evidence of this glaciation includes the grooves and U-shaped valleys formed as the glaciers advanced and retreated.

Continental drift and ocean circulation

- Movement of the Earth's tectonic plates drives continental drift (the movement of the continents). Over millions of years, the continents have split and converged many times and this has had major effects on the Earth's climate. Currently, Antarctica is surrounded by the Southern Ocean, through which flows the Antarctic Circumpolar Current. The Antarctic Circumpolar Current did not exist until the Antarctic continent separated fully from South America. It prevented warm waters from the Atlantic, the Pacific, and the Indian Oceans reaching the Antarctic. As a result, Antarctica rapidly developed a huge ice sheet that remains in place today.
- Until about 5 million years ago, North and South America were not connected. The gap between them, called the Central American Seaway, allowed tropical waters to flow between the Atlantic and the Pacific Oceans. The formation of the Central American isthmus blocked this flow and may have contributed to the beginning of the ice age, 2.7 million years ago.
- The collision of India with Europe raised the Himalayas, changing the way air currents moved about the globe. The Himalayas affect the seasonal rains in India by causing warm, moist air to rise. The cooling air then loses its moisture as precipitation as it moves south, causing the monsoons. The rain shadow effect of the Himalayas produces the large deserts of the Gobi and the Taklamakan.

40 million years ago the land bridge between Antarctica and South America prevented polar circulation of the ocean.

The appearance of the Central American isthmus prevented the flow of water between the Atlantic and the Pacific Oceans through the Central American Seaway.

ISBN: 978-1-98-856693-1

Mountain building and rain shadows

- Mountains affect climate by deflecting air currents to higher levels of the atmosphere. As the air rises, it cools and moisture in it condenses to fall as rain, producing a wet, cool climate. Having lost its moisture, the air passes over the mountain and descends as dry air, picking up moisture and producing a warm, dry climate. This effect is called a rain shadow and it occurs anywhere there are tall mountain ranges that block air flow.
- Mountain building via plate tectonics (orogeny) has occurred in many parts of the world near plate boundaries. Mountain building is a long term process, and can last tens of millions of years, thus producing long term climatic changes on large areas of land.

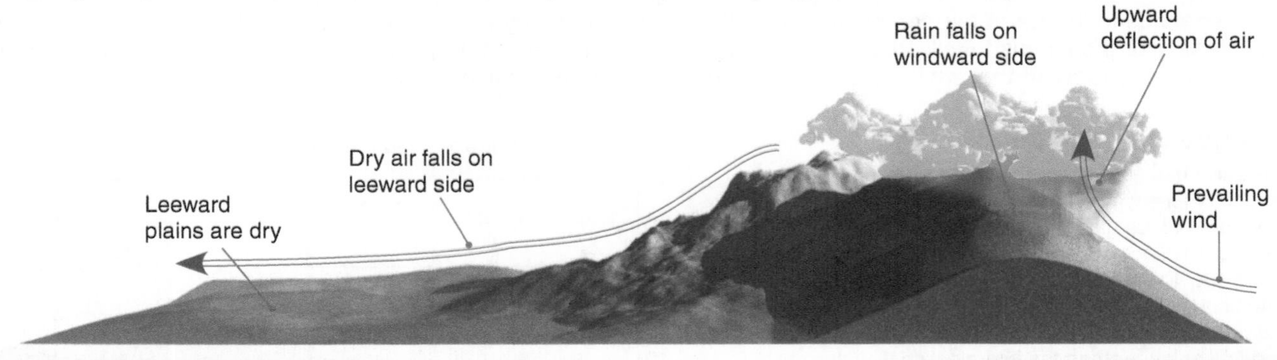

Rain shadows can cause some extreme effects. In Chile, the Andes block moist winds from the Amazon basin, producing the Atacama desert, the driest non-polar desert on Earth. The Atacama is estimated to be 3 million years old.

The Southern Alps in New Zealand produce one of the most extreme rain shadows in the world. On the western slopes, rainfall can reach 8900 mm a year. On the Eastern slopes, rainfall drops to just 380 mm in some areas.

Death Valley in California is in the rain shadow of the Sierra Nevada mountains. The valley has recorded the hottest temperatures on Earth (56.7°C). Death Valley formed after the last glacial period and receives just 60 mm of rain a year.

1. (a) When did the current ice age begin? ______

   (b) When did the last glacial period end? ______

   (c) What is the term for the current period of generally warm climatic conditions? ______

2. What are some possible reasons for the periodic occurrence of glacial periods? ______

3. Using examples, explain how continental drift can affect ocean currents and the effect this can have on climate:

4. Using examples, explain how mountain ranges can have long term effects on local climate: ______

ISBN: 978-1-98-856693-1

66 Review Your Understanding

Key Question: What processes continually shape the Earth's surface?

▸ The surface of the Earth is constantly changed by factors such as erosion, mountain building, and volcanic activity. In this chapter, you have studied the effect of these on the Earth's surface.

1. (a) List some destructive factors that shape the Earth's surface. What do these tend to do to the surface of the Earth?

   (b) List some constructive factors that shape the Earth's surface. What do these tend to do to the surface of the Earth?

NASA

   (c) The rocks making up Mt. Roraima in Venezuela (right) are 2 billion year old sandstones laid down on the bottom of what was once an ancient sea. Use constructive and destructive forces to explain Mt. Roraima's formation:

Yosemite

2. On the photograph (right), identify, label, and describe the factors that are changing the landscape:

   (a)

   (b)

   (c)

   (d)

3. Feedback loops are important drivers that both stabilize and change the climate.

   (a) What kind of feedback loop stabilizes the climate? Give an example:

   (b) What kind of feedback loop causes the climate to change? Give an example:

ISBN: 978-1-98-856693-1

67 Summing Up

1. The diagram below shows the velocity of two types of seismic waves at different depths in the Earth.

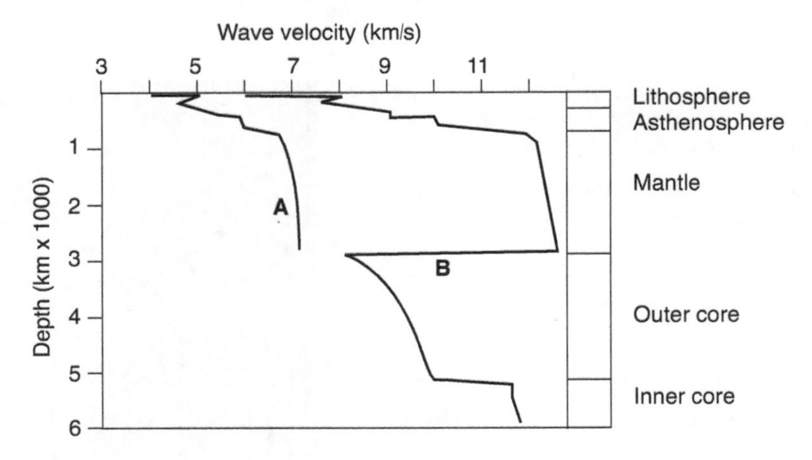

(a) Does line A show a P or S wave? ______

(b) Does line B show a P or S wave? ______

(c) How can you tell? ______

______

______

______

(d) Explain why the velocity of the waves increases with depth through the mantle: ______

______

______

2. Draw a line on the graphs below to show negative feedback over time and positive feedback over time:

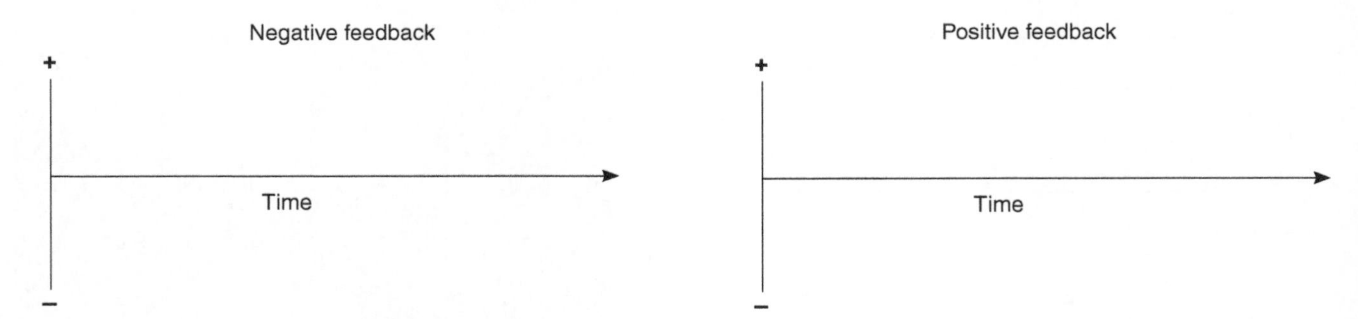

3. Study the graph below of Earth's temperature over the last 1000 years. Label the regions of apparent negative feedback and of apparent positive feedback:

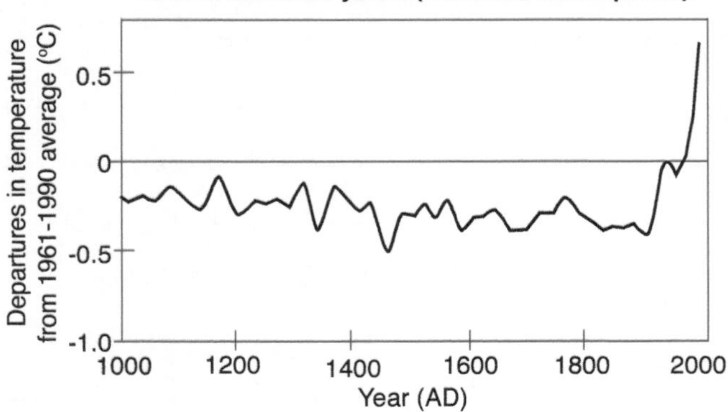

ISBN: 978-1-98-856693-1

4. The graph below shows the extent to which each component adds or removes heat to or from the atmosphere (shown as a gain or loss in temperature).

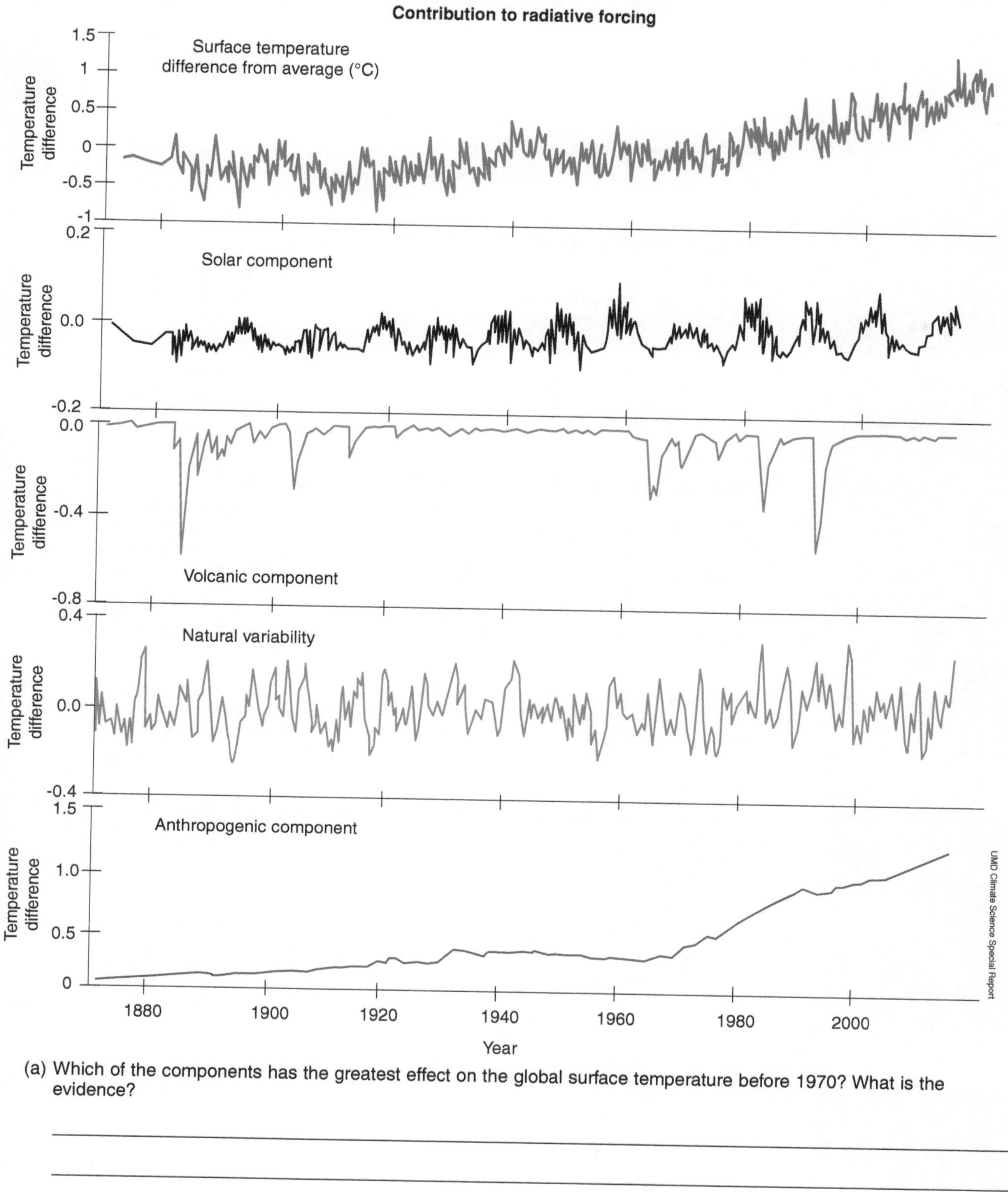

(a) Which of the components has the greatest effect on the global surface temperature before 1970? What is the evidence?

____

____

____

____

(b) Which of the components has the greatest effect on the global surface temperature after 1970? What is the evidence?

____

____

____

ISBN: 978-1-98-856693-1

Plate Tectonics

Luka Adikashvili CC 3.0

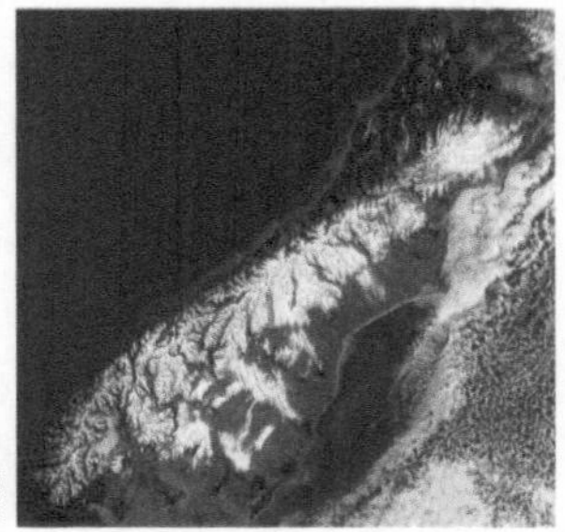

NASA

Anchoring Phenomenon

On the move: How do the continents move? — 68 74

What drives the movement in the mantle?

- ☐ 1 Describe the process of radioactive decay. Understand that both radioactive decay and heat left over from the Earth's formation provides energy that drives mantle convection, which carries heat from Earth's interior to the surface. — 69

- ☐ 2 Investigate the change in temperature with depth. Use graphs and spreadsheets to plot temperature change with depth, and use this as evidence for the Earth having layers with specific properties. — 70

How do plate tectonics shape the Earth's surface?

- ☐ 4 Explain how the theory of plate tectonics demonstrates that movement on Earth's surface is a result of convection in the mantle. Use evidence, including the age of rocks, to show that specific locations on the surface of the Earth have moved hundreds or thousands of kilometres over tens of thousands to millions of years, and are still moving. — 71

- ☐ 5 Use the presence of stationary hotspots to show the direction of movement of the plates. — 71

- ☐ 6 Use the locations of earthquakes and volcanoes as evidence for the positions of the plate boundaries. Describe the different kinds of plate boundary and their differences. Develop a model to show how convection currents in the mantle are responsible for the movement of the tectonic plates. — 71 72 75

- ☐ 7 Explain that earthquakes result from movement along plate boundaries and that volcanoes generally form along the edge of plate boundaries. Know that the amount of material lost at convergent boundaries is roughly balanced by the amount formed at divergent boundaries. — 72

- ☐ 8 Use a model based on evidence to illustrate how the continents have moved over time, and determine their locations millions of years in the past. Use models to show how evidence such as sediments can be used to determine past movements of continents. — 73

68 On the Move

Key Question: How do the continents move?

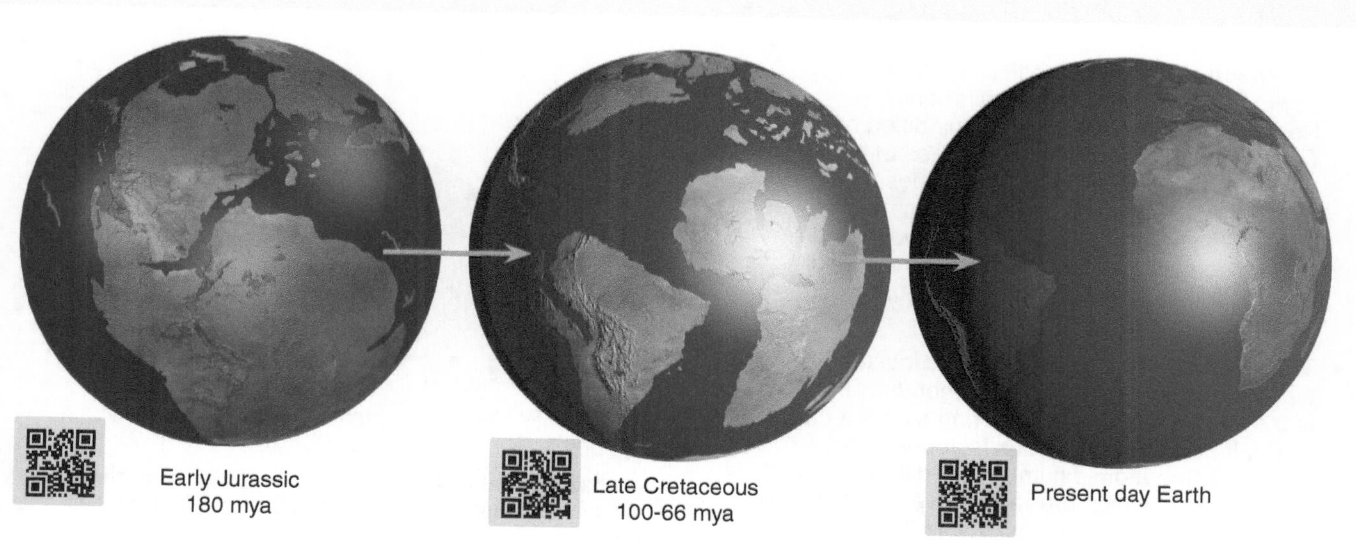

▸ The image on the far right above shows Earth as we know it today. The image on the left shows the Earth as we understand it looked during the early Jurassic period, about 180 million years ago. This is based on evidence collected over the last hundred years. The continents have separated and rejoined many times, over the billions of years of Earth's history. **Continental drift** describes the movement of the continents over the surface of the Earth. It was not until the 1960s that the theory of **plate tectonics**, which describes this movement, was confirmed. There is still a lot we do not understand about how this occurs, but clearly it involves massive energy sources beneath the Earth.

1. Write down five things that you know (or think you know) about continental drift in the space below:

   (a) ______________________________

   (b) ______________________________

   (c) ______________________________

   (d) ______________________________

   (e) ______________________________

2. Discuss your ideas with other people in your class. Do they have different ideas from you? Can they add to your current knowledge? Summarize any ideas you had not already thought of:

   ____

   ____

   ____

   ____

3. The curve below represents the surface of the Earth. Draw lines to show the layers of the Earth and to represent what mechanisms you think exist that move the continents around on the surface.

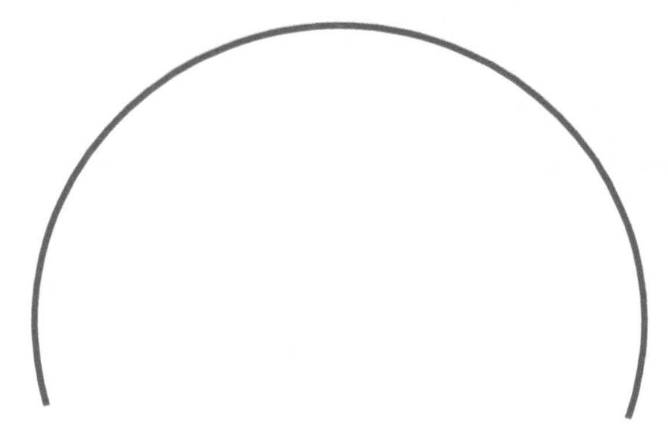

ISBN: 978-1-98-856693-1

69 The Nuclear Fires

Key Question: Where does the heat in the interior of the Earth come from?

- **Radioactive decay** is the fission (breaking down) of large atoms into smaller ones. Radioactive decay occurs in many different ways but usually involves the release of highly energetic particles, e.g. alpha particles, or electromagnetic radiation, e.g. gamma waves. These high energy particles and waves collide with objects around them, releasing heat and causing the temperature of the surrounding material to increase.
- The material that formed the Earth included elements such as uranium and thorium. Uranium is the heaviest naturally occurring element on Earth. It occurs in numerous isotopes (atoms with the same atomic number but different atomic masses) all of which are radioactive. U-238 is the most common and the most stable it has a half life of about 4.5 billion years (about the age of the Earth).
- When a U-238 atom decays, it produces a helium nucleus (which is an alpha particle) and a thorium atom. The thorium atom itself is unstable and will also decay. There is a decay chain that continues until a stable atom of lead is produced. Heat is released at each stage and this heats the interior of the planet.

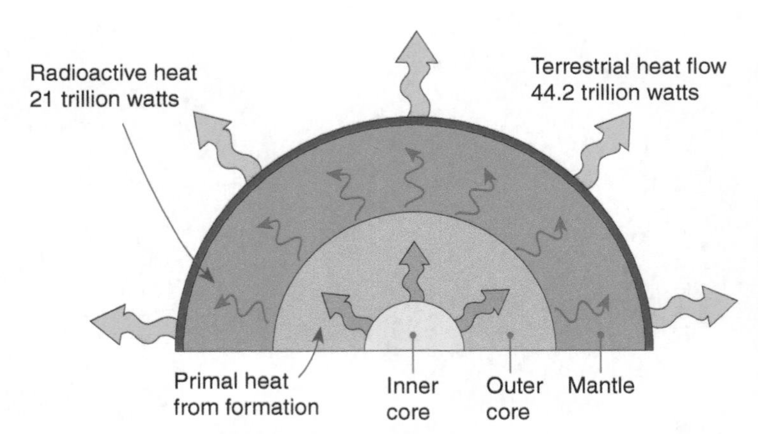

About half the heat radiated by the Earth comes from the decay of radioactive elements. Most of the rest comes from heat left over from the Earth's formation.

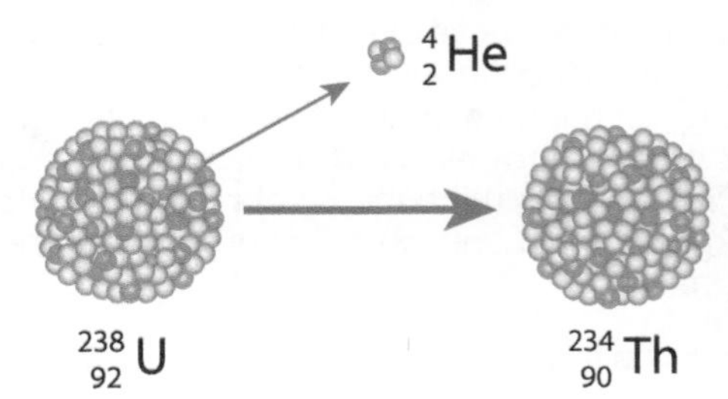

Uranium-238 has a half life of 4.5 billion years and decays to thorium-234. Thorium-234 has a half life of just 24.5 days.

Radioactive decay heats the interior of the planet. Some of this heat powers volcanic activity, helping to form volcanoes.

Earthquakes result from **convection currents** (produced by heat) moving Earth's interior and shifting surface layers.

The movement of Earth's **mantle** causes parts of the surface to collide, rising up to produce mountains, e.g. the Himalayas.

1. What is radioactive decay? ______

2. (a) How much heat is radiated by the Earth? ______

   (b) How much of this is produced from radioactive decay? ______

3. What is emitted when a uranium-238 atom decays? ______

4. Explain the importance of radioactive decay to geological processes, such as plate tectonics:

ISBN: 978-1-98-856693-1

70 The Heat of the Earth

Key Question: How does the temperature change as we go deeper into the Earth?

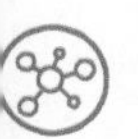

The Kola Superdeep Borehole

- There have been many attempts to drill as deep into the Earth as possible. Some of today's oil wells reach 10,000 m below the surface. Drilling to such a depth produces many problems, including those due to the effects of the high temperatures at such depths.
- Drilling boreholes into the Earth can produce a lot of useful scientific data, including the type of rock encountered and even data about past climates. The simplest, but often most interesting, is how the temperature changes with depth.
- In 1970, a scientific project was started on the Kola peninsula in Russia to drill as far as possible into the Earth's crust. The Kola Superdeep Borehole eventually reached 12,262 m before problems with high temperatures and equipment made it impossible to drill any deeper. At that depth, the temperature measured 180°C.
- Drilling was shut down in 1995, but the borehole is still the deepest artificial point on Earth. Some oil drilling projects have drilled longer boreholes but they have not reached as deep into the ground.
- One of the most interesting finds of the project was the discovery of water in the rocks nearly 7 km down. Until then, no one had thought water would exist at such a depth.
- Fossils of microscopic plankton were found 6 km down.
- Studies of seismic waves (generated by earthquakes and explosions) indicated a transition between granite above and basalt below ~7 km. Drilling found this was not the case.

The borehole has long been welded shut...

Rakot13 CC3.0

...and the buildings abandoned

Bigest CC3.0

1. (a) The data below shows the temperature data for the Kola Superdeep Borehole. Plot the data on the grid provided. When plotting depth data, the depth should be plotted descending on the y axis.

NEED HELP? See Activities 6 & 8

Depth (m)	Temperature (°C)
0	–
200	16.80
400	18.21
600	19.79
800	21.47
1000	23.32
1200	25.24
1400	27.20
1600	30.00
1800	32.46
2000	35.00
2200	37.84
2400	40.24
2600	42.90
2800	45.80
3000	47.91
3200	50.00
3400	54.51
3600	58.00
3800	61.20
4000	62.73
4200	65.10
4400	68.41

ISBN: 978-1-98-856693-1

EM ESS2.A

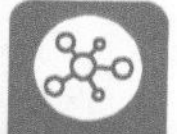

(b) Describe the shape of the graph and what it shows: ____________________

(c) Draw a line of best fit through the data and use it to determine the rate of temperature increase per meter:

(d) What would you expect to happen to the temperature if depth was increased? ____________________

2. The limits of the graph stop you from adding the temperature of the of the Kola borehole at 12,262 m (180°C). However, this can be done using a spreadsheet such as Microsoft Excel.

(a) Type the data into the spreadsheet in columns, as presented on the previous page, then add the final data points to the row underneath. Alternatively, you can use the link on **BIOZONE's Resource Hub** to download the data.

(b) Plot the data on a scatter graph (not a line graph). Use the mouse to right click the y axis and select **Format axis**. In the tab that appears, tick the box labeled **Values in reverse order**.

(c) Does the shape of the graph change from your original plot? ____________________

(d) By replotting the data with temperature on the y axis, it is possible to obtain an equation for the graph from which we can calculate temperature as depth increases.
Right click on a data point and select **Add trendline**. Then tick **Display equation on chart.**
The equation is $y = 0.0137x + 8.9026$. This means: temperature = 0.0137 x depth (meters) + 8.9026.
On average it is 6,371 km to the center of the Earth.

i. What percentage to the center of the Earth did the Kola Superdeep Borehole reach? ____________________

ii. Use the equation above to calculate the temperature at the center of the Earth, assuming the temperature keeps rising in the same pattern as your plotted data:

iii. From analysis of various studies and data, scientists estimate the temperature at the center of the Earth to be about 6000°C. Does this match with your answer above? What does this mean about how Earth is structured?

3. Scientists were surprised to find water in the rocks more than 6 km deep. Where do you think the water may have come from and why had it stayed at that depth? (HINT: Think of the increase in temperature and pressure at this depth).

4. Based on the seismic data, scientists thought that there should be a change from granite to basalt at ~7 km below the surface (because the waves travel at different speeds through the different rock types). However, the drilling showed this wasn't the case. As a group, discuss this and suggest what might account for the change in seismic wave velocity:

5. Between 1987 and 1995, Germany also carried out a deep borehole project. They recorded a temperature of 260°C at 9,101 meters. What does this tell us about the heating of the crust?

ISBN: 978-1-98-856693-1

71 Plate Tectonics

Key Question: How does the theory of plate tectonics explain the movements of the crust, and the location of earthquakes and volcanoes?

- The Earth's crust is broken up into seven large, continent-sized **tectonic plates** and about a dozen smaller plates. Throughout geological time, these plates have moved about the Earth's surface, opening and closing oceans, building mountains, and shuffling continents in a process called **continental drift**.

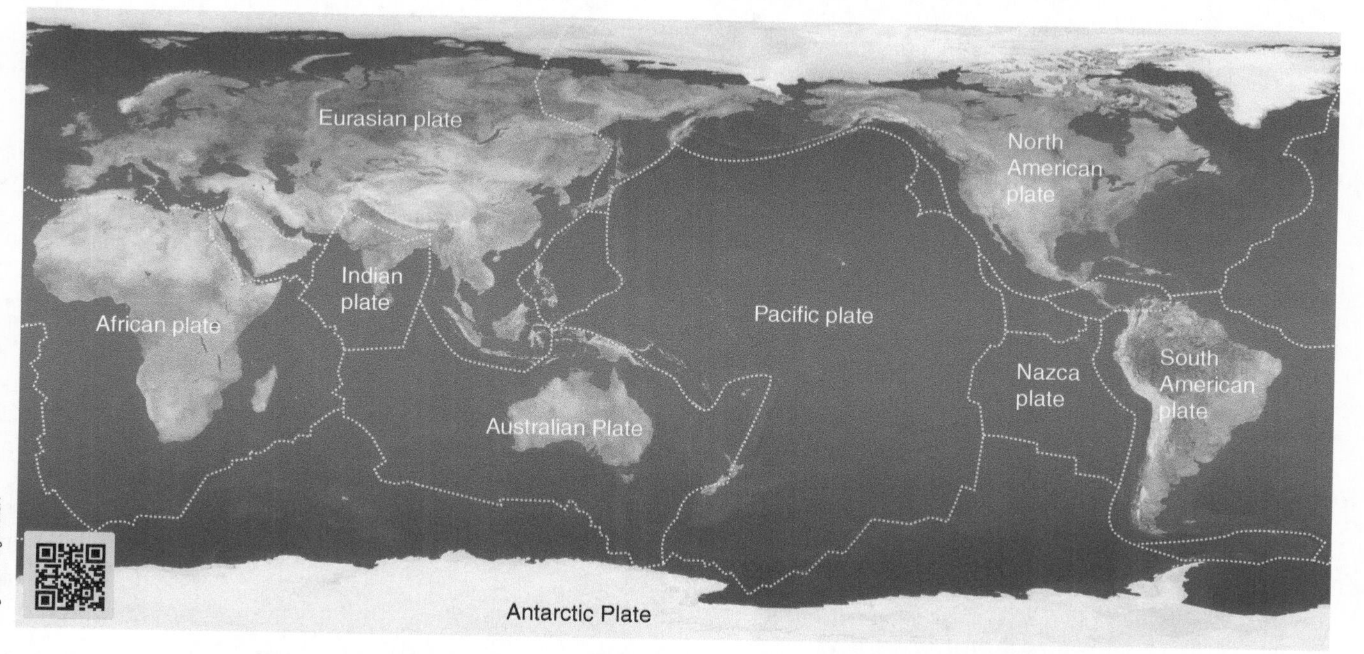

- The evidence for past plate movements has come from several sources: mapping of plate boundaries, the discovery of sea floor spreading, measurement of the direction and rate of plate movement, and geological evidence such as the distribution of ancient mountain chains, unusual deposits, and fossils. The size of the plates is constantly changing, with some expanding and some getting smaller. The extent of the tectonic plates is shown in the diagram above. The Pacific plate is by far the largest, measuring 103 million km^2.

The mechanism of plate movement

- The relatively cool lithosphere covers the hotter, plastic and more fluid asthenosphere. Heat from the **mantle** drives two kinds of asthenospheric movement: **convection** and mantle plumes. Plate motion is partly driven by the weight of cold, dense plates sinking into the mantle at trenches. This heavier, cooler material, sinking under the influence of gravity, displaces heated material, which rises as mantle plumes.
- The movements of the tectonic plates puts the brittle rock of the crust under strain, creating **faults** where rocks fracture and slip past each other. Earthquakes are caused by energy release during rapid slippage along faults. Consequently, the Earth's major earthquake (and volcanic) zones occur along plate boundaries.

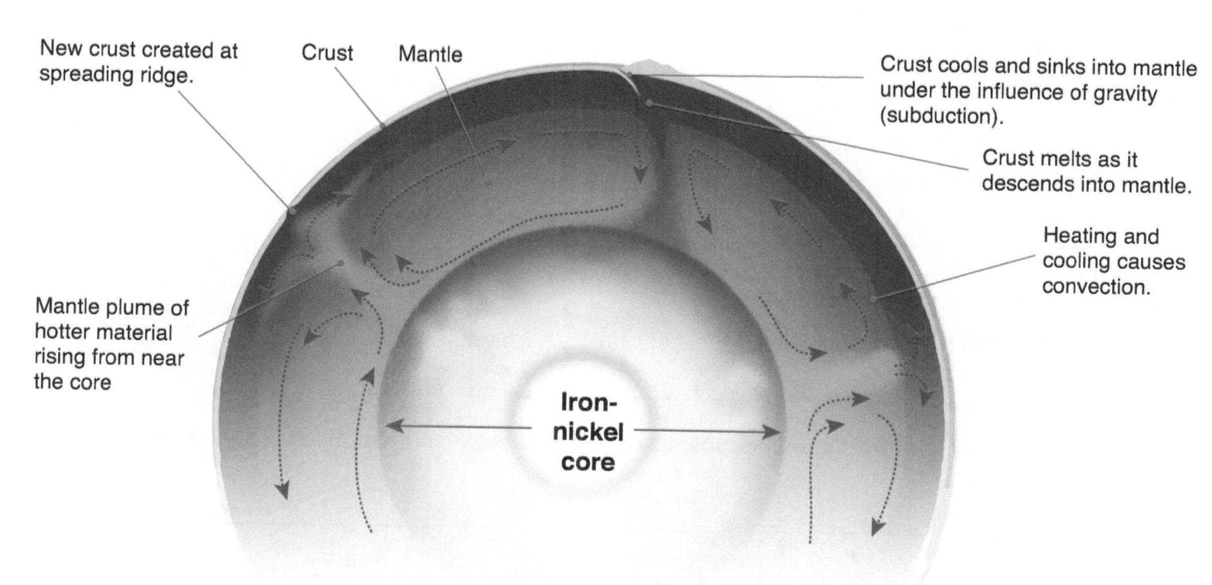

ISBN: 978-1-98-856693-1

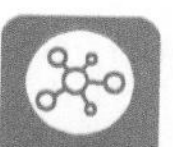

Subduction and volcanoes

Much of the Pacific plate boundaries form **subduction zones,** where one tectonic plate moves under another and into the mantle. This produces a region of extreme seismic and volcanic activity. Along with parts of the Nazca plate, it forms the Pacific Ring of Fire. Around three quarters of the world's active and dormant volcanoes are found around the edge of the ring, and nearly 90% of all earthquake activity is located there.

Subduction zones around the Pacific rim

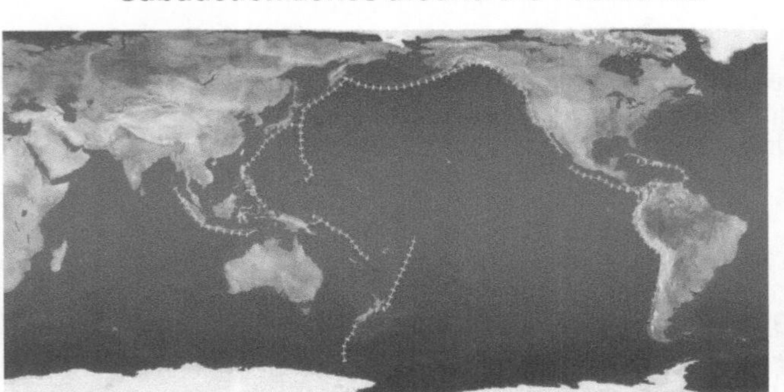

Volcanoes around the Pacific rim

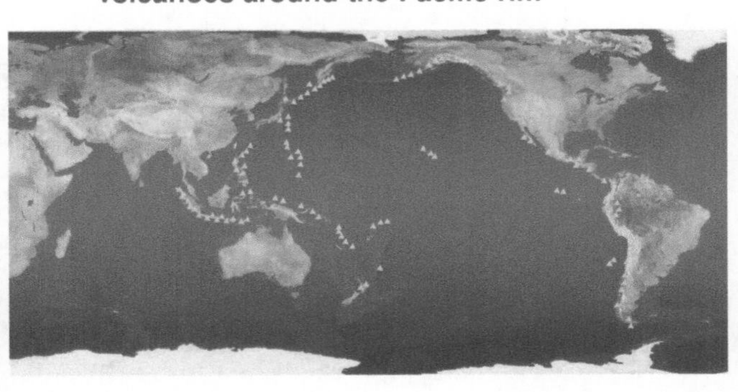

1. Name the seven major tectonic plates: ______________________________

____

2. Study the images of the Hawaiian Island chain below. These islands formed as the Pacific plate moved over a "hot spot" in the mantle. From the information, determine which direction the Pacific plate is moving at this point:

____

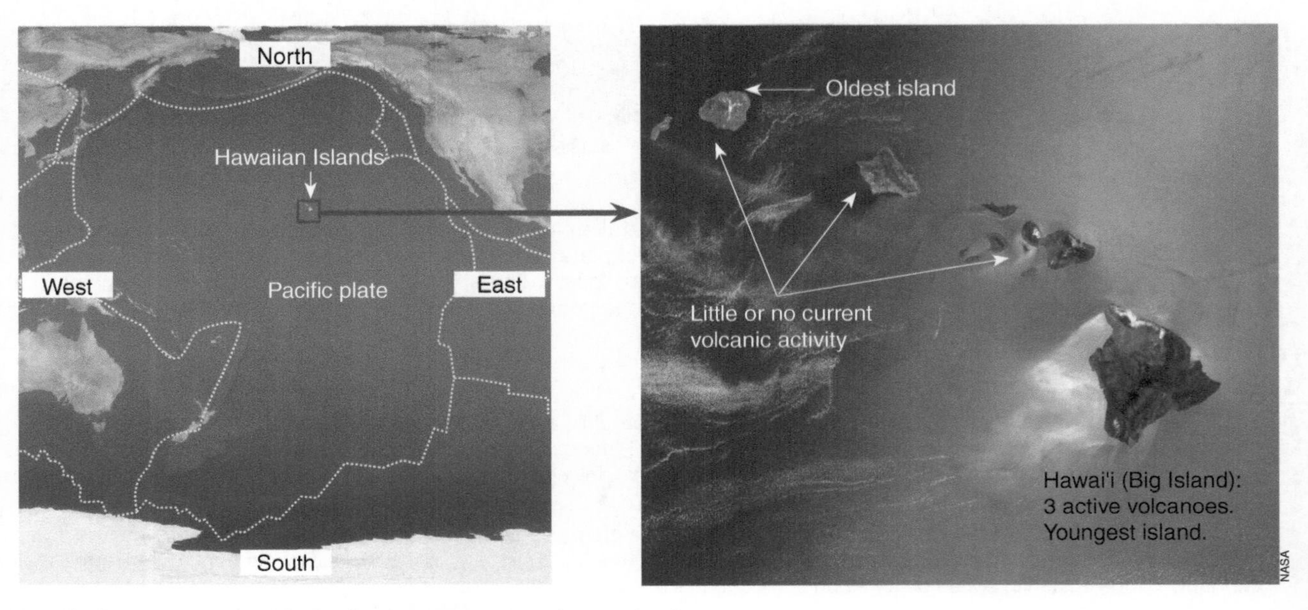

3. Identify three types of evidence for the movement of tectonic plates: ______________________________

____

____

4. (a) Describe the mechanism of plate movement: ______________________________

____

____

(b) How does this account for continental drift? ______________________________

____

5. Study the images at the top of the page. Describe the relationship between the position of subduction zones and volcanoes in the Pacific:

____

____

ISBN: 978-1-98-856693-1

6. (a) Use the information below to produce a graph of the age of the volcanoes in the Hawaiian island chain compared to their distance from the Kilauea volcano on Hawai'i (Big island).

Name	Distance from Kilauea (km)	Age (millions of years)
Kilauea	0	0
Mauna Kea	54	0.375
Kohala	100	0.43
East Maui	182	0.75
West Maui	220	1.32
East Molokai	256	1.76
West Molokai	280	1.9
Koolau	339	2.6
Waianae	374	3.7
Kauai	519	5.1
Nihoa	780	7.2
Necker	1058	10.3

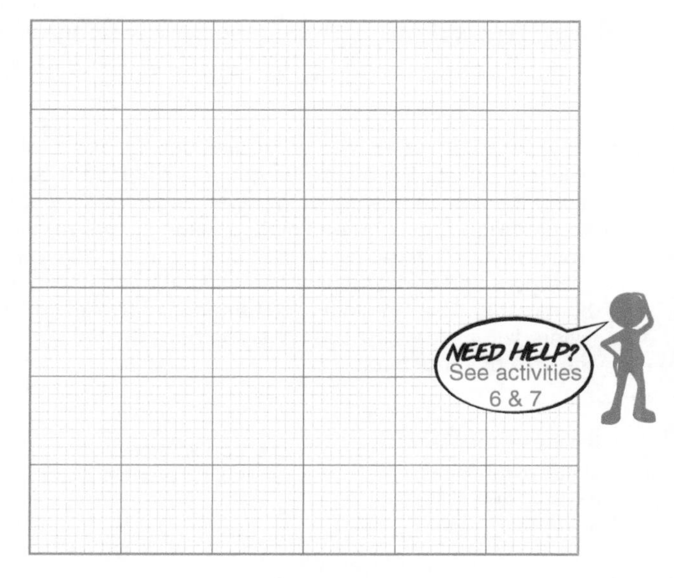

(b) Use the data to calculate the rate of the movement of the Pacific plate over the Hawaiian hot spot:

7. Using an internet browser, launch Google Earth (https://www.google.com/earth/) or type Google Earth into your search engine or follow the link on the **BIOZONE Resource Hub**. Google Earth is able to import .kml or .kmz files. These files contain data that adds layers to the globe.

i) Open another window and go to https://www.usgs.gov/media/files/plate-boundaries-kmz-file or follow the link at the **BIOZONE Resource Hub**.
ii) Download the **Tectonic Plate Boundaries** file. Save it where you can find it easily. Return to Google Earth.
iii) Click on the **Projects** tab, then click **Open,** then **Import KML file**.
iv) Click **Open file** and navigate to where you have saved the file. You can save the imported file to Google Earth so that it is also available when you open Google Earth.
v) Once the file is imported, several layers will appear showing plate boundaries and their direction and speed of movement. Click off the **Projects** tab to hide it and show the map legend.

(a) Navigate to the edge of the Pacific plate east of Aomori, Japan. Find the point labeled PA-NA. What direction is this point of the plate moving?

(b) Click on the point. An information box will appear. How fast is the plate moving?

(c) Navigate to New Zealand, east of Australia. There is an unusual situation regarding the direction of the tectonic plate movements to the north and south of the country and in the middle of the South Island. Describe the direction of the plate movements about New Zealand and predict how this might affect the shape of the country in the distant future.

(d) Navigate to California in the western United States. The San Andreas fault runs nearly the length of California. What type of fault is it? How can you tell?

(e) Find the point labeled PA-NA just south of Santa Maria. How fast is this point moving?

(f) The distance between Santa Maria and San Jose (on the opposite side of the fault) is about 285 km. How long will it take for these two places to be side by side, based on the speed of movement above?

ISBN: 978-1-98-856693-1

72 Plate Boundaries

Key Question: What occurs at the boundaries of tectonic plates, and what drives plate movement?

- Plate boundaries are marked by well-defined zones of seismic and volcanic activity. Plate growth occurs at **divergent boundaries** along the sea floor, spreading ridges, e.g. the Mid-Atlantic Ridge and the Red Sea, whereas plate attrition occurs at **convergent boundaries** marked by deep ocean trenches and **subduction zones**. Divergent and convergent zones make up approximately 80% of plate boundaries. The remaining 20% are called **transform boundaries**, where two plates slide past one another with no significant change in the size of either plate.

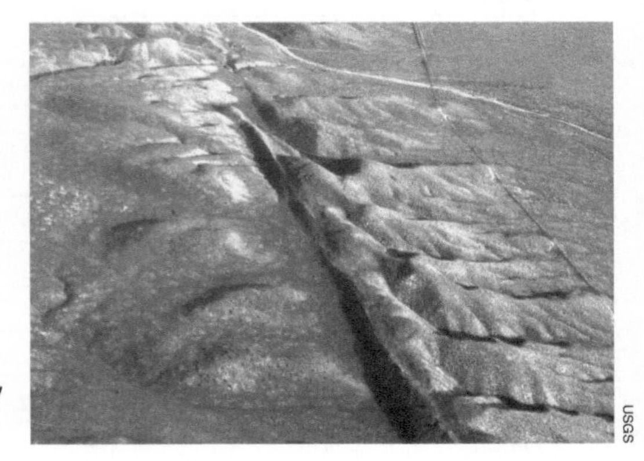

The San Andreas fault is a transform boundary running for over 1000 km through California.

Island arcs form from a chain of volcanoes parallel to the edge of a subduction zone.

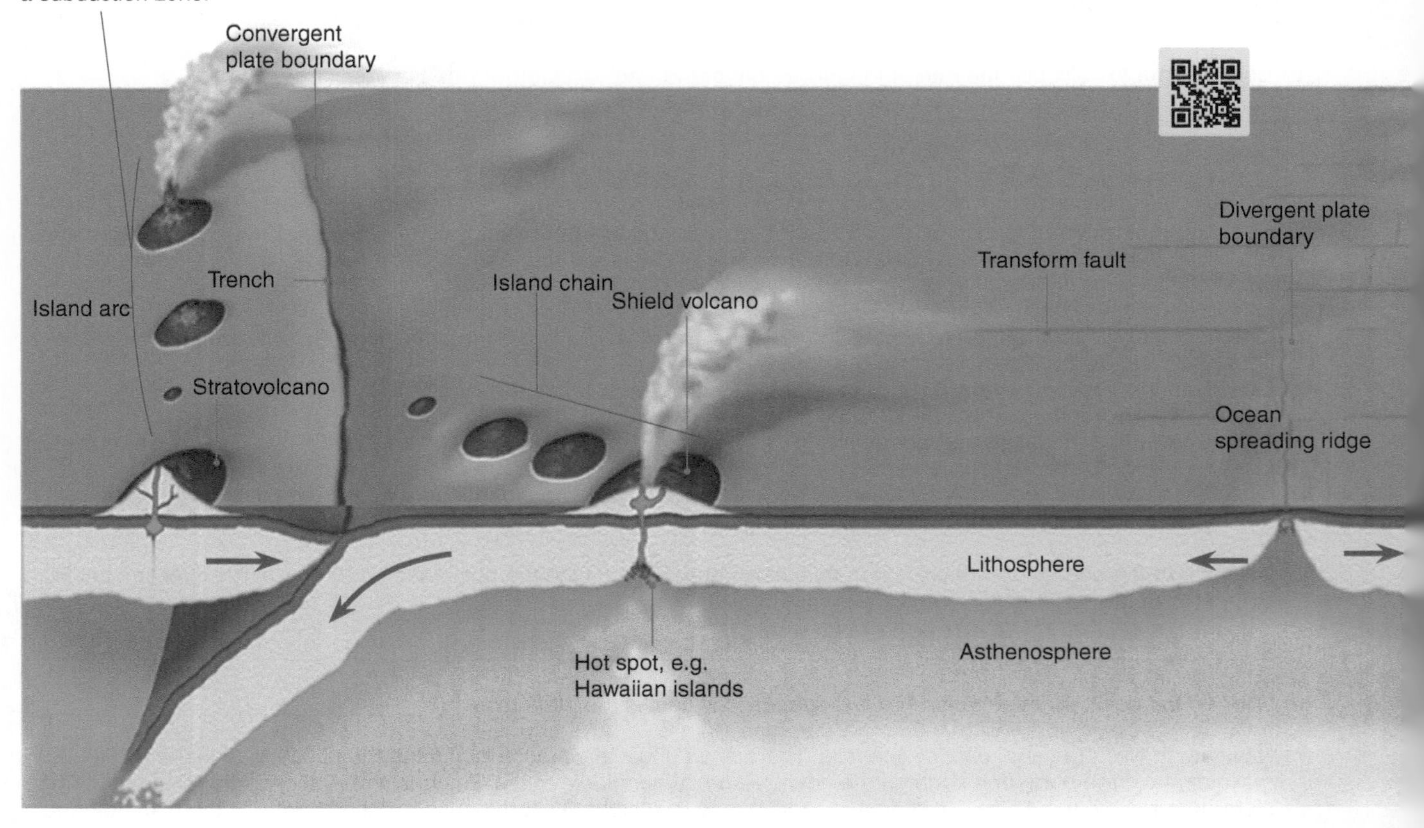

1. Describe what is happening at each of the following plate boundaries, and identify an example in each case:

   (a) Convergent plate boundary: ____

   ____

   ____

   (b) Divergent plate boundary: ____

   ____

   ____

   (c) Transform plate boundary: ____

   ____

   ____

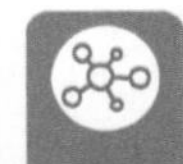

ESS2.A EM

ISBN: 978-1-98-856693-1

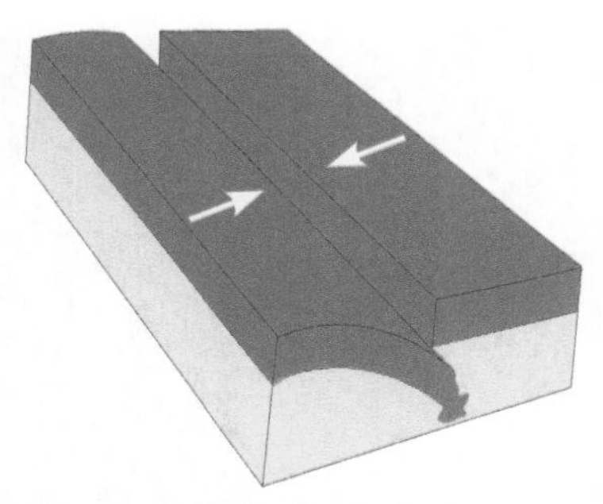

Plate boundaries moving towards each other are called **convergent plate boundaries.** Where oceanic crust and continental crust meet, the oceanic crust will subduct under the continental crust, creating a subduction zone. Volcanoes normally form along the continental border of a subduction zone. When continental crusts collide, huge mountain ranges such as the Himalayas can form.

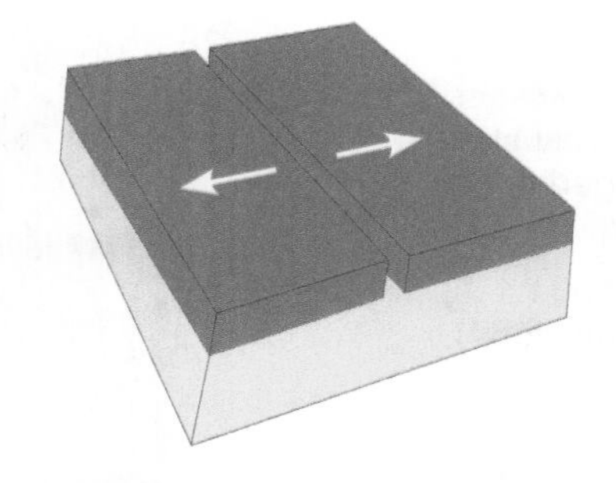

Divergent plate boundaries form where the tectonic plates are moving away from each other. These are commonly found along the mid ocean ridges, but occasionally are seen on land, as in the Great Rift Valley and Iceland. Divergent boundaries are also known as constructive boundaries as they produce new crust from the upwelling of magma.

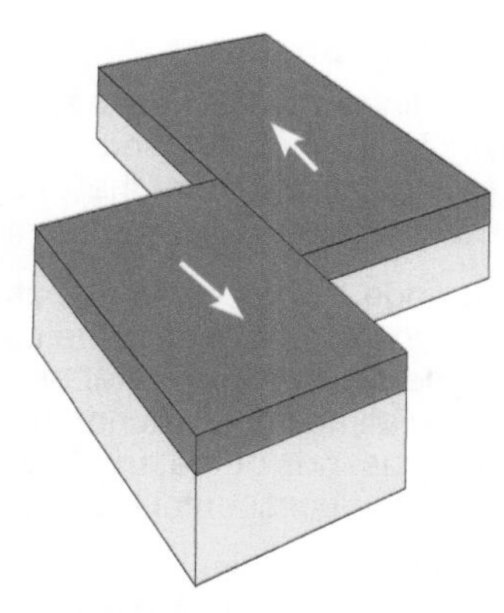

Transform boundaries are formed when the tectonic plates are moving past each other. They are, therefore, neither constructive nor destructive. Examples include the San Andreas **fault** in California and the Alpine Fault in New Zealand.

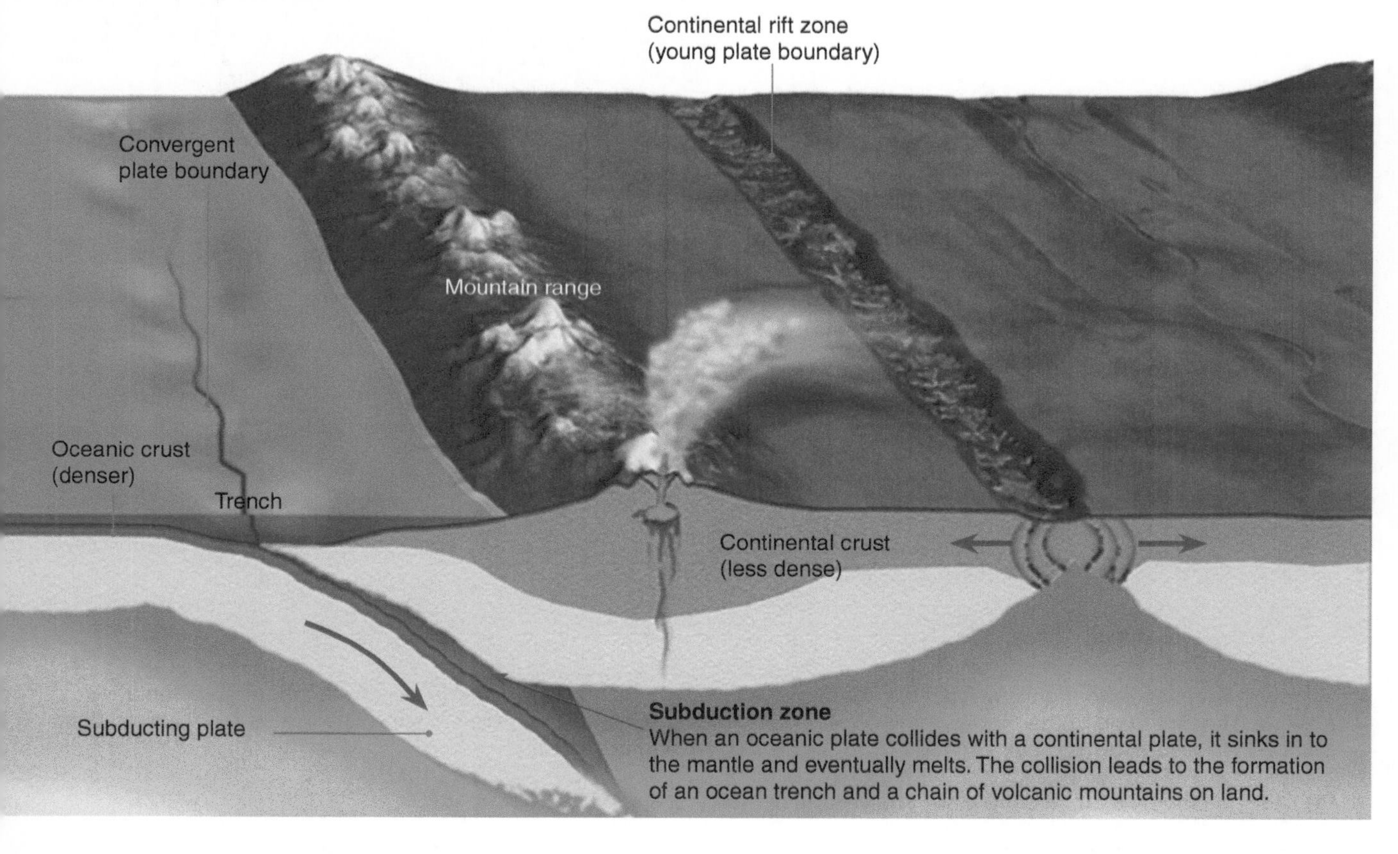

Subduction zone
When an oceanic plate collides with a continental plate, it sinks in to the mantle and eventually melts. The collision leads to the formation of an ocean trench and a chain of volcanic mountains on land.

2. Identify the type of plate boundary at which each of the following occurs:

   (a) Mountain building: ______________________ (c) Creation of new ocean floor: ______________________

   (b) Subduction: ______________________ (d) Island arc: ______________________

3. (a) Explain why the oceanic crust subducts under the continental crust in a subduction zone: ______________________

   ____

   ____

   (b) What causes volcanoes to form along the continental plate boundary of a subduction zone? ______________________

   ____

   ____

   ____

ISBN: 978-1-98-856693-1

Continental shelves

- The continents extend out beyond the shorelines, many kilometers out to sea. The continental shelf is the part of the continent that is submerged under relatively shallow water (diagram below).
- At the edge of the continental shelf, there is a sudden increase in slope (the continental slope). Here, the depth of the water suddenly increases from sometimes a few hundred meters to often many thousands of meters. This is the boundary between the continental crust and the oceanic crust.
- The continental crust is thicker and less dense than the oceanic crust. As a result, it is usually higher than the oceanic crust and much of it sits out of the surrounding oceans.
- There are exceptions to this. Most of the continental mass of Zealandia (right) is below the ocean surface, with only the narrow New Zealand archipelago sitting above the water.

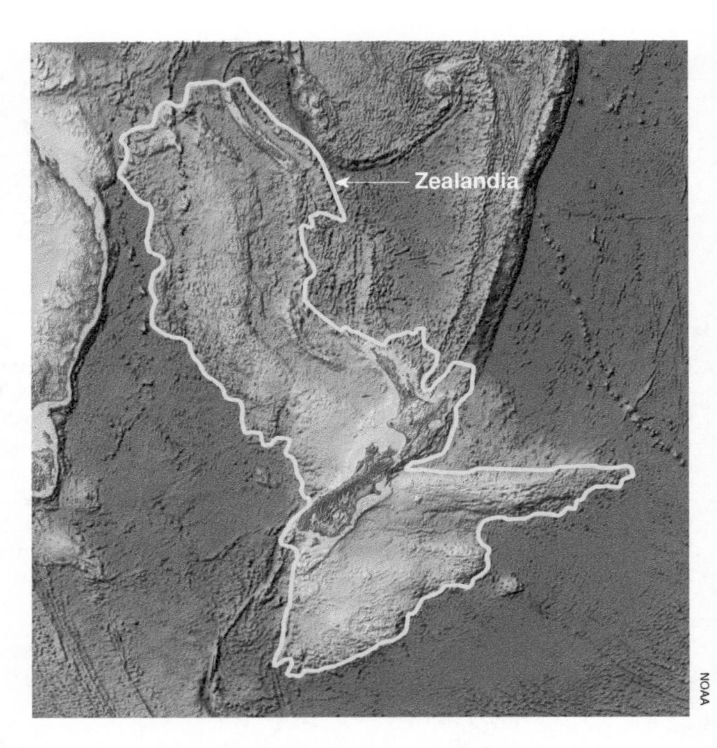

- The extent of the continental shelf around a continent varies. Some continental areas have very little shelf, especially where the edge of an advancing oceanic plate dives underneath continental crust. One example is the offshore subduction zone off the coast of Chile (compare western and eastern coasts of South America opposite).
- It is useful to study the shape of the continental shelves rather than the coastlines, because coastlines change over time as ocean levels rise and fall, e.g. when ice sheets expand and retreat. The map opposite shows the continental shelves in **dark gray** at the edges of the continents.

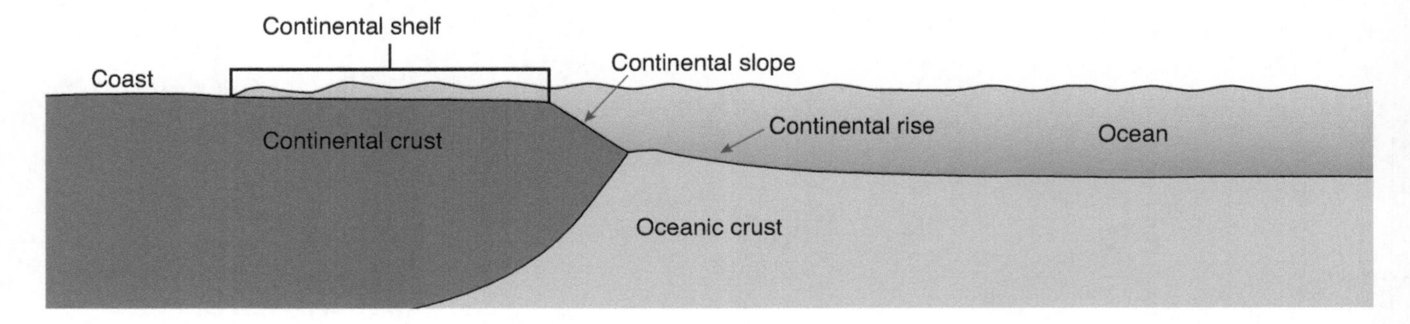

4. From the full page map (right), we can see that various continental shelves appear to match with other continental shelves. The distortion of the map at the poles makes some of these difficult to see clearly. The age of the rocks on the sea bed are also shown. These can help us to match up continental shelves.

   (a) Describe the location of continental shelves that match those identified below:

Continental shelf	Matching continental shelf
North eastern coast of North America	
North western coast of Europe	
Eastern coast of South America	
South coast of Australia	

   (b) What does the matching of these continental shelves suggest about continents and the tectonic plates?

ISBN: 978-1-98-856693-1

Map of the Earth showing the ages of the sea floor, the boundaries of the plates, the continents, and the continental shelves in dark gray. The seven major plates are as follows: **1**) Pacific Plate, **2**) North American Plate, **3**) Eurasian Plate, **4**) African Plate, **5**) Antarctic Plate, **6**) Indo-Australia Plate, **7**) South American Plate.

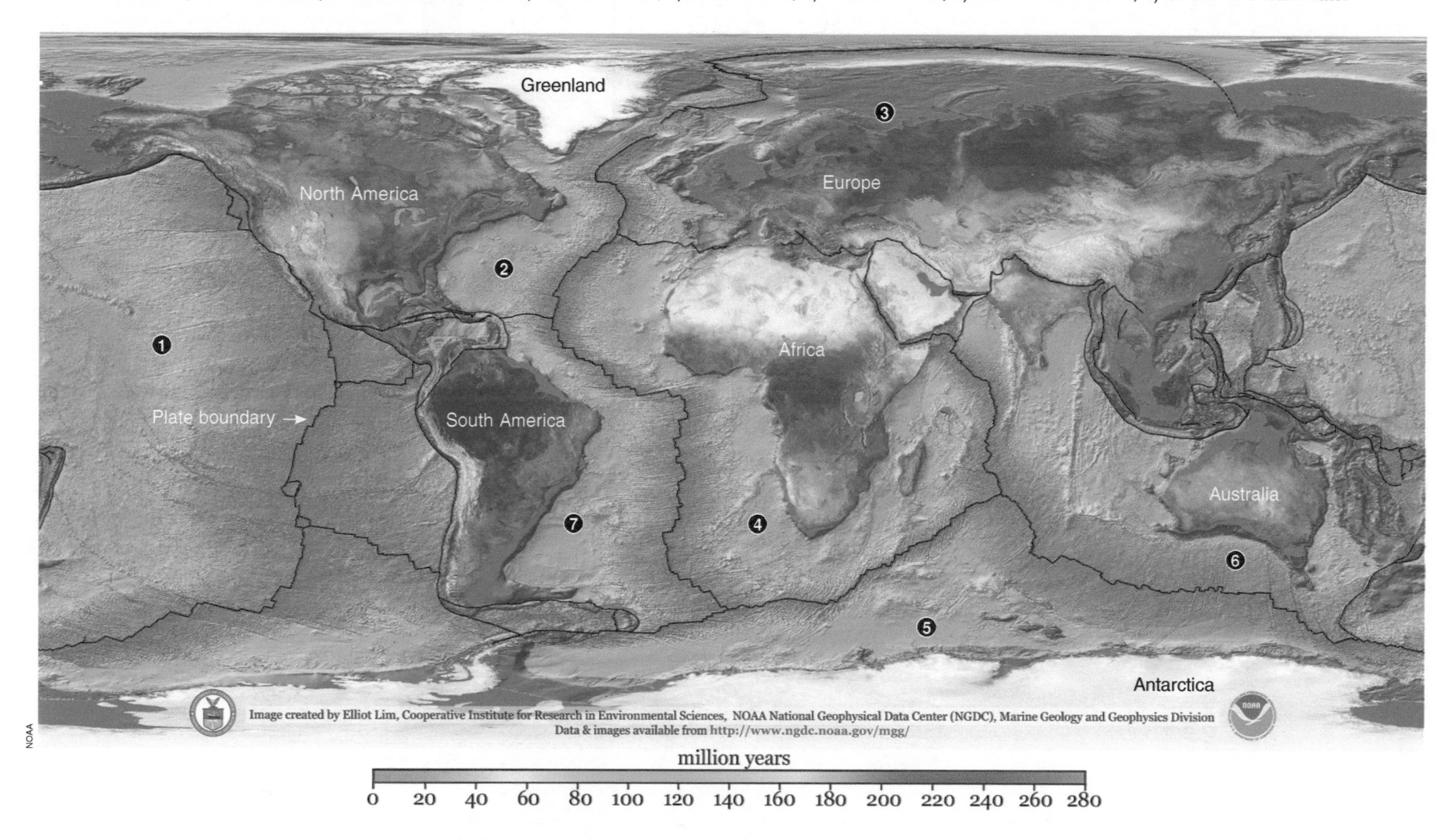

Note the ages of the rocks of the sea floor. Recall from chapter 5 that new ocean floor is formed at the mid-ocean ridge and this pushes the plates (and continents apart).

ISBN: 978-1-98-856693-1

73 Modeling Continental Drift

Key Question: How has continental drift affected the positions of the continents, over time?

▶ **Continental drift,** the movement of the Earth's continents relative to each other, is a measurable phenomenon and has continued throughout Earth's history. Movements of up to 2-11 cm a year have been recorded between continents, using GPS. The movements of the Earth's seven major crustal plates are driven by a geological process known as **plate tectonics.** Some continents are drifting apart, while others are moving together. Many lines of evidence show that the modern continents were once joined together as "supercontinents". One supercontinent, **Gondwana**, was made up of the southern continents, some 200 mya (million years ago).

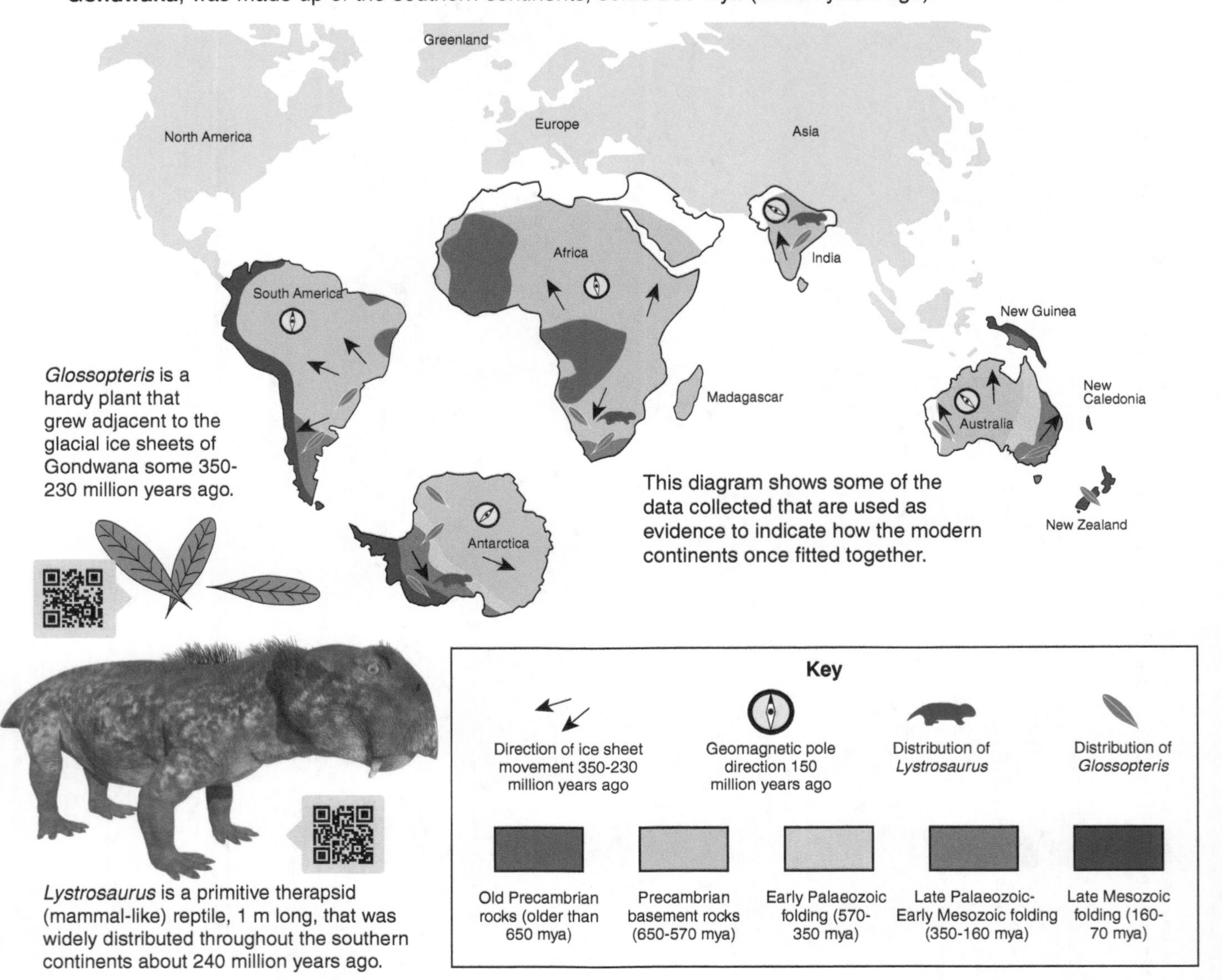

Glossopteris is a hardy plant that grew adjacent to the glacial ice sheets of Gondwana some 350-230 million years ago.

This diagram shows some of the data collected that are used as evidence to indicate how the modern continents once fitted together.

Lystrosaurus is a primitive therapsid (mammal-like) reptile, 1 m long, that was widely distributed throughout the southern continents about 240 million years ago.

Investigation 6.1 Continental drift

See appendix for equipment list.

1. Cut out the southern continents on page 167, as close to the coastline marks as possible.
2. Arrange the cut-outs onto the outline of Gondwana on page 169. Take into account the following:
   - The location of ancient rocks and periods of mountain folding during different geological ages.
   - The direction of ancient ice sheet movements.
   - The geomagnetic orientation of old rocks (the way that magnetic crystals are lined up in ancient rock gives an indication of the direction of the magnetic pole at the time the rock was formed).
   - The distribution of fossils of ancient species such as Lystrosaurus and Glossopteris.

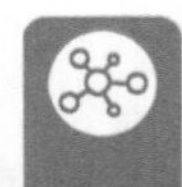

ESS2.A SC

ISBN: 978-1-98-856693-1

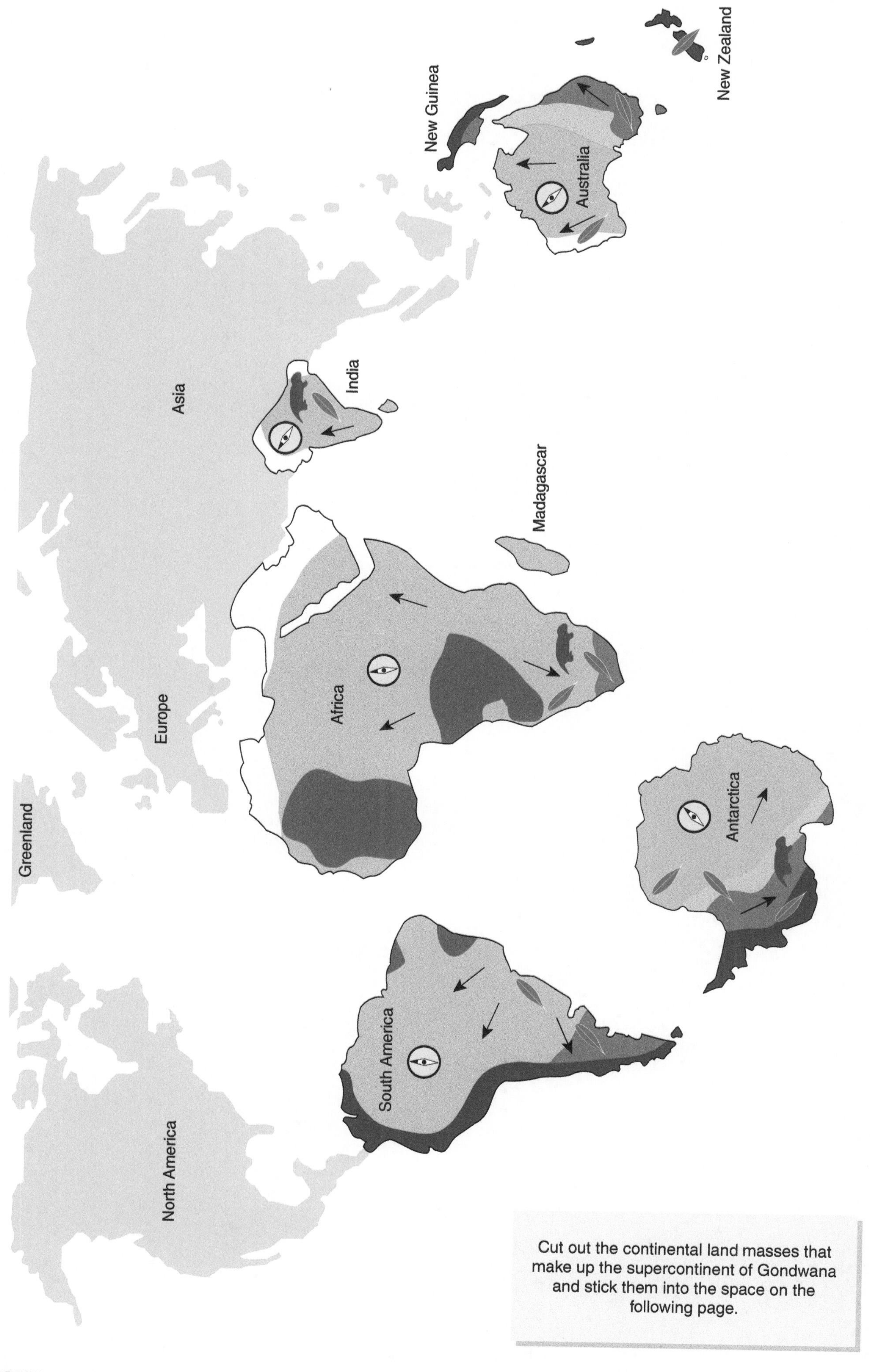

Cut out the continental land masses that make up the supercontinent of Gondwana and stick them into the space on the following page.

ISBN: 978-1-98-856693-1

This page has been deliberately left blank

ISBN: 978-1-98-856693-1

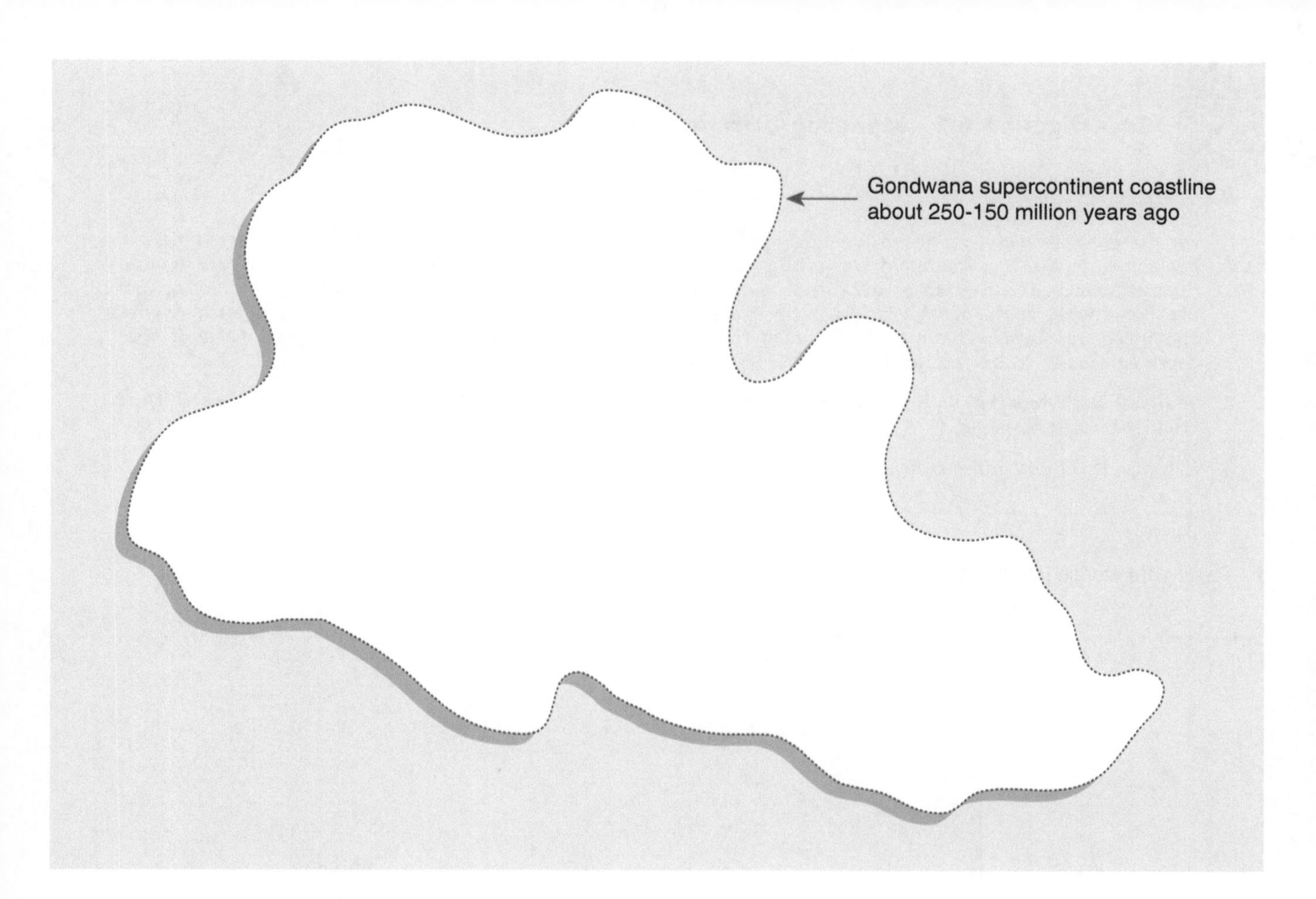

1. Once you have positioned the modern continents into the pattern of the supercontinent, mark on the diagram:
   (a) The likely position of the South Pole 350-230 million years ago (as indicated by the movement of the ice sheets).
   (b) The likely position of the geomagnetic South Pole 150 million years ago (as indicated by ancient geomagnetism).

2. State what general deduction you can make about the position of the polar regions with respect to land masses:

3. Fossils of *Lystrosaurus* are known from Antarctica, South Africa, India, and Western China. With the modern continents in their present position, *Lystrosaurus* could have walked across dry land to get to China, Africa, and India. It was not possible for it to walk to Antarctica, however. Explain the distribution of this ancient species in terms of continental drift:

4. The Atlantic Ocean is currently opening up at the rate of 2 cm per year. At this rate in the past, calculate how long it would have taken to reach its current extent, with the distance from Africa to South America being 2300 km (assume the rate of spreading has been constant):

5. How do the different lines of evidence allow scientists to recreate the positions of the Earth's continents, through time?

ISBN: 978-1-98-856693-1

Investigation 6.2 Modeling drift over time

See appendix for equipment list.

1. On the opposite page are three identical sets of four puzzle pieces. They represent three different time periods from the four continent world of Square World. Each set of four continents forms a larger square (Square World). The colored objects (red, blue, green) represent sediments found across Square World. There are three ways that Square World can be formed from the four continents. Your task is to determine what the three ways are and the order in which they "formed" (from the oldest to the youngest). None of the continents need to be rotated from their current orientation.
2. You may work together in pairs to do this activity if you wish. Cut out the three sets of "continents" (A, B, C) from the opposite page.
3. Arrange them into three complete Square Worlds.

1. Paste your worlds into the spaces provided below:

Youngest

Middle

Oldest

ISBN: 978-1-98-856693-1

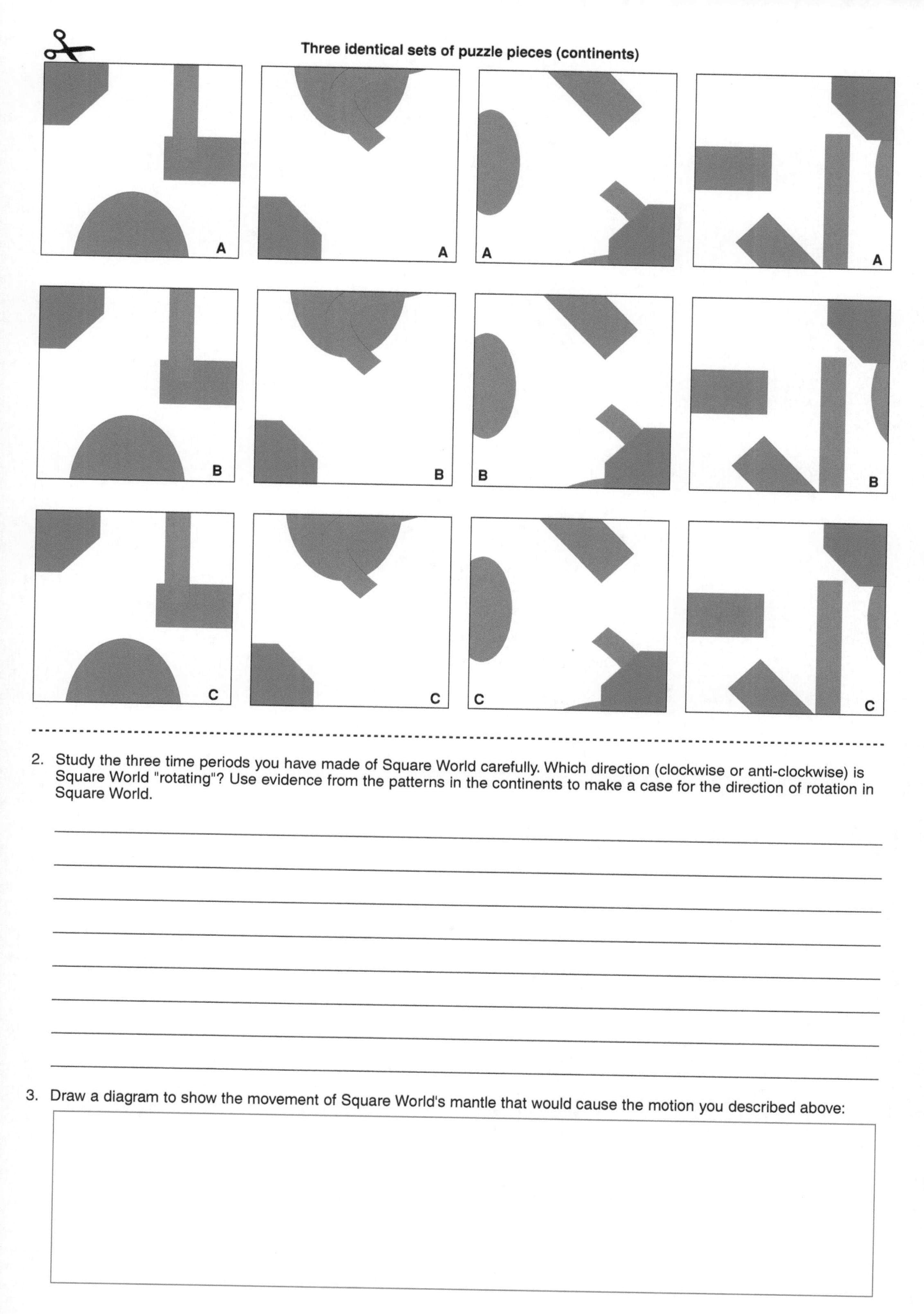

2. Study the three time periods you have made of Square World carefully. Which direction (clockwise or anti-clockwise) is Square World "rotating"? Use evidence from the patterns in the continents to make a case for the direction of rotation in Square World.

3. Draw a diagram to show the movement of Square World's mantle that would cause the motion you described above:

ISBN: 978-1-98-856693-1

This page has been deliberately left blank

ISBN: 978-1-98-856693-1

74 Review Your Understanding

Key Question: How do the continents move?

- In this chapter, you have seen that the interior of the Earth is heated by the energy produced by the decay of radioactive isotopes in the mantle, and from the heat left over from its formation.
- You have also studied the movement of the tectonic plates on the Earth's surface and the way they come together (converge) and move apart (diverge).
- You should now have enough information to build a simple model of the interior of the Earth and explain its movements.

1. At the start of this chapter, you were shown how Africa and South America were once joined and have now spread apart. You should now be able to explain how this occurs. In your explanation you should draw and explain a model of the Earth to show how convection moves the tectonic plates.

ISBN: 978-1-98-856693-1

75 Summing Up

1. Earthquakes normally occur along plate boundaries. Measuring the depth of these earthquakes can give an idea of the shape of the boundary and how the plates are interacting. The data below shows earthquake depths for the Tonga Trench in the Pacific Ocean and along the coast of Chile.

(a) Plot a scatter graph of the data on the grids provided and add a line of best fir for each graph:

Tonga trench		Chile coast	
Longitude (°W)	Depth (km)	Longitude (°W)	Depth (km)
176.2	270	67.5	180
175.8	115	68.3	130
175.7	260	62.3	480
175.4	250	62.0	600
176.0	160	69.8	30
173.9	60	69.8	55
174.9	50	67.7	120
179.2	650	67.9	140
173.8	50	69.2	35
177.0	350	68.6	125
178.8	580	68.1	145
177.4	420	65.2	285
178.0	520	69.7	50
177.7	560	68.2	160
177.7	465	66.2	230
179.2	670	66.3	215
175.1	40	68.5	140
176.0	220	68.1	130

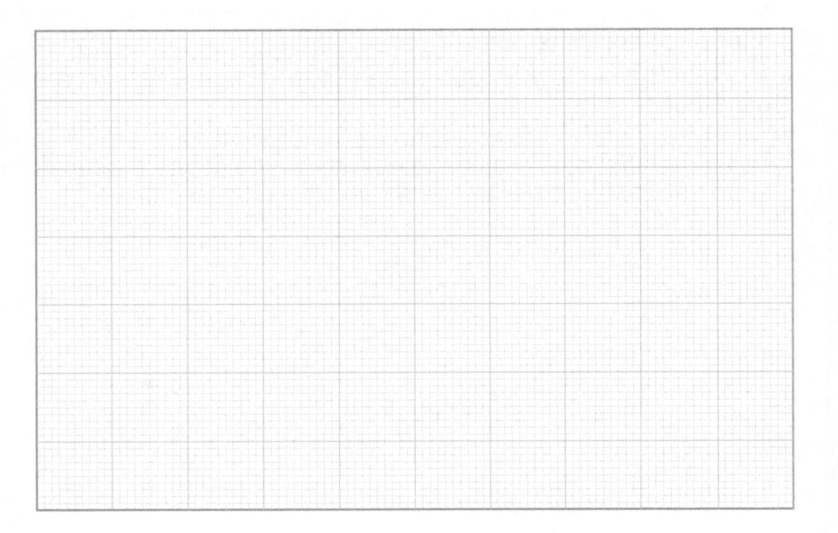

(b) What type of plate boundary appears to be present at the locations plotted?

(c) Draw a diagram in the space below to show the how the layers of the Earth are moving at the Tonga Trench:

ISBN: 978-1-98-856693-1

2. Draw a diagram in the space below to show the mechanisms of plate tectonics that shift the plates of the Earth's crust. You should make sure your diagram has divergent and convergent boundaries, and the layers of the Earth that are significant in plate tectonics.

3. Explain the significance of radioactive decay to plate tectonics: ______

4. The diagram (right) shows the Pacific plate and the Nazca plate. The white dotted line shows the location of the plate boundaries. The red dotted line shows the location of subduction zones along those boundaries.

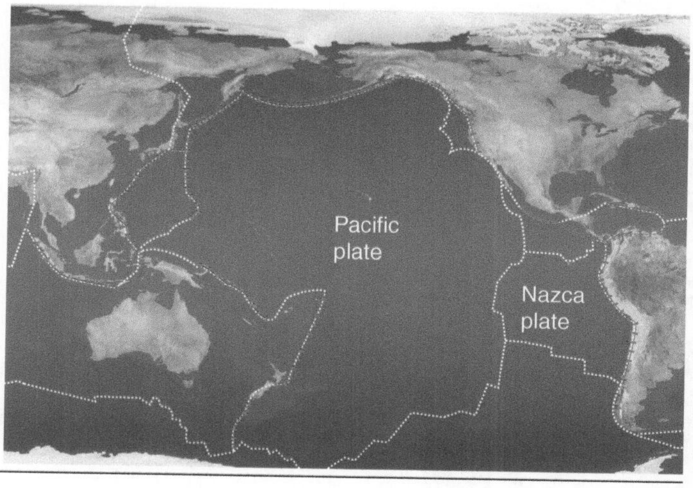

   (a) On the diagram, circle the area that would likely be a divergent plate boundary.

   (b) Where would you expect to find volcanoes on this diagram?

   Pacific plate

   Nazca plate

   (c) Explain why volcanoes form in the places you have indicated in (b): ______

ISBN: 978-1-98-856693-1

CHAPTER 7

The Roles of Water in the Earth's Surface Processes

Anchoring Phenomenon

Lets Go Spelunking: What processes helped to form the Mammoth Caves? 76 85

Why is water so important?

- ☐ 1 Link the properties of water, such as bonding, density, and state, to its structure. Draw a model of water molecules bonded to ions. 77
- ☐ 2 Interpret information in a hydrologic cycle model to explain how water moves around the Earth. Correctly label and identify features in a model representing a hydrologic cycle. 78

What processes allow rock to continuously form and reform?

- ☐ 3 Using information from a rock cycle model, identify the three main classification groups of rocks. Explain how select rocks have been formed. Investigate properties, including density, of select rocks. Use a rock key to identify select rocks. 79
- ☐ 4 Graph and analyze different concentrated ionic solutions and their respective melting points. Explain how water can lower the melting point of rocks, as part of the rock cycle. 80 86
- ☐ 5 Distinguish between weathering and erosion. Describe how weathering is able to break down rocks, as part of the rock cycle. Explain how erosion is able to break down rocks, as part of the rock cycle. 81 86
- ☐ 6 Investigate the process of frost wedging in a fair test. Critique the frost wedging model for how well it represents the actual process. 82
- ☐ 7 Investigate the process of erosion using a model of water flow through river channels. Model the process of fossilization. Describe how erosion and deposition in flood plains contribute to productive agricultural areas. 83 86
- ☐ 8 Link the moisture content of soil to erosion rate. 84 86

76 Lets Go Spelunking!

Key Question: What processes helped to form the Mammoth Caves?

- At Mammoth Cave National Park in Kentucky there is an underground limestone cave system, with around 640 km mapped out, and over 1000 km yet to be discovered by spelunkers, a term for cave explorers.
- The cave system started to form around 10 million years ago. It sits within the large Green River drainage basin, so was exposed to river water, along with slightly acidic rainwater, and ground water seeping through the rock.
- The cave system contains huge caverns, underground lakes, and sinkholes in which streams suddenly disappear into caves containing underground lakes.
- Mammoth Caves have stalactites, mineral formations that hang from the cave's ceilings, and stalagmites extending from the ground upwards.
- The oldest rocks that form the deep cave structure were laid down around 320 million years ago, on the site of a huge inland sea. On top of that are three other layers, or formations, that are successively younger.

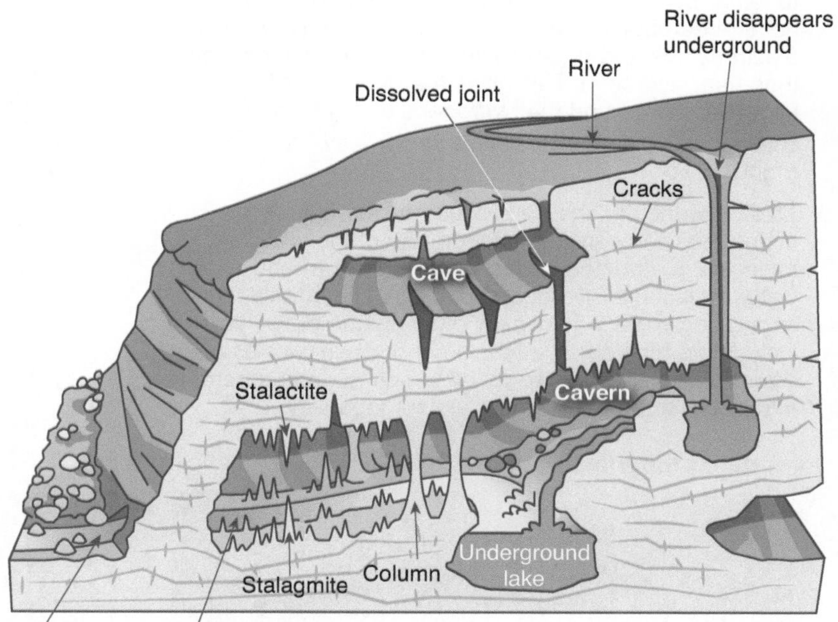

1. In groups, discuss what type of rock you think the big open caverns, containing the stalactites and stalagmites, in Mammoth Caves are made from, and how might you know that? Record a summary of your group's ideas below:

2. How do you think the Mammoth Caves might have formed? Use the space below to develop a flow chart of the processes you think might be involved in forming Mammoth Caves (you may not decide to use all four steps):

ISBN: 978-1-98-856693-1

77 The Properties of Water

Key Question: How do the unique physical and chemical properties of water make it a central chemical in many biological and geological systems?

- Water has a simple chemical formula, containing two hydrogen atoms and one oxygen atom (H_2O) held together by bonds. The electrons in these bonds are not shared equally between the atoms. On average, the electrons spend a greater amount of time near oxygen than near hydrogen. This gives the oxygen a slightly negative charge and the hydrogens a slightly positive charge, called a **dipole**. This is shown as δ^- and δ^+ (right).
- This difference in charge produces a strongly polar molecule. The positive hydrogen end of the water molecule is attracted to the negative oxygen end of other water molecules (hydrogen bonding). The attraction is strong and gives water many of its unique properties, including a high surface tension and a behavior as a powerful solvent. The tendency of one atom in a bond to attract electrons is known as electronegativity.

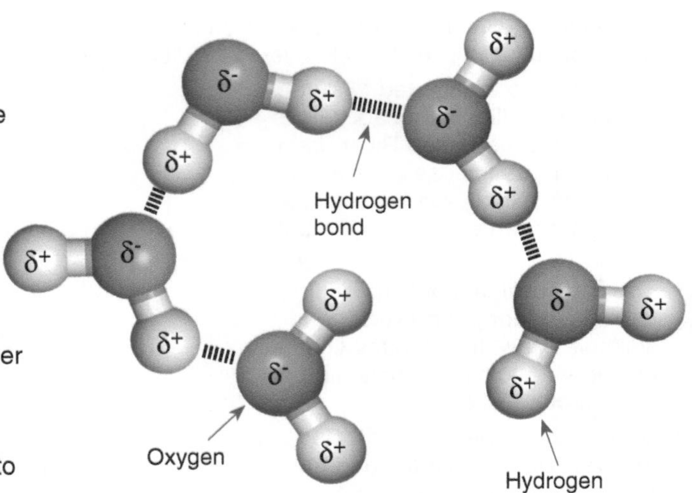

Important properties of water

Water has the highest heat capacity of all liquids. It takes a lot of energy to raise its temperature. Water has a high boiling point, because a lot of energy is need to break the hydrogen bonds between water molecules and make water boil.

Water molecules are **cohesive**, i.e. they stick together. This is due to hydrogen bonding. Cohesion allows water to form drops and is responsible for surface tension. Water molecules also **adhere** to other substances.

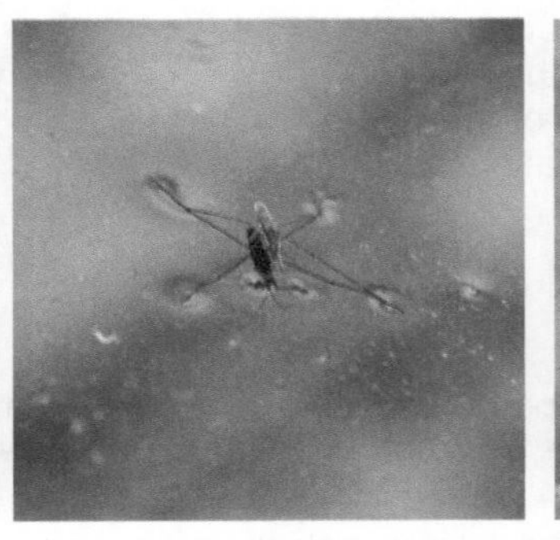

Surface tension is the ability of a fluid's surface to deform without breaking. Water can deform more than most fluids before its surface tension is broken. Thus a water skater (above) can float because it doesn't break the surface tension.

Water's polarity makes it an extremely good solvent. Substances such as salts, e.g. sodium chloride (NaCl), dissolve relatively easily in water - one of the reasons the sea is so salty (carrying 35 g/L of salt).

One of the most important properties of water is that its solid state (ice, right) is less dense that its liquid state. This means that ice floats on water. When freezing, water molecules align into a crystal structure that increases its volume by about 9% compared to liquid water at the same temperature. Water is colorless and transparent.

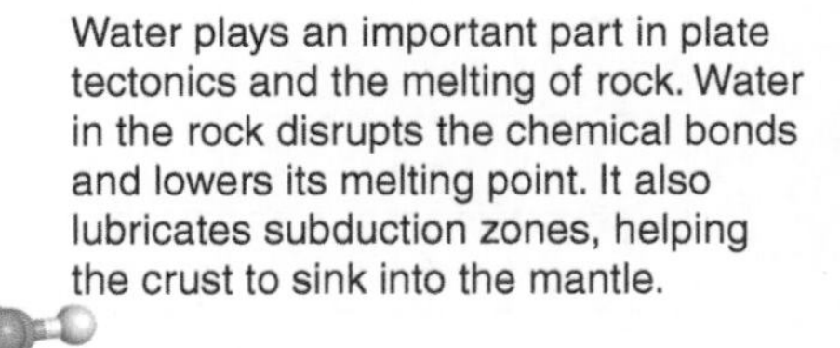

Water plays an important part in plate tectonics and the melting of rock. Water in the rock disrupts the chemical bonds and lowers its melting point. It also lubricates subduction zones, helping the crust to sink into the mantle.

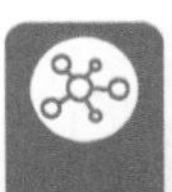

ESS2.C
SF

ISBN: 978-1-98-856693-1

Comparing water and hydrogen sulfide

Hydrogen sulfide (H_2S) has the same molecular shape as water (right), but has a melting point of -82°C and a boiling point of -60°C, far lower than water's. This is because of the difference in electronegativity of sulfur and oxygen. Even though sulfur sits directly below oxygen on the periodic table, its outer electrons are further away from the nucleus and are held more weakly. This leads to a greater difference in polarity between a H_2O molecule and a H_2S molecule.

Property	Water	Hydrogen sulfide
Formula	H_2O	H_2S
Melting point	0°C	-82°C
Boiling point	100°C	-60°C

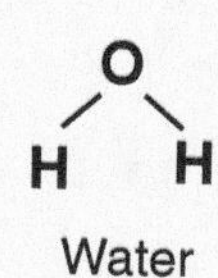

Water

Hydrogen sulfide

The bonds that water molecules form with each other require a lot of energy to break. This is why water has a much higher boiling point than hydrogen sulfide.

1. Below, are two simple diagrams of a sodium ion and a chloride ion. Note the charge they carry. In the space around them, draw three to four water molecules per ion to show how the water molecules interact with the them:

Na^+

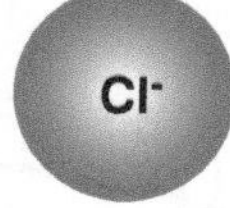

2. Explain the formation of hydrogen bonds between water molecules: ______

3. Explain why aquatic environments have relatively stable temperatures: ______

4. Why does ice float on water? ______

5. Explain why water has a high surface tension: ______

6. Why does hydrogen sulfide have a much lower melting point and boiling point than water? ______

ISBN: 978-1-98-856693-1

78 The Hydrologic Cycle

Key Question: What processes allow water to cycle from the oceans to the land, and back?

Earth's water

- About 97% of Earth's **water** is stored in the oceans, which contain more than 1.3 billion km^3 of water. Less than 1% of Earth's water is freely available fresh water (in lakes, rivers, and streams).
- Water evaporates from the oceans and lakes into the atmosphere and falls as precipitation, e.g. rain, snow, or hail. Precipitation falling on the land is transported back to the oceans by rivers and streams, or is returned to the atmosphere by evaporation or transpiration (evaporation from plant surfaces).
- Water can cycle very quickly if it remains near the Earth's surface, but it can also remain locked away for hundreds or even thousands of years, e.g. if trapped in deep **ice** layers at the poles, or in groundwater storage (aquifers).
- Humans intervene in the **hydrologic** (water) **cycle** by using water for their own needs. Withdrawing water from rivers and lakes for irrigation changes evaporation patterns, lowers lake levels, and reduces river flows.

Water is the only substance on Earth that is found naturally as a solid, liquid, or gas. It has an unexpectedly high boiling point compared to other similar molecules and requires a lot of energy to change state. This means it acts as a buffer against extreme temperature fluctuations in the environment.

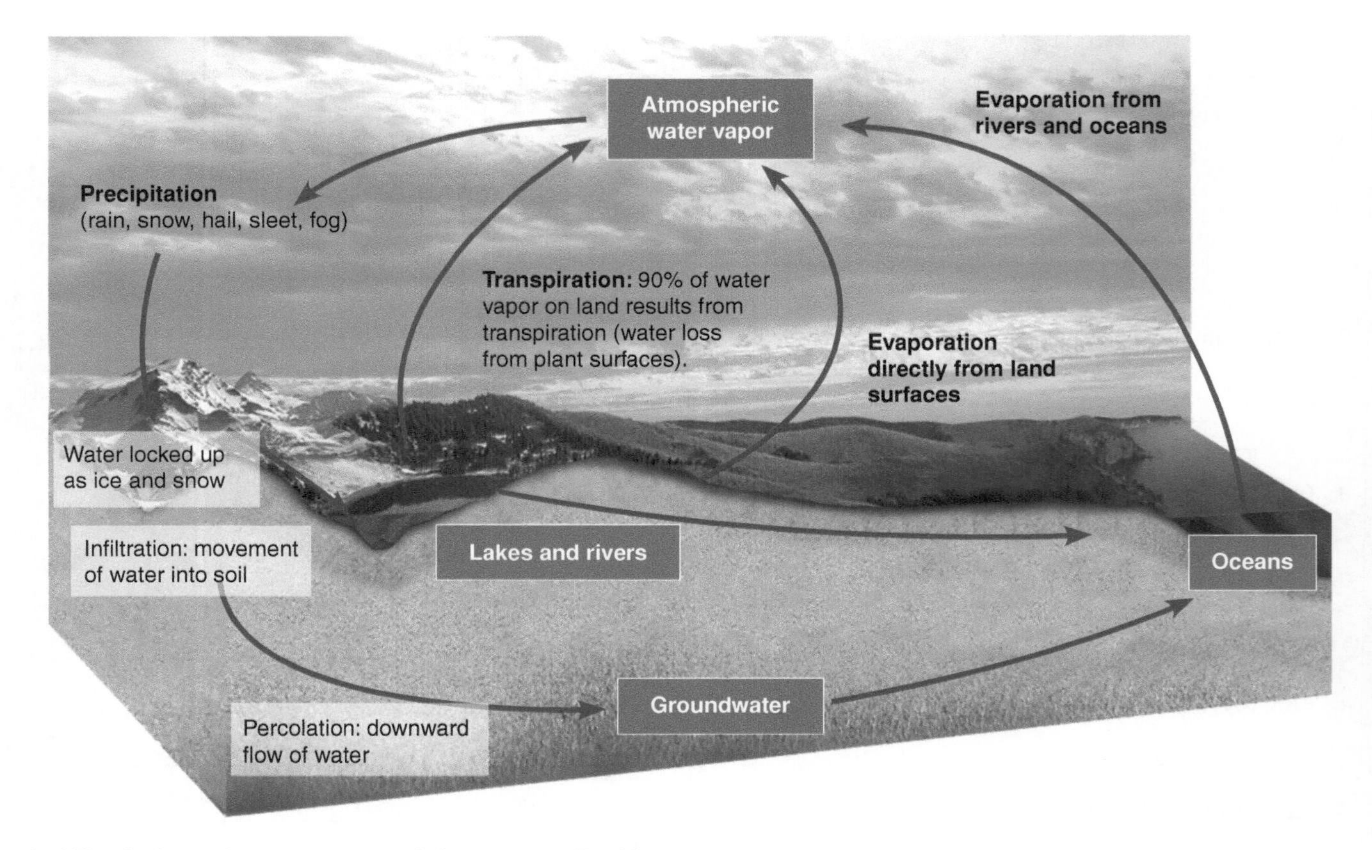

1. What is the main storage reservoir for water on Earth? ______

2. Describe the feature of water that allows it cycle, as described above: ______

3. Identify the two processes by which water moves from the land or oceans to the atmosphere: ______

   ESS2.C SF

ISBN: 978-1-98-856693-1

The water cycle is important in the transport of energy around the globe. Energy (from the Sun) is absorbed by the oceans. Water evaporates from the oceans, cooling them. This energy is released again when water vapor condenses.

Water can be held inside the Earth itself. The largest reservoir of water on Earth is in fact, in the mantle, bound with minerals. Some estimates put the amount of water in the mantle at ten times the volume in the Earth's oceans.

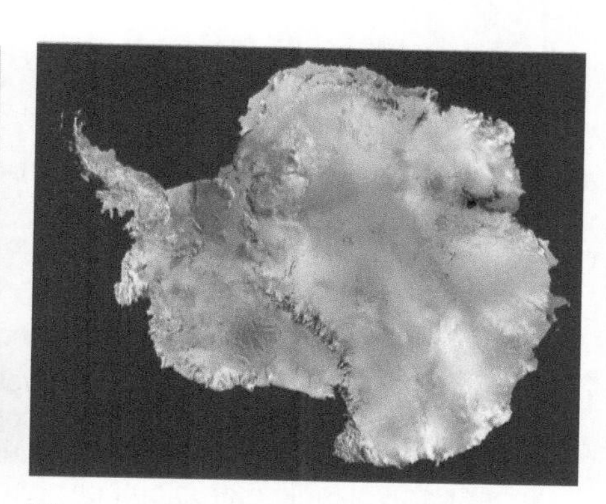

Water can be locked up in ice for tens of thousands of years. The ice in the ice sheet of Greenland is about 100,000 years old, while ice cores from Antarctica have dated some ice to at least 800,000 years old.

4. Explain how the hydrologic cycle helps to move energy around the globe: ______________________

5. How do humans intervene in the water cycle and how might this affect bodies of water such as lakes?

6. The photograph below shows a set-up for modeling the water cycle in the classroom. Use the following terms to label the model: *Clouds, oceans, rain, evaporation, land*

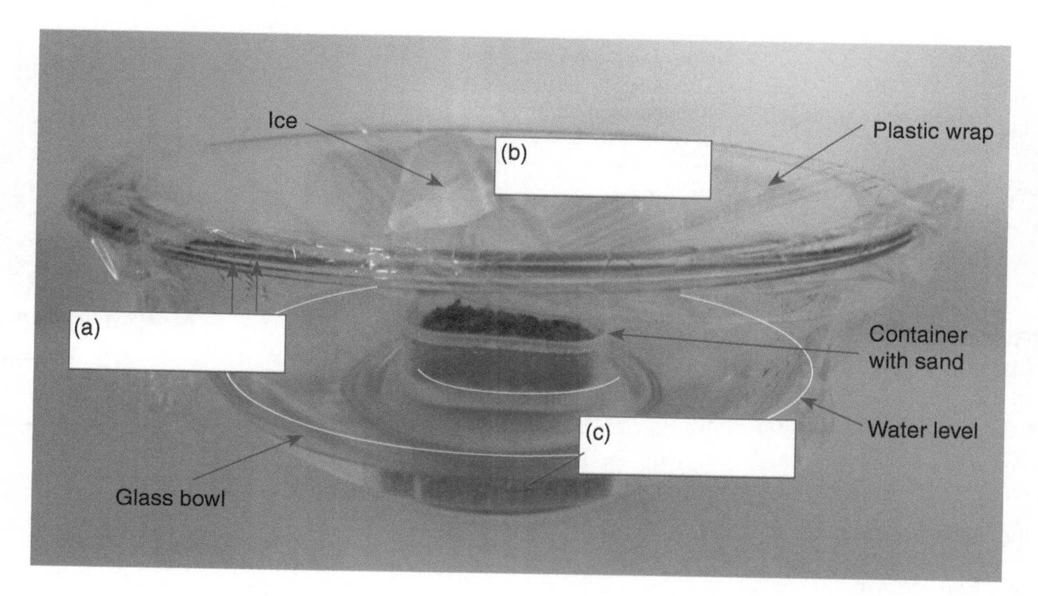

(d) What represents the clouds in the model? ______________________

(e) Explain how the "clouds" model this part of the actual water cycle: ______________________

ISBN: 978-1-98-856693-1

79 The Rock Cycle

Key Question: How do the processes of erosion, burial, melting, and reforming allow Earth's rocks to form a continuous cycle?

- The Earth's many rock types can be classified (grouped) as either **igneous**, **metamorphic**, or **sedimentary**.
- These rocks form in a continuous cycle. Erosion of surface rocks produces sediments. Burial of these, and pressure, transforms them into sedimentary rocks. Heat and pressure within the Earth can transform pre-existing rocks to form metamorphic rocks, such as slate and schist. Contact with **magma** can melt these to form igneous rock, which may appear as volcanic extrusions or plutonic intrusions (rocks formed underground, e.g. cooling magma).
- When rocks are exposed at the surface, they are then subjected to physical, chemical, and biological processes, collectively known as **weathering**. This cycle of rock formation, exposure, weathering, erosion, and deposition is known as the **rock cycle**.

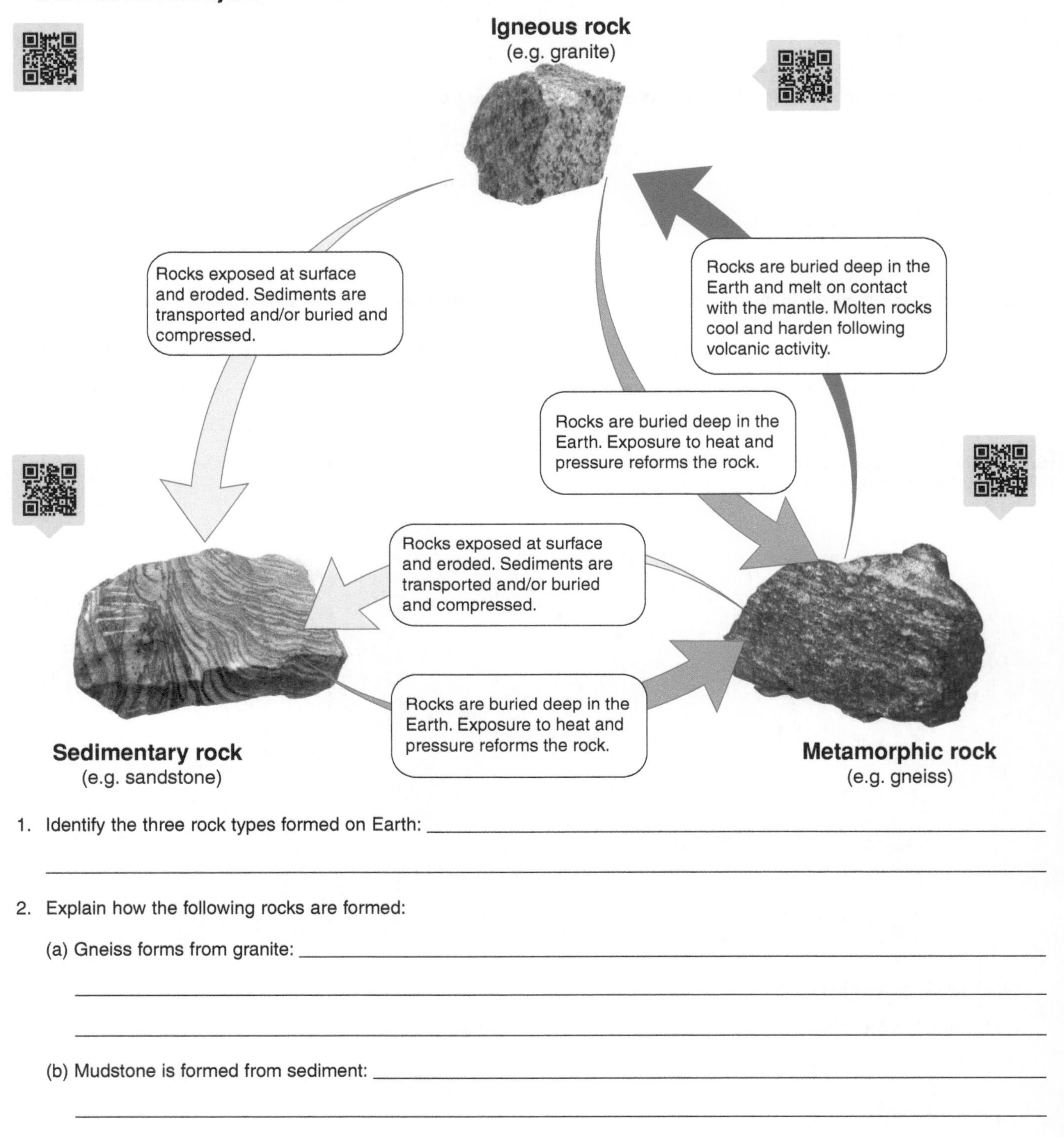

1. Identify the three rock types formed on Earth: ______________________________

____

2. Explain how the following rocks are formed:

(a) Gneiss forms from granite: ______________________________

____

____

(b) Mudstone is formed from sediment: ______________________________

____

____

   ESS2.C SF

ISBN: 978-1-98-856693-1

Investigation 7.1 Determining properties of rocks

See appendix for equipment list.

1. Gather some examples of different types of rocks. Identify the rock type using the key below, and then record in the table at step 5. Also, record the rock's classification: volcanic, metamorphic, or sedimentary.

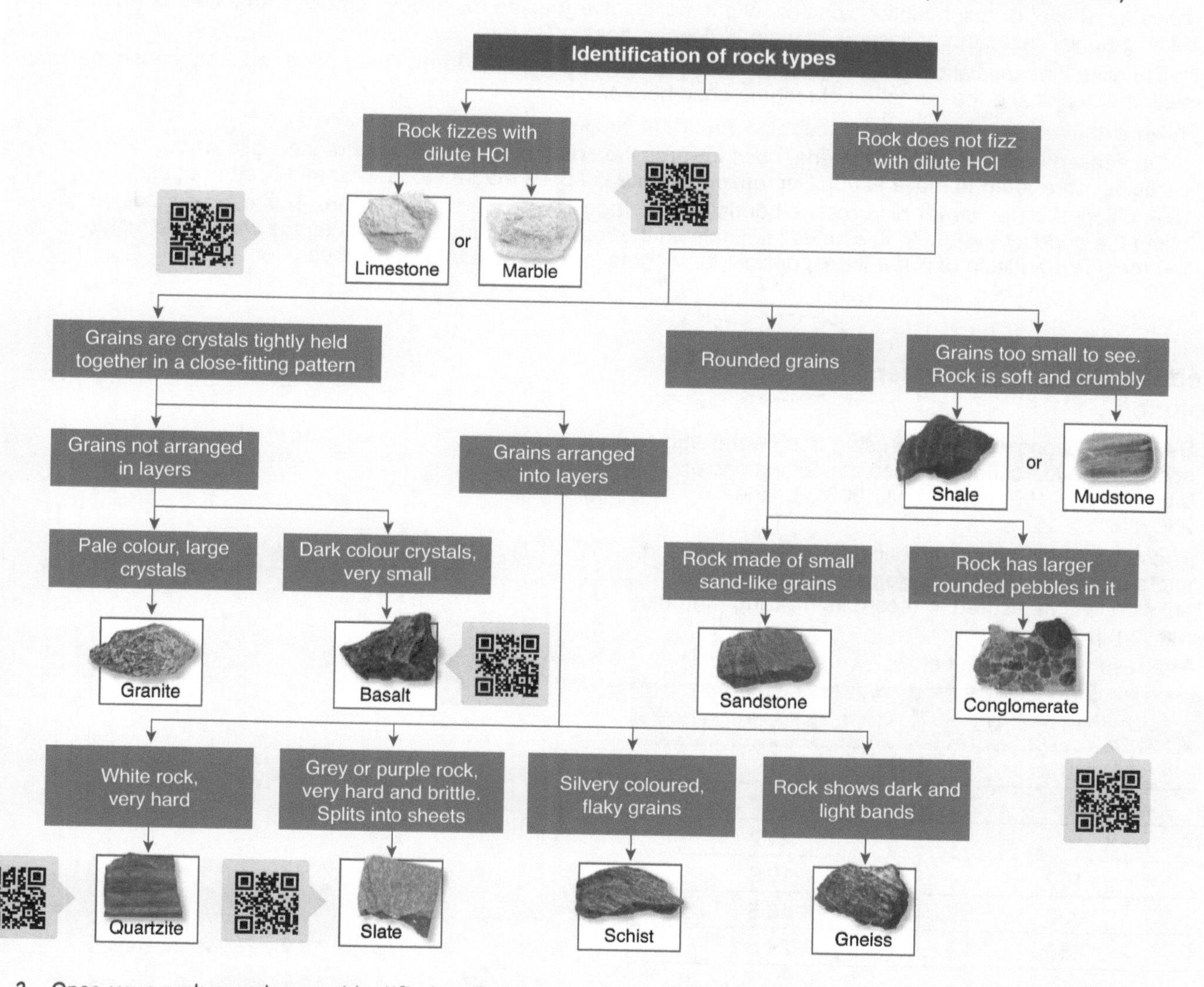

2. Once your rock samples are identified and recorded in the table below, weigh each rock and record its mass.
3. Measure the volume of each rock by filling a larger graduated cylinder with water to a known volume (e.g 200 mL) and placing the rock into it.
4. Record the increase in volume for each rock.
5. Divide the mass by the volume to find the density of each rock.

Rock sample	Rock classification	Mass (g)	Volume (mL or cm^3)	Density (g/mL or g/cm^3)

3. What type of rock had the greatest density? ______

4. The density of Earth's core is thought to be 12 g/cm^3; how does this rock's density compare to the density of the core?

______

ISBN: 978-1-98-856693-1

80 Water's Role in the Melting of Rocks

Key Question: How does water allow rocks in the solid lithosphere and asthenosphere to melt into liquid magma?

- The lithosphere and asthenosphere are solid; they are not liquid or molten. Yet volcanoes located above a hot spot or a subduction zone spew out molten lava (molten rock above ground), and magma (molten rock below ground) oozes out of fissures along mid-ocean ridges.
- This implies that special conditions must be encountered for magma to form. Three conditions that cause the local melting of rocks and the formation of magma chambers are:
- 1. Heat: the most obvious, but not the most important cause.
- 2. Decreased pressure: as hot material rises towards the crust, pressure on it decreases, allowing particles more room to move about. Decreased pressure causes magma to form at mid ocean ridges.
- 3. Addition of water: **water** disrupts the bonds in rocks and lowers their melting point. This can be modeled using **ice** and salt (NaCl). In this model, ice acts as the rock in the mantle and salt as the water held inside the rock. The addition of water is responsible for magma forming at subduction zones.

Sodium chloride and water solution

- Several solutions were made using fresh water and sodium chloride salt to produce concentrations of 0 g/L, 50 g/L, 100 g/L, 150 g/L, 200 g/L, and 250 g/L.
- These were poured into identical beakers and placed into a freezer at -50°C. The temperature of each solution was measured to record its freezing (and thus melting) point.
- The results are shown below:

Solution concentration (g/L)	Freezing/melting point (°C)
0	0
50	-3
100	-6.5
150	-10.9
200	-16.5
250	-24.5

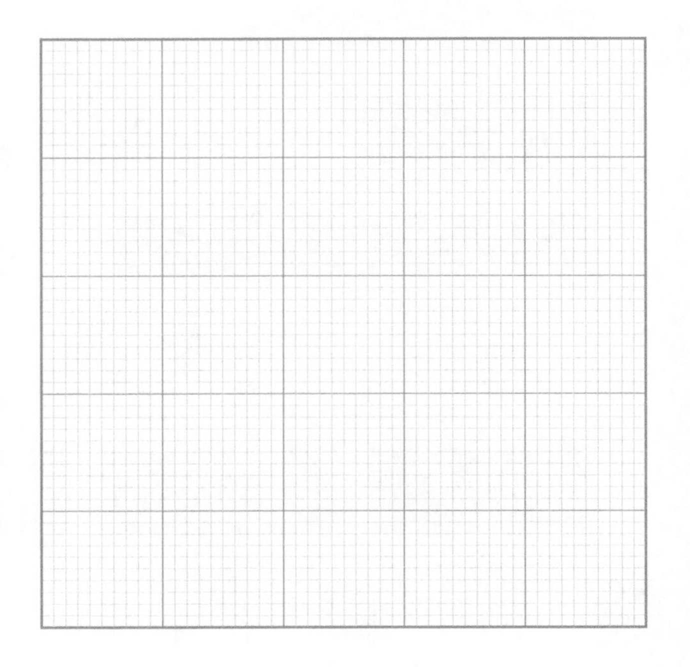

Water and plate tectonics

- As a tectonic plate descends in a subduction zone, it drags down water-laden sediment and rocks. The rocks are heated and squeezed, and at a depth of about 100 km the water is driven out and begins to rise through the rock as vapor.
- As it rises, the vapor encounters hotter rocks above, that are close to their melting point. The water vapor enters these rocks, lowering their melting point and producing magma.

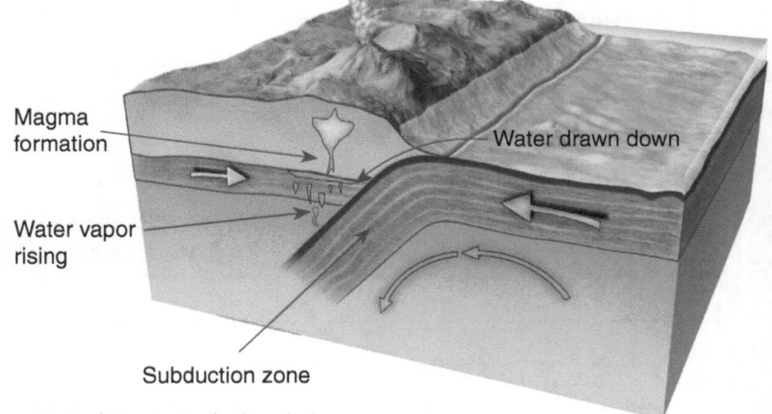

1. Use the tabulated data above to graph the melting point of the water/salt solutions:

2. Describe the shape of the graph: ____________________

3. Explain why water lowers the melting point of rocks: ____________________

____

____

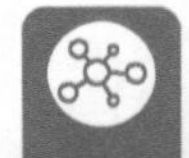

ESS2.C SF

ISBN: 978-1-98-856693-1

81 Weathering and Erosion

Key Question: How do the processes of weathering and erosion shape the Earth's surface?

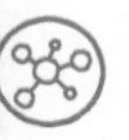

- **Weathering** and **erosion** are important processes that shape the Earth's surface. They usually work closely together and can be confused. It is important to remember that weathering and erosion are different processes.

Weathering

- Weathering is the chemical, physical, and biological process of breaking rocks and minerals down into smaller pieces.

Physical weathering

- Physical weathering occurs when rocks break apart without any change to their chemical structure. Physical weathering includes changes in pressure and temperature affecting the rock. These combine to put constant physical stress on the rock until it shatters. One way this occurs, especially in high mountains, is the process of freeze-thaw, causing frost wedging (above right and right).

Chemical weathering

- Chemical weathering is the breakdown of rock by chemical changes to the minerals it contains. This includes processes such as dissolving and oxidation. Rainwater is slightly acidic: it has a pH of about 6, due to dissolved carbon dioxide forming carbonic acid. Chemical reactions occur when it comes in contact with the minerals in rocks. An example is the weathering of limestone: the calcium carbonate in the limestone reacts with the excess hydrogen ions in the water, forming bicarbonate ions which are soluble and washed away. Another form of chemical weathering is oxidation: oxygen in the air or water reacts with iron in rocks, forming oxides or rust, which can slowly break down a rock.

Biological weathering

- Biological weathering is any weathering process carried out by a living organism. It can therefore also be chemical, e.g. by organic acids produced by organisms, or it can be physical, e.g. tree roots lifting pavements. Lichens and algae growing on the surface of rocks can slowly etch them, producing a greater surface area and slowly allowing other processes to take hold.

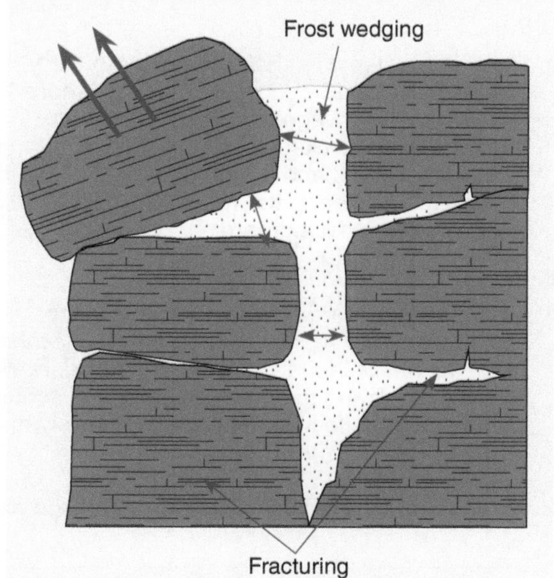

Frost wedging occurs when water seeps into cracks in rocks. As it freezes, it expands and forces the cracks open a tiny bit more. When the ice thaws, water seeps into the newly widened cracks, ready to freeze again. This continuous freeze-thaw cycle can crumble whole mountainsides over thousands of years.

1. Use the boxes below to distinguish between weathering and erosion (following page), including examples:

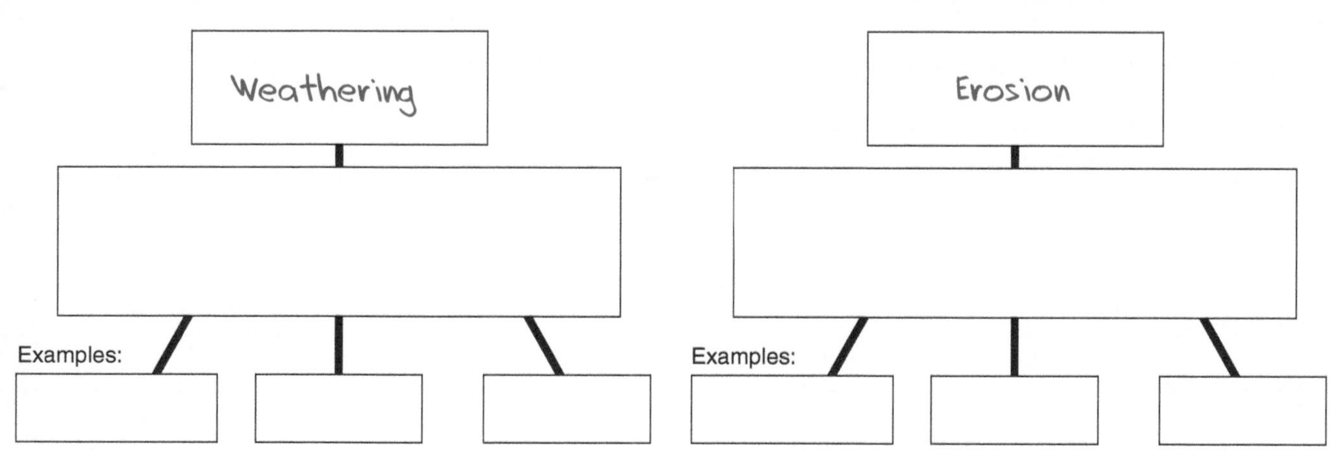

ISBN: 978-1-98-856693-1

SF

Erosion

- **Erosion** is the loosening, removal, and transport of the weathered materials. Erosion is followed by **deposition** of the material elsewhere, e.g. in a river delta. The processes of erosion combine to lower the Earth's surface.

Water

- **Water** is a major contributor to erosion. The force of water movement can be small, moving small pebbles and fine sediment, or it can be massive, such as floodwater moving huge boulders down river beds. The continual flow of water over a stony river bed, or the continual action of waves can shape the rocks into smooth, rounded shapes. The transport of sediment by rivers plays a major role in layering sediment and debris according to size and weight. In a delta, where water flow slows, heavier debris drops is deposited first, with finer sediment being carried further out to sea.

Wind

- Much like water, wind has the power to carry sediment and shape rocks. In deserts, where there is a lack of vegetation to cover the dry ground, sand is picked up by the wind and transported across continents and hurled at cliffs and mountains, physically weathering the rocks and helping to carve them into the most extraordinary shapes.

Glaciers

- Glaciers form in areas where snow and **ice** accumulate year round and flow slowly downhill. Currently, about 10% of the Earth's surface is covered by glaciers. At the height of the last glaciation, this figure was about 30%. Glaciers have enormous erosive power, and are capable of moving massive boulders and scouring out huge U shaped valleys in the process. The rock frozen in the ice acts as an effective abrasive as it slowly moves down the valley, removing soil and earth as it goes.

2. Explain how frost wedging breaks down large rocks: ______

3. Describe two ways in which chemical weathering breaks down rocks:

   (a) ______

   (b) ______

4. Explain how biological weathering can incorporate both physical and chemical weathering: ______

5. Describe how each of the following take place:

   (a) Water erosion: ______

   (b) Wind erosion: ______

   (c) Glacial erosion: ______

ISBN: 978-1-98-856693-1

Investigating Frost Wedging

Key Question: How does frost wedging contribute to the weathering of rocks?

Investigation 7.2 Investigating frost wedging

See appendix for equipment list.

1. Set up three boxes, as shown in the diagram below:

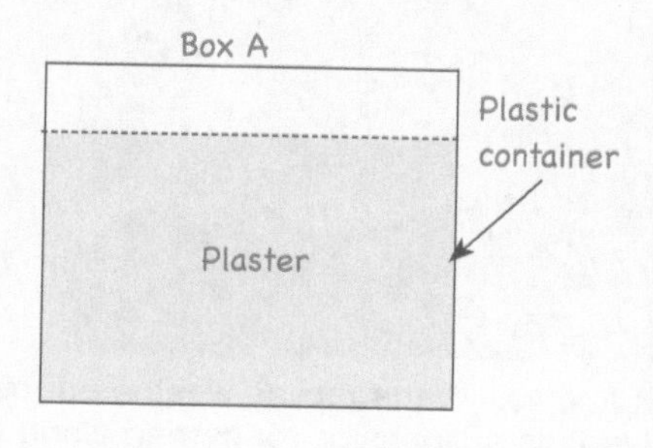

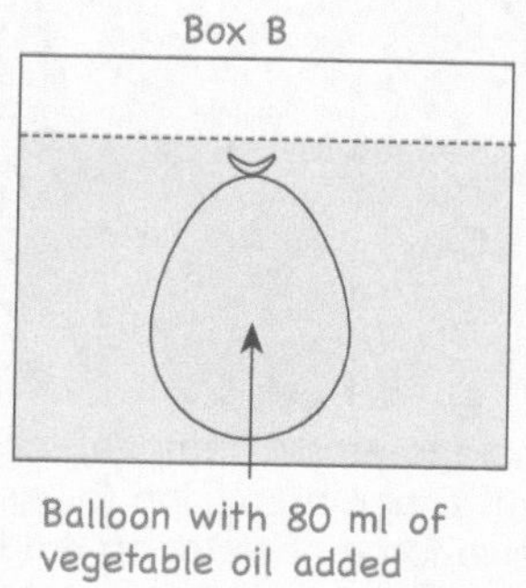

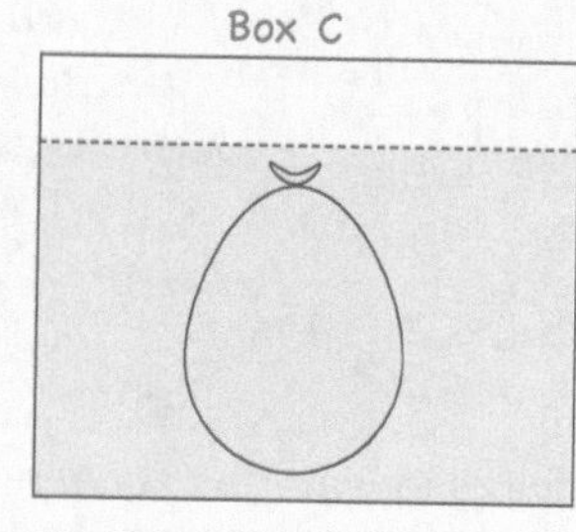

2. Allow the plaster to set, then place all three boxes in a freezer overnight.

1. Remove the boxes from the freezer and record observations below:

   (a) Box A: ______

   (b) Box B: ______

   (c) Box C: ______

2. Which box(es) acted as the control for the test? ______

3. It is expected that plastic in one of the boxes has split. Explain why this has occurred: ______

4. (a) How well does this model in the investigation represent the process of frost wedging, and why?

   ______

   (b) In what ways does the model differ from frost wedging? ______

5. Use the findings from the investigation to summarize the role water plays in rock formation: ______

ISBN: 978-1-98-856693-1

83 Modeling Erosion

Key Question: How does modeling help us to understand how erosion shapes the landscape?

Water as an agent of erosion

- **Water**, including water as snow and **ice**, is able to erode (remove) rock and soil. Water moves weathered rock to the lowest elevation possible, and transports it either in solution (dissolved), in suspension, or carried along the base of water courses as bed load. The erosive force of water on land is clearly seen where soil is removed along drainage lines by surface water runoff, or where the sea meets coastal cliffs. **Erosion** rates are variable. River banks and coastal cliffs may be very gradually undercut and then, once unstable, may slump, forming a flat surface as a large volume of material is removed.

Modeling the effect of water on the landscape

- Stream trays or tables are a simple way of modeling and observing how rivers develop and change the land by erosion and **deposition** of sediment. Any long tray can be used, as long as there is a water supply and an outlet for the water is drilled at the lower end.
- You will use your stream tray set-up to explore how water affects the landscape and what features of the landscape influence the landforms that result.

Investigation 7.3 Modeling the process of erosion

See appendix for equipment list.

1. You may work in groups. Set up the tray by placing it on a slight angle with the outlet at the lower end. Place your substrate, e.g. gravel, silt, or sand in the tray and work the sediment so that it becomes thinner near the lower end.
2. The simplest set-up is to make a sediment "mountain" near the upper end of the tray to initially block water flow, forming a "lake". See photo (right) for set-up.
3. Answer question 1 below and then begin your investigation. Record your results on the next page.

1. Before you do the modeling, record your predictions for the following:

   (a) The effect of flow velocity (rate and direction) on erosion: ______________________________

   ____

   (b) Where most of the erosion will occur in a meandering (snake-like) stream: ______________________________

   ____

   (c) Where the sediment that is moved will be deposited: ______________________________

   ____

ISBN: 978-1-98-856693-1

4. With your stream tray now operating, observe the effect of the lake overflowing (A).
5. Experiment with making different mountain shapes, then repeat the overflow scenario.
6. Experiment with different materials, e.g. gravel, sand, clay, to simulate different rock types.
7. What factors influence how the channel will form? ____

____

____

8. Now, create a river meander (sinuous track) and observe how it changes over time as water moves at different velocities around the bends, depositing and eroding material at different places (B).
9. Add larger rocks and vegetation to observe their effects on erosion and river channel formation (B).
10. Investigate the effect of increasing water velocity when banks are already undercut by erosion.

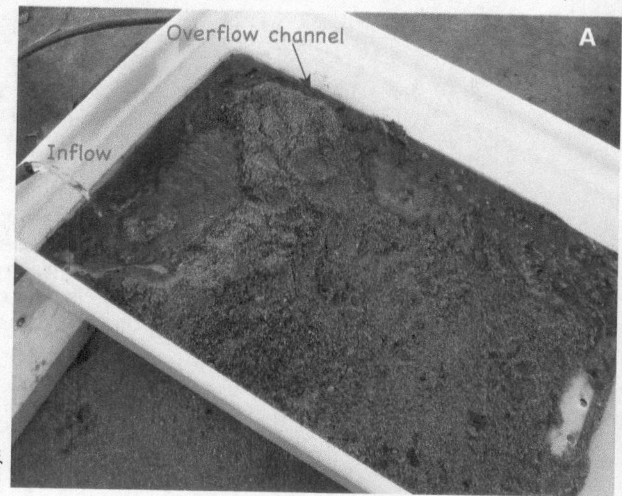

2. Draw the flow through the different models you have made. Include notes about the changes and how features such as large rocks and vegetation affect the river's shape. What is the effect of changing the velocity of water flow?

ISBN: 978-1-98-856693-1

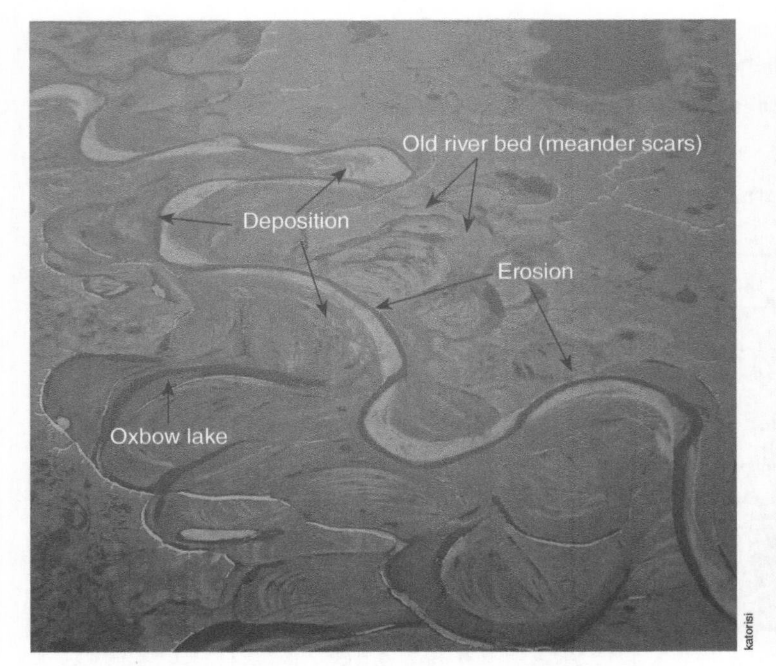

River meanders are the result of deposition on the inner bank and erosion on the outer bank. Over time, meanders become accentuated, and may meet and close up to form oxbow lakes (above). This usually occurs in the shallower end-stages of a river's course. During natural flooding events, a river may overflow its banks, depositing sediment on the surrounding land. Over time, this creates a flat, fertile floodplain.

Great Skagit Valley is a productive floodplain in Washington State. Historical flooding from the Skagit River (above) provided nutrient-rich sediment to create fertile soils that grow a wide range of commercial fruits, vegetables, and flowers. Diking to control the river began in the 1880's, reducing the regular flooding to farmland.

3. Build the gravel and sand into a mountain at the top end of the tray. Let the water flow, forming a new stream. Near the bottom of the tray, in the water flow, place a small animal or plant figurine, lying it down. Observe the build up of sediment on the figurine. This process models part of the process of fossilization:

   (a) Which step in fossilization is being modeled? ______________________________

   (b) What other process needs to occur for fossilization to proceed? ______________________________

4. (a) Use the information provided and your models to explain how river meanders arise: ______________________________

   ____

   ____

   (b) How would this pattern of deposition change during a large flood? ______________________________

   ____

   ____

   ____

5. Based on your models and your understanding, and supplementary material found in the **BIOZONE's Resource Hub**, explain how erosion and deposition form the basis of Great Skagit Valley's agricultural economy:

   ____

   ____

   ____

   ____

   ____

   ____

   ____

   ____

   ____

ISBN: 978-1-98-856693-1

84 Moisture Content and Soil Erosion

Key Question: How do the cohesive and adhesive properties of water influence the rate of erosion in soils?

Effect of soil moisture on wind erosion

- **Water** plays a major role in binding soil together. Dry soils are easily blown away by the wind. In deserts, this effect can be seen in the movement of sand dunes. The dune slowly creeps in the direction of the wind flow as dry sand is blown up a dune and tumbles over the front. When water is at low to medium concentrations, its **cohesive** and **adhesive** properties bind soil particles together into clumps, increasing soil stability and making it harder for the wind to move the soil particles.

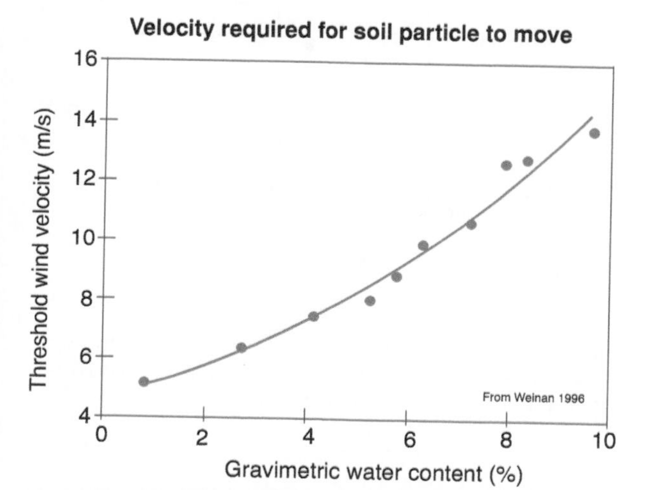

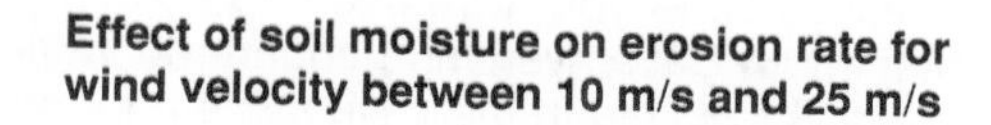

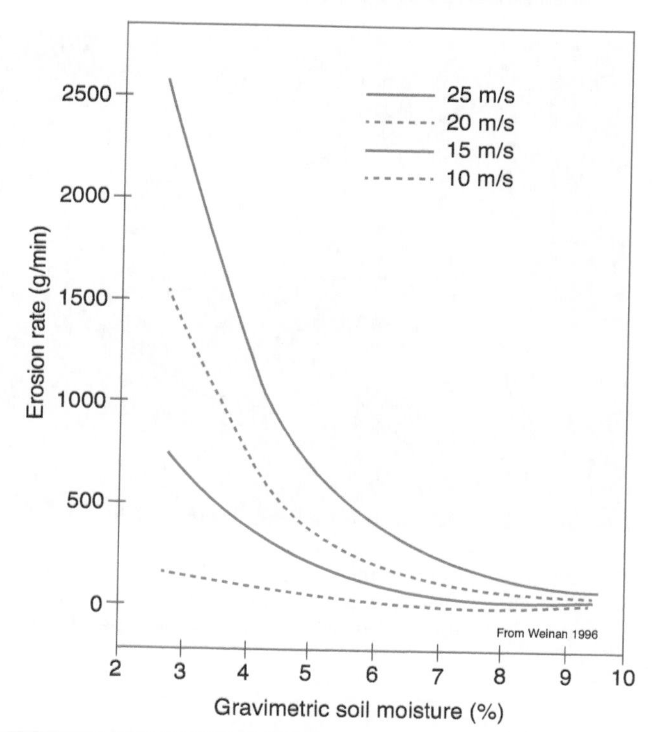

Cropping, plowing, and planting in many farms occurs in the summer months when soil moisture is low (but growing conditions are favorable). Valuable top soil can be lost if the land is struck by high winds at this time. Soil moisture may be reduced due to drought, poor irrigation management, or a lack of vegetation cover. The lack of moisture in soil also contributes to dust storms.

Although water helps bind soil particles, there is a point at which the soil becomes saturated and cannot hold more water. At this point (or even before, depending on the soil type), the soil will no longer be able to maintain its structure. If this happens on a hillside, a landslide may occur. Landslides also occur if soil is above an impermeable layer that water cannot penetrate, producing a lubricated area that the soil will slide over.

1. Which properties of water affect soil stability? ______

2. Study the left graph above:

   (a) What is the wind velocity needed to move soil with a moisture of 3%? ______

   (b) What is the wind velocity needed to move soil with a moisture of 8%? ______

3. How many times more erosion occurs in a soil with 3% moisture than a soil with 7% moisture is a 15 m/s wind?

   ______

4. At what soil moisture does wind speed make little difference to erosion rate? ______

ISBN: 978-1-98-856693-1

SF 

85 Review Your Understanding

Key Question: What processes helped to form the Mammoth Caves?

In this chapter you have seen how water plays a role in developing the Earth's surface features, like the vast Mammoth Cave system encountered in the anchoring phenomenon. You should now be able to better describe the process involved in the cave system formation, and the interaction between **water** and rocks.

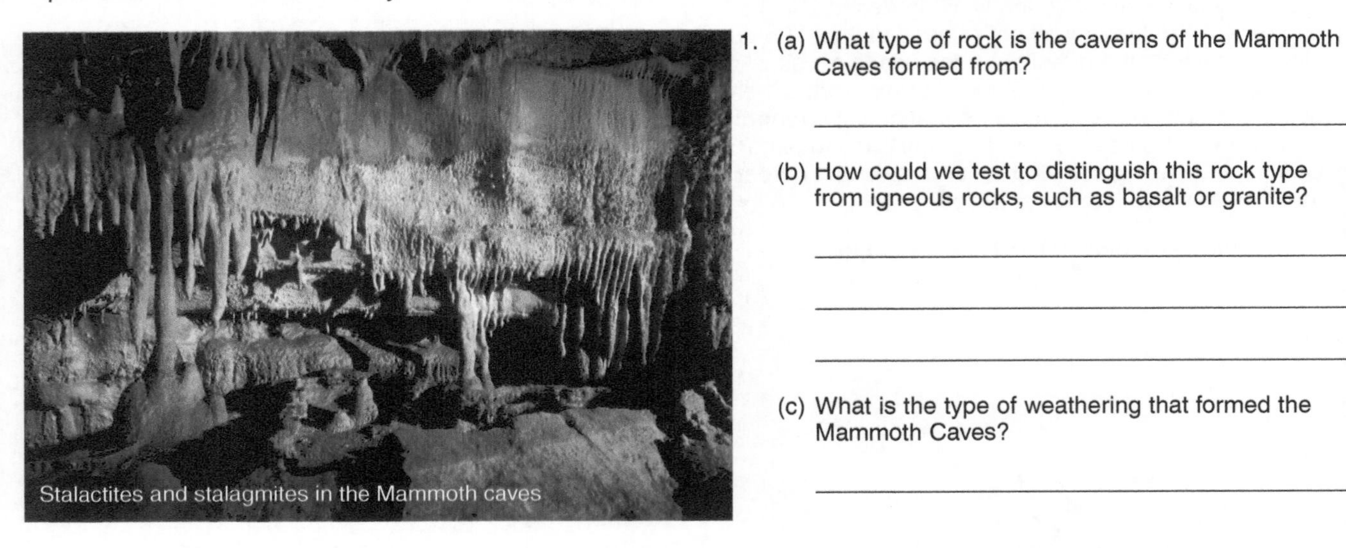

Stalactites and stalagmites in the Mammoth caves

1. (a) What type of rock is the caverns of the Mammoth Caves formed from?

   (b) How could we test to distinguish this rock type from igneous rocks, such as basalt or granite?

   (c) What is the type of weathering that formed the Mammoth Caves?

2. At the start of the chapter, you developed a flow chart of how you thought the Mammoth Cave system may have formed. You will now refine this flow chart by creating a simple annotated diagram below, using the correct scientific vocabulary, as well any rock cycle processes and the type of weathering leading to the Mammoth Cave formation.

ISBN: 978-1-98-856693-1

86 Summing Up

1. Wind is an agent of soil erosion. How much it erodes, depends on the moisture content of the soil. The data below shows the effect of wind velocity on the erosion of soil:

	Soil lost (kg/m²/min)	
Wind velocity (m/s)	2.67% moisture	5.20% moisture
2	0.2	0.1
4	0.8	0.2
6	1.3	0.35
8	2.2	0.6
10	3.6	0.8

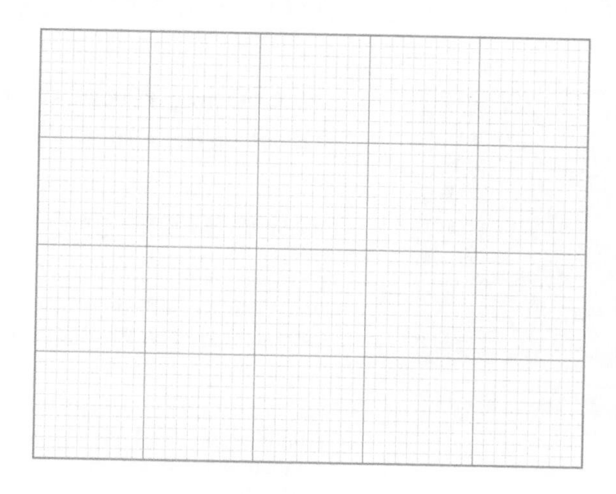

(a) Graph the data on the grid provided:

(b) Describe the shape of the lines: ____

(c) What is the effect of soil moisture on erosion? ____

(d) What is the effect of wind velocity on erosion? ____

2. Identify the type of weathering occurring in the following photos.

(a) ____________________ (b) ____________________ (c) ____________________

3. The diagram below shows the current shape of a short part of a river's course. Draw over the diagram to show what you might expect the river to look like, some time in the future:

4. When the mineral peridotite is in the presence of water, its melting point is about 800°C. When water is absent, it melts at about 1500°C. Explain what causes this change in melting point and the effect of this on volcanic activity and magma/lava formation:

____

ISBN: 978-1-98-856693-1

CHAPTER 8

Weather, Climate, and Biogeography

NASA

Anchoring Phenomenon

It's Getting Hot in Here: Why is the world heating up? — 87 101

How does energy flow in and out of Earth change the climate?

☐ 1 Calculate incoming and outgoing energy in a model of earth's energy budget. Discuss how Earth's climate is affected by the angle of incoming light. Calculate the amount of solar energy received at specific points. — 88 102

☐ 2 Use information from models of the Earth's shape, tilt, and rotation to explain how they influence the distribution of energy around the globe, create the seasons, and affect atmospheric circulation. Investigate how the angle of incoming light affects the amount of energy received. — 89

☐ 3 Explain the role of the atmosphere. Explain the phenomenon of aurora. — 90

☐ 4 Use models to explain how atmospheric circulation influences the climate of different biomes. — 91

How has life and Earth's systems co-evolved over time?

☐ 5 Explain how life on Earth and the environment influence each other. — 92

☐ 6 Discuss both seasonal and long term changes of carbon dioxide in the atmosphere. — 93

Hcrepin

☐ 7 Explain the origin of atmospheric oxygen and link it to the process of photosynthesis. Use evidence to identify historical changes in oxygen levels, including the "Great Oxygenation Event". — 94 102

☐ 8 Link changes in life on Earth to influences on biodiversity change. Discuss how plants co-evolved with soil development on Earth. Explain the relationship between coral reefs and mangroves, and their influence on developing surface features on Earth. — 95 96 97

How does carbon cycle through the hydrosphere, atmosphere, geosphere, and biosphere?

☐ 9 Calculate quantitative shifts of carbon into different reservoirs, using models of the carbon cycle. Construct your own model to demonstrate movement of carbon through the atmosphere, hydrosphere, geosphere, and biosphere. — 98 102

☐ 10 Use a spreadsheet model to investigate carbon cycle changes. — 99

Graeme Churchard

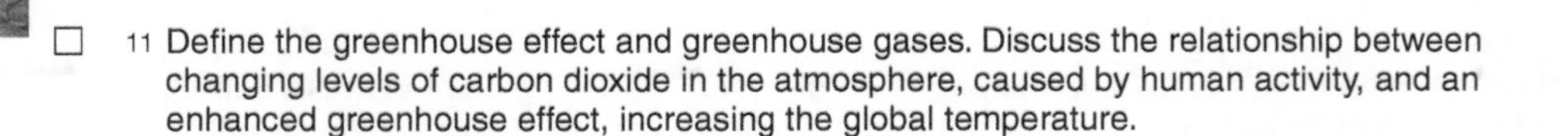

☐ 11 Define the greenhouse effect and greenhouse gases. Discuss the relationship between changing levels of carbon dioxide in the atmosphere, caused by human activity, and an enhanced greenhouse effect, increasing the global temperature. — 100 101

87 It's Getting Hot in Here

Key Question: Why is the world heating up?

▶ Statements that the Earth is warming are often accompanied by images such as the one shown below to gain peoples attention. Although these images may be overly dramatic, data from observatories around the world do show the Earth's surface temperature is increasing, as is the surface temperature of the oceans.

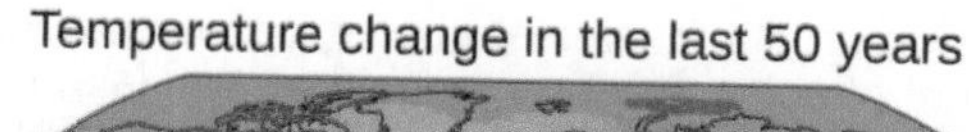

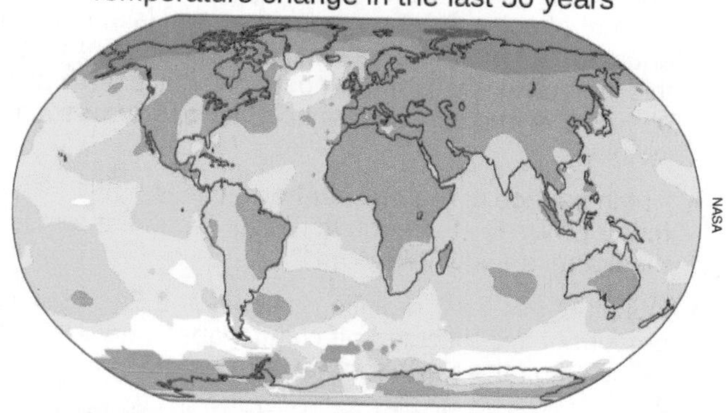

2011-2021 average vs 1956-1976 baseline

-1.0	-0.5	-0.2	+0.2	+0.5	+1.0	+2.0	+4.0 °C
-1.8	-0.9	-0.4	+0.4	+0.9	+1.8	+3.6	+7.2 °F

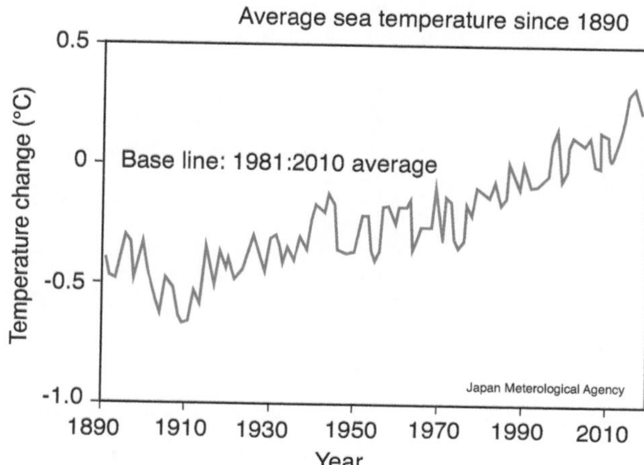

1. In groups, discuss why the globe appears to be warming. What might be causing the observations shown in the graph and map above? Summarize your ideas below:

2. Climate change is a controversial topic, with some people contesting the scientific evidence, or providing contradictory arguments. In groups, discuss climate change and the various arguments around it. Summarize your discussion below:

ISBN: 978-1-98-856693-1

88 Energy From the Sun

Key Question: How is the energy from the Sun distributed over the Earth?

- The Sun produces almost unimaginable amounts of energy. The amount of solar radiation reaching Earth is about 174 petawatts, equal to 174 quadrillion joules per second (174 x 10^{15} J/s). To put this in context, the world's most powerful lasers can produce power of 1.25 PW and only keep this up for one picosecond (1 x 10^{-12} seconds).
- At the surface of the **atmosphere**, this is 1.361 kilowatts per square meter ($kW\,m^{-2}$) at the equator. Over the entire surface of the Earth, the figure is about 342 W/m^2.
- Not all of this solar radiation reaches the Earth's surface. A large amount of it is reflected off clouds, absorbed by the atmosphere, or reflected off the Earth's surface.
- The energy from the Sun is also not distributed evenly about the globe. Because the Earth is spherical the poles receive less energy per square kilometer than the equator. Earth's angle of rotation further influences the uneven distribution of the energy received.

1. Complete the diagram below of incoming and radiated energy.

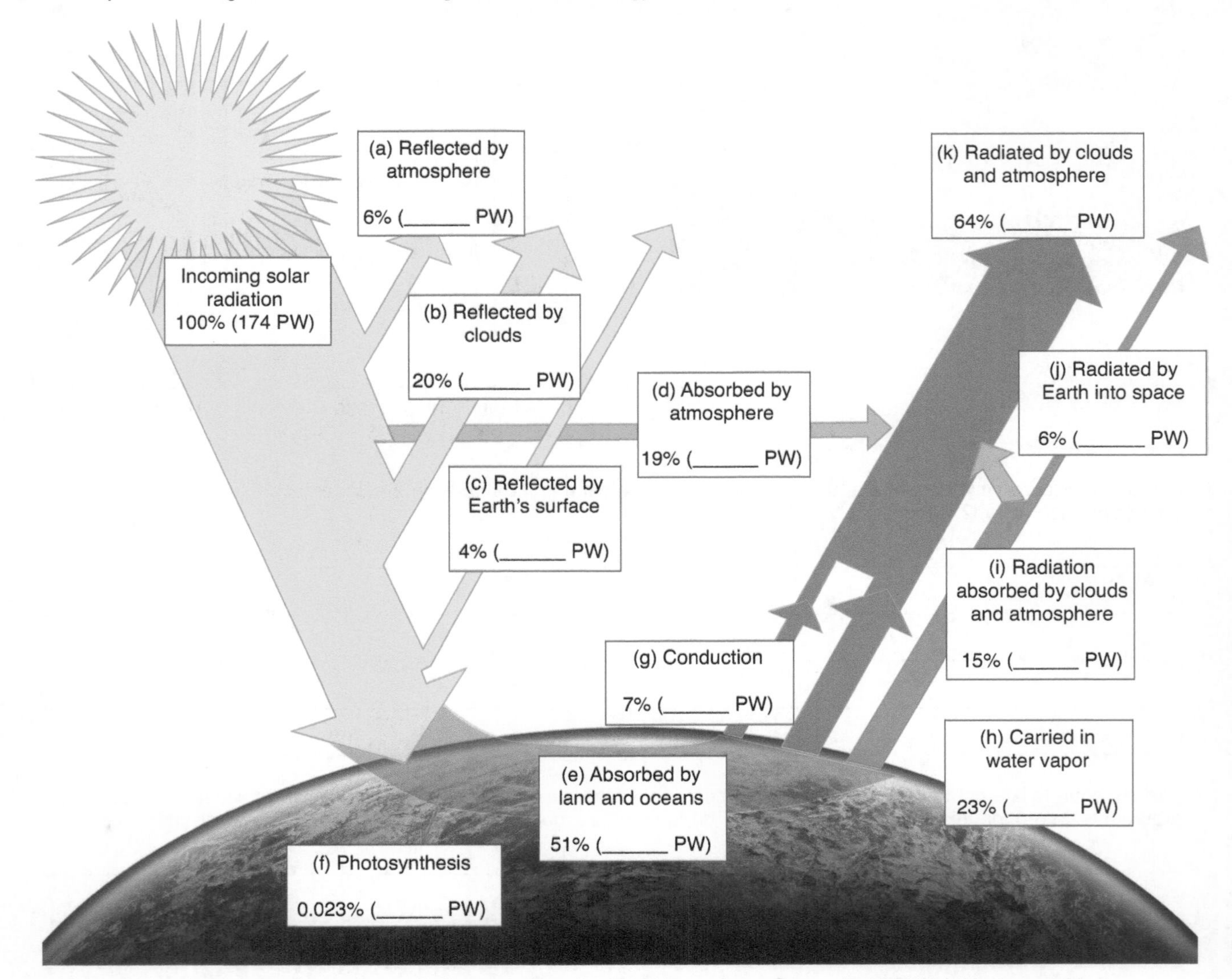

- About 51% of the incoming solar radiation reaches the Earth's surface. Some (0.023%)of this is used by photosynthesis in plants to build organic molecules. The rest drives atmospheric winds and ocean circulation and eventually radiated back into space.

  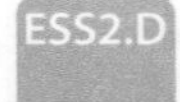 

ISBN: 978-1-98-856693-1

- The curvature of the Earth changes the angle at which solar radiation hits the planet's surface. At the equator, the Sun is directly overhead and solar radiation hits the Earth perpendicular to the surface (at noon). The Tropic of Cancer and the Tropic of Capricorn are lines of latitude on the Earth that denote the limit of the Sun being overhead at noon (depending on the **season**).
- Outside the tropics, solar radiation continues to hit the Earth more and more obliquely towards the poles until it hits virtually parallel with the surface. This makes an enormous difference to the amount of useful solar radiation received. At the equator, almost 100% of the light to reach the surface is available, while at the poles almost none is. Moreover, light at the poles has to travel through more of the **atmosphere** and so even less light actually reaches the surface.

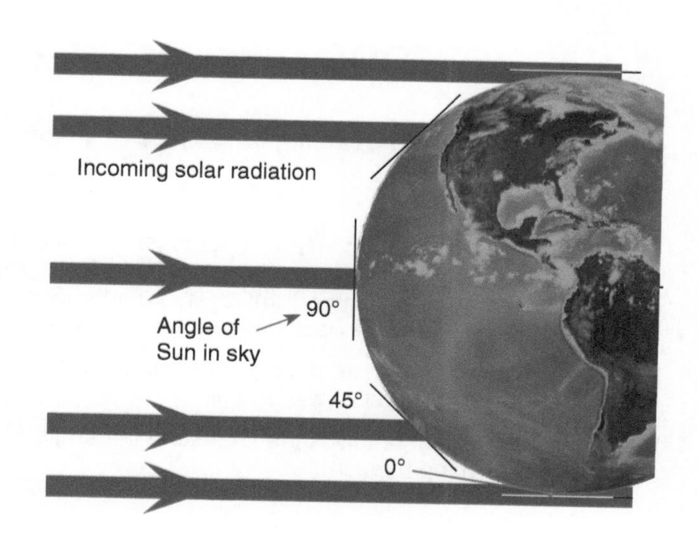

Below the Arctic and Antarctic circles, the Earth receives only about 40% of the solar energy that is received at the equator.

The tropics receive the full amount of sunlight and energy available. This causes heating, which carries water into the air, creating a hot, wet climate.

Differential heating between the tropics and poles drives air currents from the tropics towards the poles. This is because as air rises at the equator and falls at the poles.

2. (a) Describe the relationship between the curvature of the Earth and the amount of solar energy received at the surface:

(b) Explain how this affects the climate at the following points:

i: The equator:

ii: The poles:

3. The amount of solar energy received at any point on the Earth can be calculated using the equation:

$$A' = A \times \text{cosine } x$$

Where **A** = the amount of solar radiation at the equator, **A'** = the amount of solar radiation at latitude x. **x** = the latitude of the point on the Earth.

For each of the following lines of latitude, calculate the amount of solar energy received, assuming 700 $W m^{-2}$ of energy is received at the equator and no tilt to the Earth (i.e. at the spring and fall equinoxes). The first one is completed for you. (Note that your calculator must be set to use degrees, not radians):

(a) Tropic of Cancer (23.5° North): $A' = 700 \times \cos 23.5 = 700 \times 0.917 = 641.9\ W/m^2$

(b) 45° North:

(c) Arctic circle (66° North):

(d) North pole (90° North):

ISBN: 978-1-98-856693-1

89 Seasons

Key Question: How does the Earth's tilt cause alternate heating (summer) and cooling (winter)?

- The Earth is tilted at 23.4° with respect to its axis of orbit around the Sun. The angle remains the same as it travels around the Sun. This results in the North pole pointed towards the Sun during the months of June, July, and August, (the northern summer) and away from the Sun six months later during December, January, and February (the northern winter). The opposite happens in the Southern Hemisphere (below).
- The change in temperature during the **seasons** is a direct result of this change, depending on whether the pole points towards the Sun or away from it.
- The observed effect of this is the change in the angle of the Sun at noon during the summer (more overhead) and winter (lower to the horizon).

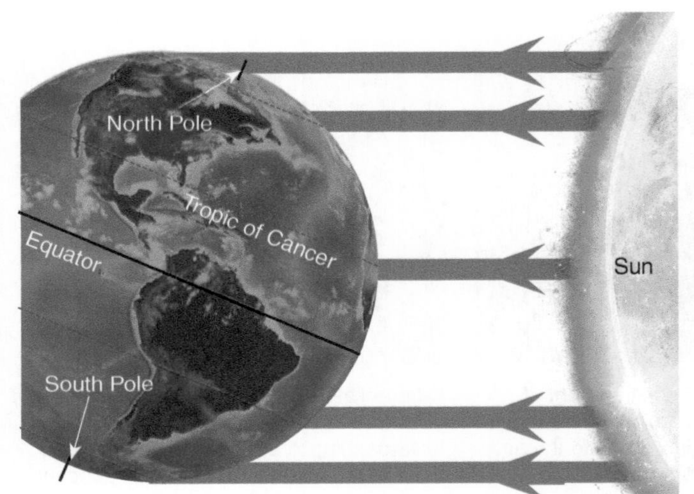

Northern Hemisphere: Summer
Southern Hemisphere: Winter

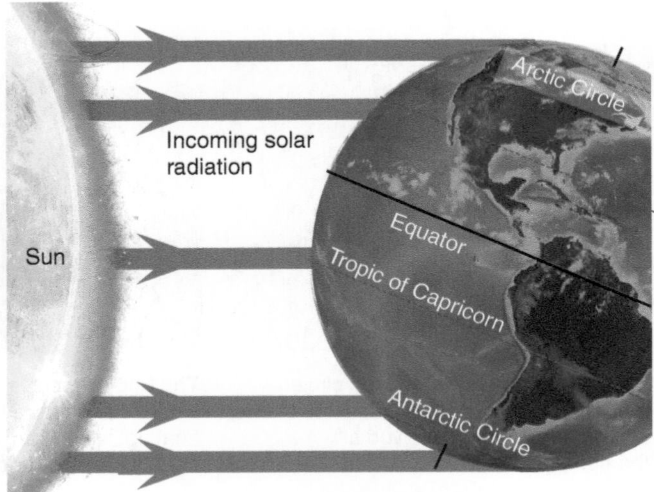

Northern Hemisphere: Winter
Southern Hemisphere: Summer

- The energy received from the Sun is more or less constant, so why is it so much colder during the winter? The answer is that the energy from the Sun is spread over a much larger area during the winter because the angle of sunlight hitting the ground so much less in winter.
- For example a shadow at noon in the summer is short. The shadow represents the area of ground that the sunlight would have hit. In winter the shadow is much longer and therefore the area of ground the sunlight would have hit is greater. Thus the energy per square meter is less, resulting in a lower overall temperature.

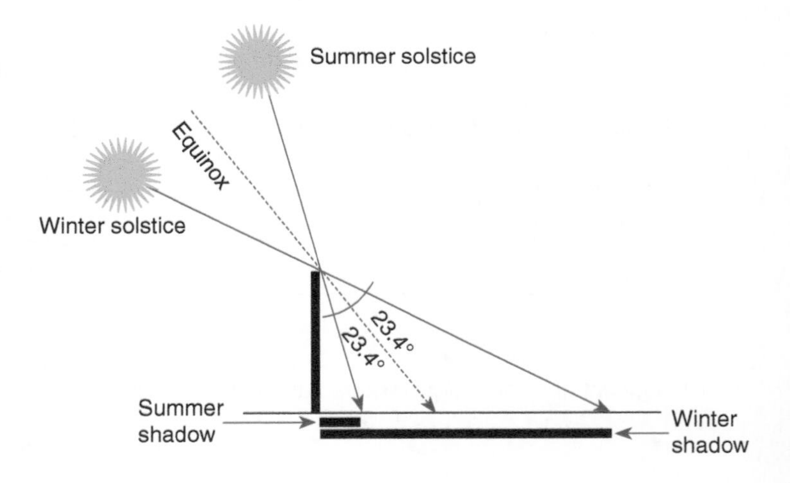

1. What causes the change in seasons on Earth? ________________________________

____

2. What effect does the change of seasons have on the angle of the Sun above the horizon at noon?

____

____

3. Compare the length of a shadow at noon in summer and winter: ________________________________

____

ISBN: 978-1-98-856693-1

Investigation 8.1 Measuring Energy

See appendix for equipment list.

1. Using a stand and protractor to measure angle, set up a flashlight pointing straight down (90° angle) at a piece of grid paper from a distance of 30 cm (a darkened room works best) as shown in the diagram below

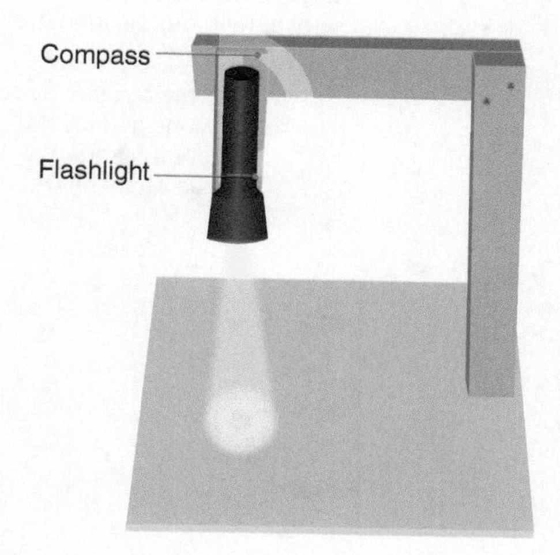

2. Draw around the illuminated part of the grid paper and then use the grid paper to help find the area illuminated.
3. Area illuminated (90°): ______________________________
4. Tilt the clamp stand to a 66° angle, measuring 30 cm from the center of the flashlight front along the angle to the center of the illuminated area on the grid paper. Again, draw around and calculate the area of grid paper illuminated.

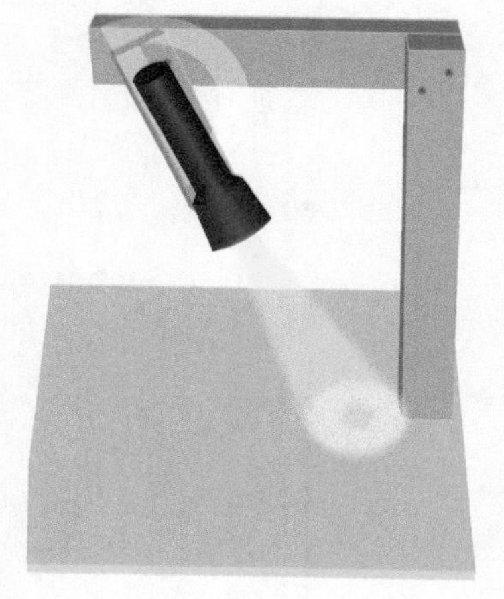

5. Area illuminated (66°): ______________________________
6. Repeat this procedure for 45° and 33°.

   Area illuminated (45°): ____________________ Area illuminated (33°): ____________________

4. (a) How does the area of graph paper illuminated change with the angle of the flashlight? ______________________________

____

____

(b) For each angle of the flashlight, calculate the amount of light energy (watts) received per cm^2 on the grid paper. You could use a light meter to measure the light output of the flashlight if you don't know it or (assuming its output is constant) start with a general light output of 3 W. (Hint if the light bulb is a 3 W bulb, each square cm of paper is receiving how many watts?). Write your answers next to your outlines on the graph paper.

(c) Attach all your graph paper records to this page.

ISBN: 978-1-98-856693-1

90 The Earth's Atmosphere

Key Question: How does the atmosphere help to carry energy from the Sun around the globe?

- The Earth's **atmosphere** is a layer of gases surrounding the globe and retained by gravity. It contains roughly 78% nitrogen, 20.95% oxygen, 0.93% argon, 0.038% carbon dioxide, trace amounts of other gases, and a variable amount (average around 1%) of water vapor.
- This mixture of gases, known as air, protects life on Earth by absorbing ultraviolet radiation and reducing temperature extremes between day and night. The atmosphere consists of layers around the Earth, each one defined by the way temperature changes within its limits.
- The outermost **troposphere** thins slowly, fading into space with no boundary. The air of the atmosphere moves in response to heating from the Sun and, globally, the atmospheric circulation transports warmth from equatorial areas to high latitudes and returning cooler air to the tropics.

The exosphere extends from about 1000 km above the Earth to about 10,000 km above the Earth. Gases are very spread out. Beyond this is the vacuum of space.

Thermosphere
This layer extends as high as 1000 km. Temperature increases rapidly after about 88 km. However even though the temperature of each molecule is very high, the amount of heat per volume of space is very low because there is almost a vacuum.

Mesosphere
Temperature is constant in the lower mesosphere, but decreases steadily with height above 56 km.

Stratosphere
Temperature is stable to 20 km, then increases due to absorption of UV by the thin layer of ozone.

Troposphere
Air mixes vertically and horizontally. All weather occurs in this layer.

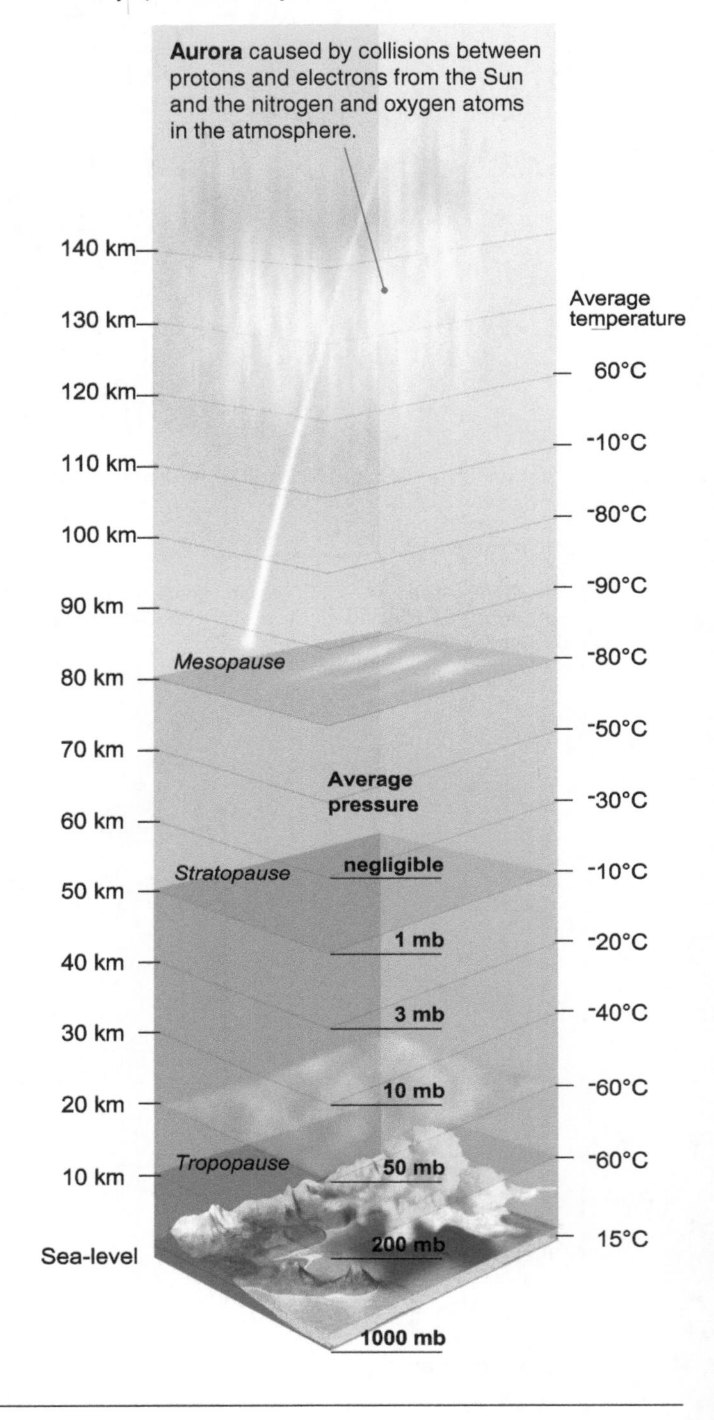

1. Describe two important roles of the atmosphere: ______________________________

____

2. What causes aurora? ______________________________

____

____

____

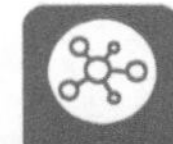

ISBN: 978-1-98-856693-1

91 Atmospheric Circulation and Climate

Key Question: How does the rotation and differential heating of the Earth effect the circulation of the planet's atmosphere, and therefore climate?

Atmospheric circulation and the tricellular model

- High temperatures over the equator and low temperatures over the poles, combined with the rotation of the Earth, produce a series of separated atmospheric cells that circulate at specific areas in the **atmosphere**. This model of atmospheric circulation, with three cells in each hemisphere, is known as the **tricellular model**.

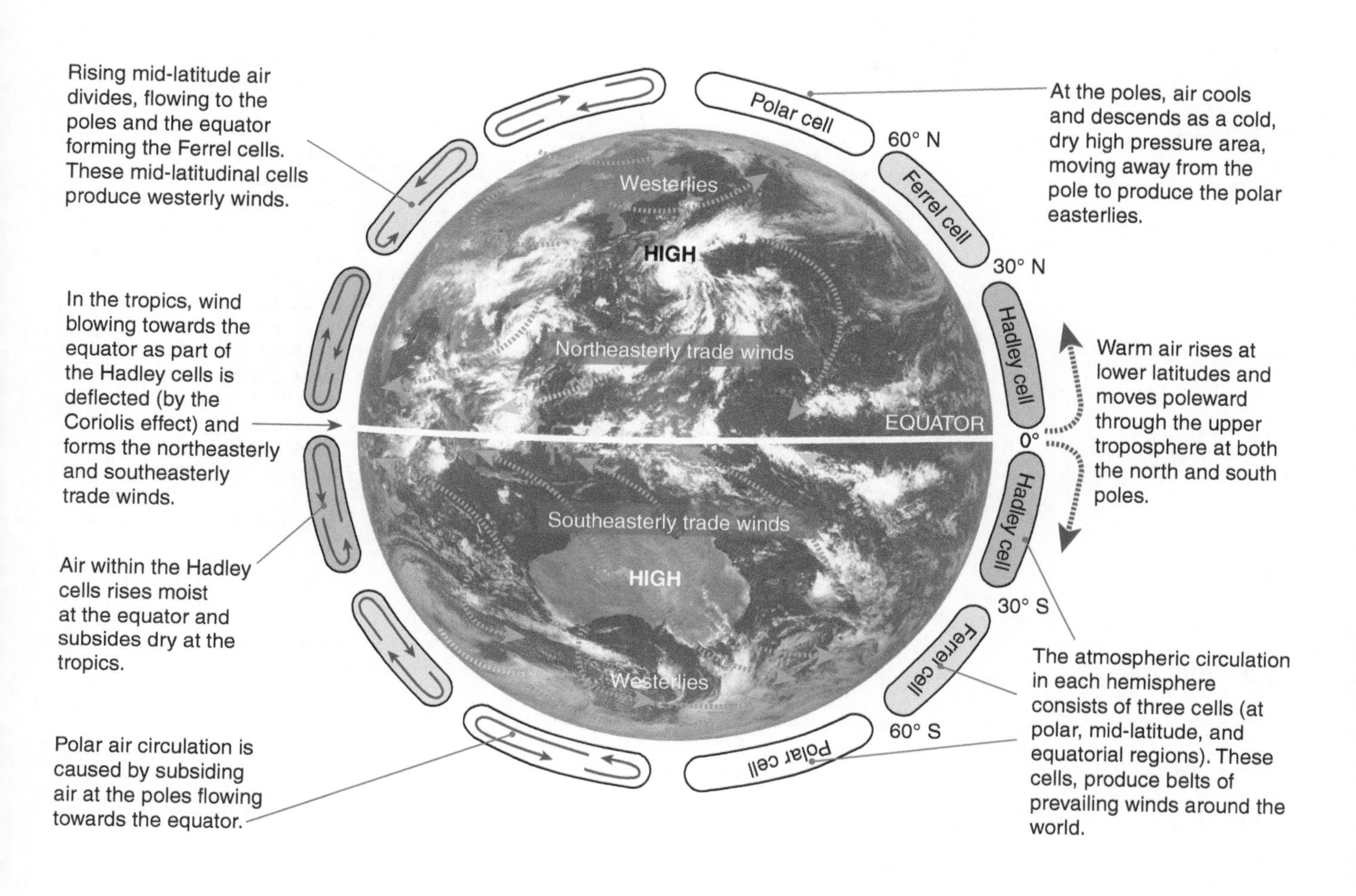

- The energy gained from solar radiation becomes progressively less from the equator to the poles. Heat gained at the tropics is transferred to cooler regions by atmospheric circulation, producing a more even spread of temperatures over the globe than would otherwise occur if there was no atmosphere. Similarly heat gained by the oceans also transfers heat about the globe. The ice caps of the poles reflect so much of the sunlight they receive that they produce a permanently cold **climate**.
- If there was no heat flow, the poles would be about 25°C cooler and the equator about 14° C warmer.

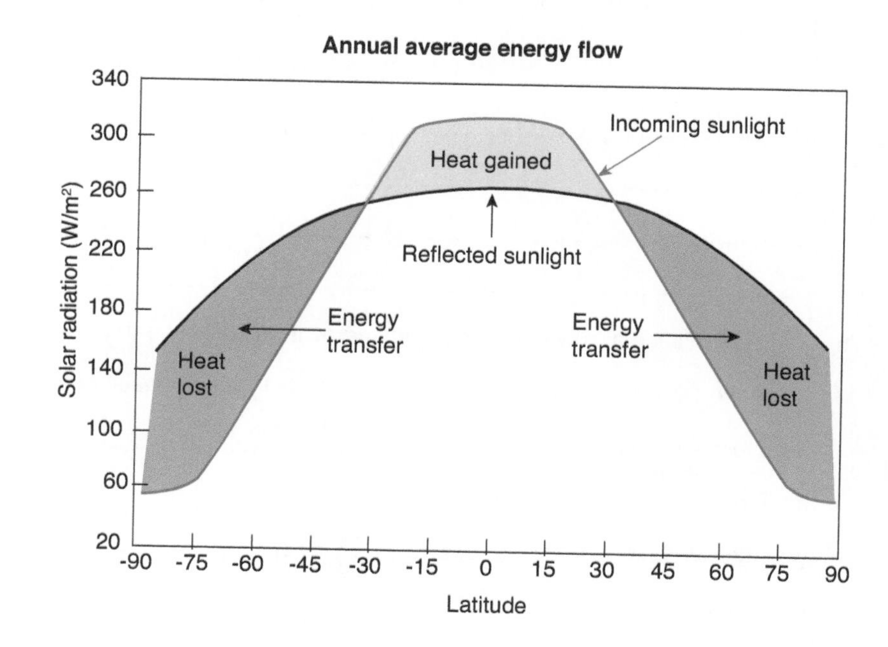

ISBN: 978-1-98-856693-1

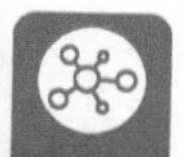

Atmospheric circulation influences climates and biomes

- The **climate** is affected by the circulation of the **atmosphere**. Air rising at the equator produces a warm wet climate. As the air travels away from the equator, it cools and descends as dry air.
- The division of atmospheric circulation into three separate cells in each hemisphere produces climatic conditions that are mirrored on each side of the equator. These conditions produce **biomes**, large areas with the same climatic conditions and vegetation characteristics. Tropical rainforests are one such biome and are found circling the equator, bordered by deserts, then temperate forests, and finally polar deserts.

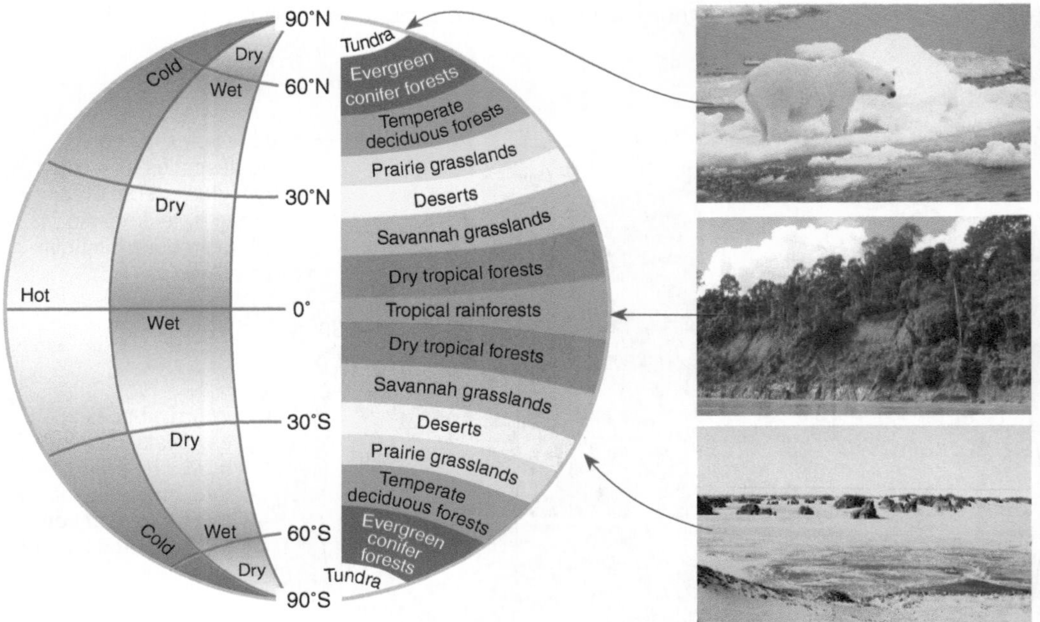

Cool dry air descending at the poles produces polar deserts. Because water remains locked up as ice, these are some of the driest places on Earth.

Warm air rising at the equator carries moisture with it, which falls as rain in often violent rainstorms. The warm wet climate produces the most biodiverse regions on Earth.

Dry air descending beyond the tropics strips moisture from the land as it travels back to the equator. Deserts have the most extreme temperature changes because there is no moisture or clouds to regulate the heat.

1. Identify the latitudes that each of the atmospheric cells lie between:

   (a) Polar cell: ____________________

   (b) Ferrel cell: ____________________

   (c) Hadley cell: ____________________

2. Identify the cell that produces mid latitude westerlies: ____________________

3. Which cell is responsible for producing the trade winds? ____________________

4. How does the tricellular model explain why the tropics are hot and wet and the deserts to either side of the tropics are hot and dry:

5. State the latitude at which the incoming energy from sunlight equals the energy lost: ____________________

6. Using the diagram above, identify the approximate latitude of each of the following biomes and describe their climate:

   (a) Evergreen conifer forest: ____________________

   (b) Temperate deciduous forest: ____________________

   (c) Tropical rainforest: ____________________

   (d) Deserts: ____________________

ISBN: 978-1-98-856693-1

92 The Coevolution of Earth's Systems

Key Question: How did the Earth and life on it evolve together, and shape each other?

- Life began on Earth about 3.8 billion years ago. Life takes resources from its surroundings, modifies them, and then uses them to replicate itself. In doing this, life modifies the environment, either by modifying chemicals and structures in the environment directly or by adding chemicals from waste or through decay after death.
- The modification of the environment produces new conditions for the evolution of life and as life evolves so does the environment, forcing more change upon life.
- This reciprocal influence is termed **coevolution** and it is a common phenomenon in biology. One example is the species of yucca plants, which are only pollinated by species of yucca moths. In Earth science, an example is the formation of the Earth's atmosphere by early photosynthetic organisms that produced oxygen as a waste product.
- The diagram right illustrates key stages of the coevolution of Earth's systems and life showing how changes in one influenced changes in the other.

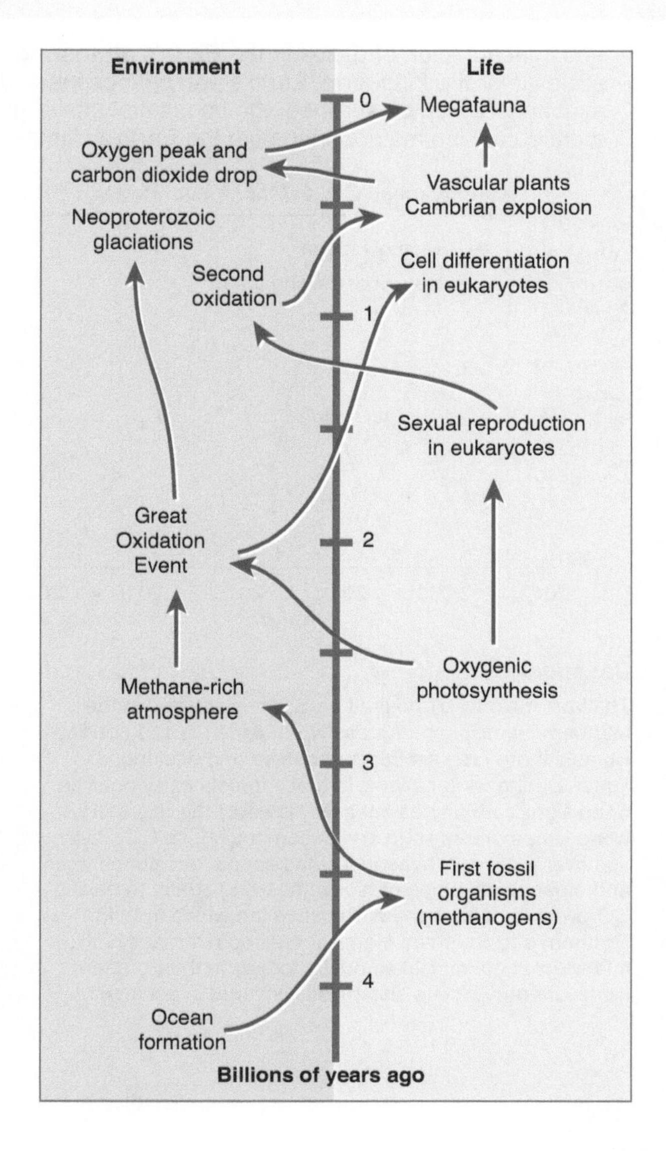

Mangroves have evolved to inhabit estuarine environments. They modify the estuary by collecting sediment and so the environment evolves into a terrestrial instead of a marine one.

1. What is meant by coevolution? ______________________________

2. Describe how life causes the environment to change: ______________________________

3. How does the environment allow for life to evolve? ______________________________

4. Describe a specific example of life modifying the environment: ______________________________

ISBN: 978-1-98-856693-1

93 Changes in Earth's Atmosphere

Key Question: How have the concentrations of gases in the Earth's atmosphere changed over time?

▸ The concentration of gases in the Earth's **atmosphere** fluctuate on small scales over the short term, and on large scales over the long term. Earth's early atmosphere was very different to today's. Even after a nitrogen-oxygen atmosphere was established, the concentrations of gases such as oxygen and carbon dioxide (CO_2) changed greatly, causing major changes to the Earth's climate.

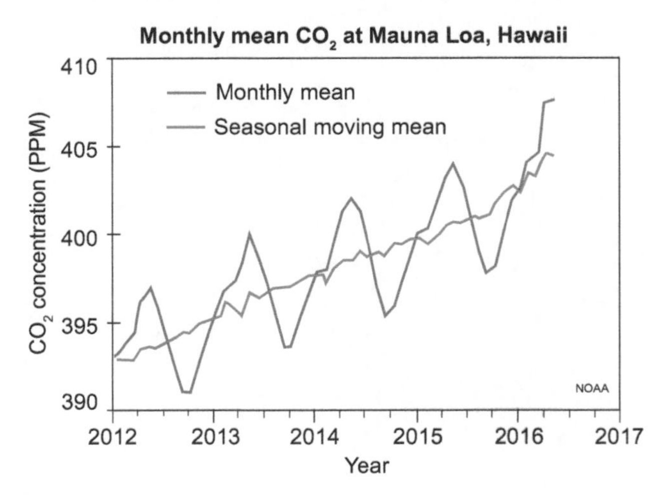

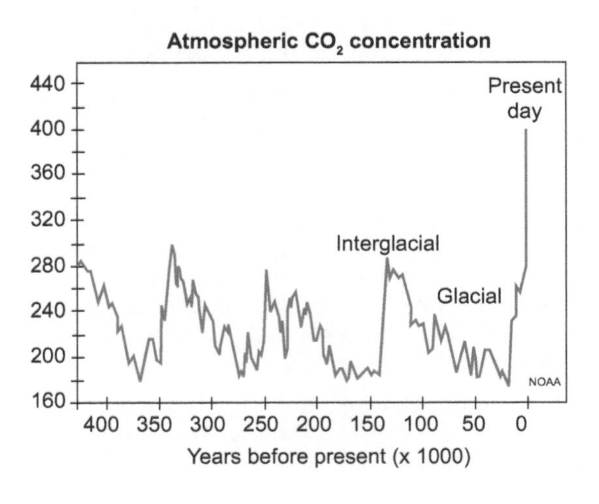

Seasonal CO_2

The vast majority of the land on Earth is situated in the Northern Hemisphere. Across North America and northern Eurasia there are vast tracts of conifer and deciduous forest. During winter, plants in these forests carry out little or no significant photosynthesis. However the rest of the world keeps on respiring and decomposing, so CO_2 levels rise over the winter season. During spring, deciduous trees and other plants begin photosynthesizing again, removing CO_2 from the atmosphere. Because the winds from the Northern and Southern Hemispheres do not readily mix, this effect is not cancelled out by forests in the Southern Hemisphere (which is also mostly covered in oceans).

Long term CO_2

The concentration of CO_2 has cycled relatively consistently over the last several hundred thousand years. The rise and fall of the atmosphere's CO_2 concentration correlates with the rise and fall of the Earth's surface temperature over at least the last 400,000 years. Although CO_2 is not the direct cause of the change in temperature (which is actually caused by changes in Earth's orbit) it does contribute to a positive feedback effect that helps warm the planet. The steep rise in CO_2 concentration over the last 60 years has been attributed to the burning of fossil fuels. **Climate** scientists fear that an atmospheric CO_2 concentration "point of no return" may soon be reached.

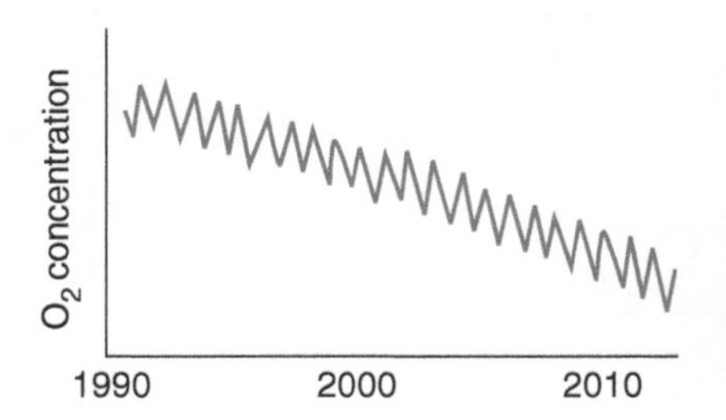

The oxygen concentration in the atmosphere is currently 21%. It rises and falls seasonally in a similar way to the CO_2 concentration. Measurements show that overall concentration has been reducing since the 1950s.

Atmospheric oxygen peaked at about 35% 300 million years ago during the Carboniferous period. During this time, huge insects, such as the giant dragonfly *Meganeura*, could exist because the high oxygen concentration allowed oxygen to easily diffuse into their bodies

The Earth has had at least three atmospheres. The earliest was probably similar to the atmospheres of the solar system's giant gas planets or the moon Titan (above). Oxygen didn't exist in the atmosphere in any large amount until about 2.4 billion years ago.

1. What causes the seasonal changes in CO_2 concentration? ____________________

____

____

2. What global changes over the last 400,000 years correlate with the rise and fall of CO_2 concentrations?

____

ISBN: 978-1-98-856693-1

94 The Great Oxygenation Event

Key Question: How did oxygen, produced as the waste product of oxygenic photosynthesis, fundamentally change the Earth's atmosphere and lead to a snowball Earth?

- The rise of photosynthetic life produced changes to the Earth that, in turn, affected life itself. Photosynthesis requires electrons in order to fix CO_2 as organic compounds. Early photosynthetic prokaryotes probably used H_2S as a source of electrons, producing sulfur compounds as waste (as do sulfur bacteria today). The evolution of an oxygen-producing photosynthetic process filled the **atmosphere** with oxygen and provided a new way for life to extract energy from organic molecules.
- It also changed Earth's rocks, created new minerals, formed the ozone layer, and plunged the Earth into a 300 million year long ice age. The initial rise in free oxygen is called the **Great Oxygenation Event** (GOE).
- The rise in oxygen allowed aerobic organisms, including eukaryotes, to evolve. There is evidence to suggest that the evolution of multicellular algae (e.g. seaweeds) triggered another ice age by extracting CO_2 from the atmosphere faster than it was being replaced, thus reducing its **greenhouse effect**.

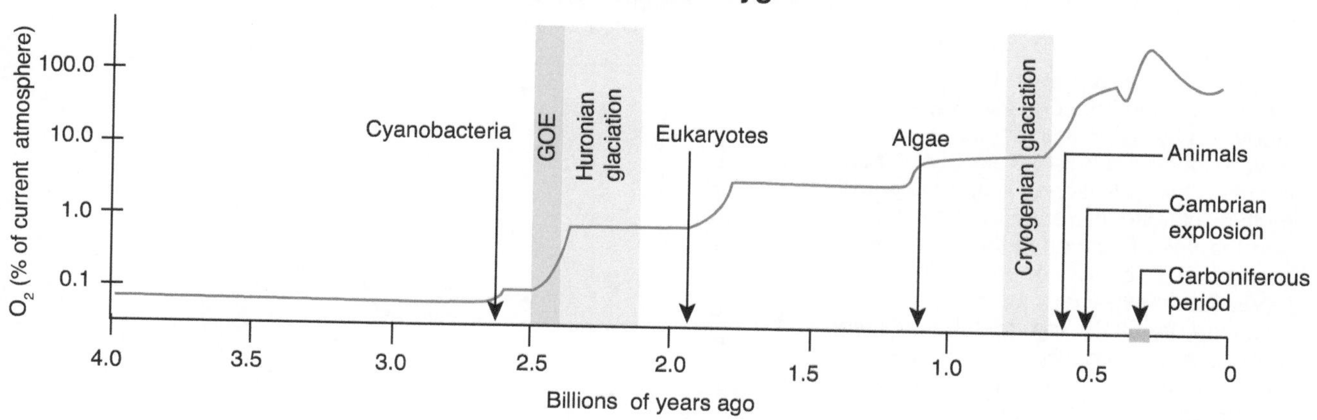

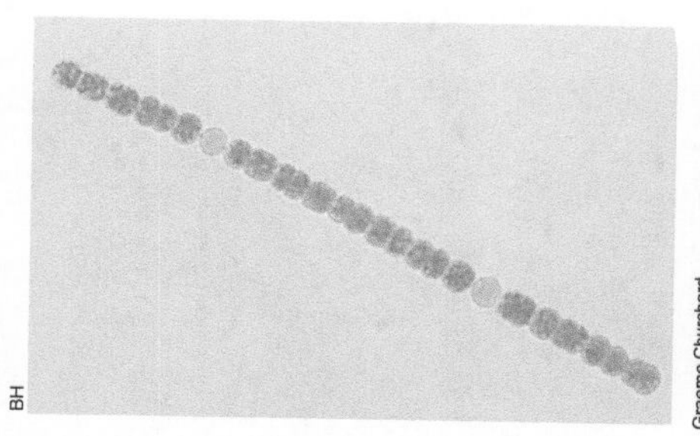

A key step in the evolution of photosynthesis was to use H_2O as an electron donor for the process, releasing O_2 gas as a by-product. This occurred in cyanobacteria (above) more than 2.4 billion years ago.

At first this new oxygen reacted with iron in the sea forming vast tracts of banded iron formations (above). These are mostly dated between 2.4 and 1.9 billion years old. The oceans and other rocks and minerals also acted as oxygen sinks.

Oxygen also reacted with CH_4 in the atmosphere, forming CO_2, a less potent **greenhouse gas**. This caused a decrease in the Earth's temperature, triggering the Huronian glaciation, a **Snowball Earth** that lasted for 300 m.y.

1. Where did Earth's atmospheric oxygen originally come from? ______________________

____

2. (a) Why did the oxygen in the atmosphere not increase for millions of years after oxygenic photosynthesis evolved?

____

____

(b) What evidence is there for the Great Oxygenation Event? ______________________

____

3. Identify two geological events probably caused by the rise of biological oxygen production: ______________________

____

ISBN: 978-1-98-856693-1

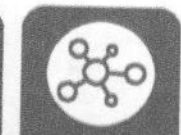

95 Changes in Biodiversity

Key Question: How have changes to the Earth affected the biodiversity of life throughout Earth's history?

- Although the biodiversity of this planet has not increased at a steady rate since the evolution of life, it has nevertheless become greater over time. Biodiversity is closely related to the environment. As biodiversity has increased over time, so it has affected the environment and produced new conditions for organisms to exploit. Examples include cyanobacteria producing the first oxygen **atmosphere**, which allowed the rise of eukaryotes, and microbes in the ground helping to produce the first soils, which helped plants to colonize the land.

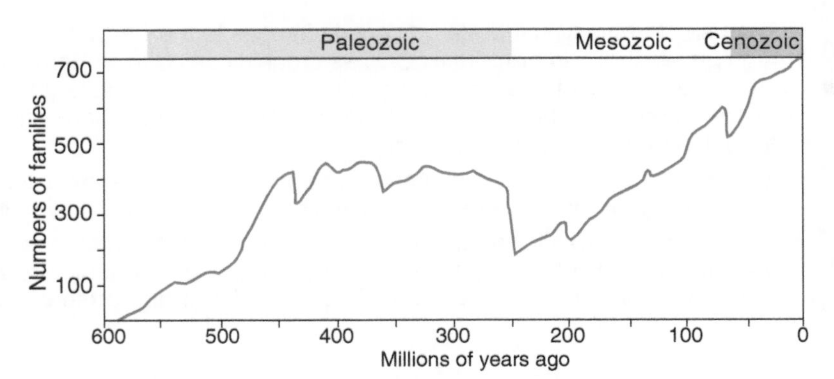

The graph above shows how the number of families of organisms has changed over time.

- The rise of free oxygen in the atmosphere had a profound effect on life. A 2009 study, led by paleobiologist Jonathan L. Payne, found that there were correlations between the evolution of eukaryotes and multicellular life, increase in body size, and the rise of oxygen in the atmosphere (right). The body size of organisms increased in two sharp jumps: at the evolution of eukaryotes, and the evolution of multicellular organisms. Both these events correlate with sharp increases in the amount of available oxygen.

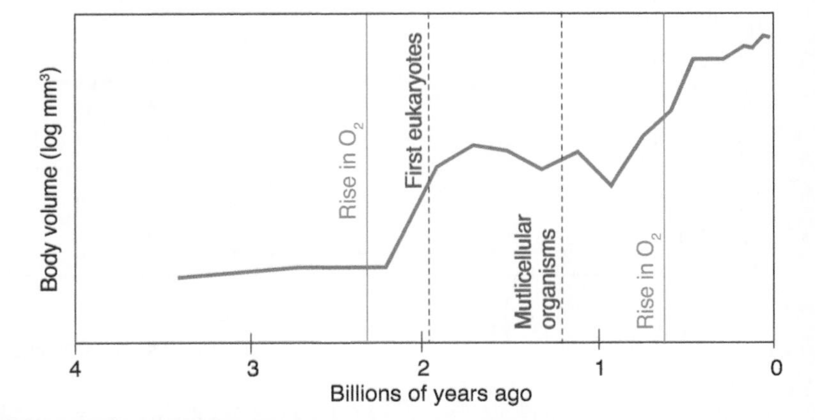

The Carboniferous period saw significant changes to the atmosphere and biodiversity. New land plants locked up large amounts of carbon and raised atmospheric O_2 to 35%. The plants formed huge tracts of coal and insects grew to huge sizes in the high oxygen atmosphere.

The environment can be affected by extraterrestrial sources. The impact of a giant asteroid 66 million years ago produced a nuclear winter that ended the reign of the dinosaurs. In their place, mammals diversified and became the dominant large terrestrial animal life form.

A period of **climate** change 53 to 47 million years ago saw a rise in the biodiversity of mammals in North America. The number of genera increased to a record of 104, and the land was covered in rainforest.

1. Give two examples to illustrate how life modifies the environment and then diversifies into the new, modified environment:

(a) ______________________________

____

____

(b) ______________________________

____

____

ISBN: 978-1-98-856693-1

96 Soils and Microbes

Key Question: How do microbes play an important role in producing soil from weathered rock and organic material?

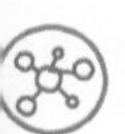

- Soils are a complex mixture of unconsolidated weathered rock and organic material. Before microbes invaded the land, the Earth had no soil, simply rock and earth produced by weathering and erosion.
- Soils didn't begin to appear until about 500 million years ago. Microbes used chemicals in the rocks to build their bodies and, when they died, they added their organic matter to the developing soils.
- Once simple soils developed, the first land plants could establish. This resulted in further development of the soils through biological weathering and the addition of dead material to accumulate organic matter.
- The developing soil provided new habitats for the early animals that invaded the land. They too helped soil development by churning the soil and adding organic matter.

The parent rock is broken down by weathering. Some minerals are available, others are locked up in rocks.

Microbes invade the land and make minerals locked in rocks available. Organic material from microbes builds up.

Early plants invade the land. They mix early soils and add organic matter. Microbes, including fungi, help plants access minerals.

The first soils have developed by 500 million years ago. The final conditions depend on the regional conditions and rock type.

1. When did the first soils appear? ______________________________

2. Describe the role of weathering in soil formation: ______________________________

____

____

3. Describe the role of microbes in soil formation: ______________________________

____

____

4. Describe role of plants in soil development: ______________________________

____

____

5. How did soils influence the evolution of plants and soil organisms? ______________________________

____

____

____

ISBN: 978-1-98-856693-1

97 Reefs and Estuaries

Key Question: How can the development of landforms be influenced by living organisms?

Reefs

- Coral reefs are relatively common throughout tropical oceans. They are formed by colonies of millions of tiny animals called polyps. The polyps use calcium carbonate to form the coral skeleton. Different species form different shaped corals. Over thousands of years, the coral reef can build up to cover thousands of square kilometers (e.g. the Great Barrier Reef). The first corals appeared about 500 million years ago, although modern coral reefs appeared only about 10,000 years ago.
- The evolution of reefs has had land-forming effects on the tropical coastlines of continents and islands, altering the seascape and the landscape. As reefs grow and eventually reach the sea surface, wave action erodes them, producing deposits that form small coral islands (especially around subsiding volcanoes). These islands and reefs absorb and slow waves so that erosion on the beach behind the coral island is slowed and any sediment from the land remains where it was deposited.
- Coral reefs also provided a variety of new habitats for marine life. In fact, 25% of all marine species are found on coral reefs.

Reefs provide a vast array of habitats into which animals can diversify

Estuaries

- Estuaries are places rich in nutrients. However the mud of the estuaries is unstable and often anoxic (lacking oxygen). Any plant that could evolve to live on the unstable mud would have access to a large supply of nutrients. Mangroves are plants adapted to the estuarine environment.
- An important feature of mangroves is that they have roots that spread out from the central trunk and grow upwards out of the mud. This causes them to accumulate sediment and their growth stabilizes the mud. Over time, the tangle of roots allows the mud to accumulate above sea level and form land. At the same time, the seaward edge of the mud flat moves out to sea as sediment accumulates and the landward edge is taken over by land plants. Thus the mangrove forest produces land from the sea.

1. What percentage of marine species inhabit coral reefs? ______________________

2. (a) What is the effect of coral reefs on wave movement? ______________________

   (b) What effect does this have on coastal development? ______________________

3. Explain how mangroves produce new land: ______________________

ESS2.E SC

ISBN: 978-1-98-856693-1

98 Carbon Cycling

Key Question: How does carbon cycle between the atmosphere, biosphere, geosphere, and hydrosphere?

- Carbon is the essential element of life. Its unique properties allow it to form an almost infinite number of different molecules. In living systems, the most important of these are carbohydrates, fats, nucleic acids, and proteins.
- Carbon in the **atmosphere** is found mainly as carbon dioxide (CO_2) and methane (CH_4). In rocks, it is most commonly found as either coal (mostly carbon) or limestone (calcium carbonate).
- The most important processes in the **carbon cycle** are photosynthesis and respiration. Photosynthesis removes carbon from the atmosphere and converts it into organic molecules. This organic carbon may eventually be returned to the atmosphere as CO_2 through respiration (the oxidation of glucose to produce usable energy for metabolism). The activity of volcanoes also releases CO_2 into the atmosphere, although the volumes are relatively small.
- Carbon cycles at different rates depending on where it is. On average, carbon remains in the atmosphere as CO_2 for about 5 years, in organisms for about 10 years, and in oceans for about 400 years. Carbon can remain in rocks (e.g. coal) for millions of years.

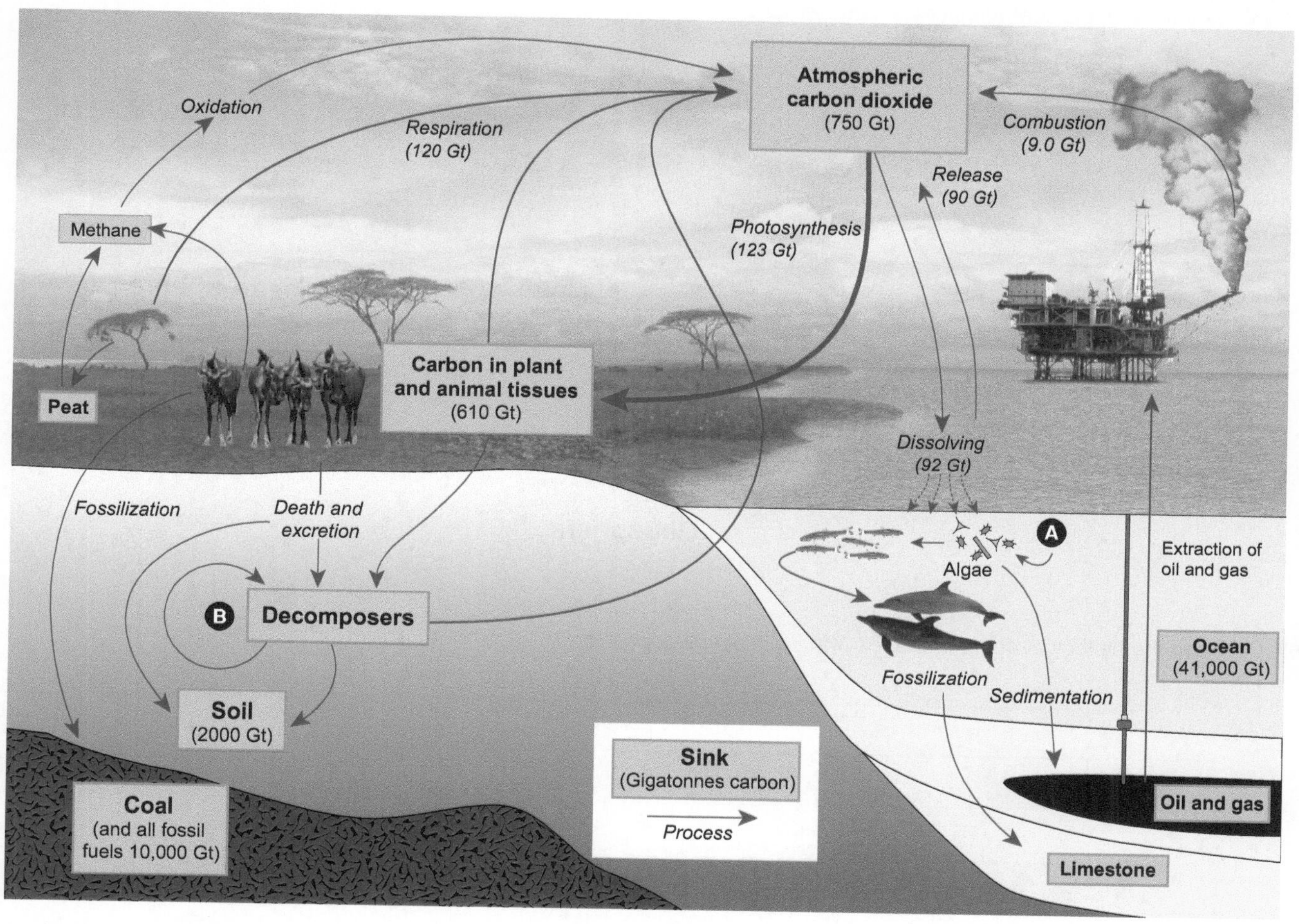

1. (a) What are the two main forms of carbon in the atmosphere? ________________
   (b) In what important molecules is carbon found in living systems? ________________
   (c) In what two forms is carbon found in rocks? ________________
2. (a) Name two processes that remove carbon from the atmosphere: ________________
   (b) Name two processes that add carbon to the atmosphere: ________________
3. (a) What is the role of decomposers in the carbon cycle? ________________
   (b) What is the role of fossilization in the carbon cycle? ________________

ISBN: 978-1-98-856693-1

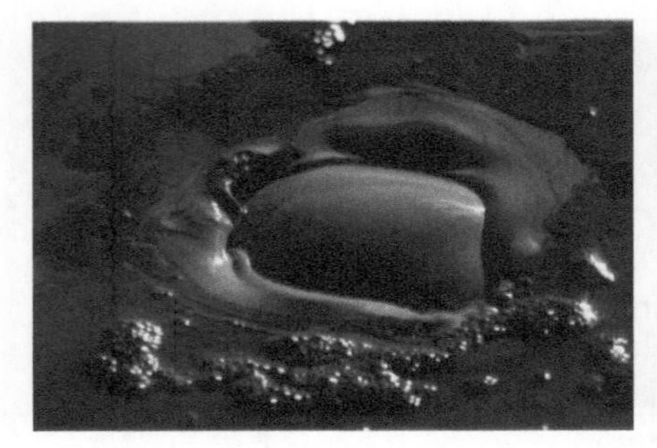

Oil and natural gas formed when dead algae and zooplankton settled to the bottom of shallow seas and lakes. These remains were buried and compressed under layers of non-porous sediment. Oil and gas, like coal, are extracted by humans.

Limestone is a type of sedimentary rock containing mostly calcium carbonate. It forms when the shells of mollusks and other marine organisms with $CaCO_3$ skeletons become fossilized. Weathering of exposed limestone releases carbon.

Coal is formed from the remains of terrestrial plant material buried in shallow swamps and subsequently compacted under sediments to form a hard black material. Coal is composed primarily of carbon and is a widely used fuel source.

4. Use the space below to complete a model to show how carbon cycles through the biosphere, geosphere, hydrosphere, and atmosphere. Include quantities where relevant:

Atmosphere

Biosphere

Hydrosphere

Geosphere

5. Describe the biological origin of the following geological deposits:

(a) Coal: ______________________________

(b) Oil: ______________________________

(c) Limestone: ______________________________

6. (a) What is the effect of human activity on the amount of carbon stored in sinks? ______________________________

(b) Describe two global effects resulting from this activity: ______________________________

ISBN: 978-1-98-856693-1

99 Modeling the Carbon Cycling

Key Question: How can modeling be used to show us the cycling of carbon through the hydrosphere, geosphere, and biosphere?

Modeling changes to the carbon cycle

- Scientists has been able to estimate the mass of carbon stored in the Earth's various reservoirs (e.g. rocks). They have also been able to estimate the rate at which carbon cycles from reservoir to reservoir.
- This data can be used to produce a crude but informative model of the **carbon cycle**. The table below shows the quantity and exchanges of carbon in each reservoir.

Reservoir	Amount in reservoir (gigatonnes (Gt))	Exchanges
Atmosphere	750	Movements included absorption and release by the ocean, and living organisms. Combustion of fossil fuels is adding carbon dioxide to the atmosphere.
Biomass	2610 (610 in plants and animals, ~ 2000 in soil)	Approximately 123 Gt per year is absorbed by photosynthesis, with 120 Gt per year being released by respiration.
Ocean	41,000	About 92 Gt per year is absorbed but 90 Gt per year is released.
Sedimentary rocks	60 million	Exchanges between rocks and other reservoirs and generally very small.
Fossil fuels	10,000	About 9 Gt per year into atmosphere from combustion of fossil fuels.

Investigation 8.2 Modeling carbon cycle changes

See appendix for equipment list.

1. Open a spreadsheet and type in headings for the rates of exchange and their values (below). Enter column headings for year and the mass of carbon and the effect of this on surface temperature. Enter headings for the other reservoirs in the cells below this (below):

	A	B	C	D	E	F
1	**Exchanges (Gt)**		**Year**	**Atmospheric carbon dioxide (Gt)**	**Cumulative gain in temperature (°C)**	
2			0			
3	Combustion of fossil fuels		1			
4	9		2			
5			3			
6	Absorbed by ocean		4			
7	92		5			
8			6			
9	Released by ocean		7			
10	90		8			
11			9			
12	Rate of photosynthesis		10			
13	123					
14						
15	Rate of respiration					
16	120					
17						
18		**Reservoir (C in Gt)**				
19	Year	Ocean	Living organisms	Fossil fuels		
20	0					
21	1					
22	2					
23	3					
24	4					
25	5					
26	6					
27	7					
28	8					
29	9					
30	10					
31						
32						
33						

2. The change in atmospheric carbon is the sum of the exchanges between the reservoirs. This can be written as a simple spreadsheet formula. In cell D2 enter the value for atmospheric carbon (840). Now, in cell D3 enter the formula for the change in atmospheric carbon: =D2+$A$4+$A$10+$A$16-$A$7-$A$13. It is important that the cells and $ symbol are entered correctly so that cell references remain constant.

ISBN: 978-1-98-856693-1

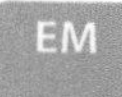

3. Copy this formula into down to cell D12 using the fill down feature of the spreadsheet:

	C	D	E
1	Year	**Atmospheric carbon dioxide**	**Cumulative gain in temperature (°C)**
2	0	750	
3	1	=D2+$A$4+$A$10+$A$16-$A$7-$A$13	=(D3-D2)*0.0017
4	2	=D3+$A$4+$A$10+$A$16-$A$7-$A$13	=E3+(D4-D3)*0.0017
5	3	=D4+$A$4+$A$10+$A$16-$A$7-$A$13	=E4+(D5-D4)*0.0017
6	4	=D5+$A$4+$A$10+$A$16-$A$7-$A$13	=E5+(D6-D5)*0.0017
7	5	=D6+$A$4+$A$10+$A$16-$A$7-$A$13	=E6+(D7-D6)*0.0017
8	6	=D7+$A$4+$A$10+$A$16-$A$7-$A$13	=E7+(D8-D7)*0.0017
9	7	=D8+$A$4+$A$10+$A$16-$A$7-$A$13	=E8+(D9-D8)*0.0017
10	8	=D9+$A$4+$A$10+$A$16-$A$7-$A$13	=E9+(D10-D9)*0.0017
11	9	=D10+$A$4+$A$10+$A$16-$A$7-$A$13	=E10+(D11-D10)*0.0017
12	10	=D11+$A$4+$A$10+$A$16-$A$7-$A$13	=E11+(D12-D11)*0.0017
13			

4. Formulae for the changes in the other reservoirs can be entered in the appropriate cells. First enter the initial value for the reservoir. Fill the cells down to the ten years shown:

17				
18		**Reservoir (C in Gt)**		
19	Year	Ocean	Living organisms	Fossil fuels
20	0	41000	2610	10000
21	1	=B20+$A$7-$A$10	=C20+$A$13-$A$16	=D20-$A$4
22	2	=B21+$A$7-$A$10	=C21+$A$13-$A$16	=D21-$A$4
23	3	=B22+$A$7-$A$10	=C22+$A$13-$A$16	=D22-$A$4
24	4	=B23+$A$7-$A$10	=C23+$A$13-$A$16	=D23-$A$4
25	5	=B24+$A$7-$A$10	=C24+$A$13-$A$16	=D24-$A$4
26	6	=B25+$A$7-$A$10	=C25+$A$13-$A$16	=D25-$A$4
27	7	=B26+$A$7-$A$10	=C26+$A$13-$A$16	=D26-$A$4
28	8	=B27+$A$7-$A$10	=C27+$A$13-$A$16	=D27-$A$4
29	9	=B28+$A$7-$A$10	=C28+$A$13-$A$16	=D28-$A$4
30	10	=B29+$A$7-$A$10	=C29+$A$13-$A$16	=D29-$A$4
31				

5. Lastly a formula for the effect of atmospheric carbon on the temperature can be entered into cell E2. A 2016 study found that there is a global temperature increase of 1.7 °C per trillion tonnes of CO_2. We can therefore work out the temperature change per tonne of carbon dioxide and multiply that by the mass of extra carbon dioxide in the atmosphere (remembering that our values are in gigatonnes) to find the cumulative change in temperature over time. In cell E3 enter the formula =(D4-D3)* 0.0017. In cell E4 enter the formula =E3+(D4-D3)* 0.0017. Fill this down.

1. (a) Using your spreadsheet, what is the net gain per year of atmospheric carbon dioxide? ______

(b) Explain your answer to (a): ______

2. You can vary the rate of exchange between the reservoirs. Try changing the rate of combustion.

(a) What the effect of increasing the rate of combustion on the amount of carbon dioxide in the atmosphere?

(b) What about decreasing it? ______

3. Research the carbon cycle, especially the exchanges of carbon between reservoirs. How can the spreadsheet be improved to better model the changes in atmospheric carbon dioxide?

ISBN: 978-1-98-856693-1

100 Atmospheric Changes and Climate Change

Key Question: How does the combustion of fossil fuels, which returns ancient carbon to the atmosphere, cause warming?

- The Earth's **atmosphere** comprises a mix of gases including nitrogen, oxygen, and water vapor. Small quantities of carbon dioxide (CO_2), methane, and a number of other trace gases are also present. Together, water, CO_2, and methane produce a **greenhouse effect** that moderates the surface temperature of the Earth.
- The term greenhouse effect describes the natural process by which heat is retained within the atmosphere by these **greenhouse gases** letting in sunlight, but trapping the heat that would normally radiate back into space. The greenhouse effect results in the Earth having a mean surface temperature of about 15°C, 33°C warmer than it would have without an atmosphere. About 75% of the natural greenhouse effect is due to water vapor, however CO_2 is a more significant factor.

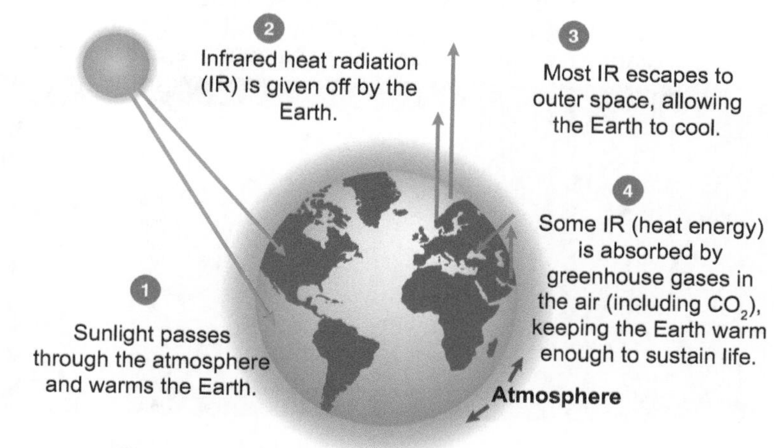

5 **Enhanced greenhouse effect:** Increasing levels of CO_2 increase the amount of heat retained, causing the atmosphere and Earth's surface to heat up.

- Fluctuations in the Earth's surface temperature as a result of **climate** shifts, albeit slow and gradual, are normal and have occurred throughout the history of the Earth. However, since the mid 20th century, the Earth's surface temperature has been increasing at a rapid rate. This phenomenon is called global warming and leads to climate change. Scientific evidence shows it can be directly attributed to increasing atmospheric levels of CO_2 and other greenhouse gases emitted into the atmosphere.

Potential effects of climate change

Sea levels are expected to rise by up to 58 cm by the year 2090. This is the result of the thermal expansion of ocean water and melting of glaciers and ice shelves. Many of North America's largest cities are near the coast. The predicted rises in sea levels could result in inundation of these cities and entry of salt **water** into agricultural lands.

The **ice**-albedo effect refers to the ability of ice to reflect sunlight. Cooling tends to increase ice cover, so more sunlight is reflected. Warming reduces ice cover, and more solar energy is absorbed, so more warming occurs. Ice has a stabilizing effect on global climate, reflecting nearly all the sun's energy that hits it.

The continuing effect of climate change depends upon the complex interactions of the gases in the atmosphere, solar input and ocean currents. Outcomes can be predicted using modeling programs, which depend on predictions of the amount of greenhouse gases produced by humanity. Thus, a range outcomes is possible.

1. Which gases are responsible for the greenhouse effect on Earth? ______________________________

____

2. Which of these gases is most responsible for human-caused climate change? ______________________________

3. What is the difference between the greenhouse effect and climate change? ______________________________

____

____

4. What are two possible effects of climate change and what are their consequences? ______________________________

____

____

ISBN: 978-1-98-856693-1

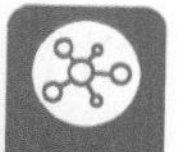

Visualizing a warming world

- It can be difficult to see the trends in the complex patterns of hurricanes and other events. Probably the simplest or most obvious aspect of **climate** change that can be directly measured is the change in the surface temperature of the Earth over time. This has been measured in meteorological stations around the globe.
- The diagrams below visualize the annual temperatures globally and North America. The color scale is ± 2.6 standard deviations from the annual average temperature for each area (thus the same colors in different visualizations may be different temperatures). Red are above average years, blue are below average years. The bottom graph presents the North America data in a second format. Explore for yourself at *www.showyourstripes.*

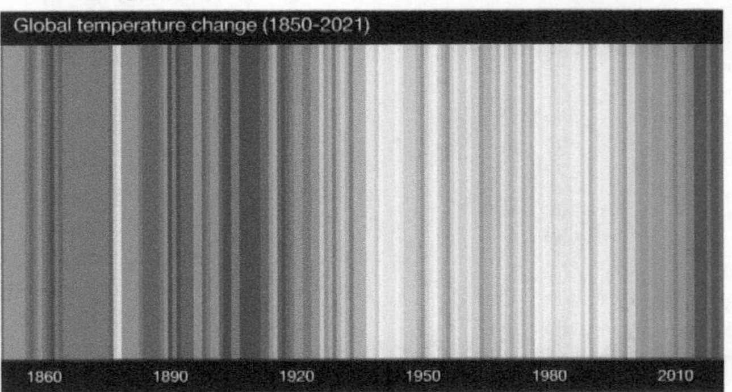

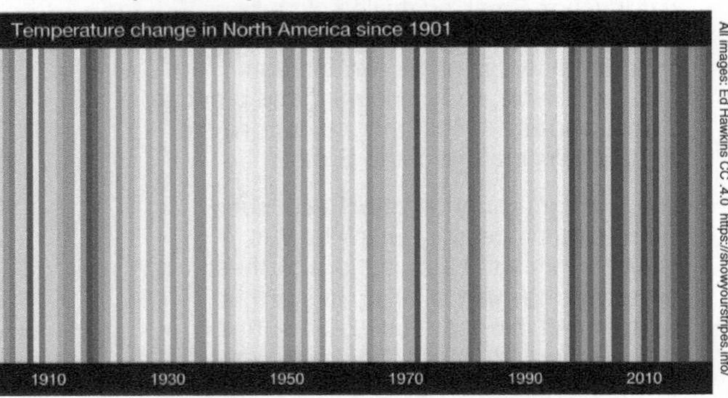

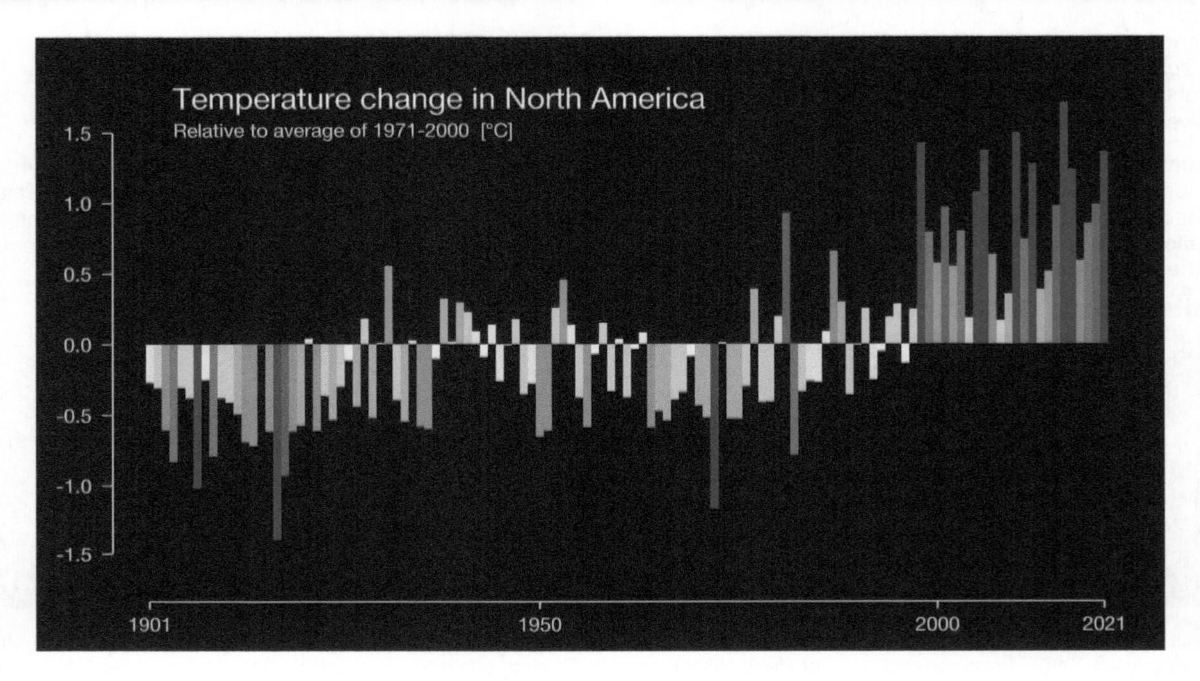

5. What features of the two top 'stripes' models above make them a 'powerful' means to visualize the change in global and North America temperature since 1800?

6. What are the advantages and disadvantages of using an alternate model like the graph, to inform the general public about the impacts of climate change?

7. Summarize how anthropomorphic (human caused) emissions of CO_2 into the atmosphere are linked to climate change:

ISBN: 978-1-98-856693-1

101 Review Your Understanding

Key Question: Why is the world heating up?

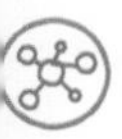

- In this chapter you have been shown several lines of evidence for how CO_2 acting as a **greenhouse gas** in the **atmosphere**, increasing global temperatures, and anthropomorphic (human) greenhouse gas emissions, are linked.

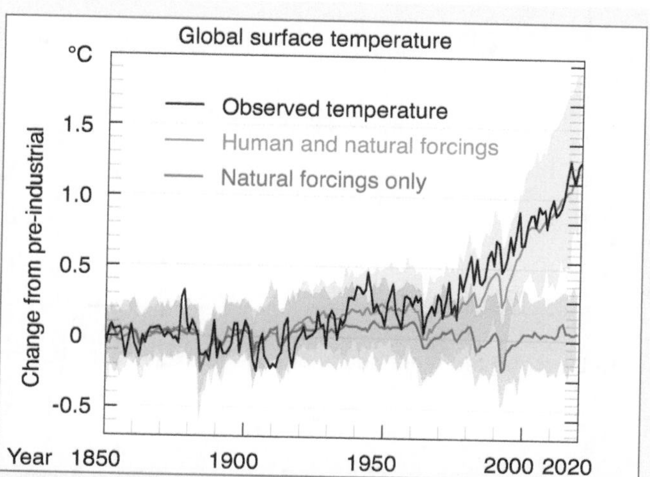

Global temperature changes on Earth are due to both natural and human induced forcings; energy imbalances impacting the climate system. By separating out the two sets of forcings, we are able to see the impact of each.

- You should now be able to better describe the complex phenomenon of global temperature rise due to increasing atmospheric carbon dioxide, and the evidence that supports it.

1. Create a model, either digitally, on paper, or constructed from other materials, to show the links between carbon cycling, anthropomorphic carbon dioxide release, the greenhouse effect and resulting energy flow, the albedo effect, and the impact of temperature increases on climate change. Publish your work in a shared forum so that others can comment or critique your work and you can develop or strengthen your writing as needed. Use the space below to create a mind map (network of connected ideas) to help you plan your model:

ISBN: 978-1-98-856693-1

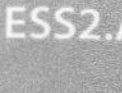

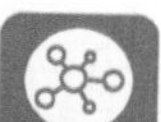

102 Summing Up

1. (a) Draw a diagram in the space below to show absorption and reflection of incoming solar radiation as it arrives from the Sun and passes through the Earth's atmosphere to the surface and is reflected back into space:

(b) Describe the greenhouse effect and explain why it is important to Earth's climate: ______________________

2. (a) What was the Great Oxygenation Event (GOE): ______________________

(b) What subsequent events in Earth's history occurred as a consequence of the GOE: ______________________

3. (a) Use the following labels to complete the diagram of the carbon cycle shown right: *atmosphere, geosphere, oceans, respiration (R), photosynthesis (PS).*

(b) Add arrows to show deforestation (D) and combustion (C) of fossil fuels:

(c) Combustion and deforestation result in another 9 petagrams of carbon being added to the carbon cycle. Add this value to the diagram.

(d) About 3 petagrams is taken up by photosynthesis and 2 petagrams is taken up by the oceans. Add these values to the appropriate labels on the diagram.

(e) How much extra carbon is actually added to the atmosphere by deforestation and combustion?

____

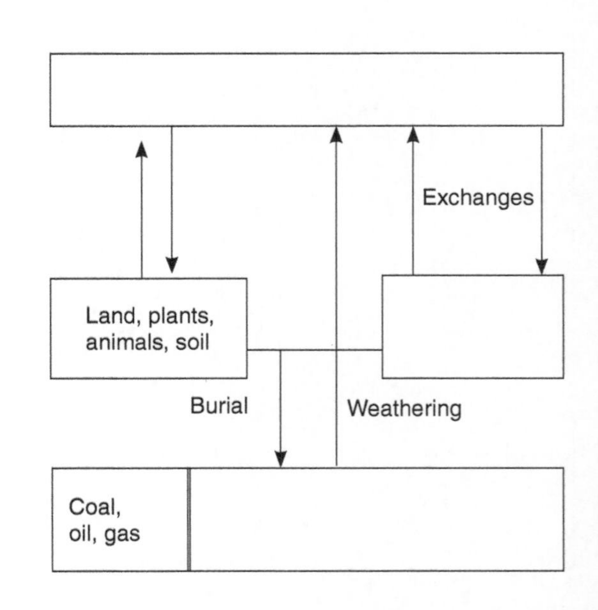

ESS2.D ESS2.E EM SC

ISBN: 978-1-98-856693-1

Earth and Human Activity

Concepts and connections
Use arrows to make connections between related concepts in this section of the book

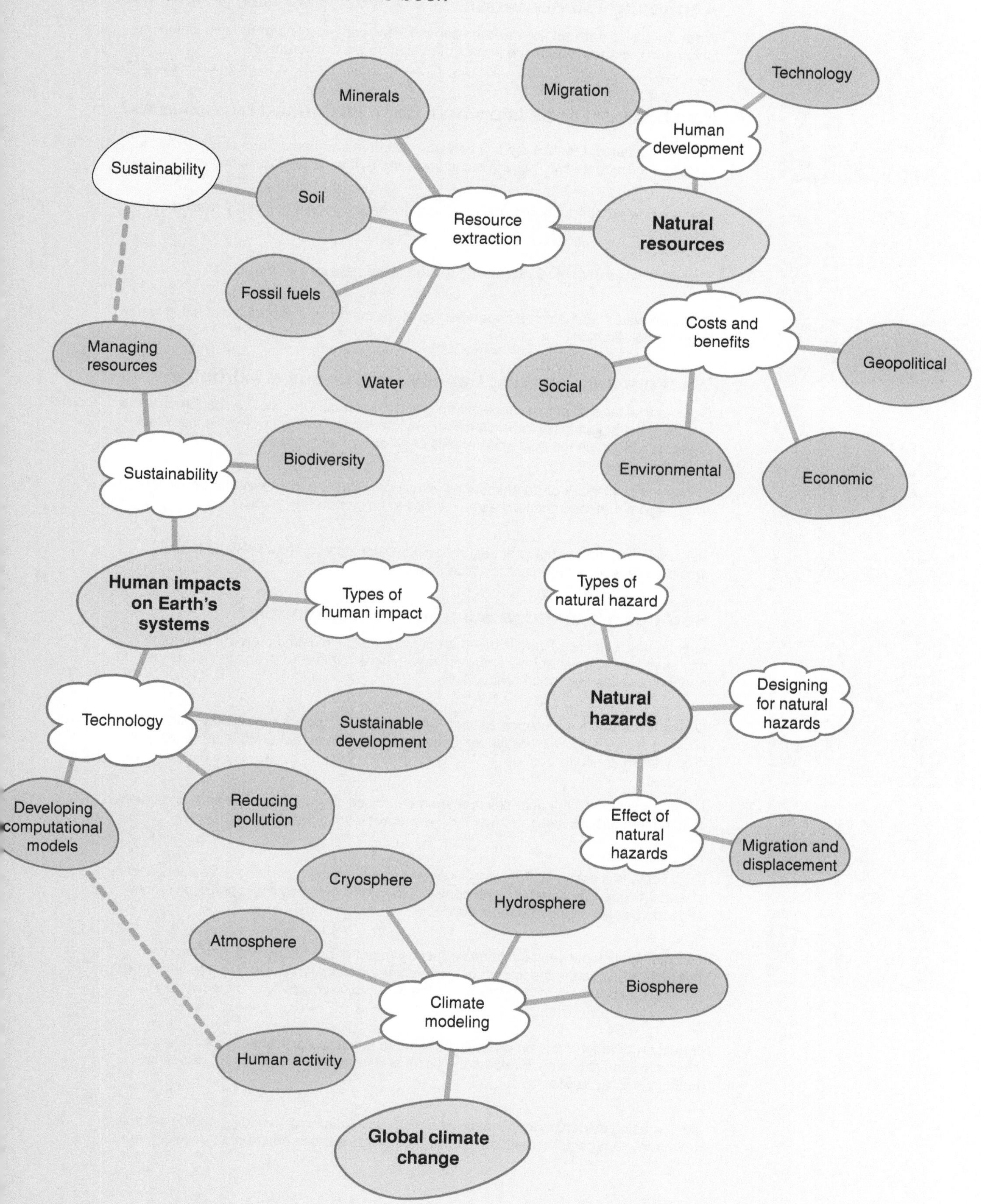

CHAPTER 9

Natural Resources

Anchoring Phenomenon

What do we do with all the dead batteries? How can recycling or reusing lithium in lithium-ion batteries reduce the impact of mining on the environment? 103 120

How has human development been influenced by resources?

- ☐ 1 Define a resource. Discuss the link between resource and human population location. Discuss the link between modern technology and human population location. 104 105
- ☐ 2 Discuss how human technological development has aligned with energy resources requirements. 106
- ☐ 3 Use world water resource information to identify humans use of water. 107
- ☐ 4 Compare water use between countries. Compare the costs and benefits of using water to generate electricity. 108

What are the costs and benefits from resource extraction?

- ☐ 5 Discuss the benefits of fossil fuels as an energy resource. Discuss the cost/benefit factors of extracting fossil fuels. Consider environmental factors involved in fossil fuel extraction. Evaluate the cost and benefits of an oil extraction scenario. 109 110
- ☐ 6 Relate the term 'peak oil' to efficient oil extraction. Evaluate the costs and benefits of two different methods of oil extraction, linked to environmental impact. 111
- ☐ 7 Describe costs and benefits of coal production. Considering the costs and benefits, provide a reasoned argument for mine site location. 112

How can we manage our resources sustainably?

- ☐ 8 Explain how pesticides, fertilizers, and antibiotics allow maximum production from minimum land. Consider how energy usage may be minimized in an agricultural setting, and the possible impact on productivity. 113
- ☐ 9 Define sustainable agriculture. Explain how agriculture can manage biodiversity, water, and soil sustainably. Discuss issues between future human demand, and resource and crop yield in agriculture. 114
- ☐ 10 Identify soil types. Link poor soil management to soil degradation. Compare and contrast farming methods. Investigate the physical properties of different soil types. 115
- ☐ 11 Participate in a jigsaw activity to evaluate a farming practice in terms of its sustainability characteristics. Link terracing and contour plowing to reducing soil loss. Explain how vegetative cover reduces soil erosion. 116 117
- ☐ 12 Discuss the link between sustainable management of rangeland and increased productivity. Describe the impact of overgrazing on rangelands. Discuss the link between grazing management of rangeland and the resulting productivity and biodiversity. 118
- ☐ 13 Identify why recycling is an essential method to manage Earth's resources. Evaluate alternatives to recycling. Evaluate the costs and benefits of two different recycling options in a city scenario. 119
- ☐ 14 Justify, using evidence, the location of human developments, including mining sites, and resource management. Discuss the link between resources and human development. 121

103 What do we do with all the dead batteries?

Key Question: How can recycling or reusing lithium in lithium-ion batteries reduce the impact of mining on the environment?

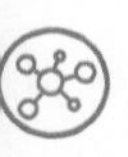

- The shift from **fossil fuel** powered vehicles to electric vehicles has greatly increased the demand for lithium, the main chemical element used in electric (EV) car 'lithium-ion" batteries.
- Over 50% of lithium is currently mined from the ground in Australia, which is extracted from 'mixed compound' ores in the rocks.
- Lithium is also found dissolved into underground pools of water in the dry Atacama Desert of Chile, and Argentina. The 'saltwater' is brought to the surface and evaporated to separate the lithium.
- Lithium-ion batteries currently have a life-span of 10-20 years. Current recycling processes 'melt' the whole battery down into a black 'gloop', that makes it hard to recycle and separate the valuable lithium to place back into new batteries.

Cut away of electric vehicle chassis showing lithium-ion batteries connected together to power the car.

1. What technology do you, your family, or community, regularly use that might rely on rechargeable batteries?

2. Can you recycle batteries where you live? and if not, what do you do with 'used up' batteries?

3. What effect do you think of NOT recycling rechargeable batteries, which are likely to contain lithium, might have on the environment, both locally and globally, in the future?

4. In small groups, develop some initial suggestions for how the resource of lithium might be reused or recycled to minimize impacts on the environment:

ISBN: 978-1-98-856693-1

CE

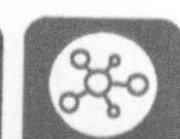

104 Humans and Resources

Key Question: What are the Earth's resources, and how are they important to human society?

What is a resource?

- Resources are substances that can be used for beneficial purposes. Water is the most fundamental, but there are many other resources important to human society. Resources can be divided into many different kinds, e.g. energy, land, and food. Resources can also be **renewable** (continuously replenished e.g. water) and **non-renewable** (not replenished e.g. fossil fuels).
- **Natural resources** are those that are derived from the environment. Important natural resources include water, **minerals**, **fossil fuels**, and fertile soils. The availability of these resources determined where population centers became established and flourished and had a large impact on human technological and social development.

Fossil fuels

Human development in the last 200 years has been based on fossil fuels. Peat and **coal** had been burned for hundreds of years but it was not until the Industrial Revolution that fossil fuels became so important. They are so cheap, energetically concentrated, and easy to transport that they have yet to be equalled by any other kind of energy source.

Water

Fresh water is the most important of all resources. It is essential to all life's processes and is important in industry where it is used as a solvent and a coolant. Water covers nearly 75% of the Earth, but only a tiny fraction of this is fresh. Of that, an even smaller amount is available on the surface.

Minerals

Fertile soils

Minerals

Human technology is built on minerals. Minerals are solids made up of atoms arranged in a fixed composition, e.g. lime, quartz, and magnetite. Minerals are important both in their natural form (e.g. diamond coated saws) and as ores (e.g. magnetite as an ore for iron). Metals extracted from ores have been important as a basis for currency (e.g. gold) and in electrical and mechanical products (e.g. iron and copper).

Fertile soils

Soil fertility refers to the soil's ability to supply the nutrients for plant growth. A fertile soil is rich in nutrients and the soil microbes that make the nutrients accessible to plants. The availability of fertile soil was an important factor in the development of agricultural societies and the first towns and cities.

1. What is a resource? ______________________________

____

____

2. Why is water the most essential resource? ______________________________

____

____

3. (a) What two components are important contributors to soil fertility and why? ______________________________

____

(b) How might soil fertility have contributed to the location of major population centers? ______________________________

____

____

4. Why are fossil fuels such an important and useful resource? ______________________________

____

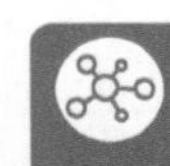

ESS3.A CE

ISBN: 978-1-98-856693-1

105 Resources and Civilization

Key Question: What is the link between human civilization and settlement and the location of important resources such as water, minerals, and fossil fuels?

- Human civilization and settlement is, for the most part, found around **natural resources**, be they recently found or ancient. Water is the most important natural resource and cities originally developed near water supplies such as rivers or natural springs. Today water is still important but other commodities such as **fossil fuels** and **minerals** (e.g. gold, iron, and copper) are important for economic wealth and growing populations.
- **Soil** is also an important resource. Across the Midwest of North America, parts of southern South America, Western Europe, and South East Asia fertile soils allow the growth of vast crops. Modern technology has boosted the size of these crops. The United States alone produced 58 million tonnes of wheat in 2013, the third largest global production, behind China and India.
- As human civilization has expanded and our ability to move resources about the globe has become more efficient, the largest population centers no longer need to be close to areas of major resources. The USA exports 50% of its wheat production. Similarly important minerals are often mined in remote parts of the world and shipped to smelters closer to population centers.

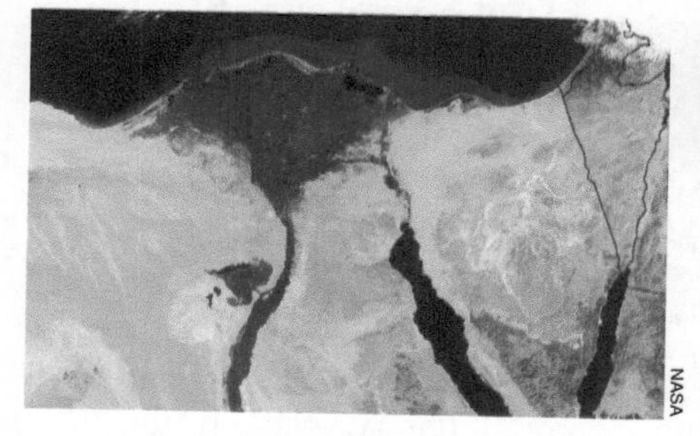

The Nile delta represents a classic case of human civilization developing around natural resources. The Nile provides water for drinking and irrigation, and its fertile soils allow numerous crops to be grown. However, just outside the delta lies a vast desert wasteland.

The Fertile Crescent is another area where human civilization developed around the resources of water and soil. The area is often referred to as one of the cradles of civilization. It has a large biodiversity due to its location between Africa and Eurasia.

Mesoamerica has many ancient abandoned cities that were once thriving centers. However the overuse of soil resources, possible drought, and overpopulation caused the collapse of many of these cities around 800 -1000 AD.

World's major natural resources

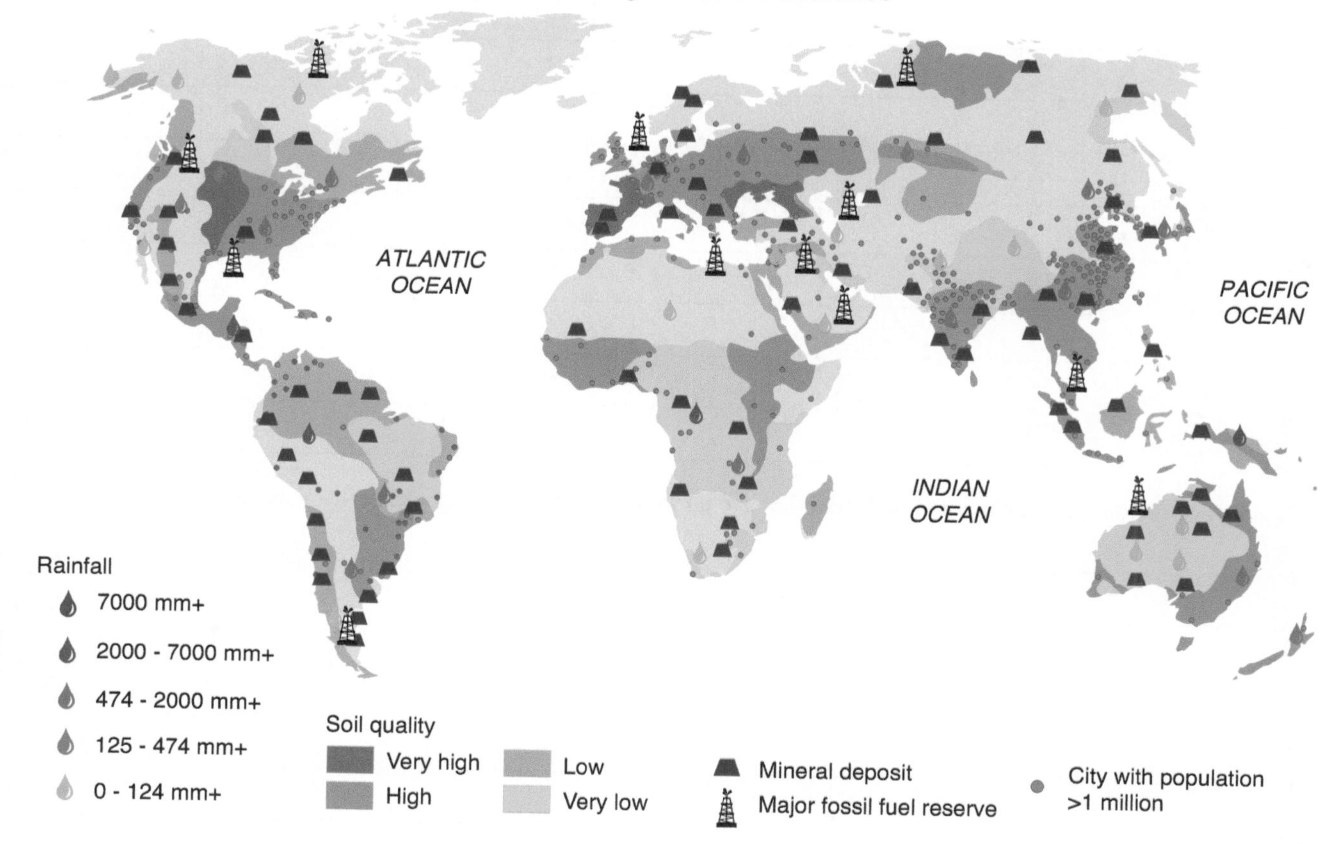

ISBN: 978-1-98-856693-1

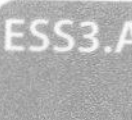

- The image below is a composite showing the Earth at night. The bright areas are cities and population centers. In general, the brighter the area, the bigger the human population there.

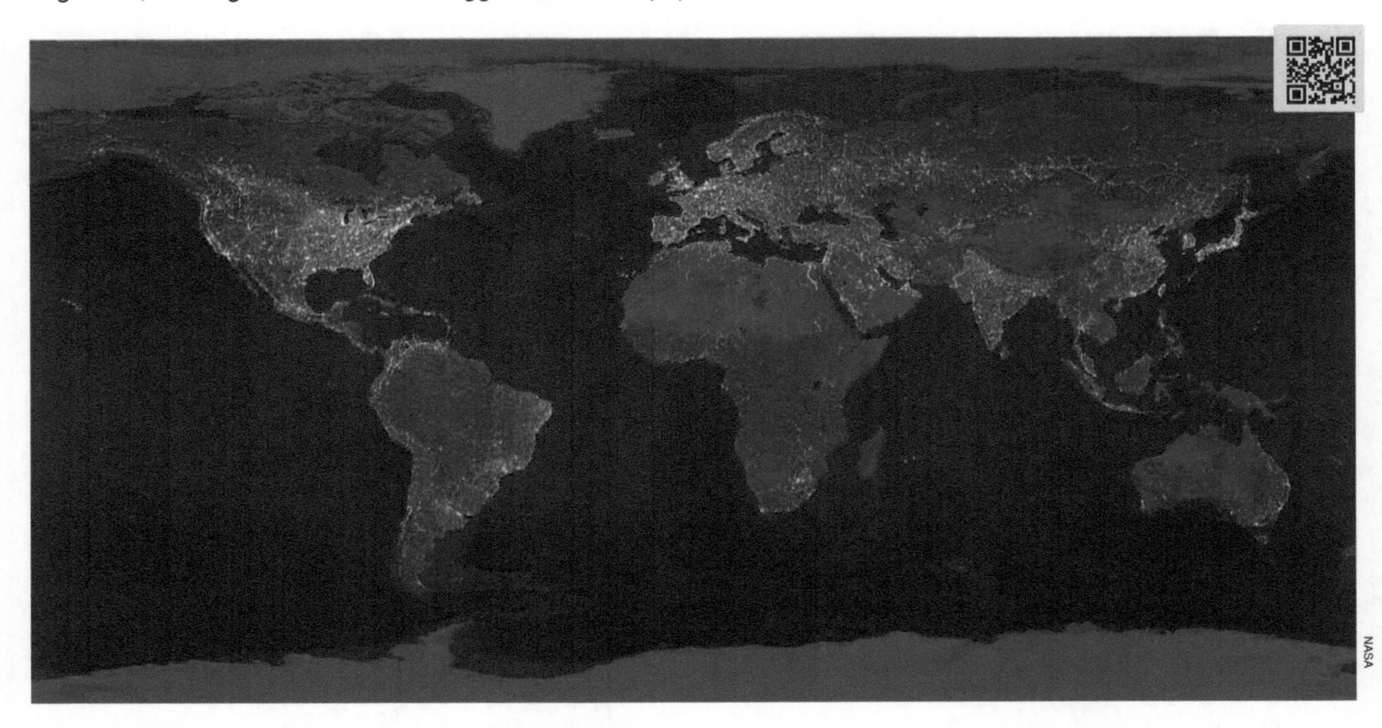

- Notice the location of large populations. For example, the majority of Australia's population live on the east coast. Although Australia's outback is rich in minerals such as bauxite, zinc, uranium, and iron, it has very little water, making it impossible for large populations to live there.
- In Egypt, the bright line of light leading to the Nile delta shows the large populations living around this important water source. Water is the most important natural resource and civilization in Egypt is focused around the Nile delta.
- Places such as Las Vegas in Nevada were only small towns just a few decades ago. The ability of humans to redirect water from rivers and store it in reservoirs has allowed these places to grow to huge population centres.

1. Study the map on the preceding pages and the image above. Discuss the relationship between resources (soil, minerals, rainfall, fossil fuels) and population centers. Use examples to highlight this relationship:

2. Explain how modern technology now influences where large populations can be become established:

ISBN: 978-1-98-856693-1

106 Energy, Resources, and Technology

Key Question: How are the use of resources, transformation of energy, and development of technology, integrally linked with human history?

- There is an argument that the history of human social, technological, and cultural development is linked directly to our ability to harness and transform energy. One of the earliest uses of energy was the invention of ways to provide reliable fire. Energy could then be used to cook food, hunt animals, produce weapons, and provide light.
- Domesticating animals and using them to provide mechanical power (horsepower) increased the work that could be done by one person. Using **coal** and charcoal to provide heat enabled the smelting of iron and metal alloys, expanding the range of tools that could be used.
- The development of the steam and internal combustion engines provided ways for heat to be transformed into reliable and powerful mechanical work. Harnessing other types of mechanical work to drive electrical turbines (e.g. water turbines) produced reliable **electrical energy**.
- At each of these steps, the ability of one person to do work increased. At each step, the **resources** that became available to a person increased. But the resources required also increased. Iron production requires **coal** and charcoal to provide heat and act as reducers. Iron machinery allows the components of engines to be manufactured (again from iron). Engines need fuel - coal and **oil**. And so there is a continuing increase in resources required and produced.

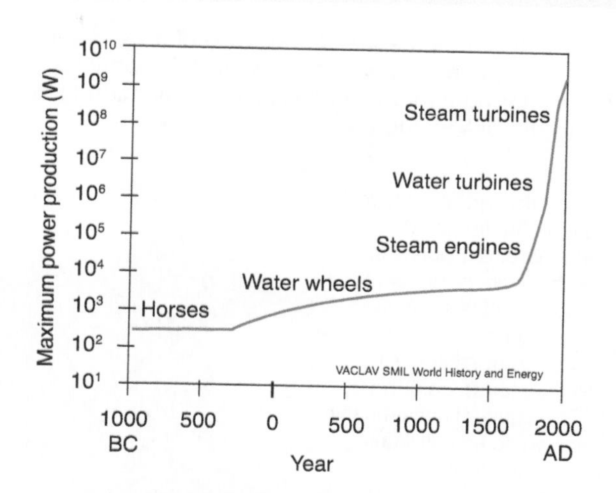

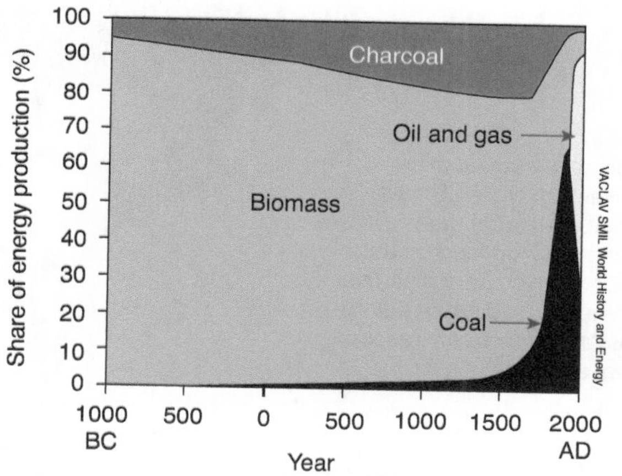

Domesticating horses and cattle allowed one person to plow an entire field, drive a mill, or carry a greater load. This allowed the utilization of more resources and their more efficient use.

More efficient ways of using energy resources increased the power available. A tractor can do the work of many horses. Now many fields can be plowed and planted by one person, allowing more food to be produced.

Transforming energy into electricity makes usable energy available to the masses. 100,000 years ago the average person used about 20,000 kJ of energy a day. Today it is close to a million kJ a day, from using cars, computers, and appliances.

1. In the last 3000 years, which two technological developments signalled sudden increases in the energy available to humans to do work:

2. Discuss how energy and resources have shaped human social and technological development:

ISBN: 978-1-98-856693-1

107 Global Water Resources

Key Question: How do rivers, lakes, and aquifers act as key water sources to provide water, transport routes, and energy for human use?

- The Earth is an aqueous planet; 71% of its surface is covered by water. Only about 0.0071% of the world's water exists as usable freshwater at the Earth's surface (in lakes, rivers, and wetlands). Rivers and lakes provide sources of water for human use, especially the irrigation of crops. Some of the largest and most important water courses are shown below and opposite.

The **Ogallala aquifer** is a vast water-table aquifer located beneath the Great Plains in the US. It covers portions of eight states and is extensively used for irrigation. 30% of it has already been used and 70% of it is expected to be gone by 2065. The aquifer is essentially non-renewable as it will take thousands of years to recharge.

The **North American Great Lakes** are the largest group of freshwater lakes on Earth, containing 22% of the world's fresh surface water.

The **Colorado River** runs through seven states of Southwestern United States. It has several large dams including the Hoover dam and the Glen Canyon dam. The river is so heavily used for irrigation purposes its flow rarely reaches the sea anymore

The **Mississippi River** drains most of the area between the Rocky Mountains and the Appalachians. A series of locks and dams provide for barge traffic.

The **Amazon River** accounts for 20% of the world's total river flow and drains 40% of South America. The Amazon is the largest rainforest in the world and has the world's highest biodiversity

Rivers have been vital transport routes since ancient times. Cities and towns could transport goods and resources along rivers for trade. Large rivers such as the Mississippi, above, are able to accommodate large ships for much of their length. Adding locks to the river can extend the distance a ship can travel.

Hullwarren

Rivers provide vital water for irrigation of crops and act as reservoirs for town supplies. However, overuse of a river for irrigation or building dams can lower its level and reduce the downstream flow. This can cause warming of downstream river waters which can lead to degradation of the riverine habitat.

The flow of water in a river provides a way of generating electricity by driving turbines in dams. The damming of rivers severely affects flow rates downstream. Dams are often used for flood control, but this often means floodplains no longer receive a supply of vital nutrients during floods, lowering the fertility of the soils.

ISBN: 978-1-98-856693-1

The **Volga River** and its many tributaries form an extensive river system, which drains an area of about 1.35 million km^2 in the most heavily populated part of Russia. High levels of chemical pollution currently give cause for environmental concern. The Volga River receives the majority of its water supply from snow melt, and the water is extracted by many urban areas along its path. Water loss, evaporating from dams, or diverted for agricultural irrigation, have greatly reduced the flow released at the river mouth, and therefore, the volume of the Caspian Sea it enters.

The fertile **Ganges Basin** is central to the agricultural economies of India and Bangladesh. The Ganges and its tributaries currently provide irrigation to a large and populous region, although a recent UN climate report indicates that the glaciers feeding the Ganges may disappear by 2030, as the temperature rise from climate change can not longer sustain them, leaving it as a seasonal system fed by the monsoon rains.

From glacial origins, the **Yangtze River** flows 6300 km eastwards into the East China Sea. The Yangtze is subject to extensive flooding, which is only partly controlled by the massive Three Gorges Dam, and it is heavily polluted. The polluted water has degraded the aquatic ecosystems, as well as reducing drinkable water supplies. Glacial melt that supplies the headwater is likely to reduce due to climate change impacts, and available water resources will decline significantly.

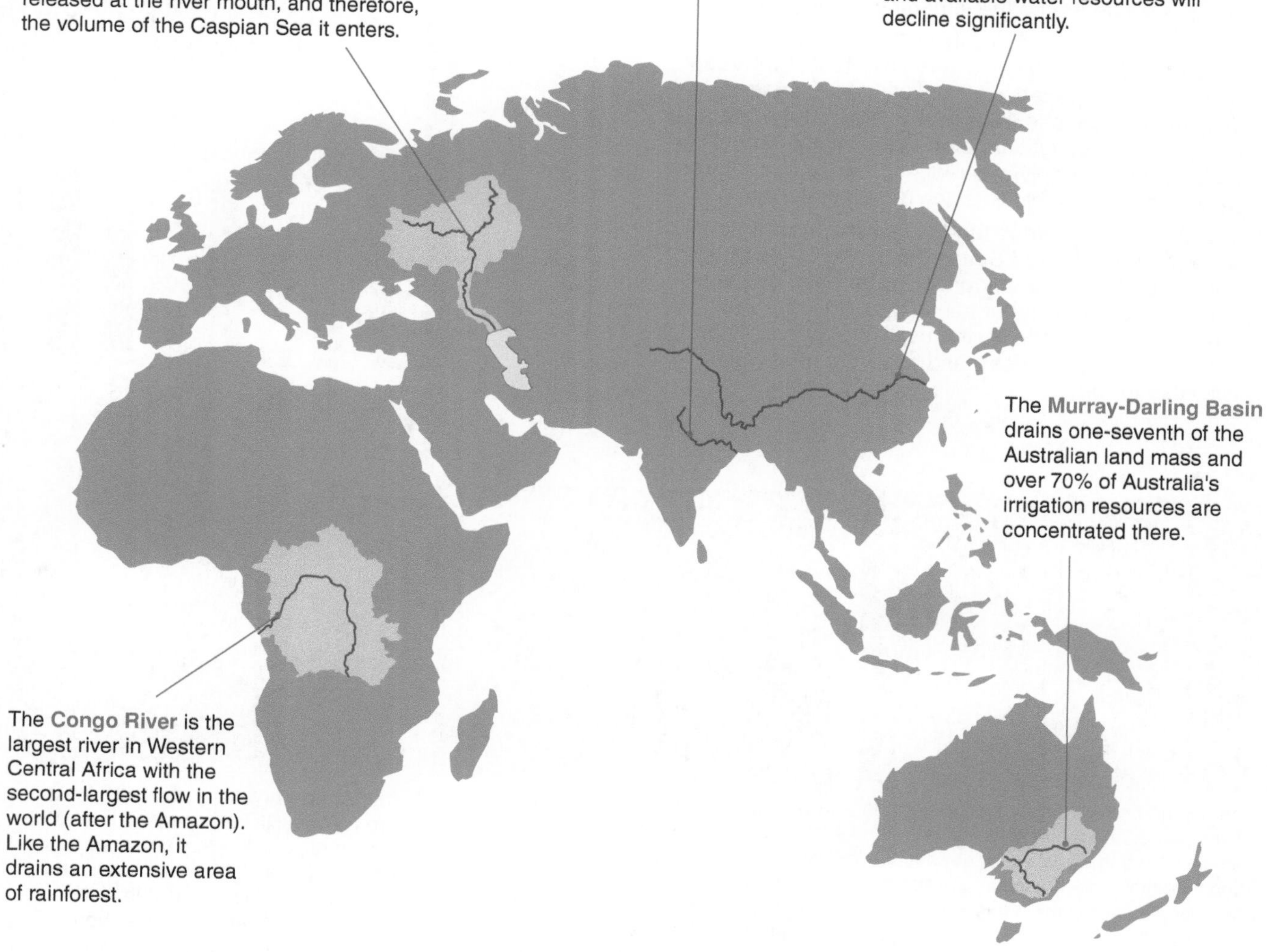

1. Explain why some deep but extensive aquifers, such as the Ogallala, are considered non-renewable: ______________

____

____

2. Identify three uses of river by humans:

   (a) ____

   (b) ____

   (c) ____

3. Describe some of the negative aspects of human use of global water resources: ______________

____

____

____

ISBN: 978-1-98-856693-1

108 Water and People

Key Question: What are some of the important uses of water to humans?

- Water is the most important substance on the planet. Life could not exist without it. There are approximately 1.4 billion trillion liters of water on Earth and Earth is the only planet in the solar system where large volumes of water are found on the surface in liquid form.
- However, water is not evenly distributed throughout the globe. Deserts receive very little rainfall whereas other places experience large volumes of seasonal or daily rainfall. Despite the enormous amount of water on this planet, wasteful usage and poor management of treatment and supply has reduced the amount of fresh water that is available to much of humanity.
- Industrialized countries tend to use the most amount of water, with the United States being one of the largest domestic users. The amount of water used by people in domestic situations depends upon the efficiency of the water use, its cost to the user (higher supply prices usually mean lower use), and the amount of water available for use.

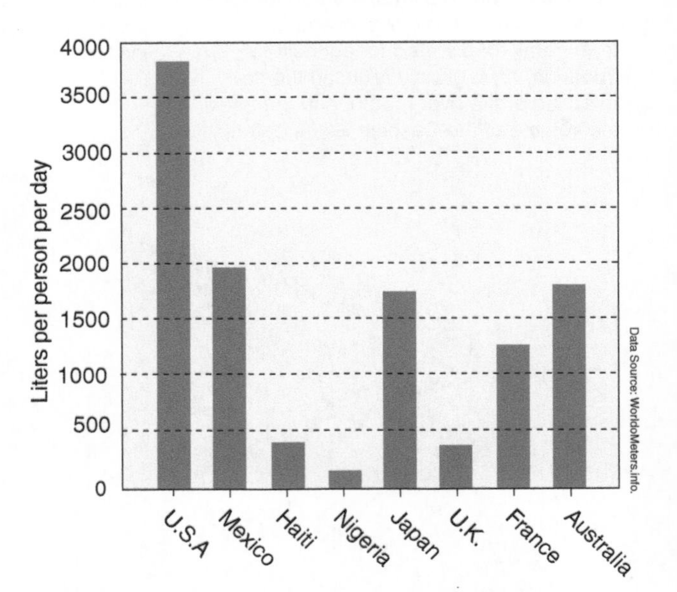

The human body is nearly 70% water and health authorities recommend drinking between 1.8 and 2 L of water per day to keep it healthy and functioning. In some countries, access even to this small amount is difficult. In some areas, people may use just 15 liters of water per day for all of their domestic uses including drinking water (compared to over 570 liters per person per day in the United States).

Nearly half of the water supplied by municipal water systems in the US is used to flush toilets and water lawns, and another 20-35% is lost through leakages. Treatment of waste water places major demands on cities yet there are few incentives to reduce water use and recycle. Providing reliable clean water remains a major public health issue in many poorer regions of the world.

Potable water (water suitable to drink) is a rare resource in large parts of the world. Access to potable water is limited by the availability of suitable water resources (e.g. rivers), its ease of distribution, and level of water treatment (water-borne diseases and dissolved toxins need to be removed). In many countries, distribution of water is difficult and storage of large amounts is almost impossible.

1. What factors limit water supply to some countries? ______________________________

2. (a) Which type of countries tend to use the most amount of water? ______________________________

   (b) What is the major use of water in these countries? ______________________________

3. Why is potable water such a rare resource in many countries? ______________________________

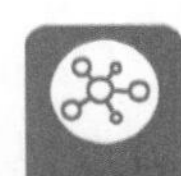    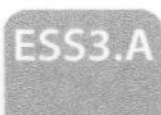

ESS3.A CE

ISBN: 978-1-98-856693-1

Costs and benefits of using water: hydroelectric dams

Damming a river...

...helps burn less coal.

- Water has been used to generate usable energy for hundreds of years. The water wheel allowed the gravitational potential energy in water at the top of a waterfall to be converted to the kinetic energy of a spinning wheel. The spinning wheel could then be used to drive mechanical devices such as grain mills. This principle is still used today. Water turbines are used in dams to spin giant electric generators to produce electricity.
- Electricity production is of fundamental importance in our world today. Without electricity, our standard of living would plummet. As we use more high demand devices we require more and more electricity generating schemes (even with more efficient devices).
- **Fossil fuel** fired power stations produce by far the most amount of electricity in the world today. However they are also responsible for producing huge volumes of CO_2, which is linked to climate change.
- Hydroelectric power reduces the need to use **coal** by using a **renewable resource** (water flow) and thus reducing CO_2 production and the consumption of a **non-renewable resource** (coal).
- However, there are important environmental costs to be considered when building hydroelectric dams.

Costs	Benefits
Construction costs	Electricity generation
Flooded land	Reduction in CO_2 production from fossil fuels.
Disruption of river habitat	Water storage for irrigation and domestic use.
Relocation of families	

- Cost/benefit analyses are carried out when planning dams. To do this, monetary values are often assigned to resources, giving them a quantitative value. For example, a forest that will be flooded by the reservoir behind a dam may be worth $1 million a year in tourism or $10 million in clear-felled timber. The loss of this monetary value can then be compared to the monetary benefit of the dam, e.g. the dam will produce $5 million worth of electricity per year and save $2 million of coal a year. Comparing these cost and benefit values over the lifespan of the dam can help in making decisions about its economic viability. However, cost-benefit analyses are by no means the only consideration and it may not be possible to assign an economic value to some factors.

Chongkian

4. How can water be used to generate electricity? ______________________

5. (a) Identify some costs and benefits of hydroelectric dams: ______________________

   (b) Explain how these costs and benefits can be evaluated and compared to produce a cost/benefit ratio: ______________________

6. What costs and benefits might be difficult to quantify in monetary terms? ______________________

ISBN: 978-1-98-856693-1

109 Non-Renewable Resources

Key Question: What are Earth's non-renewable resources, and where do we find them?

- The Earth contains enormous mineral resources, which can be obtained and used with relative ease to produce usable energy. Mineral resources are **non-renewable**. Some are in relatively short supply (e.g. coal and oil) while others are essentially limitless (e.g. iron).The most commonly used of these are the **fossil fuels**, i.e. **coal**, **oil** and **natural gas.** These can be burned immediately to produce heat energy or they can be refined to provide a variety of energy or material needs. Around 80% of the world's energy needs comes from burning fossil fuels.
- The use of fossil fuels as an energy source is a relatively cheap and efficient way of producing energy. However, the 'cost' to environment, with the modeled impact of increasing concentrations of greenhouse gas forcing climate change, is shifting the cost-benefit calculation of using fossil fuels. As **renewable** and 'green' energy technology is becoming cheaper and more accessible, the % of energy reliant on fossil fuel use is decreasing.
- Oil and natural gas are usually found together. Crude oil is a thick black liquid. Oil reservoirs occur underground where the oil is trapped between two layers of impermeable rock. The oil and gas can be extracted by drilling into the reservoir and pumping the fossil fuel out.
- **Minerals** are important resources. These are mined when the concentration is high enough to make extraction economical. For example, gold has an average abundance of 0.004 ppm in the Earth's crust. To be mined economically it needs to be about 0.5 ppm. A variety of geophysical processes can produce these economic accumulations.

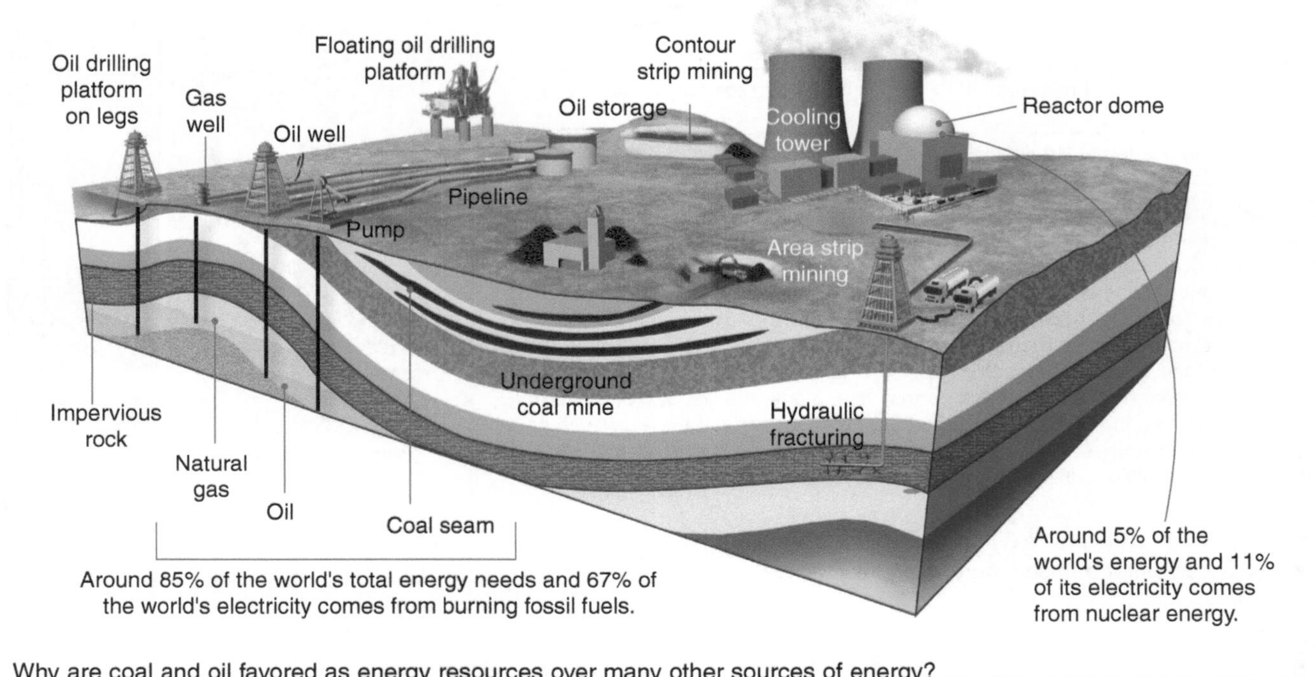

1. Why are coal and oil favored as energy resources over many other sources of energy? ______________________

2. Describe some differences between coal and oil and their extraction from the ground: ______________________

3. What factors determine whether or not it is worth mining a mineral? ______________________

   ESS3.A 

ISBN: 978-1-98-856693-1

110 Environmental Issues of Oil Extraction

Key Question: How does the location of non-renewable resources determine the type of extraction used, and the subsequent environmental costs?

- **Oil** extraction is associated with a number of environmental issues, even before considering its transportation and use. Drilling for oil on land risks groundwater pollution, oil spills from drilling offshore affect vast areas, and the mining of oil sands and oil shales destroys thousands of hectares of forests.
- However, oil is still the most important fuel for the world's transportation industry and is integral to our daily lives. Some of the issues associated with oil extraction are described below.

In situ extraction

In situ extraction is a method of removing oil from oil sands that are too deep to mine. It uses large amounts of energy and water. The water must be stored in tailings ponds for decontamination. Extraction produces up to three times as much CO_2 as the same quantity of conventional oil.

Offshore oil platform

Oil platforms disrupt the seabed when wellheads and pipelines are laid down. There is the potential for oil spills to affect large areas of the ocean. The flaring of the gases contributes to global warming.

Hydraulic fracturing well

In this method, oil-containing rock is fractured by high pressure fluid. The fracking fluid is mostly water with numerous additives to enhance oil mobility. The water must be stored and storage ponds may contaminate groundwater. Groundwater can be contaminated by additives and oil if the well casings are not sealed correctly or fissures link fractured layers to groundwater.

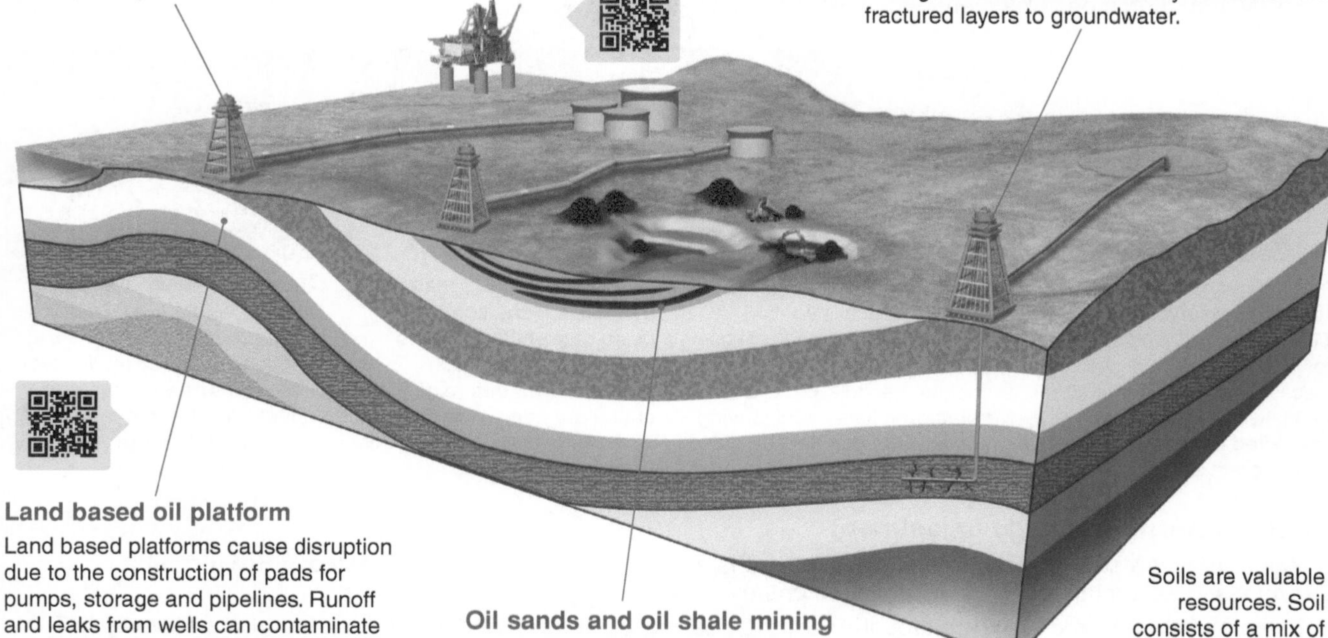

Land based oil platform

Land based platforms cause disruption due to the construction of pads for pumps, storage and pipelines. Runoff and leaks from wells can contaminate ground and surface water. Accidental release of air pollutants, such as methane, contributes to global warming. There is the possibility of land subsidence above oil or gas fields.

Oil sands and oil shale mining

This requires the removal of vast tracts of forest. It produces large volumes of solid and liquid toxic tailings which require huge tracts of land. Leakages of tailings ponds contaminate water.

Soils are valuable resources. Soil consists of a mix of minerals and organic matter. The intensive use of soils can deplete the mineral and organic content, which must be replaced with fertilizers.

1. What environmental issues do hydraulic fracturing and the mining of oil sands and oil shales have in common?

2. Explain why an oil spill from offshore oil extraction can potentially affect huge marine areas:

3. In groups, discuss the following scenario and evaluate the costs and benefits associated with it:
"*In situ* extraction of oil uses enough clean burning natural gas in one day to heat 3 million homes. It has an Energy Return on Energy Investment (ERoEI) of 5:1 (see activity 111 for definition), but produces large amounts greenhouse gases compared to other extraction methods". Include reference to energy inputs and outputs, environmental issues, and pros and cons of energy intensive oil extraction. Attach your group's summary to this page.

ISBN: 978-1-98-856693-1

111 Oil and Natural Gas

Key Question: How does the location and type of oil influence extraction costs and returns on investment?

- **Oil** is formed from the remains of algae and zooplankton which settled to the bottom of shallow seas and lakes about the same time as the coal-forming swamps. These remains were buried and compressed under layers of nonporous sediment. The process, although continuous, occurs so slowly that oil (like coal) is essentially **non-renewable**.
- Oil and natural gas are both composed of a mixture of hydrocarbons and are generally found in the same underground reservoirs. Natural gas is generally defined as a mixture of hydrocarbons with four or fewer carbon atoms in the chain (as these are gaseous at standard temperatures and pressures). Oil is defined as the mixture of hydrocarbons with five or more carbon atoms in the chain.
- Crude oil can be refined and used for an extensive array of applications including fuel, road tar, plastics, and cosmetics.
- Oil and natural gas are valuable for their energy content. Extraction can be costly and returns on investment dependent on the location and type of oil.

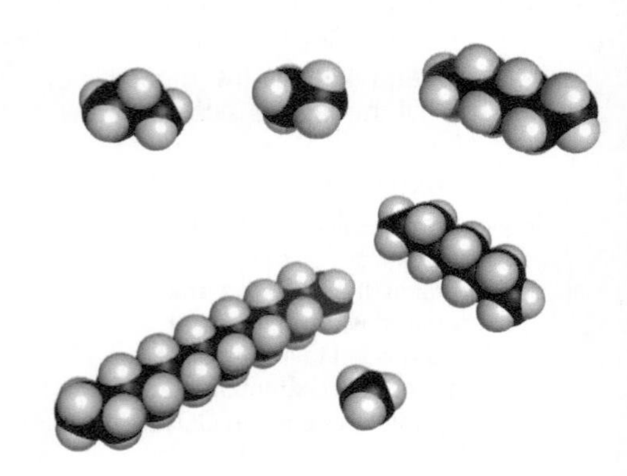

Natural gas is often found in the same reservoirs as oil. Drilling rigs require specialized facilities to store the gas. Because of this, much natural gas is either vented, or reinjected to maintain pressure in the reservoir.

Transport of natural gas requires specialized equipment. Liquid natural gas (LNG) tankers are able to cool the gas to -162 °C and transport it as a liquid (saving space). Gas can also be piped to shore if facilities are nearby.

USDE

Oil may be found in materials that make extraction using conventional drilling impossible. These **non conventional oils** (e.g. oil shale) are often mined in the same way as coal and the oil washed from them.

Crude and heavy oils require refining before use. Crude oil is separated into different sized fractions by a distillation tower. Heavy oils may be heated under pressure to break them into smaller more usable molecules.

Energy return on energy investment

- The energy invested to produce a barrel of oil or the **energy return on energy invested** (**ERoEI**) can be expressed as a ratio of energy expended to energy gained.
- In the early 1900s, the ratio was around 100:1 (100 barrels of oil were produced from 1 barrel of oil invested). The ratio has reduced over time to between 30:1 and 10:1, as the resources become increasingly difficult to harvest and process.

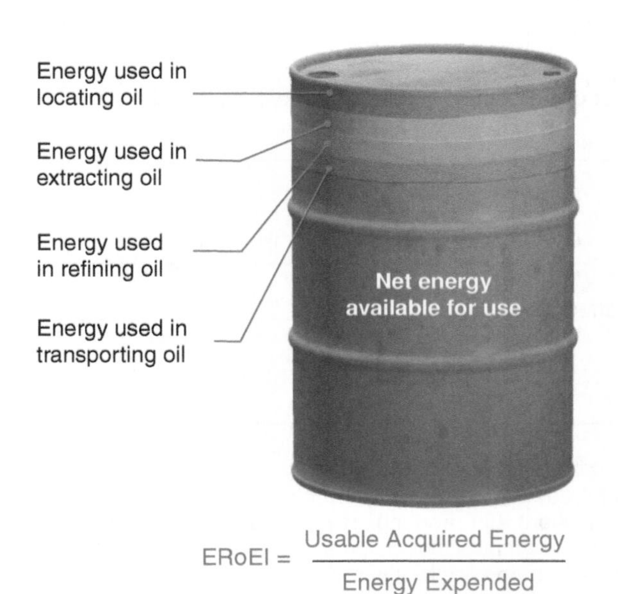

$$\text{ERoEI} = \frac{\text{Usable Acquired Energy}}{\text{Energy Expended}}$$

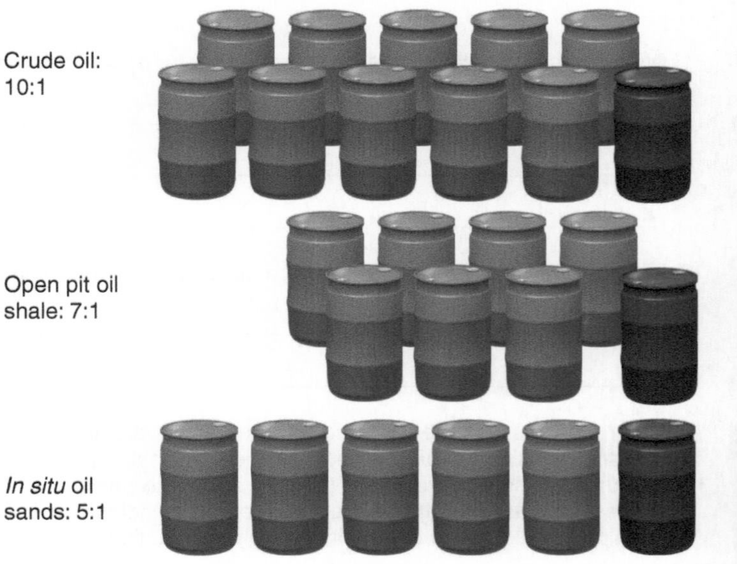

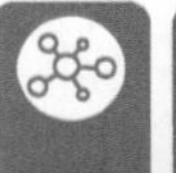     

ESS3.A

ISBN: 978-1-98-856693-1

Peak oil

- The future of the production of any **mineral** can be estimated from its current and historical production rates. Called a Hubbert Curve after its discoverer, it shows that the extraction rate of any **non-renewable resource** will fit into a bell shape curve (right). Plotting the amount of mineral extracted on a graph gives the shape of part of the curve, from which the rest can be estimated. Using these curves, peak production and the time until the resource runs out can be estimated.
- Hubbert curves are constantly applied to estimate peak oil. Peak **oil** is difficult to accurately predict and depends on what type of oil is included in the prediction (e.g. crude, oil shales etc) and how much new oil is being discovered (e.g. the Lula field off the coast of Brazil discovered in 2006).Global oil production decreased dramatically in the mid 1970s and it was thought peak oil may have been reached, but production has since continued to increase.

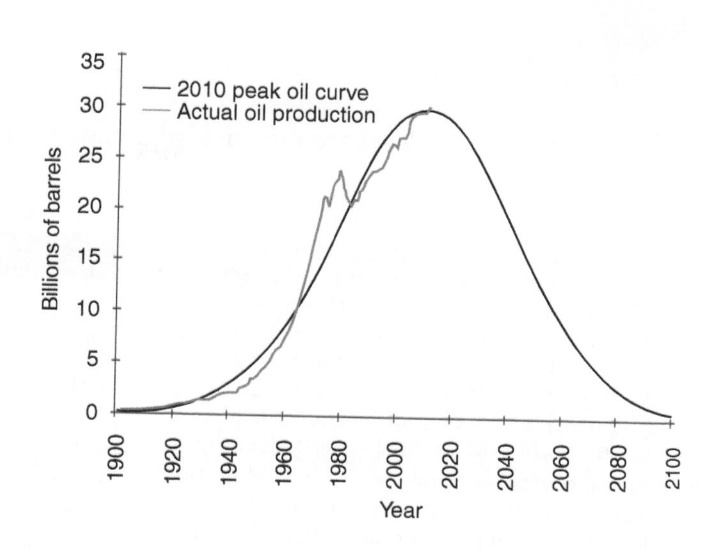

Major world oil reserves

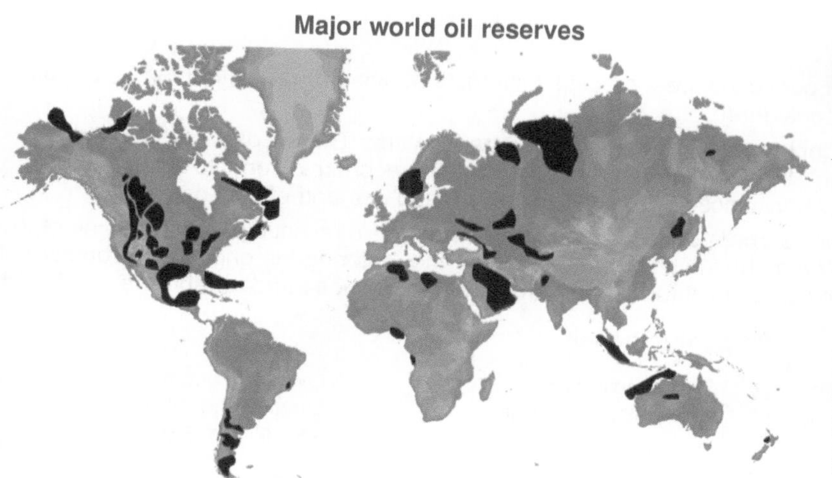

Oil	
Benefits	Costs
Large supply	Many reserves are offshore and difficult to extract
High net energy gain	High CO_2 production
Can be refined to produce many different fuel types	Potential for large environmental damage if spilled
Easy to transport	Rate of use will use up reserves in near future

1. Describe the difference in the composition of natural gas and oil: ______

2. (a) Discuss the significance of peak oil: ______

   (b) What factors affect our estimate of peak oil? ______

3. An oil company located a new area of oil sands and began an analysis of two possible extraction methods. The oil is heavy oil, making pumping difficult. The first method of extraction analyzed was Cold Heavy Oil Production with Sand (CHOPS).The system is relatively cheap but extracts only about 10% of the available oil. It also produces a lot of contaminated sand that must be disposed of. The second method is Steam Assisted Gravity Drainage (SAGD). SAGD requires two parallel wells, one above the other. Steam is pumped into the upper well. The steam heats the heavy oil, which drains into the lower well and is pumped out. This method extracts up to 80% of the oil but is very costly as it requires heating water to steam. No contaminated sand is produced, but oil-contaminated water is.

   Evaluate the costs and benefits of each of these extraction methods and identify any other factors that could affect the decision of which method to use: ______

ISBN: 978-1-98-856693-1

112 Coal

Key Question: What are the costs and benefits of coal mining?

- **Coal** is a valuable **mineral**. Its mining produces economic and energy benefits, but also social and environmental costs. Coal is formed from the remains of terrestrial plant material buried in vast shallow swamps during the Carboniferous period (359 to 299 mya) and subsequently compacted under sediments to form a hard black rock.
- Burning coal produces about a third of the world's energy needs. Nearly eight billion tonnes of coal are produced globally each year. Burning coal produces vast quantities of greenhouse gases and pollutants, contributing to smog and climate change.

Using coal	
Benefits	**Costs**
Huge supplies (billions of tonnes)	High CO_2 production when burned
High net energy yields.	High particle pollution from soot
Can be used to produce syngas and converted to other fuels.	Low grade coals produce high pollution and contribute to acid rain
Relatively easy to extract when close to the surface	High land disturbance through mining, including subsidence
Important in industry as coke (reducer)	Noise and dust pollution during mining

Best practice coal production

- When plans are put in place for opening a coal mine, best practice dictates that economic, environmental, social, and even political costs and benefits are considered.
- By considering these aspects, the net benefit (or cost) of the mine can be identified. Some costs and benefits of coal production are indicated above right, but there are many more including economic benefits such as the creation of jobs and building of industry, or social costs, such as the loss of land use and effects on health.
- It is preferable (and appropriate) that a mine's operators allocate some of the mine's revenue to pay for some of the environmental and social costs, including repairing environmental damage and restoring the original environment (if possible) when the mine closes. Large mines can cost tens of millions of dollars to close and rehabilitate.

Preparing the mine

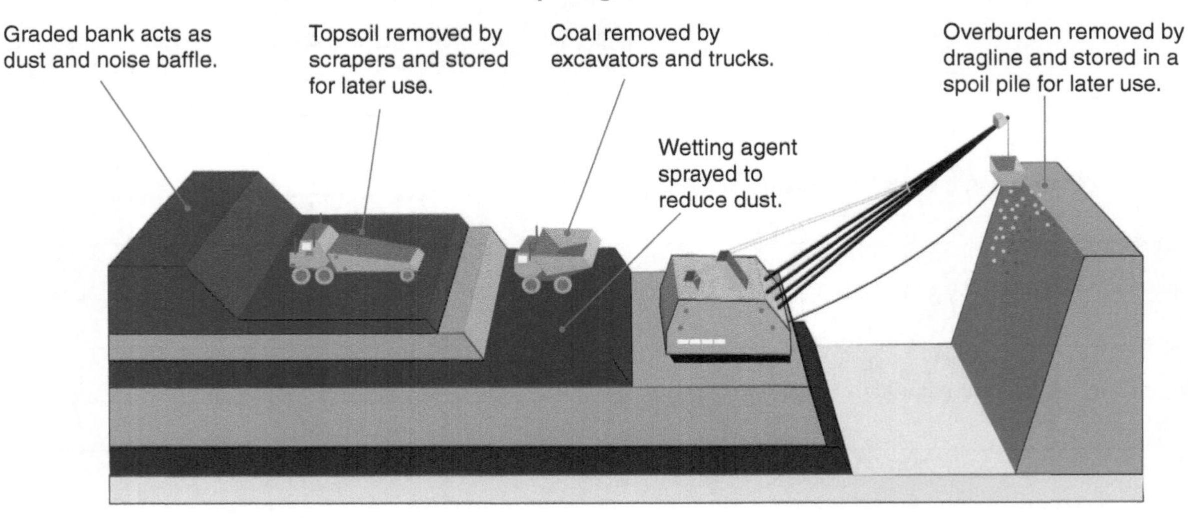

Remediating the mine

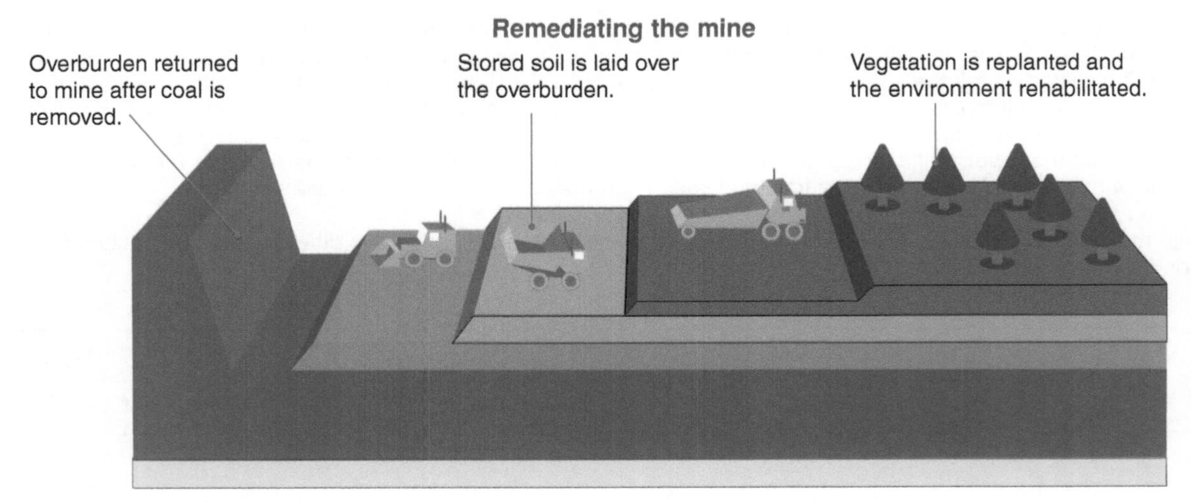

ESS3.A

ISBN: 978-1-98-856693-1

Major world coal reserves

Coal is pulverized and used to fuel thermal power stations. In developing countries, it is often used for home heating and cooking. This can lead to health problems if furnaces or stoves are not properly vented or coal ash is handled improperly, as coal can contain many toxic substances.

1. For each of the following, list two benefits of coal production:

   (a) Economic benefits: ______________________________

   (b) Social benefits: ______________________________

2. For each of the following, list two costs of coal production:

   (a) Environmental costs: ______________________________

   (b) Economic costs: ______________________________

   (c) Social costs: ______________________________

3. The diagram below shows a simplified map of a region where two possible areas could be surface-mined for coal. Use the information below and in this activity to evaluate the costs and benefits of mining at each proposed site. On a separate sheet, produce a reasoned argument for which mine site is best. Staple your sheet to this page.

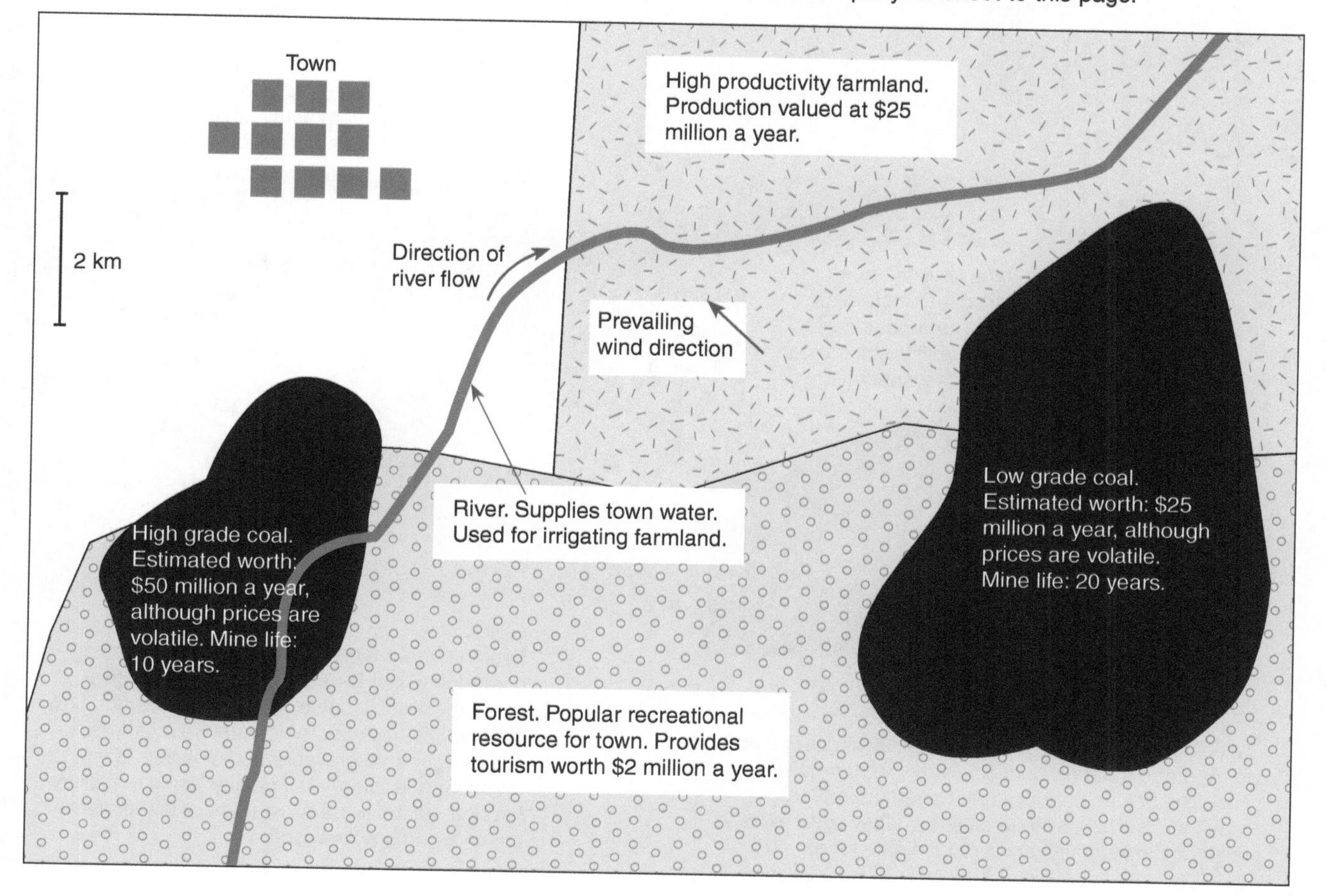

ISBN: 978-1-98-856693-1

113 Intensive Agricultural Practices

Key Question: How can agriculture produce the maximum yield possible from minimum land use?

- Producing food from a limited amount of land presents several challenges: to maximize yield while minimizing losses to pests and disease, to ensure **sustainability** of production, and (in the case of animals) to meet certain standards of welfare and safety.
- By maximizing the efficiency of **resource** use and energy conversion into product, industrialized intensive agricultural systems meet these demands by using high inputs of energy to obtain high yields per unit of land farmed. Such systems apply not just to crop plants, but to animals too, which are raised to slaughter weight at high densities in confined areas (a technique called factory farming).

Some features of industrialized agriculture

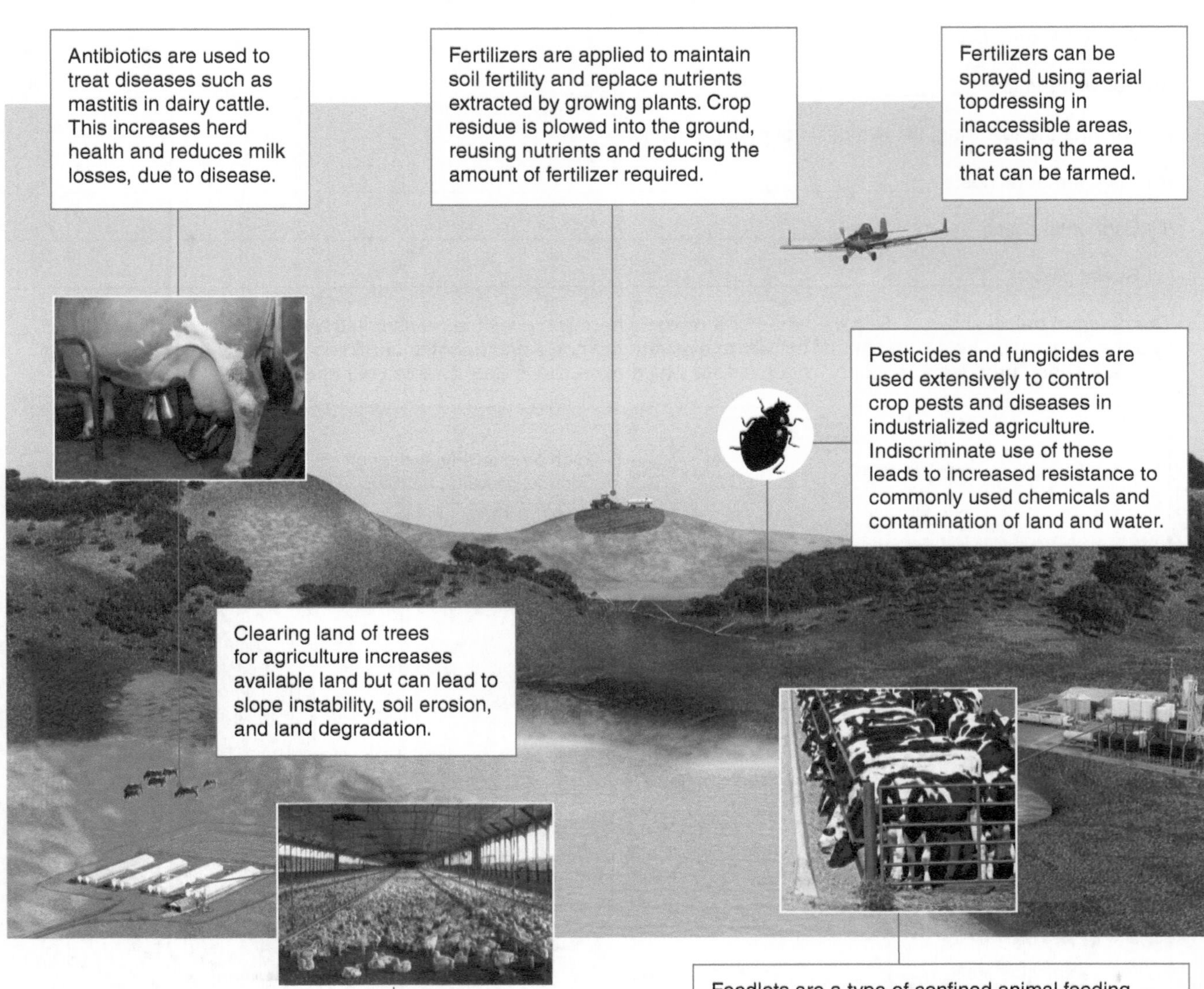

Antibiotics are used in the intensive farming of poultry for egg and meat production. Proponents regard antibiotics as an important management tool to prevent, control, and treat disease, allowing farmers to raise healthy animals and produce safe food.

Feedlots are a type of confined animal feeding operation which is used for rapidly feeding livestock, notably cattle, to slaughter weight. Diet for stock in feedlots are very dense in energy to encourage rapid growth and deposition of fat in the meat (marbling). As in many forms of factory farming, antibiotics are used to combat disease in the crowded environment.

ESS3.A

CE

ISBN: 978-1-98-856693-1

Agriculture and productivity

Increasing net productivity in agriculture (increasing yield) is a matter of manipulating and maximizing the conversion of energy into useful product, e.g. maximizing the grass grown to feed to livestock. On a farm, the simplest way to increase the net productivity is to produce a monoculture. Monocultures reduce competition between the desirable crop and weed species, allowing crops to put more energy into biomass. Other agricultural practices designed to increase productivity in crops include pest control and spraying to reduce disease. Higher productivity in feed-crops also allows greater secondary productivity (production of consumer biomass) in livestock. Here, similar agricultural practices make sure the energy from feed-crops is efficiently assimilated by livestock.

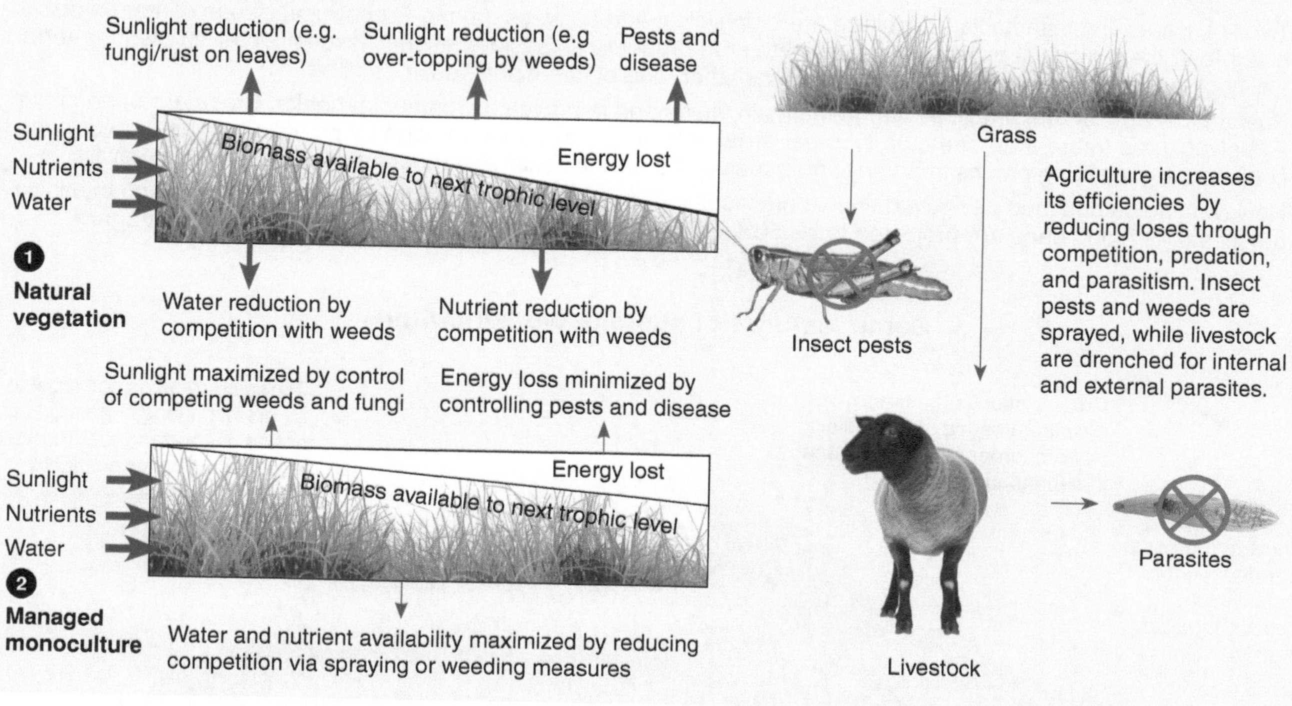

1. Explain the need for each of the following in industrialized intensive agriculture, including how they help to maximize production while minimizing land use.

   (a) Pesticides: ______________________________

   (b) Fertilizers: ______________________________

   (c) Antibiotics: ______________________________

2. Conventional intensive agriculture requires the input of large amounts of energy. Identify places where this energy input occurs and how it might be reduced, considering any effects this might have on production:

____

ISBN: 978-1-98-856693-1

114 Sustainable Agricultural Practices

Key Question: How can sustainable agricultural practices focus on maintaining crop yields while still maintaining ecosystem health?

- Sustainable agriculture refers to farming practices that maximize the net benefit to society by meeting current and future food and material demands while maintaining ecosystem health and services.
- Two key issues in sustainable agriculture are biophysical and socio-economic. Biophysical issues center on soil health and the biological processes essential to crop productivity. Socio-economic issues center on the long-term ability of farmers to manage **resources**, such as labor, and obtain inputs, such as seed.
- Sustainable agricultural practices aim to maintain yields and improve environmental health. Crops are often grown as polycultures (more than one crop type per area), which reduces pest damage by providing a trap crop or pest confuser (e.g. planting onions in a carrot crop masks the carrots' odor and reduces damage by carrot sawfly)
- However, yields obtained using sustainable practices can be up to 25% lower than those obtained using intensive practices. As food needs are projected to be 50% greater by 2050 than today this is a major disadvantage.

Some features of sustainable agriculture

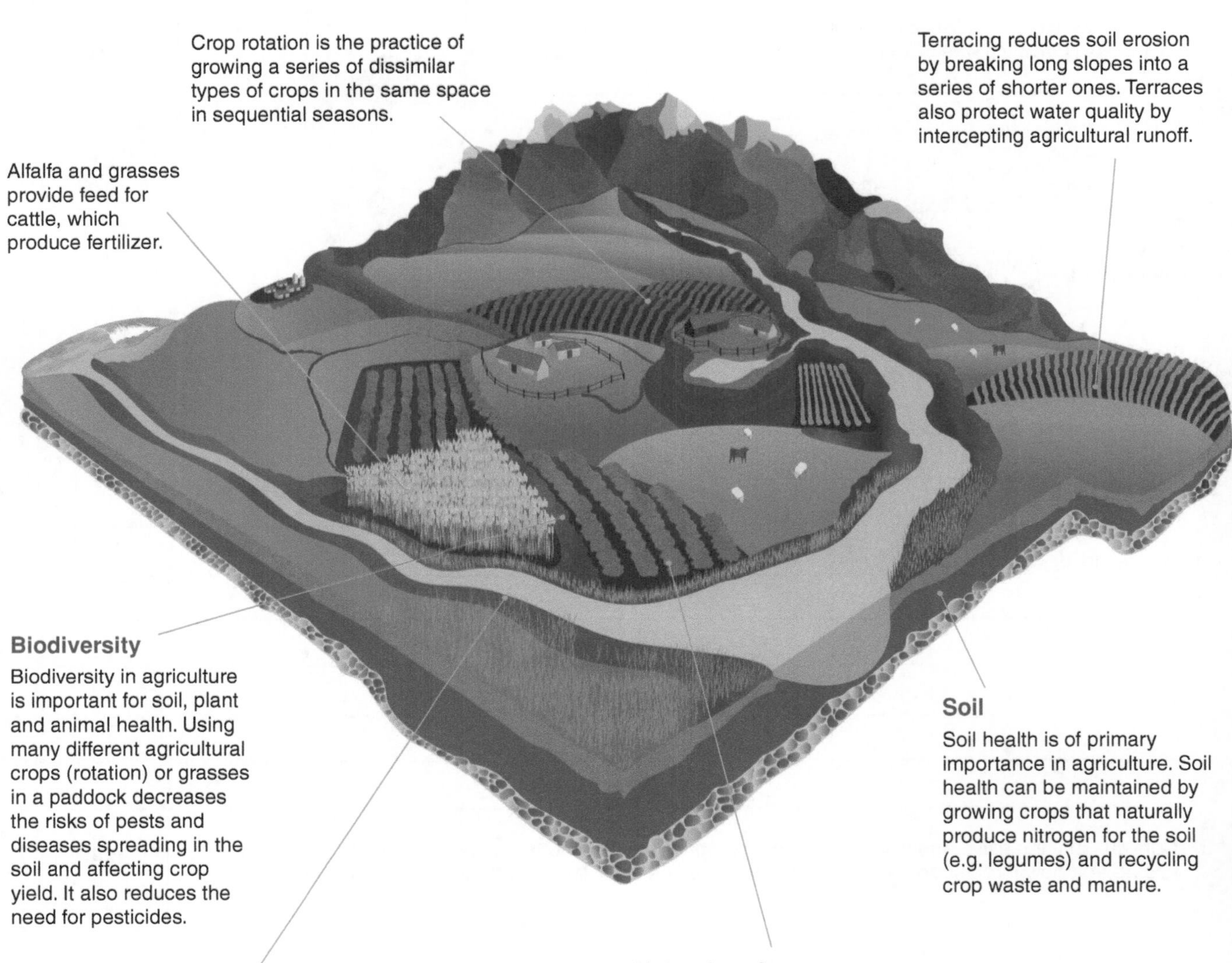

ISBN: 978-1-98-856693-1

Many sustainable practices don't yet include the use of high yielding genetically modified organisms (GMOs), such as rice and wheat. GMOs that can maximize yield with minimum resource use or in marginal growing environments will have to be a serious option to feed the world's rapidly growing population.

Mineral resources, such as rock phosphate and calcium sulfate, supply many of the nutrients needed to maintain agricultural production. Peak phosphorus is expected in 2030. After this, we will need to find new ways to produce phosphorus for fertilizers, such as reclaiming it from plant and animal matter.

Sharon Loxton

Nitrogen fertilizers require ammonia which is made from nitrogen and hydrogen via the Haber process. This requires large amounts of energy and hydrogen, both of which usually come from fossil fuels. To make fertilizers truly sustainable, renewable energy sources and hydrogen supplies are needed.

1. What is sustainable agriculture? ______________________________

2. Explain how sustainable agriculture manages each of the following resources to meet its goals of long term sustainability:

(a) Biodiversity: ______________________________

(b) Water: ______________________________

(c) Soil: ______________________________

3. Discuss the issues associated with resource use and crop yield in agriculture. Produce a reasoned argument as to the best agricultural practice to feed the growing human population over the next 30 years:

____

ISBN: 978-1-98-856693-1

115 Soil Management

Key Question: How does the type of soil make a difference to how it should be used and managed?

- **Soil** is a valuable but rather fragile **resource** and can be easily damaged by inappropriate farming practices. For example, attempts to clear rainforest and bring it into agricultural production have not proved sustainable. These soils are thin and nutrient poor. After only a few years farming they may be abandoned due to poor production.
- Overgrazing and deforestation may cause desertification. When cultivating soils, farmers must be careful not to compact soil, which would leave it lacking structure. The continual use of heavy machinery can cause soil compaction.
- Healthy soils are 'alive' with a diverse community of organisms, including bacteria, fungi, and invertebrates. These organisms improve soil structure and help to create humus.
- Soils known as loams consist of around 20% clay, 40% sand, and 40% silt. Loams are generally considered the most ideal soil, as they retain water and nutrients, but drain freely (right).

Soil type diagram

Percentage clay: 100, 90, 80, 70, 60, 50, 40, 30, 20, 10
Percentage silt: 10, 20, 30, 40, 50, 60, 70, 80, 90, 100
Percentage sand: 100, 90, 80, 70, 60, 50, 40, 30, 20, 10

Read clay in this direction

Read silt in this direction

Read sand in this direction

Clay, Sandy clay, Silty clay, Clay loam, Silty clay loam, Sandy clay loam, Loam, Sandy loam, Silt loam, Loamy sand, Sand, Silt

	Clay	Silt	Sand	Loam
Nutrient holding capacity	++	+	0	+
Water infiltration capacity	0	+	++	+
Water holding capacity	++	+	0	+
Aeration	0	+	++	+
Workability	0	+	++	+

0 = low + = medium ++ = high

- The capacity of soil to be worked and produce viable crops depends on its mixture of particles. Silt provides a moderate capacity in all areas due to its intermediate particle size.
- By itself, it is a poor soil as it too easily turns to mud when wet and is blown away by winds when dry. Loam consists of a variety of particle sizes and maintains a more consistent texture when both wet and dry.

1. Explain the term loam and how it applies to the soil properties: ______

2. Using the scale on soil samples 1 and 2 (right), calculate the percentage of sand, silt and clay in each sample and then use the soil triangle to identify the type of soil:

   Soil sample 1: % sand: ______ % silt: ______ % clay: ______

   Soil type: ______

   Soil sample 2: % sand: ______ % silt: ______ % clay: ______

   Soil type: ______

3. How does poor soil management lead to soil degradation? ______

Clay
Silt
Sand

Soil sample 1

Clay
Silt
Sand

Soil sample 2

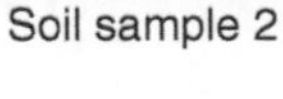

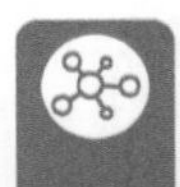

ISBN: 978-1-98-856693-1

No till farming

- Tillage is the mechanical agitation of the ground by plowing and overturning the soil. It has several benefits including the aeration of the soil, mechanical destruction of weeds, and plowing the nutrients in green crops into the ground ready for the next crop.
- However there are several disadvantages to tillage, including the exposure of soil to the wind, increasing erosion and loss of water. One method of reducing soil erosion is the no-tillage system (right and below) in which the residue of the previous crop is left on the surface and seed is planted beneath the ground with special machinery.

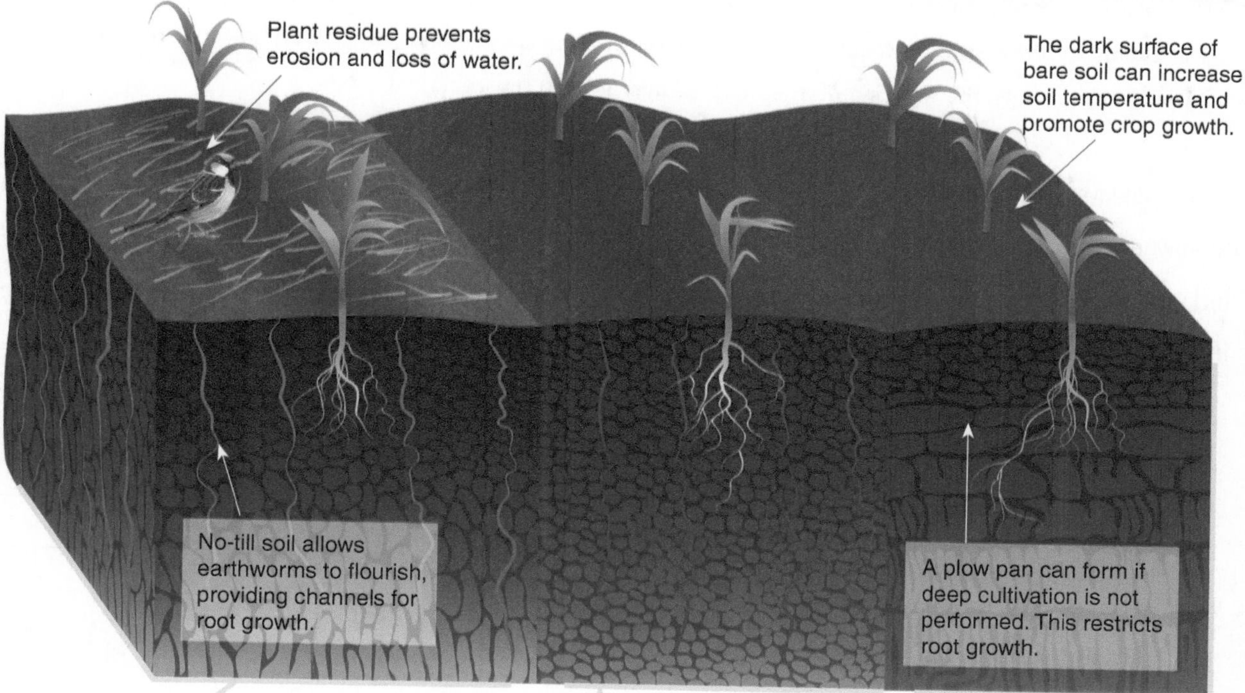

No-tillage systems

The vegetation remaining after harvest is mowed, rolled, or sprayed to begin its break down. Seeds are planted into the ground with seed drills. Residue from the previous harvest helps to reduce loss of water and soil, and prevents weeds becoming established. No-tillage is an extreme form of conservation tillage.

Conservation tillage

Conservation tillage reduces disturbance and retains crop residues. Up to 50% of the crop residue is plowed and buried but the soil is not inverted. Seed is planted into the soil beneath the residue. Conservation tillage reduces overall fuel use and labor costs, and increases carbon storage in the soil.

Intensive tillage

Up to 90% of crop residue is plowed and buried. Fields are tilled with machinery to break up soil and produce a smooth surface for planting. This disturbance to the soil can help if soils are wet or compacted but leads to greater loss of soil carbon and reduced biological activity. After planting, cultivators and herbicides are used to prevent weeds growing.

4. Explain why loamy soils are more easily worked and produce higher crop yields than other soil types:

____

____

____

5. (a) Describe the main difference between no-till and tillage farming methods: _______________

____

(b) Contrast the effort required for no-till and intensive tillage methods and suggest when each of these methods might be advantageous.

____

____

____

____

ISBN: 978-1-98-856693-1

Investigation 9.1 Identifying soil type part 1

See appendix for equipment list.

1. Your teacher has a supply of sand, silt, and clay in separate containers. Obtain three measuring cylinders and place a 20 mL sample of either sand, silt, or clay in each one.
2. Study each sample. Note the texture of each type and the particle size.
3. Now place all three samples into one measuring cylinder. Add enough water to cover them completely.
4. Thoroughly mix the samples together using a stirring rod or spatula and leave to settle for a few minutes.
5. After settling study the layering of the mixture and answer the questions below:

6. (a) In what layer did the **sand** settle after the mixing? ____________________

   (b) In what layer did the **clay** settle after the mixing? ____________________

   (c) In what layer did the **silt** settle after the mixing? ____________________

   (d) How could you use this layering to work out the percentage of sand, silt, and clay in a soil sample?

Investigation 9.2 Identifying soil type part 2

See appendix for equipment list.

1. Your teacher also has three soil samples of unknown type labeled 1, 2, and 3.
2. Your task is to design an investigation that will identify the type of soil (using the soil triangle on the previous page) for each soil sample. Use the space below to write your method, results table, and conclusions:

ISBN: 978-1-98-856693-1

116 Soils, Agriculture, and Solutions

Key Question: How can different farming practices lead to sustainability?

- You have seen how human populations rely on healthy productive soils in order to produce enough food and increased production has historically been driven by the application of fertilizers. Yet fertilizers and industrialized farming practices are costly in terms of energy.
- The challenge for farmers and researchers now and in the future is to manage the physical, chemical, and biological processes controlling soil carbon, nitrogen dynamics, and greenhouse gas emissions from soils.
- The table below outlines seven agricultural and land management practices that aim to provide for human needs into the future and reduce greenhouse emissions from agriculture. Carbon sequestration is important. This is the removal of carbon from the atmosphere to storage.

What does a sustainable future for farming look like?

Farming practice	Definition	Effect on greenhouse gas emissions	Environmental benefits
1 Cover crops	Crops planted to protect and improve soil and nutrients rather than for harvest, especially when the land would otherwise have been barren.	Sequesters carbon in plants and soil. Adding a cover crop to a conservation tillage system can nearly double the rate of carbon sequestration.	Decrease in soil erosion, better retention of nutrients, increased soil organic matter, improved water quality.
2 Conservation tillage	Leaving 30% or more of the crop residue behind after planting. No-till avoids tilling completely (soil is undisturbed).	Soil is disturbed less, so carbon storage in the soil is increased. Reduces carbon dioxide emissions from farm equipment.	Reduces erosion and water pollution because runoff from the soil is reduced.
3 Organic agriculture	Crop rotation, compost, and biological pest control are used to maintain soil productivity and control pests without synthetic pesticides and fertilizers.	On average, organic agriculture involves 60% less direct energy input compared to intensive production. Soils under organic production can store more carbon.	Organic farming has been shown to lead to better retention of soil nutrients, reduced rates of soil erosion, and reduced runoff of water and nutrients.
4 Grazing land management	Modifying grazing practices to reduce greenhouse gas emissions (e.g. rotational grazing and reduced livestock densities).	Reduces soil compaction and maintains ground cover so increases carbon sequestration by the soil. Lower stocking rates reduce emissions of CH_4 and N_2O.	Reduces erosion and water pollution because ground cover is maintained and runoff is reduced.
5 Sustainable forest management	Managing plants to provide wildlife habitat, increase biodiversity, and capture carbon.	Increased plant growth increases carbon sequestration in plant biomass.	Improves water quality and ecosystem resilience (ability of the ecosystem to resist damage and recover from disturbance).
6 On-farm anaerobic digesters	Digesters extract methane from animal waste. The methane can be used as fuel to generate electricity.	Significantly reduces methane emissions. Potential to significantly reduce fossil fuel consumption.	Improved air quality and reduced odor.
7 Retaining or restoring native ecosystems	Returning land its natural state or preventing them from being destroyed through development.	Improved carbon sequestration in accumulated leaf litter, increased organic matter in soils, and increased plant root mass.	Reduced erosion and improved water quality. Improves ecosystem resilience overall.

ISBN: 978-1-98-856693-1

Figure 1: Cover crops can provide the nitrogen needed for optimal growth of corn.

Figure 2: Since 2000, anaerobic digesters on livestock farms in the US have reduced direct and indirect emissions by 34.6 MMTCO2e (million metric tons CO_2 equivalent).

Treatment	Soil loss (tonne/ha)
Bare plot	73.8
Conventional tilling	17.3
Minimal tillage	2.1

Table 1: Soil loss for three tillage systems on a typical agricultural soil in Venezuela.

	Moisture retention in soil (%)			
	Maize	Pigeon peas	Soybeans	Cowpeas
Plowed	9.7	10.8	7.3	12.3
No tillage	13.3	12.1	10.6	15.4

Source FAO.org

Table 2: Effect of tillage regime on soil moisture retention at 0-10 cm depth under different crops two weeks after planting.

Site	Regime	Soil C (tonne C/ha)
Site 1	MiG_{21}	46.6*
	Ext_{50+}	40.4*
Site 2	MiG_{25}	36.2
	Ext_{50+}	32.2
Site 3	MiG_{5}	59.5*
	Ext_{50+}	45.1*
Site 4	MiG_{3}	50.9*
	Ext_{50+}	42.8*

Source Conant, R.T. (2003)

Table 3: Total soil carbon for the top 50 cm of soil at four sites (VA, USA). **MiG** = Management-intensive grazing or short rotational grazing. **Ext** = extensive grazing (low stocking continuous). Subscript refers to number of years under that regime. Asterisks indicate a significant difference between management treatments.

Data from numerous field studies indicate short rotation grazing regimes (MiG) can increase productivity and lead to substantially higher soil carbon. In one study of grazing regimes in the southeastern US (Conant, 2003), total organic soil carbon average 22% greater under MiG. However, the benefits are dependent on available moisture and the findings may not apply to arid lands or during drought conditions.

1. (a) The class will be divided into groups. Each group should choose one of the farming practices described on the previous page and evaluate its features and design in terms of its capacity for sustainable use of a resource (soil) and its ability to sequester carbon and reduce greenhouse gas emissions. Some additional data has been provided in the tables and figures above. You may use this information and any other research or case studies to support your evaluation (visit the **BIOZONE Resource Hub** for more information). Summarize the main points of your group's evaluation in a shared document, including any supporting evidence.

(b) Present your group's findings to the class. The class must then decide collectively what goal and targets are required to conserve the soil resource and best manage it to sequester carbon.

(c) It is not practical to implement all of these farming practices at the same time. In your original groups, select two farming practices that you think are compatible and would provide the greatest benefits in terms of use of the soil resource and reducing greenhouse gas emissions. Write your two practices below and briefly explain why you made this choice. Include a summary of the likely costs and benefits involved, including social, environmental, energetic, and economic considerations. Share your findings with the class.

ISBN: 978-1-98-856693-1

117 Reducing Soil Erosion

Key Question: How can soil conservation practices ensure valuable topsoil resources are not lost?

- Good **soil** is vital for productive agriculture. Most modern cropping techniques use heavy machinery to turn over the remnants of harvested crops, break up the soil, and smooth it flat to form a planting surface. This leaves the soil exposed, and large volumes of topsoil can be lost through wind or rain before there is sufficient crop cover to protect it.
- Even when a crop is fully established, there may still be exposed ground from which soil can be lost. Alternative planting techniques such as no-till farming, terracing, contour plowing, windbreaks, and intercropping reduce the exposure of soil to the elements.

Crops are often planted parallel to the slope of the land so that machinery can move through them easily. This orientation produces channels down which water can easily flow, taking valuable top soil with it.

USDA

Plowing and planting across, rather than down, slopes produces contours that slow water runoff and reduce soil loss by up to 50%. Water has more time to settle into the soil, reducing the amount of irrigation required.

Terracing converts a slope into broad strips, slowing or preventing water and soil runoff and reducing erosion. This technique is commonly used in paddy fields. Terraces also help to control flooding downstream.

USDA

Windbreaks reduce soil erosion by reducing wind speed close to the ground. They also reduce water loss, and so lower irrigation requirements. Windbreaks placed near drainage ditches help to reduce erosion because the tree roots stabilize soil at the edge of the ditch.

Wawny

Agroforestry is a combination of agriculture and forestry. Crops or stock are raised on the same land as a stand of woody perennials. Biodiversity levels are often higher than in conventional agricultural systems and soil loss is much reduced.

Cropping system	Average annual soil loss (t/ha)	Percent rain runoff
Bare soil	41.0	30
Continuous corn	19.7	29
Continuous wheat	10.1	23
Rotation: corn, wheat, clover	2.7	14
Continuous grass	0.3	12

Cunningham- Saigo

Soil erosion is significantly reduced when the vegetative cover over the soil is maintained (above). Continuous cover can be achieved by using machinery to plant crops directly into the soil beneath the existing ground cover, often along with fertilizers and pesticides.

1. Explain how terracing and contour plowing reduce soil loss compared to plowing parallel to the slope: ____________

____

____

____

2. Explain how maintaining vegetative cover reduces soil erosion: ____________

____

____

____

ISBN: 978-1-98-856693-1

CE

ESS3.A

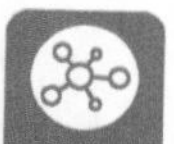

118 Managing Rangelands

Key Question: How can we manage fragile rangeland ecosystems?

- Rangelands are large, relatively undeveloped areas populated by grasses, grass-like plants, and scrub. They are usually semi-arid to arid areas and include grasslands, tundra, scrublands, coastal scrub, alpine areas, and savannah.
- Globally, rangelands cover around 50% of the Earth's land surface. The USA has about 3.1 million km^2 of rangeland, of which 1.6 million km^2 is privately owned. Rangelands cover 80% of Australia, mostly as the outback, but only 3% of Australia's population live in rangeland areas.
- Rangelands are often used to graze livestock (e.g. sheep and cattle) but they regenerate slowly because of low rainfall. Careful management is required to prevent damage and soil loss as a result of overgrazing.

USDA

- Grasses grow continuously from a plant meristem (dividing cells) close to the ground, so the leaf can be cropped without causing growth to stop. This allows a field to be grazed in a near-continuous fashion. Grazing by animals stimulates grass to grow and removes dead material. Grasslands cropped at their optimum capacity can be much more productive than if left uncropped (right).
- Overgrazing occurs when too many animals are grazed for too long on a section of pasture and the grass does not have enough time between cropping to regrow. Overgrazing may destroy the meristem, in which case plant regeneration stops. Exposed soils may become colonized by invasive species or eroded by wind and rain.

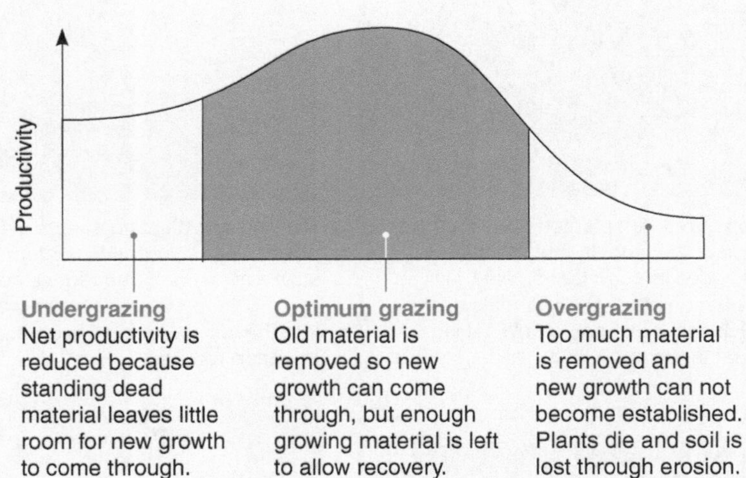

Total net primary production and efficiency of grazed and ungrazed grasslands			
		Net production (kcal/m^2)	Efficiency (%)
Grazed	Desert	1081	0.13
	Shortgrass plains	3761	0.80
	Mixed grasslands	2254	0.51
	Prairie	3749	0.77
Ungrazed	Desert	1177	0.16
	Shortgrass plains	2721	0.57
	Mixed grasslands	2052	0.47
	Prairie	2220	0.44

From Ecology and Field Biology, R. Smith

1. Using evidence from this page, explain how carefully managed grazing on a rangeland can increase its productivity:

2. Why can rangelands easily become overgrazed?

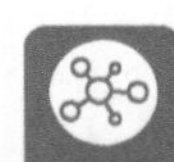    ESS3.A  CE  

ISBN: 978-1-98-856693-1

Rotating livestock

- Sustainable management of **natural resources** such as soil and grasslands is necessary if those **resources** are to be available in the future. Calculating stocking rates for an area to be grazed is important to ensure that the land is not overgrazed and stock rotations are sustainable. Livestock are selective grazers, so care must be taken when grazing only one livestock species that particular grasses or shrubs are not eaten to local extinction.

Rotating grazing

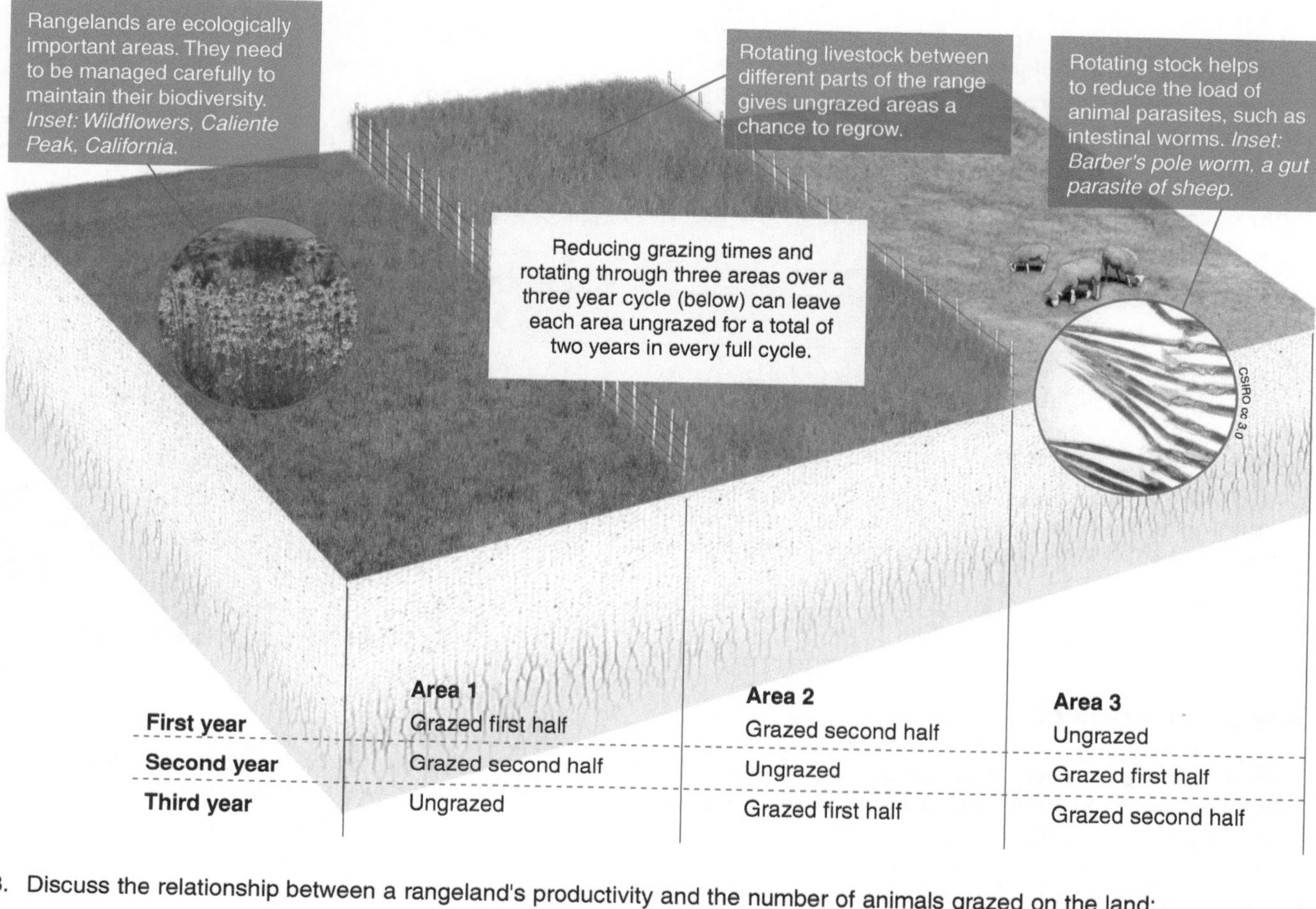

	Area 1	**Area 2**	**Area 3**
First year	Grazed first half	Grazed second half	Ungrazed
Second year	Grazed second half	Ungrazed	Grazed first half
Third year	Ungrazed	Grazed first half	Grazed second half

3. Discuss the relationship between a rangeland's productivity and the number of animals grazed on the land:

4. (a) Describe the effects of livestock rotation on pasture and rangeland biodiversity:

   (b) Which type of grassland is the most productive when grazed?

   (c) Which type of grassland has the greatest increase in productivity when grazed?

5. Explain why overstocking could eventually lead to ecosystem collapse:

ISBN: 978-1-98-856693-1

119 Living With Limited Resources

Key Question: What practices can we use in our daily lives to live sustainably?

Recycling in your neighborhood

- Many cities, towns, and neighborhoods have recycling facilities. Some require a person to take the recycling to a specific centre. Others have trucks that pick up the recycling from the curb.
- Some places only recycle certain materials while others recycle a wide range of materials.

1. (a) Does your neighborhood have recycling collection? ____________

   (b) If yes, do you have to sort the recycling into different containers or is there just the one container?

   ____

   ____

   (c) Does the recycling need to be cleaned before pick up?

   ____

2. When you are away from home (e.g. at the mall or school) are there recycling facilities? Are the garbage cans separated out into plastics and glass for example, or is there only one garbage can for all?

   ____

   ____

Waste management

- Much of the waste produced by industrialized countries contains valuable **resources**, which could be used again if properly processed. As resources become limited and competition for them grows, individuals and companies are exploring ways to use resources as efficiently as possible. This includes reusing waste materials.
- Although most materials can theoretically be reused or recycled, there are always some situations where it is impractical. In those cases, waste may be burned to extract energy or taken directly to a landfill (garbage dump).
- The schematic below shows an integrated resource recycling scheme, which reduces waste as much as possible.

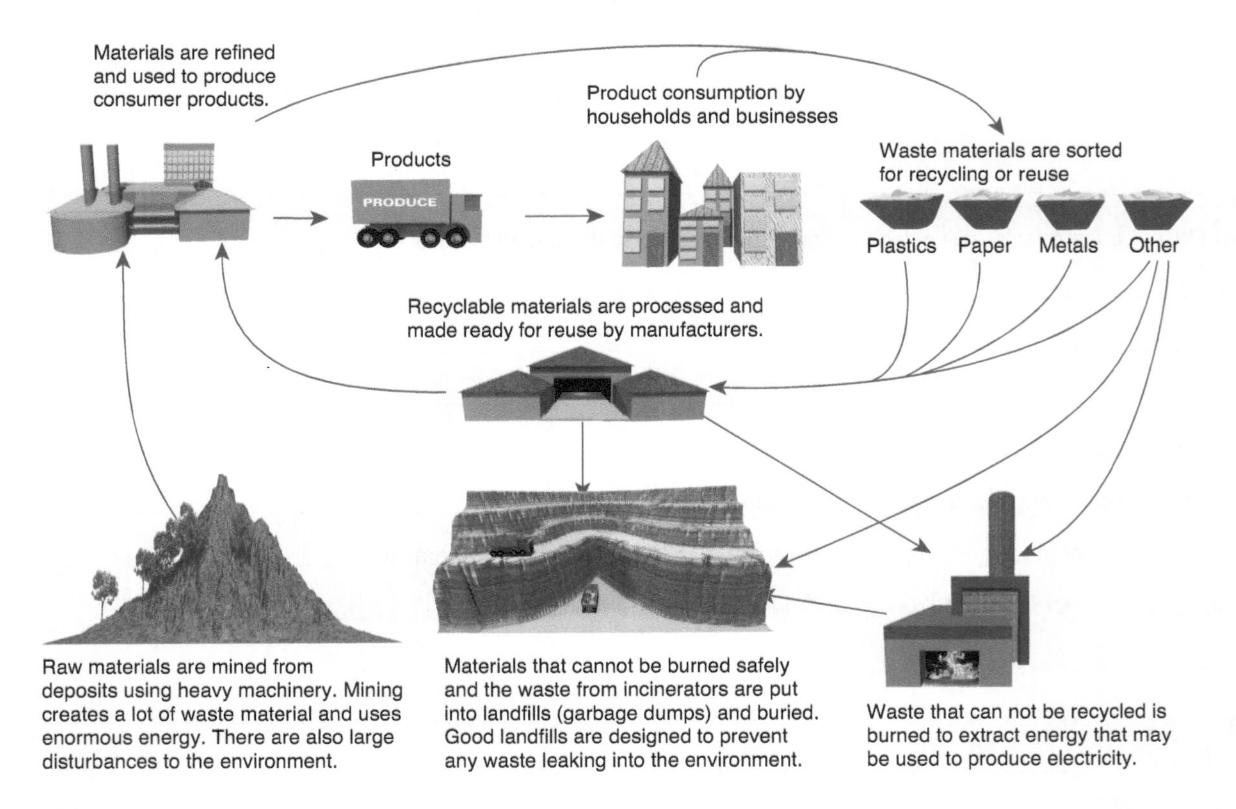

ESS3.A

ISBN: 978-1-98-856693-1

3. List three reasons why waste should be recycled: ______________________

4. Why is putting waste in a landfill the least preferred option of a waste management scheme? ______________________

5. (a) In what way is incinerating (burning) waste a useful part of a management scheme? ______________________

(b) Why is incineration one of the least preferred options in a management scheme? ______________________

Recycling, reusing, energy, and cost

- Recycling, like any resource extraction method, requires energy. This may be in the form of collecting and sorting material, transport to manufacturers, and the energy used in melting or remelting a material. In order for recycling to be advantageous, it must cost less energy than producing a new item or material from the original resource.
- Some materials returned from recycling do not return the same quality of product as new material (e.g. wood) and are often made into inferior product (a process called down-cycling). In these cases, new material needs to be added, so recycling is not a closed loop or a total solution. However, it does significantly reduce the need for new materials, extending the life of the resource and reducing the energy spent on producing new material.
- In general, metals can be 100% recycled. They are relatively easy to melt down and recover from scrap. Aluminum requires 96% less energy to make from recycled cans than it does to process from bauxite (ore). What matters the most when producing materials is the cost of extracting and refining the raw materials versus the cost of collecting, sorting, and reprocessing used materials.
- New technology for recycling has helped to reduce the cost of collecting and sorting. For example, in San Francisco, no pre-separation of recyclable material is needed. Although some workers are still required, most of the separation work is carried out by the city's state-of-the-art recycling facility. Magnets remove steel, eddy currents separate aluminum, and vacuum tubes and separators remove plastics.

Reusing sometimes takes a while

- Reusable objects, such as reusable shopping bags or take away coffee cups, have recently become fashionable. However many people do not realize how long these things need to be reused before they become "environmentally friendly". For example a single use paper cup has a cost of production and a cost of dumping. These costs are fixed for every cup A reusable cup has a much higher cost of production and a cost of cleaning. In this case, the production cost reduces over time while the cleaning cost remains the same.

Glass recycling. Modern recycling plants can sort materials automatically using the physical properties of the materials.

Energy savings using recycled material

Recycled material	Energy saving (%)
Aluminum	95
Plastic	88
Copper	75
Steel	60
Paper	60
Glass	34

Energy cost of reusable vs disposable cups

Cup type	Cup mass (g)	Material specific energy (MJ/kg)	Energy per cup (MJ/kg)
Ceramic	292	48	14
Plastic	59	107	6.3
Glass	199	28	5.5
Paper	8.3	66	0.55
Foam	1.9	104	0.20

Environmental Management Vol.18 1994

ISBN: 978-1-98-856693-1

- The data at the bottom of the previous page and the graph (right) show how many uses it takes before recyclable items (glass, plastic, or ceramic) reach the same energy per cup value as single use items (paper and foam). It does not account for the cost of disposal.

Energy cost per cup per use

Energy per use (MJ): 0, 0.2, 0.4, 0.6, 0.8, 1.0

Number of uses: 0, 50, 100, 150, 200

Ceramic, Plastic, Glass, Paper, Foam

6. Explain why recycling saves energy compared to mining and refining new materials:

7. Estimate the energy per use after 100 uses of:

   (a) A foam cup:

   (b) A ceramic cup:

   (c) A plastic cup:

Costs and convenience

8. You are the mayor of a city. Counselors have come to you with two possible recycling programs for the city. Evaluate the programs from the information below and decide which would be most effective in increasing participation in recycling from the public, reduce the amount of waste being taken to the land fill, and be the most cost effective (considering social, environmental, and economic costs).

KP

System one: Recycling is mixed (all recyclable items in one bin). A single hauler picks up curbside recycling, which is charged to users at a fixed fee (every household pays the same regardless of waste generated). Drop off facilities are available. High value recyclable waste, such as aluminum, is paid for at the recycling station on a per kilogram basis.

System two: Recycling must be presorted into glass, plastic and metals, and paper. Households can choose between two haulers which charge a pay-as-you-throw fee (the more waste generated the more they are charged. Charges also depend on the hauler). Households can bypass this fee by taking recyclables to a recycling facility for free. High value recyclable wastes such as aluminum cans are not paid for.

In both systems, a separate hauler takes rubbish to the landfill. This is charged at a fixed fee for all households.

Present your reasoned decision here. You can use more paper if you wish and attach it to this page:

ISBN: 978-1-98-856693-1

120 Review Your Understanding

Key Question: How can recycling or reusing lithium in lithium-ion batteries reduce the impact of mining on the environment?

- At the beginning of the chapter, we were introduced to the growing problem of demand for lithium, used in rechargeable batteries of electric vehicles, and the need to recycle the lithium to minimize environmental impact.
- Experts estimate we could have anywhere between 15 and 50 years supply left of readily available lithium to mine or extract, so recycling and reusing lithium contained in 'dead' batteries is essential.
- New technology, and the desire to reduce environmental impact on both mining sites, and battery dumps, are driving the ways in which we view recycling.

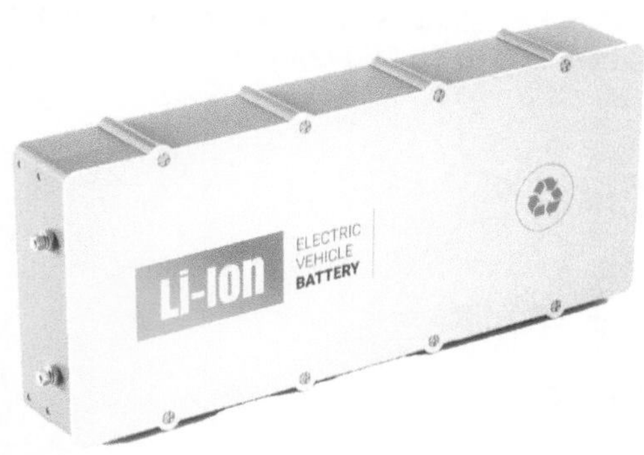

1. Lithium is one of Earth's resources. It is a silver metal that reacts readily with other elements, so is found in its ion state (Li^{+}), as a compound in solid ore in Australia, and in a water solution in underground lakes in Chile and Argentina. Use the **Resource Hub**, and your own research, to answer how the different types of mining for lithium might advantage and disadvantage these regions? Consider environmental, social, and economic factors in your answer:

2. Demand for lithium-ion batteries is likely to increase by ten-fold over the next decade. This will also mean the world will be faced with an increasingly large stock pile of 'dead' car batteries, while the demand for new batteries grows. How can reusing or recycling lithium from the batteries reduce impact on the environment?

3. How can recycling technology be solution for the growing demand for lithium resources to supply lithium-ion batteries?

ISBN: 978-1-98-856693-1

121 Summing Up

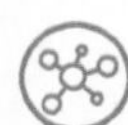

Resource Island is located 35° South, 1540 km from the nearest land mass. It is 21 km wide at its widest point and 843 m above sea level at its highest point, the table-topped Mount Kiilua. The prevailing winds come from the west. Rainfall is around 1000 mm per year, 65% of which falls during March to September. Currently undeveloped, Resource Island is to be colonized. Scientists think that if the island is managed carefully, it may one day be able to sustain up to 15,000 people.

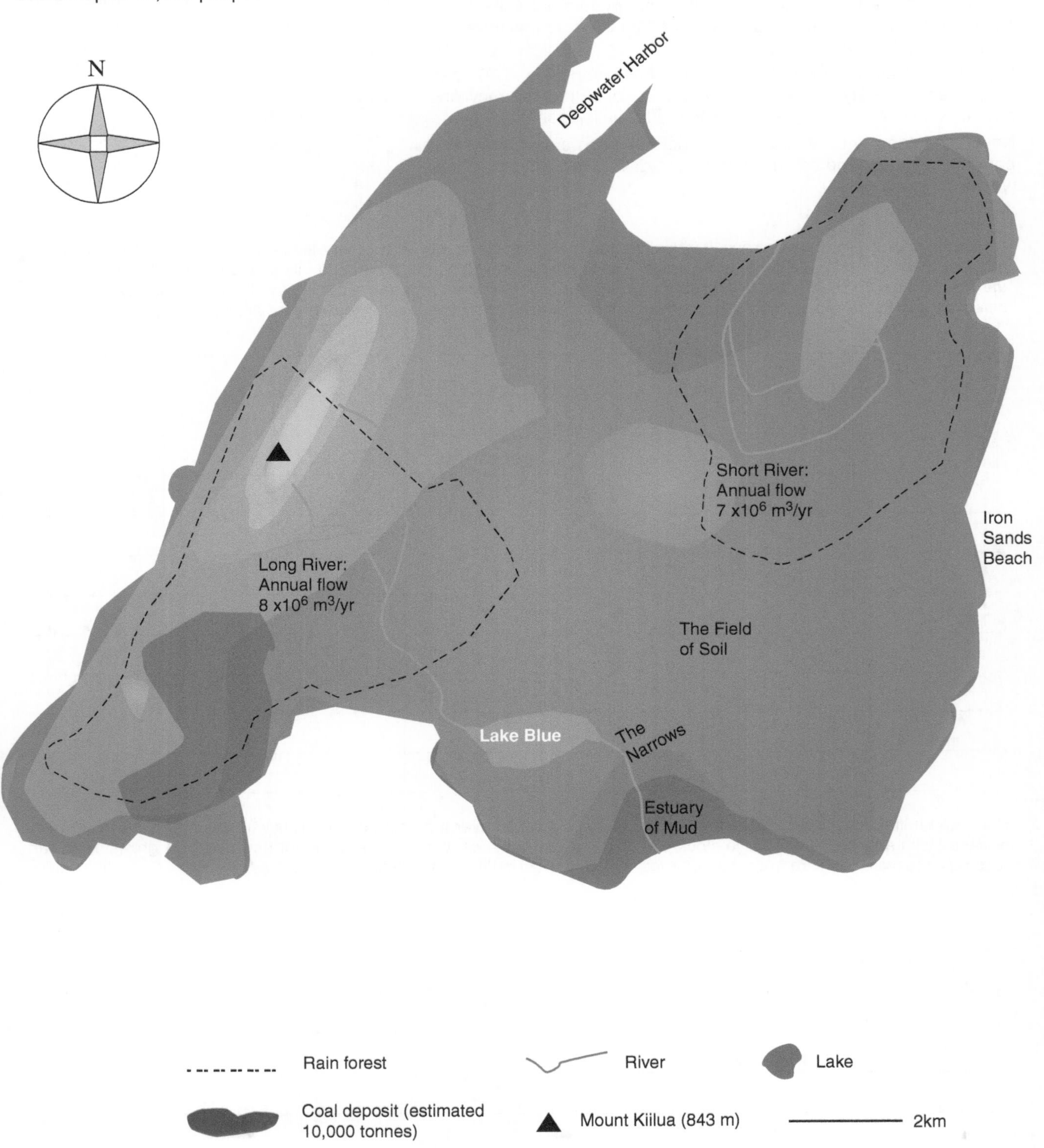

1. Resource Island will eventually host a population of 15,000 people. Mark out where you would place the main city and fields for crops and livestock. Suggest how energy and building resources will be sustained in the long term. Attach a separate sheet explaining how you would produce the enough power for 15,000 people, deal with both solid and liquid waste, and ensure adequate water supplies for drinking and irrigation. Your decisions must take into account and justify the impact on the environment.

ISBN: 978-1-98-856693-1

2. A mining company explores two potential surface mining areas using a drill to provide core samples. The costs and mineral content of each site is shown below:

	Area 1 (surface area approximately 20 km^2)	Area 2 (surface area approximately 14 km^2)
% gold (value per kilogram = $43,000)	0.00008%	0.00005%
% silver (value per kilogram = $650)	0.005%	0.007%
% copper (value per kilogram = $4.70)	0.08%	0.2%
% lead (value per kilogram = $1.80)	2%	3%
% zinc (value per kilogram = $2.15)	1.2%	2.1%
Average depth of ores (m)	100 m	50 m
Access to mine site	Moderate	Difficult
Start up cost	$40 million	$50 million
Extraction rate (total rock + ore per day)	5000 tonnes	4800 tonnes
Cost of running mine facility	$9 per tonne	$7.40 per tonne
Cost of restoring the environment per km^2	$1,200,000	$2,100,000
Approximate mine lifetime	15 years	12 years

Use the data to decide which of these areas is the most suitable for mining, giving any reasons and calculations to support your decision:

3. Explain how resources (fuel, water, soil) influence human social and technological development and activity. Provide evidence for your explanation. You may use extra paper if required and attach it to this page.

ISBN: 978-1-98-856693-1

CHAPTER 10

Natural Hazards

Anchoring Phenomenon

Weather Whiplash: What influences the frequency and extremity of weather events? 122 130

What are natural hazards, and what are the factors that influence their impact?

- ☐ 1 Define and identify a natural hazard. Describe ways in which humans can reduce the risk and impact of natural hazards. Explain how natural hazards have impacted the patterns of human settlement. 123
- ☐ 2 Distinguish between natural hazards and natural disasters. Describe features of natural hazards that can influence their impact. 124

How have natural hazards impacted the distribution of human populations?

- ☐ 3 Discuss how natural hazards, including drought and flooding due to sea level rise, have displaced human populations over time. Discuss reasons why displaced people may not return to their homes after a natural hazard. 125
- ☐ 4 Use evidence to discuss how the western United States drought may impact human activity in the present and future. 126
- ☐ 5 Discuss reasons for the differing impact of drought in different regions of the world, based on the economic situation. Describe ways in which human populations can prepare for and lessen the impact of droughts. 127
- ☐ 6 Use case study information of tundra fires in the Arctic to discuss global consequences of this natural hazard. Use California wildfire and rainfall data to identify the relationship between the two factors. Discuss the relationship between wildfire frequency and severity, changes in climate, and human activity. 128
- ☐ 7 Explain how levees may have created downstream issues in the context of the Louisiana flood event. Discuss positives and negatives of climate migration in Louisiana. Use evidence to suggest solutions that lessen impacts of flooding in the future. Explain how we can interpret evidence from our understanding of extreme climate events to attribute these to climate change.. 129
- ☐ 8 Explain how the frequency and severity of natural hazards could be linked to climate change, and how these events may impact ecosystems, biodiversity, and people. 130
- ☐ 9 Examine the relationship between number of hurricanes and energy of hurricanes in the North Atlantic. Predict the impact of natural hazards leading to sea level rise on small, low-lying islands. In the context of the Sidoarjo mudslide, discuss the impact on the surrounding population, and the resulting displacement. 131

122 Weather Whiplash

Key Question: What influences the frequency and extremity of weather events?

What causes extreme weather events?

- The sudden swing in weather conditions from one extreme to the another is called weather whiplash. California's climate naturally fluctuates between dry summers and wet winters. Historically, large swings between the extremes have been quite rare, only occurring every 100-200 years.
- The Great **Flood** of 1862 affected several states, including California. So much rain fell on the Central Valley and the Los Angeles Basin over 45 days that a large area was turned into an inland sea. An area 480 km long, averaging 32 km in width and covering 13,000 to 16,000 km^2 was under water. Towns and infrastructure were swept away and agricultural lands were ruined.
- The United States Geological Survey (USGS) has studied and mapped the flood to predict the effect of another such megastorm on modern day California. The predicted flood event is officially called the ARkStorm. It is unofficially called "the other big one".
- Some researchers predict weather extremes like the one causing The Great Flood will become more common in California, as the influences of global warming are felt.
- California has experienced many **droughts**, including one that lasted from 2012-2017. This period was the driest on record since monitoring was started. This drought was followed by the wettest winter ever recorded in Northern California. The rainfall was greater than the conditions that caused The Great Flood of 1862. Water reservoirs were replenished, but the flooding caused widespread damage. The Fresno River is normally dry at the construction site of the Fresno River Viaduct, but was filled with water during the 2017 flood. The images on the right show this.

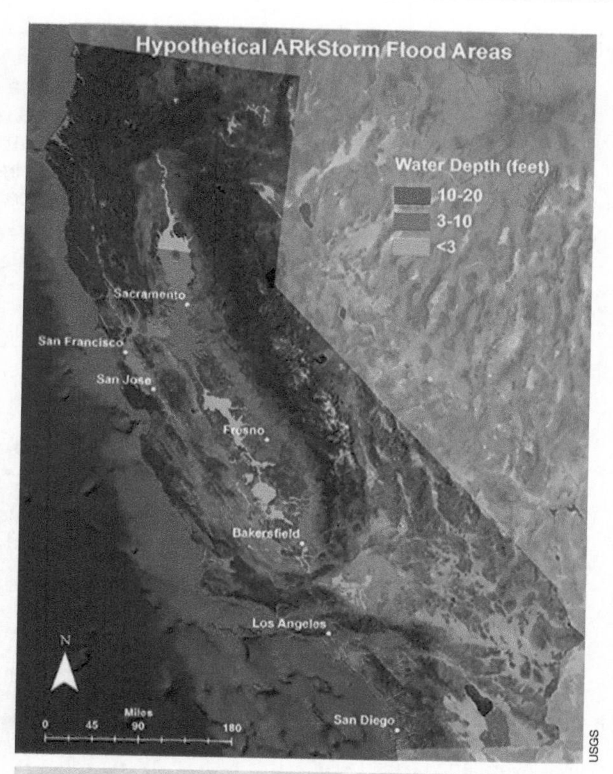

USGS

Fresno River Viaduct 2016

Fresno River Viaduct 2017

Images: California High-Speed Rail Authority (public domain)

1. Would you consider the events described for California (2012-2017) as a weather whiplash? Explain why or why not:

2. In small groups, research the occurrence of weather whiplash events in California. Has there been a change in their frequency? If so, explain the changes observed:

ISBN: 978-1-98-856693-1

123 What Are Natural Hazards?

Key Question: How can Earth's natural hazards be classified?

- The Earth can be a hazardous place. The processes that shape the surface of the Earth can also produce surface disturbances on vast scales, e.g. tropical cyclones. **Natural hazards** are any natural event that may cause damage on a small or large scale. They can be grouped into biological, e.g. disease, and geophysical hazards. Geophysical hazards include geological events (ground occurring, e.g. earthquakes) or meteorological events (atmospheric, e.g. hurricanes).
- It is important to distinguish between a natural hazard, e.g. a volcanic eruption, and a natural disaster, e.g. the wide scale loss of life and property caused by a volcanic **eruption**.

Storms can produce large scale effects. Hazards include lightning strikes, wind and water damage, flooding, and landslides due to water-logged soil.

Flood hazards are possible near rivers and lakes, called fluvial flooding. People living on the floodplains of large rivers are often inundated when rivers burst their banks. Many rivers near towns have levees or stopbanks to contain the water and prevent flooding, although these mechanisms can just transfer the flooding issues further downstream.

1. Identify the natural hazards associated with each of the following phenomena:

   (a) Storm: ______________________

   (b) Volcano: ______________________

   (c) High mountains: ______________________

2. Identify ways to reduce the risk of damage from each of the following hazards:

   (a) Drought: ______________________

   ____

   (b) River: ______________________

   ____

   (c) Seaside: ______________________

   ____

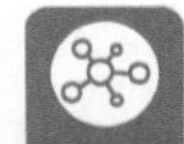   ESS3.A ESS3.B SC

ISBN: 978-1-98-856693-1

Hazards in high mountains include rock falls, blizzards, and avalanches. Avalanches occur when the snowpack loses adhesion and slides down the mountain face. More than 100 people a year are killed in avalanches, despite the large effort that is put into reducing the damage they cause.

Tropical cyclones, typhoons, and **hurricanes** present hazards around the tropical regions of the world. Damage may occur due to 200 km/h winds and flooding from rainfall and storm surges. Large cyclones can cause damage up to 40 km from the coast. Climate change may increase the frequency of cyclones.

Many areas of land used for grazing or cropping are prone to drought. Drought causes enormous economic damage as it seriously reduces farm productivity. Efforts to reduce drought damage include building dams to store water and planting drought tolerant crops. Climate change may increase the occurrences of drought.

Landslides are common on mountains and steep terrain. Every year, many thousands of homes are destroyed by landslides.

Tsunamis result from movements of the sea floor caused by earthquakes or subsea landslides. Waves may reach more than 10 m high when they reach the shore. Many high risk areas (such as Japan) have high sea walls to reduce **tsunami** damage.

Earthquakes result from the sudden movement of the ground along fault lines. They present a hazard with the potential to cause enormous damage. Billions of dollars a year is put into recovery from **earthquakes** or planning and building to minimize damage risk.

3. (a) Identify one significant natural hazard in your local area: ______________________________

(b) How does your local area prepare for, or reduce the risks posed by, this natural hazard? ______________________________

(c) Why do you think people might have settled in the area, despite the presence of this hazard? ______________________________

ISBN: 978-1-98-856693-1

124 The Effects of Natural Hazards

Key Question: What are some factors influencing the impact of natural hazards?

- The impact a **natural hazard** has depends on the features of the natural hazard itself, the natural features of the land affected, and a region's economic development. Natural hazards are not recent phenomena. They have been (and will continue to be) caused by the same processes that have always occurred, e.g. movement along a fault line produces **earthquakes**. However, some natural hazards have been made more common through human activity, e.g. forest fires, or **flood** events caused by changing the course of a river.

Many factors influence the impact of a natural hazard

- **Natural features**
  Natural features of the Earth and the environment can have a significant influence on how much damage a natural hazard can cause. For example, the angle of the coastline (steep or gentle incline) will influence how much damage will be caused by a storm surge (right).
- **Magnitude**
  The size (or magnitude) of the event has a significant impact on the damage that the natural hazard causes. For example a 2.5 magnitude earthquake is not usually felt, but a 7.0 magnitude earthquake in the same location can cause serious damage.
- **Frequency**
  The frequency of a hazard (how often it occurs) will directly affect how a particular area responds and recovers from the most recent event. For example, areas prone to frequent flood events may be severely damaged with each event and also do not have time to recover between floods.

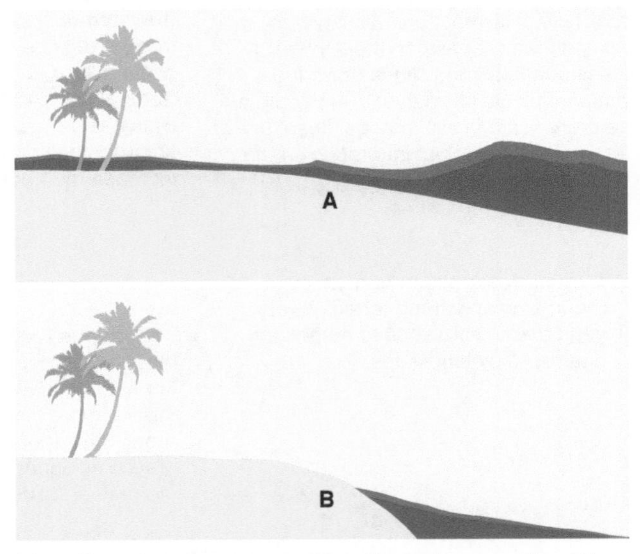

The effect of storm surge on a gently sloping coastline (A) and a steep coastline (B) is shown above. The storm surge travels much further inland when the coastline has a gentle slope, potentially damaging more land and property. A steeper slope at the coastline prevents or limits inundation, and acts as a natural protective barrier.

Many factors influence the impact of a natural disaster

- When a natural hazard event affects human life or property, the event is called a **natural disaster**. The extent of the natural disaster depends not only on the features of the natural hazard, but social factors too.
- **Level of development**
  The level of development, e.g. infrastructure and money, of an area will contribute to how well that region can respond to a natural disaster. Better economically developed regions will have the resources to respond more quickly and more efficiently than lesser economically developed regions.
- **Preparedness**
  How ready the population is to respond to a natural disaster will influence how well they cope immediately after the event. Factors include constructing buildings to withstand earthquakes in vulnerable areas, e.g. San Francisco, or having resources ready to be distributed after the event. Early warning systems, such as the **tsunami** warning system, are designed to give coastal residents time to evacuate to higher ground.
- **Accessibility**
  Remote or severely damaged areas can be difficult for disaster teams to access. If support cannot be provided to the affected population, death rates may rise. For example, if the water supply has been contaminated, disease may spread through the population. Without access to clean water and medical supplies, people may die from causes secondary to the disaster event itself.

United nations Logan Abassi cc2.0

Kobe (1995) and Haiti (2010 and 2021) were both struck by similar sized earthquakes. The damage was less severe in Kobe because Japan's strict building codes reduced the number of collapsed buildings. Regular earthquake drills meant the population were well rehearsed for an earthquake and emergency services were able to deliver supplies quickly. The death toll was much lower in Kobe and recovery was much faster because Japan has a higher level of economic development and preparedness than Haiti.

ISBN: 978-1-98-856693-1

Natural hazards can cause natural disasters

- The Atlantic **hurricane** season refers to a period (June to November) when hurricanes usually form in the Atlantic Ocean. During this period, the East Coast of the US can expect a number of hurricanes ranging in intensity from category 1-5. Anything above category 3 is a major hurricane. An average of 6 hurricanes develop during the Atlantic season, with 2-3 of these developing into category 3 or greater.
- Hurricanes are a regular **natural hazard**, but some have greater impact than others. The devastation caused in New Orleans by Hurricane Katrina in 2005 was due to a combination of the intensity of the hurricane and the physical land features of New Orleans. Hurricane Katrina varied in intensity, reaching category 5 before reducing in intensity to category 1-2 when it reached New Orleans. The prolonged heavy rain and storm surge (up to 9 meters) meant that many of the levees and floodwalls failed, resulting in **flooding** of up to 80% of the city (right). Many of the 1464 deaths associated with Hurricane Katrina were a result of levee failure.

US Coastguard Public domain

A history of flooding in New Orleans

New Orleans was originally built on natural levees along the Mississippi River. New Orleans is completely surrounded by water: the Mississippi River on one side and Lake Pontchartrain on the other. As the city grew and demand for land increased, people settled the lower lying land, which was more prone to flooding. Houses were built elevated above ground to cope with the frequent flood events. Over time, a series of drains, levees and floodwalls were developed to help protect New Orleans from flooding. Today, much of the city lies below sea level (right), relying on the levees and floodwalls to protect it. During Hurricane Katrina, the strong storm surges and prolonged rain caused most of the levees to fail, resulting in widespread flooding and destruction. (NGVD is the National Geodetic Vertical Datum, a reference point for elevation).

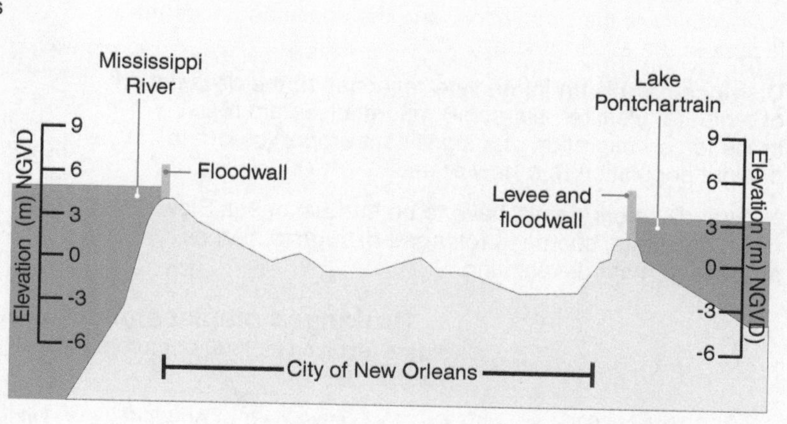

1. Describe some features of natural hazards that can increase their impact: ____________________

2. Using an example, explain how a country's level of economic development can affect the impact of a natural disaster?

3. What factors contributed to Hurricane Katrina significantly damaging New Orleans? ____________________

ISBN: 978-1-98-856693-1

125 Natural Hazards and Human Migration

Key Question: How is migration used as a survival response by people facing the prospect, impact, or aftermath of natural hazards and disasters?

Natural hazards can force migration

- Throughout history, **natural hazards**, or the natural disasters that may arise as a result of them, have significantly altered the size of human populations or forced **migration** away from the affected area. Sometimes, these movements are temporary and areas affected by the hazard are eventually repopulated. However, in some cases, people never return, because they settle permanently elsewhere or because the damaged area is no longer capable of sustaining them.
- The impact of a natural disaster depends on a variety of factors, including the time of day that the hazard strikes, the vulnerability of the population, and the social and economic factors in the environment.
- **Displacement** is an immediate response to the devastation of a natural disaster, but some natural disasters result in the forced migration of a significant proportion of the original population to a new area.
- Natural disasters do not have to be sudden onset. Slow onset disasters, such as prolonged **droughts**, can be among the most devastating.

The 2011-2012 sub-Saharan drought caused a severe food crisis across East Africa and affected 9.5 million people in four countries. Such slow onset disasters force mass movements of people in search of food and water. Many die, and survivors face uncertain futures in transitory and temporary refugee camps.

Prolonged displacement following disasters

Disasters resulting in 9000 or more people still displaced in 2015 noted

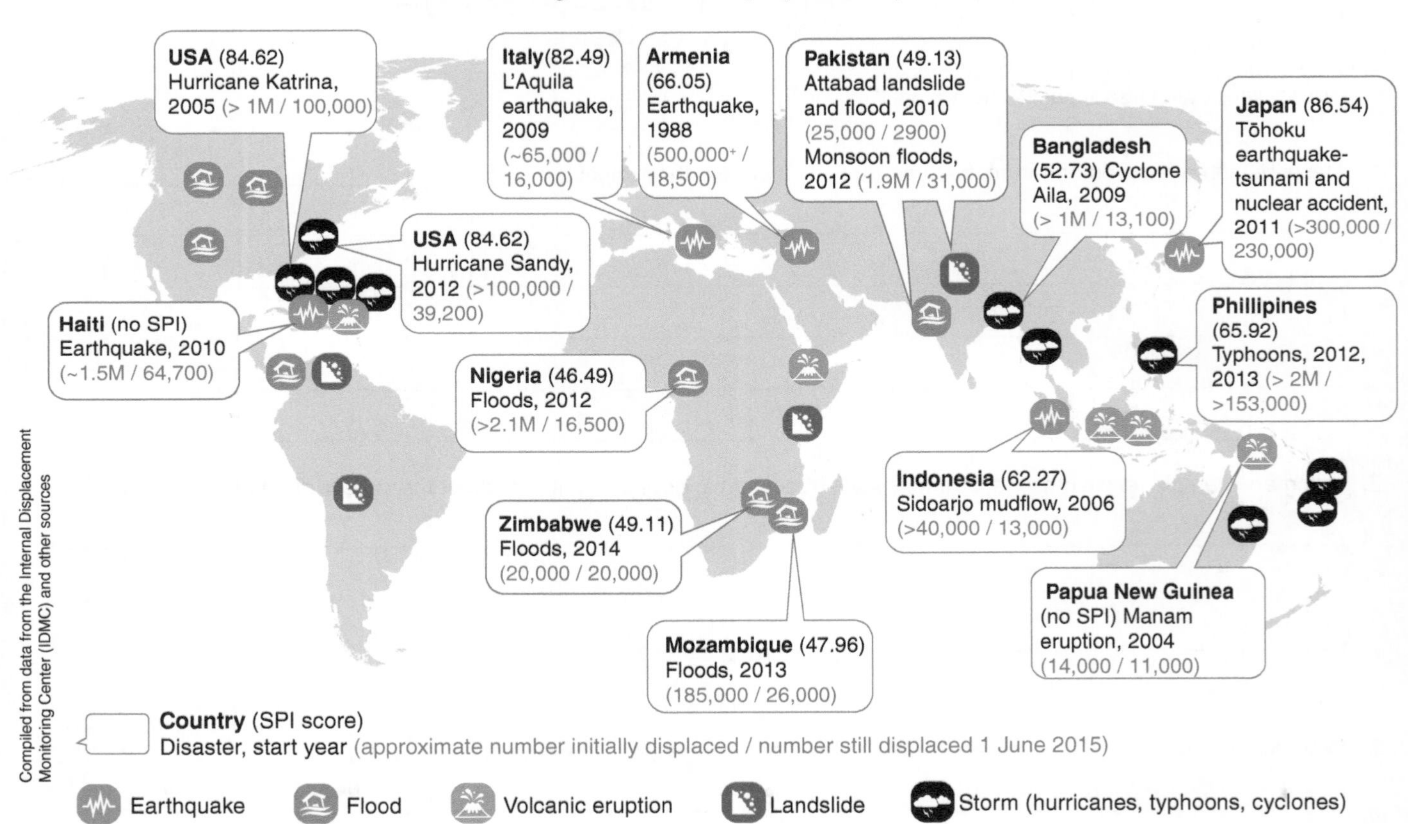

People displaced after disaster may never return

The map above indicates the location of some natural disasters in the last decade or so, with some specific events identified. The blue numbers indicate the number of people still displaced as a result of the disaster (as of 2015). The Social Progress Index (SPI) score is given for the countries indicated. This index is based on 54 indicators in the areas of basic human needs, e.g. sanitation, water, safety, freedom. It therefore indicates the extent to which countries provide for the social and environmental needs of their citizens.

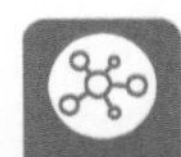

ESS3.A ESS3.B SC

ISBN: 978-1-98-856693-1

Climate change and the fate of island nations

- Even under the most conservative projections of **climate change**, rising sea levels will place many coastal and low lying regions of the world at risk of inundation. Many of these at-risk island nations are located in the Pacific and Indian Oceans and, for many populations, permanent relocation is the only viable option for the future.
- Mean sea level rose by about 15 cm during the 20th century and a further rise of up to 58 cm is projected before 2090. A rise in global mean sea level of 1 m would inundate many island groups and coastal communities.

Govt of Kiribati CC 3.0

Kiribati's capital and most populated region on Tarawa atoll

The island nation of Kiribati is made up of 33 atolls and reef islands and one raised coral island. More than 33% of its 100,000+ inhabitants live in an area of 16 km^2. Although atolls and reef islands can respond to sea level by increasing in surface area (through greater coral growth), there is no increase in height, so they are still vulnerable to inundation and salt water intrusion.

Davidarfonjones CC 3.0

Storm dunes, Funafuti atoll, Tuvalu, the highest point on the atoll.

Some 2800 km south of Kiribati, the tiny island nation of Tuvalu (maximum elevation 4.6 m) is also under threat from climate change, being vulnerable to tropical cyclones, storm surges, and king tide events. A sea level rise of 20-40 cm will make Tuvalu unhabitable for its population of around 11,000 and already its leaders are making plans for evacuation, probably to nearby Fiji.

1. Study the map opposite. Suggest three reasons why those initially displaced by natural disasters may not have returned:

   (a) ______________________________

   (b) ______________________________

   (c) ______________________________

2. How might the Social Progress Index indicate vulnerability of the population to the effects of natural hazards?

   ____

   ____

3. Slow onset disasters, such as drought and associated famine, are wide-reaching humanitarian crises affecting millions. Explain why those displaced are less likely to return home than those affected by sudden-onset disasters:

   ____

   ____

4. What social, economic, and cultural problems are likely to result in the forced migration of people from their homes because of natural hazards?

   ____

   ____

   ____

5. (a) Why are the people of low lying island nations at high risk of forced migration? ______________________________

   ____

   (b) Coral atolls can be relatively resilient to sea level rise by increasing surface area. Why is this unlikely to help the people of island nations threatened by sea level rise and increased air and sea surface temperatures?

   ____

   ____

ISBN: 978-1-98-856693-1

126 Case Study: The Western United States Drought

Key Question: How is the likelihood of increasing frequency and severity of droughts influencing decision-making and behavior in human populations?

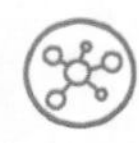

The western US 20 year drought

- The 'mega' **drought** gripping the western United States in 2022 is the longest recorded dry spell in the area going back at least 1200 years. Data from annual tree rings, thinner in dry seasons, was able to verify the historical drought claims.
- The two largest lakes used as reservoirs on the Colorado River system, Lake Mead (right) and Lake Powell, reached their lowest recorded water level in recorded history, at around 30% capacity. The Colorado River has had to place almost total restrictions on water extraction from its remaining small flow.

What caused the 2022 drought?

- Scientists have partly linked the severity and length of this drought with environmental conditions brought about from **climate change**. The drought was made more severe from higher than normal water loss from plants and early snow pack melting, both increased by warmer temperatures.
- The impacts of this exceptional drought included dead or dying crops, dry wells, harm to wildlife, loss of hydropower, and increasing risk of intense wildfires in the surrounding areas.

At Lake Mead on the Colorado river, the white 'bathtub' ring (arrowed) on the cliff shows how high the water once sat. View from Hoover Dam at Nevada and Arizona border, USA.

United States Drought Monitor - May 31, 2022

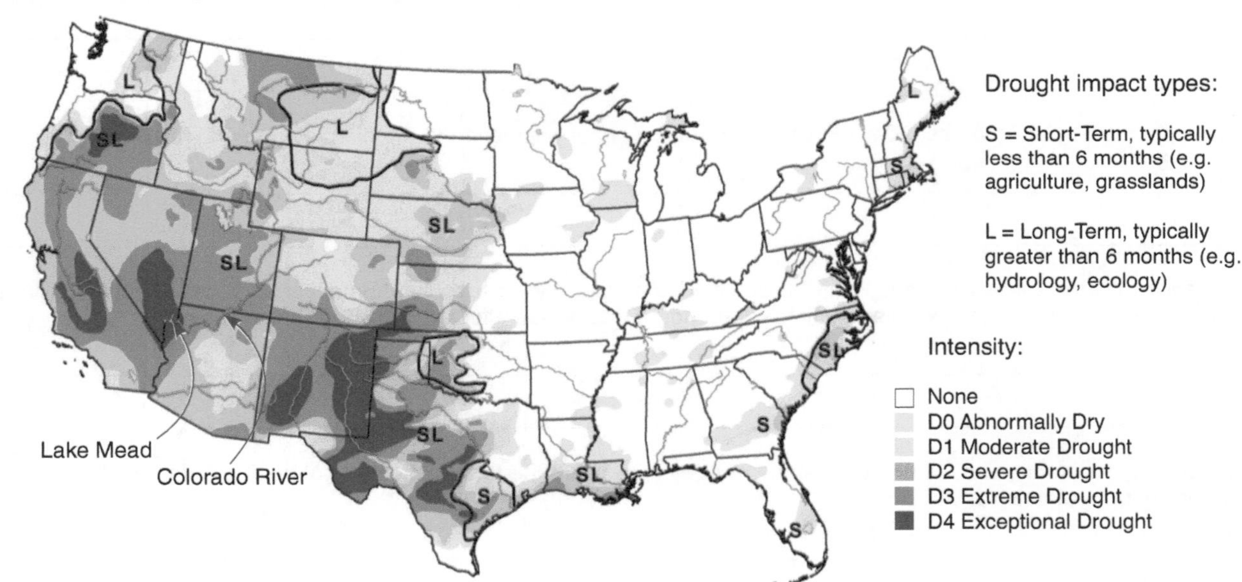

1. The 2022 drought affected areas of the western United States that are typically arid (dry), but still supported agriculture and urbanization due to irrigation and water extraction from rivers. What might the increasing impact of climate change induced droughts mean for human activity in built up urbanized areas in the future?

ISBN: 978-1-98-856693-1

Designing for Natural Hazards

Key Question: How can forecasting and preparing for drought reduce the impact of its effect?

Droughts affect nations

- In Africa, up to 80% of the population is employed in agriculture, meaning millions of people are dependent on agriculture for their income. **Drought** brings food insecurity, a loss of income, malnourishment, and susceptibility to disease, which can place the lives of these people in jeopardy. The effects of drought in developing nations can be widespread and affect a large proportion of a country.
- In more developed countries, such as the US, the effects of drought are mostly limited to farmers, as these nations have other industries to support them. However, the current, prolonged western United States drought is affecting not only the country's agricultural production, but also the urban water supply, and it is driving up the cost of food.

Dry river bed in California (2009).

Preparation and preparedness can reduce the impact of a drought

- Drought is sometimes called a creeping **natural hazard** because it develops over a period of time. It is therefore possible to plan ahead to reduce its impact. Often, being well prepared for a drought is more effective and costs less money than an emergency response, such as supplying aid. The African Climate Policy Center has been established to provide information and strategies to help African countries adapt to shifting rainfall patterns and drought. Some of these strategies are described below.

SuSanA cc2.0

Rainwater harvesting from rooftops (above) during the rainy season allows water to be stored and used in times of shortage. The water can be used for drinking and cooking, and also to supplement the watering of crops or livestock.

Evances CC 4.0

In areas of Kenya, the use of drought resistant strains of sorghum and millet has seen harvest yields double. Yields can also be increased by using fast maturing crops, or through planting less traditional crops which are quite resilient to a range of conditions, e.g. potatoes.

Infiltration pits are trenches to capture and store water when it rains. The simplest are holes dug around a plant, others are larger, lined, and filled with rocks. Rainwater soaks down through the pit instead of running off across the soil. These pits also reduce erosion.

1. Why does drought affect a larger proportion of the population in less developed nations than in more developed nations?

2. (a) Why is it possible to prepare for drought?

   (b) Describe the ways in which people can prepare for drought and reduce its impact:

ISBN: 978-1-98-856693-1

128 Wildfires

Key Question: What is the impact of wildfires, locally and globally?

- Forest fires have always been part of nature, with fire seasons occurring every year but the decade 2010 to 2020 saw a massive increase in the number, area, and intensity of forest and bush **fires** around the world.
- The last decade has seen fires begin earlier in the season and become larger and more frequent. Some of these fires are deliberately lit, either through arson or farm fires that get out of control. In some cases, the fires are set to clear debris after land has been logged, and so are not the direct cause of **deforestation**. Some arise naturally from lightning strikes and, since the world is warming, the results of these lightning strikes are far more severe, especially after **droughts**, which themselves are becoming more frequent.
- Recent years have seen fires in the Alaskan and Siberian tundra which threaten to affect permafrost and fundamentally change the Arctic landscape.

Arctic tundra

- The Arctic region is warming at twice the rate of the rest of the world. This heating is melting permafrost and then drying out the tundra, making it extremely susceptible to fire.
- Because of the freezing temperatures, there is little decay of plant material on the tundra. A large amount of organic material therefore builds up over the centuries. This has helped to store vast quantities of carbon.
- Now that the Arctic is warming, that carbon is under threat of decaying and burning, both of which release carbon dioxide. And the more warming there is, the more carbon dioxide (and trapped methane) could be released, and so there is more warming, leading to **climate change**.
- Tundra in Alaska, Canada, Greenland, and Eastern Siberia has been affected. In 2019, more than 3 million hectares of tundra was affected by fire. The fires can be typical large surface fires, but they can also form slow smoldering fires underground. These fires can persist through cold and wet conditions, and relight as "zombie fires", months later. Because they burn longer, these fires can actually transfer heat deeper into the soil and permafrost, melting and burning it.
- Tundra fires in 2019 released at least 100 million tonnes of carbon dioxide.

Tundra fires, seen from space

NASA

Tundra fires, Siberia

NPS CC 2.0

1. Describe two ways in which large fires can contribute to climate change: ______

2. Why might the fires in the Arctic be much worse for climate change than they might first appear (or compared to forest fires)?

3. Although the Arctic region is isolated and far from many other countries, explain why the impact of the tundra fires have global consequences:

ESS3.A ESS3.B SC

ISBN: 978-1-98-856693-1

California wildfires

- California's hot dry environment is particularly prone to wildfires. Since the start of the century, these wildfires have been becoming more intense. Fourteen of the largest 20 wildfires in California have occurred since 2007, and there are 78 more annual fire days now than 50 years ago.
- A number of factors influence the frequency and severity of fires (how often and how much land is burned). These include moisture level, the amount of undergrowth, tree density, and the types of trees present.
- Climate variability, especially moisture levels, is the main driver of forest **fires**. When fires become more frequent and more intense, the forest may be less able to regenerate (grow again with a similar makeup). There are several reasons for this:
  - Trees do not have time to regenerate or grow between fires, they reestablish more slowly, or fail to reestablish at all.
  - Fast growing shrubs and grasses establish more quickly than tree seedlings, which then cannot compete for resources, e.g. sunlight and space. Fewer tree species will establish, and the make-up of the area will change.
  - Seed stock is reduced, so fewer seedlings grow after a fire.

USDA

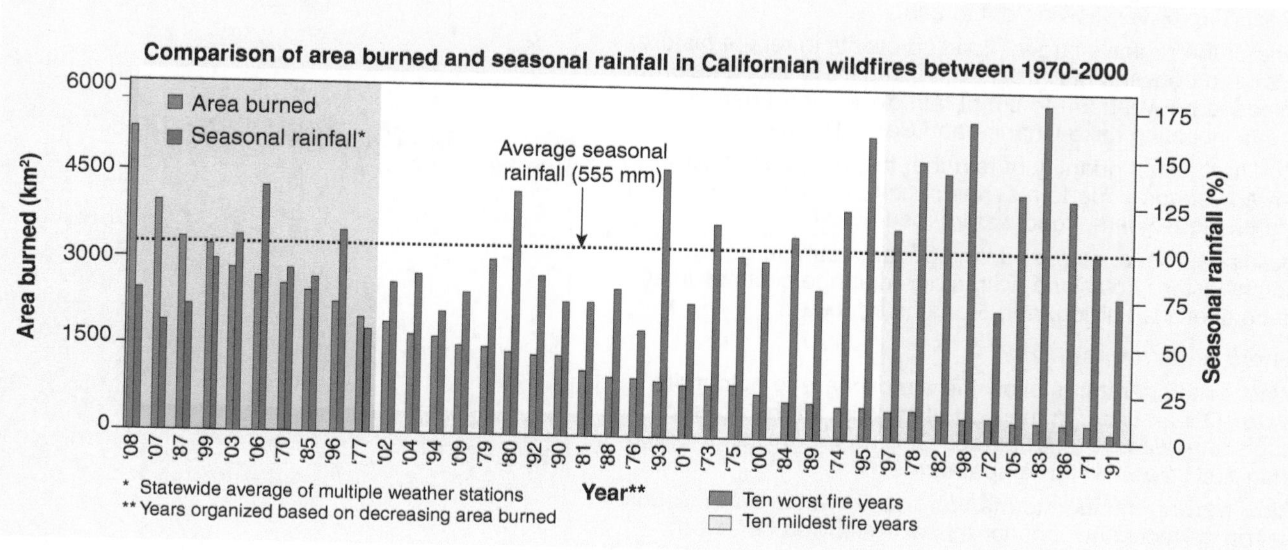

Adapted from Rogers, P (01 June, 2010). Do wet winters mean bad summer fire season in California? Not usually according to History. Bay Area News
Original data from Cal fire, U.S. Forest Service and NOAA data

4. Study the graph above. What is the relationship between rainfall in California and the area burned? ____________________

5. Why are the wildfires in California more immediate problems and receive more intense fire suppression than Arctic fires?

6. What is the link between increasing frequency and severity of wildfires, changes in climate, and human activity?

ISBN: 978-1-98-856693-1

129 Flooding

Key Question: How does the 2021 Louisiana flooding help us understand the link between extreme weather events, a changing climate, and future migrational shifts?

Louisiana Flooding

May 2021 Louisiana Flooding

- **Flooding** in Louisiana, United States, is not an uncommon event, especially near the coastal areas. The state has a significant region of low-lying swampy wetlands, called the bayou, with numerous river deltas, including that of the Mississippi River, flowing out to sea.
- One of the region's largest flooding events in recent history occurred between May 15-19th, 2021. Heavy thunderstorms released between 24-44 cm of rain over a short period, in areas including Lake Charles and Baton Rouge.
- Due to the vast quantity of rain that fell, on ground that was already sodden due to a series of extreme weather events in the previous years, flood waters rose quickly.
- Buildings, roads, cars, and land became submerged in southwestern Louisiana, with storm damage costs estimated to be over $1.4 billion, and 5 deaths attributed.

Levees (raised banks) along the Mississippi River increased flooding further downstream

Why did so much rain fall?

- Warmer temperatures allow the atmosphere to hold more water. Ocean water in the Gulf of Mexico, off the coast of Louisiana, was up to 4 degrees Celsius warmer on average than 1981-2010 water temperatures.
- Slow-moving thunderstorms and heavily water-laden clouds, set up perfect conditions for this extreme weather event.
- Scientists normally do not attribute individual extreme events, such as the Louisiana flooding, to climate change. However, scientists can use climate modeling to show the link between the increase of frequency and severity of extreme weather events and **climate change**.

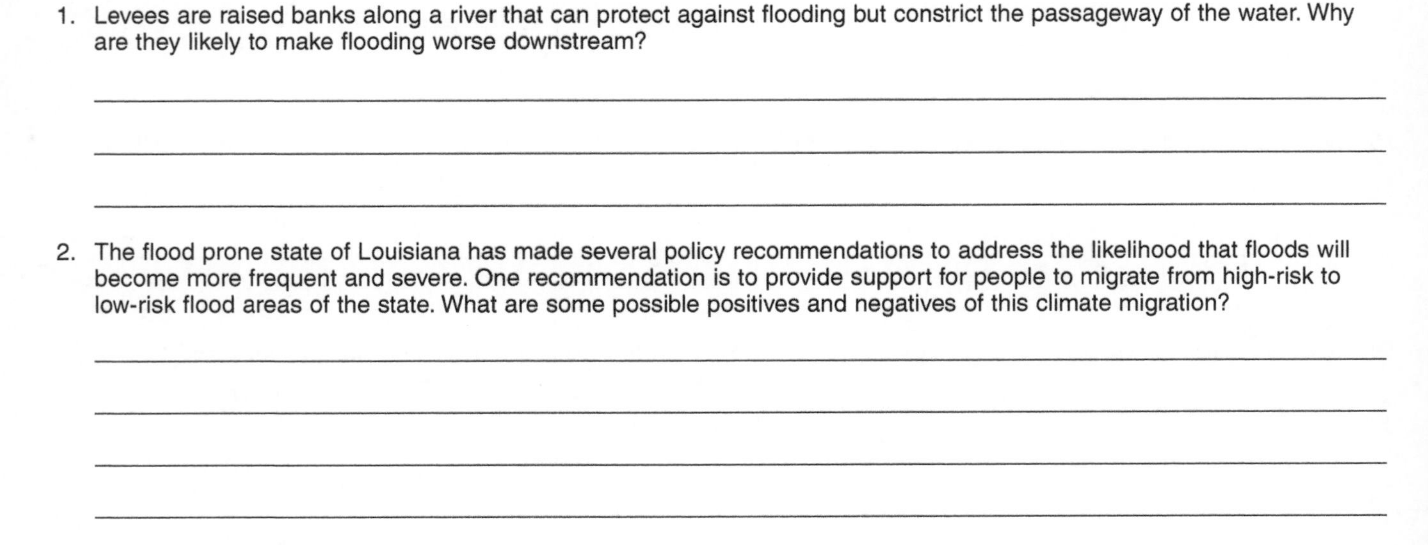

1. Levees are raised banks along a river that can protect against flooding but constrict the passageway of the water. Why are they likely to make flooding worse downstream?

2. The flood prone state of Louisiana has made several policy recommendations to address the likelihood that floods will become more frequent and severe. One recommendation is to provide support for people to migrate from high-risk to low-risk flood areas of the state. What are some possible positives and negatives of this climate migration?

ESS3.A ESS3.B SC

ISBN: 978-1-98-856693-1

Types of Flooding

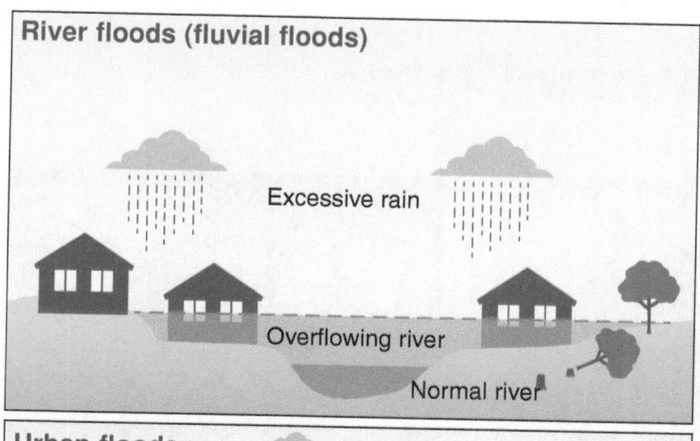

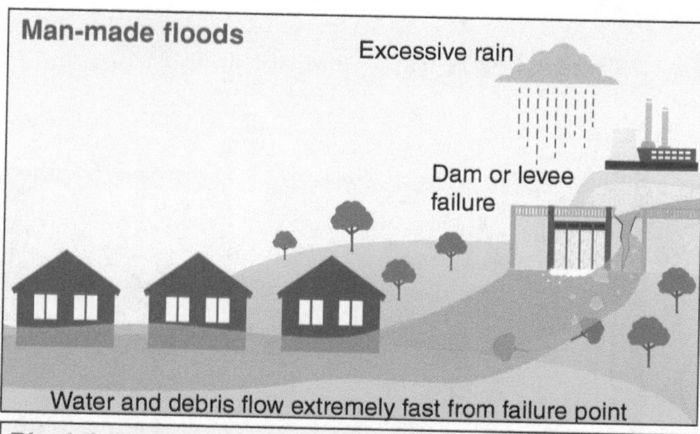

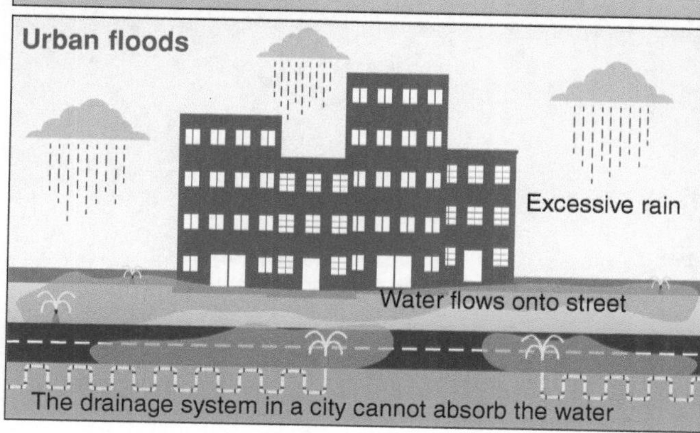

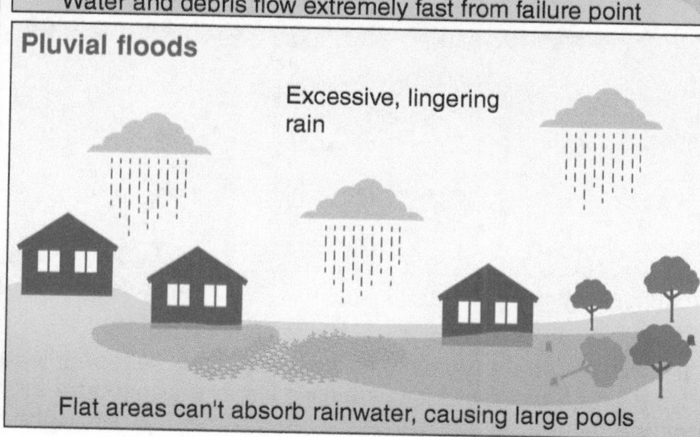

3. The different types of floods above all originate from excessive rain. However, a range of solutions can be used to lessen the impact on human populations affected. Select one scenario and suggest one or more solutions that could be used:

4. The graph below shows various extreme weather events, and the confidence with which we can attribute their occurrence to climate change.

(a) Which types of events can be most confidently assigned to climate change?

(b) Suggest why there is such a range in the ability to assign events to climate change.

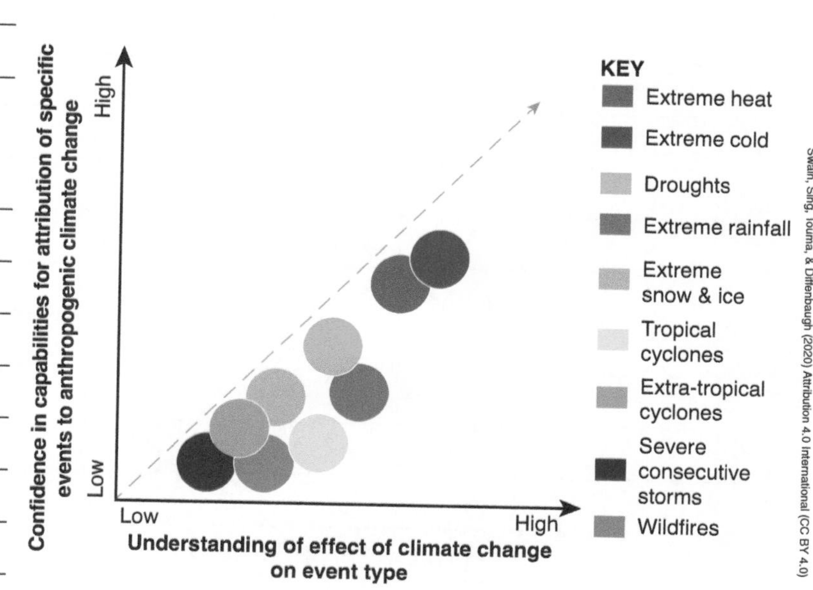

ISBN: 978-1-98-856693-1

130 Review Your Understanding

Key Question: What influences the frequency and extremity of weather events?

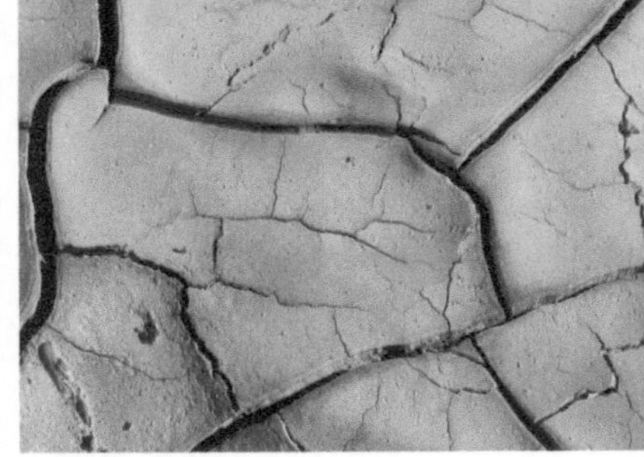

Drought affected land

NASA Jeff Schmaltz public domain

Three cyclones over the Western Pacific

Tuxyso CC SA 3.0

Flash flooding in Death Valley

California's climate typically features cyclical, seasonal weather events (dry to wet and dry again). These cycles are normal and important for sustaining life and agriculture in the region. However, in recent times, the swing between seasonal events has become more extreme, e.g. **drought** to **flood**. These events are called weather whiplash.

1. Using what you have learned in this chapter, explain how climate change can contribute to the frequency and severity of such events. Discuss the potential effects of these events and how they may affect ecosystems, biodiversity, and people:

ESS3.A ESS3.B SC

ISBN: 978-1-98-856693-1

131 Summing Up

The number of **hurricanes** forming during the North Atlantic hurricane season are monitored. The Atlantic Database Reanalysis Project, run by the National Oceanic & Atmospheric Administration (NOAA) aims to correct and add new information about past North Atlantic hurricanes. Going back to 1851, and revisiting storms in more recent years, information on tropical cyclones is revised using enhanced historical meteorological data in the context of today's scientific understanding and analysis techniques. The plots below represent data collected during the project.

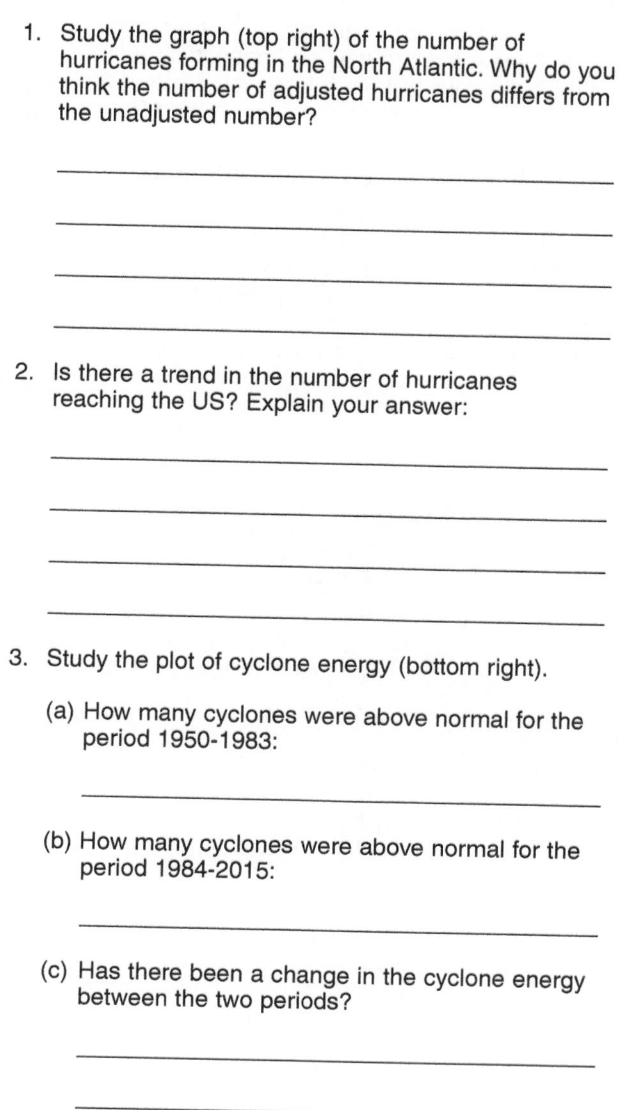

1. Study the graph (top right) of the number of hurricanes forming in the North Atlantic. Why do you think the number of adjusted hurricanes differs from the unadjusted number?

____

____

____

____

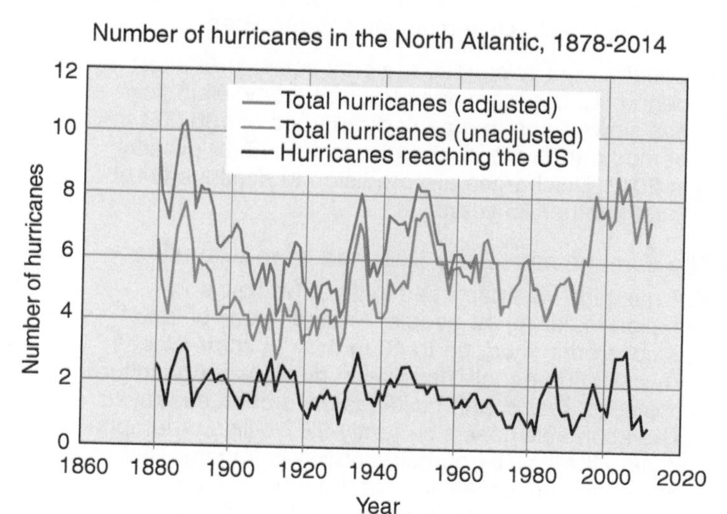

2. Is there a trend in the number of hurricanes reaching the US? Explain your answer:

____

____

____

____

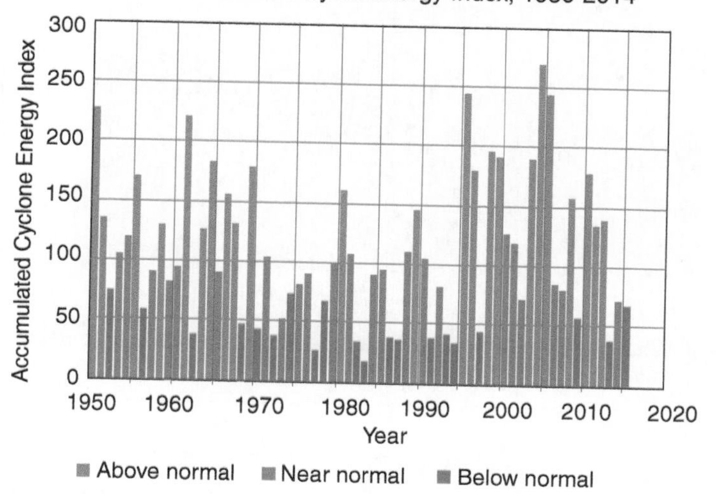

Data: NOAA, 2015. The Atlantic Hurricane Database Reanalysis Project

3. Study the plot of cyclone energy (bottom right).

   (a) How many cyclones were above normal for the period 1950-1983:

   ____

   (b) How many cyclones were above normal for the period 1984-2015:

   ____

   (c) Has there been a change in the cyclone energy between the two periods?

   ____

   ____

4. Malé (right) is the capital of the Republic of Maldives. The city is built on the North Malé Atoll, and is elevated 2.4 m above sea level. The city is one of the most densely populated in the world, with 133,412 people living within 5.8 km^2.

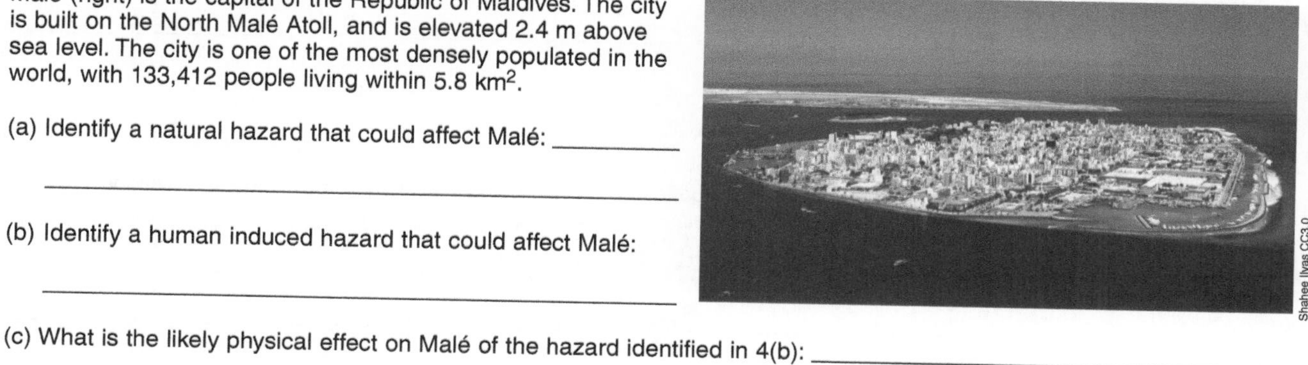

Shahee Ilyas CC3.0

   (a) Identify a natural hazard that could affect Malé: _______________

   ____

   (b) Identify a human induced hazard that could affect Malé:

   ____

   (c) What is the likely physical effect on Malé of the hazard identified in 4(b): _______________

   ____

   (d) Predict what would happen to the population of Malé as a result of the hazard identified in 4(b): _______________

   ____

ISBN: 978-1-98-856693-1

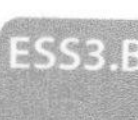

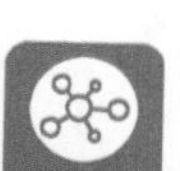

Case study: The Sidoarjo mud flow

- Mud volcanoes are vents or fissures in the ground that discharge hot mud. They are fairly common and vary in size from one meter high and two meters wide, to 700 meters high and 10 kilometers wide.
- In May 2006, mud began **erupting** from the ground in the Sidoarjo district in Jakarta, Indonesia. This newly formed mud volcano was named Lusi and, to date, is the most destructive mud volcano recorded.
- Usually, mud volcanoes are only active for a short period but Lusi continues to erupt today. Mud flow has slowed from the peak discharges of 180,000 m^3 of mud per day to discharges of 10,000 m^3 per day in 2011. Discharges are predicted to continue for at least another 25 years.

The damage caused by Lusi has been extensive

- A gas pipe was damaged in the mud flow and exploded, killing 12 people. Around 7 km^2 of land is covered in mud, up to 40 m thick in some places. Over 39,000 people have been displaced. Agriculture, business, roads, and buildings have been destroyed. The economic cost is currently $2.7 billion. Attempts to stop the flow by pumping concrete into the vent have been unsuccessful, but the mud has been contained using large concrete walls and trenches.

A school destroyed by the mud flow

hughe82 cc3.0

What caused the Sidoarjo mud flow?

There is controversy about what caused the Sidoarjo mud flow. Some people suggest it was a natural event, whereas others think the disaster was caused by human activity. Still others believe it was caused by a combination of the two. The two most common hypotheses are given below.

1. Man made: caused by drilling for gas

On May 28th, a company drilling for gas removed a drill from the exploration well and noticed an influx of water into the well's borehole, which cracked the surrounding rock. The next day Lusi erupted from a fault plane.

2. Natural hazard: caused by an earthquake

Two days before Lusi erupted, a 6.3 magnitude earthquake struck 250 km away. Shaking may have caused liquefaction of the clay layer, releasing gases. This may have caused a pressure change, which reactivated a nearby fault and created a path for mud to flow through until it was able to escape to the surface.

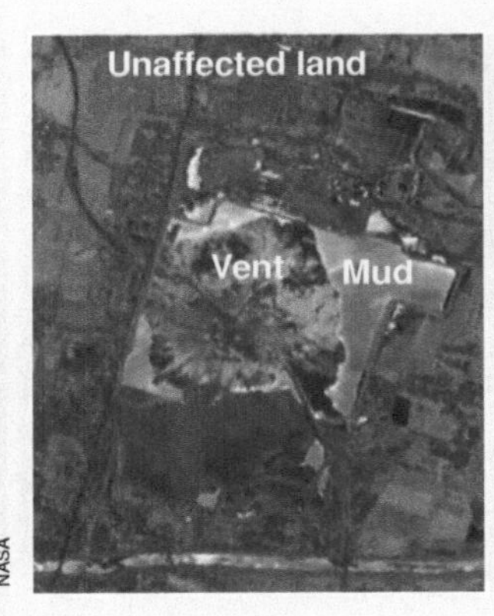

NASA

This image of Lusi (left)was captured by NASA in 2009. The mud is restricted to a rectangular shape because walls have been build to contain it.

5. What features of the Sidoarjo mud flow have made it so destructive? ____________________

6. Identify design solutions that have been utilized to stop or restrict the flow of mud. Comment on their success: ____________________

7. Thousands of people have been displaced by the mudflow. What impact is this likely to have on the development and economic viability of the region?

8. Two hypotheses are given as to what may have caused the Sidoarjo mud flow. Research both, and summarize your findings on a separate piece of paper. Decide which hypothesis you think is most likely and justify your reasons.

ISBN: 978-1-98-856693-1

CHAPTER 11

Human Impacts on Earth Systems

Anchoring Phenomenon

Room for More?: How can our Earth and its resources sustain more people? 132 145

What are the demands on Earth's resources?

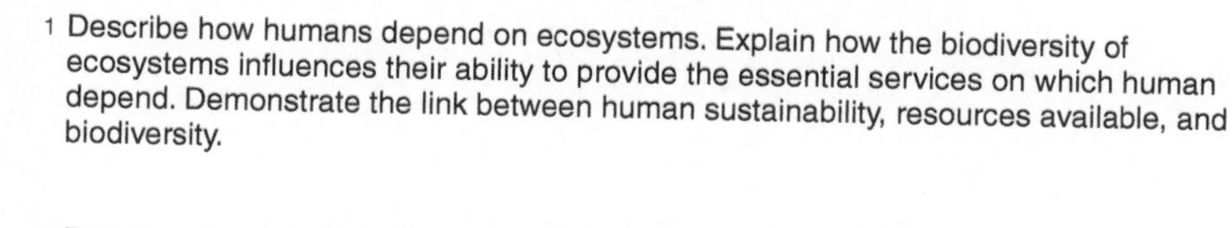

☐ 1 Describe how humans depend on ecosystems. Explain how the biodiversity of ecosystems influences their ability to provide the essential services on which human depend. Demonstrate the link between human sustainability, resources available, and biodiversity. 133

☐ 2 Develop a formula that can be used to calculate population growth. Analyze trends in population data. Calculate population growth and the resulting resource demands. 134

☐ 3 Create a computational model or simulation to illustrate the relationship between the management of natural resources, the sustainability of human populations, and biodiversity. 146

How are humans impacting Earth and its resources?

☐ 4 Summarize key impacts of human activity on the ocean environment. 135

☐ 5 Define fishing bycatch and describe ways that it could be reduced. Define the term "maximum sustainable yield". Discuss the implications of overharvesting for fish stocks. 136

☐ 6 Understand the extent of plastic pollution in the oceans. Explain how micro and nano plastics can be harmful to organisms. Evaluate how plastic-consuming bacteria could be a useful solution for removal of plastic waste. 137

☐ 7 Analyze the cost-benefit of preventing oil spills. Evaluate the use of hydrocarbon-metabolizing bacteria in cleaning up oil spills. 138

☐ 8 Discuss the impacts of human activity on the land, specifically desertification and salinization. 139

☐ 9 Discuss trends in global deforestation and evaluate some possible technological solutions to slow, halt, or reverse the trend. 140

☐ 10 Calculate densities of human population. Graph data showing change in available land over time. 141

☐ 11 Explain why people may move into concentrated urban regions. Discuss a range of harmful consequences of urbanization on the environment. Describe some positive effects that urbanization might have on the environment. 142

How can technology help remediate the consequences of human impact?

☐ 12 Explain the purpose of environmental remediation. 143

☐ 13 Evaluate a solution that reduces the impact of environmental contamination caused by humans. 144

132 Room for More?

Key Question: How can our Earth and its resources sustain more people?

The human population is expanding rapidly. It is currently approximately 7.9 billion and is expected to increase to 9.7 billion by 2050, peaking at around 11 billion by 2100. The current population is using up Earth's resources almost twice as fast as they can be renewed by natural processes. Land must be developed in order to provide enough food, housing, and resources to sustain growth of the human population.

1. Working in pairs or a small group, list some ways that humans alter the environment: ______

2. In what way could the activities you listed above have a negative effect on the populations of organisms living in the environment?

3. Can you think of any benefits of concentrating human populations in high-density areas such as towns and cities?

ISBN: 978-1-98-856693-1

133 Humans Depend on Biodiversity

Key Question: What ecosystem services do humans depend upon?

Ecosystems provide services

- Humans depend on Earth's ecosystems for the services they provide. These **ecosystem services** include **resources** such as food and fuel, as well as processes such as purification of the air and water. These directly affect human health.
- The **biodiversity** of an ecosystem affects its ability to provide these services.
- Biologically diverse and resilient ecosystems that are managed in a sustainable way are better able to provide the ecosystem services on which we depend.
- The UN has identified four categories of ecosystem services: supporting, provisioning, regulating, and cultural.
- Regulating and provisioning services are important for human health and security (security of resources and security against natural disasters).
- Cultural services are particularly important to the social fabric of human societies and contribute to well being. These are often things we cannot value in monetary terms.

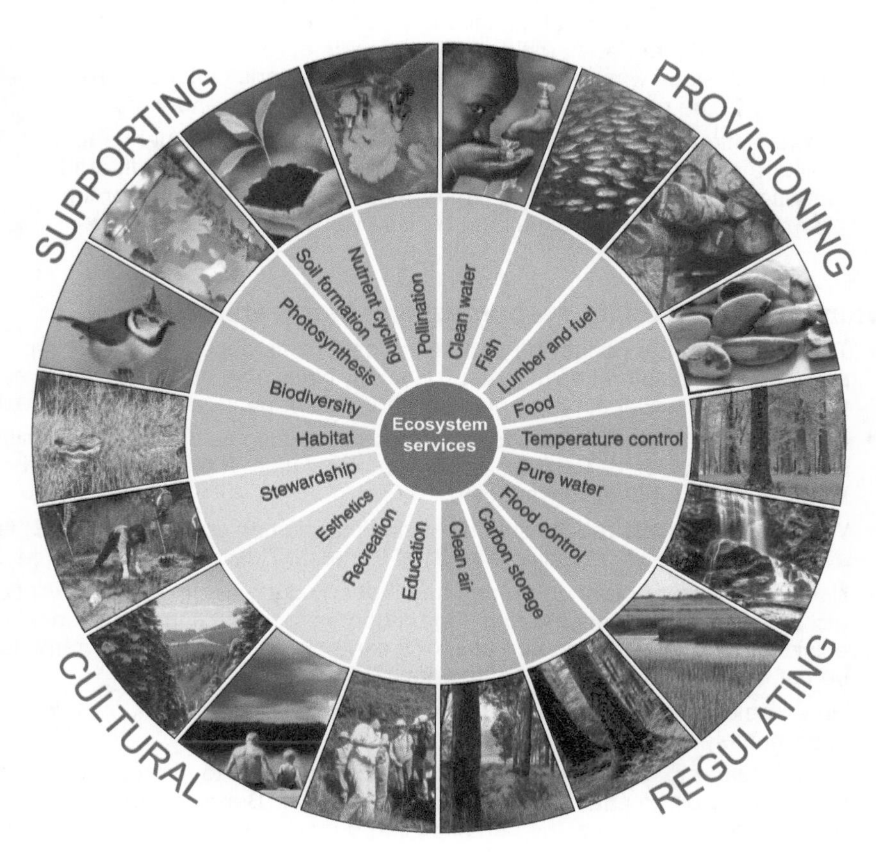

Rust on wheat stem

Biodiversity is important in crop development, e.g. promoting disease resistance. Many medical breakthroughs have come from understanding the biology of microbes and wild plants and animals.

Ebola can be spread from infected bush meat to humans

Edwin S

High biodiversity creates buffers between humans and infectious diseases (e.g. Ebola) and increases the efficiency of processes such as water purification and nutrient cycling.

Landslide

Biodiversity and ecosystem health are essential for reducing the impact of human activities (e.g. pollution) and the effects of environmental disasters (e.g. eruptions and landslides).

1. What are ecosystem services, and why are they important to humans? ______________________

2. What is the relationship between biodiversity and the ability of an ecosystem to provide essential ecosystem services?

ISBN: 978-1-98-856693-1

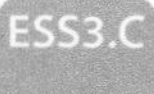

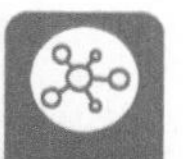

Ecosystem services: a case study

- It is difficult fully quantify the value of **ecosystem services**. One way of doing this is to estimate what people would pay for the services the ecosystem provides. This is illustrated by the following case study:
- The Peconic Estuary in Long Island has many wetlands and mudflats. Development of the area has caused these to degrade. Management programs are needed to estimate the benefits of rehabilitating the estuary. A study was carried out to estimate the contributions of the estuary to the production of wildlife, e.g. shellfish, fish, and birds.
- It was estimated that a hectare of eelgrass is worth $2631 per year, a hectare of saltmarsh is worth $835 per year, and a hectare of intertidal mudflat is worth $168 per year, in terms of commercial values for the fish, viewing values for birds, and hunting values for waterfowl.

Doug Kerr

Human sustainability, resources, and biodiversity

- The **sustainability** (longevity) of human populations depends on the responsible management of the **resources** provided by the natural environment. Healthy, biodiverse ecosystems are essential to sustainability, as these provide the essential services on which humans depend, e.g. clean air, fresh water, and carbon storage.
- If the quantity and quality of essential resources, such as water, are diminished, human sustainability is detrimentally affected. This also applies to biodiversity. If this decreases, the essential ecosystem services on which humans rely are negatively affected.
- We can express this relationship by saying that human sustainability (HS) is approximately equal to the resources available (RA) and the biodiversity (B) of the area. This could be written as a simple equation: $HS \sim RA + B$.
- Using this simple equation, we can see that any decrease in RA or B will cause a decrease in HS. However, human technology can compensate to a certain degree for reduction in resources or biodiversity. Technology (T) can help efficiency and reduce resource use, or it can help conservation programs to improve biodiversity. These factors can be put into our first equation so that now: $HS \sim (RA + T_1) + (B + T_2)$.
- Here, the equation now shows HS can remain stable even if RA or B decrease, provided that T_1 or T_2 increase appropriately.
- It is important to remember that technological solutions to reduced resources or biodiversity require both effort and money. They come at a cost (C), so that $C \sim T_1 + T_2$. Benefits (Bt) from the system described are effectively equal to human sustainability (i.e. the benefit is that humans survive) so that $HS \sim Bt$.
- These simple equations show only a small part of the complex human relationship with the environment, but they do provide a way to visualize and compute the effects of simple changes to a system.

3. (a) Describe a way of putting a value on ecosystem services: ______________________

   (b) What is the purpose of putting a value on ecosystem services? ______________________

4. Use the equations above to describe what would need to happen in the following scenarios:

   (a) Keeping HS stable while allowing B to decrease: ______________________

   (b) Keeping HS stable while reducing the need for resources (RA): ______________________

   (c) The effect on cost (C) of allowing either (a) or (b) to occur: ______________________

   (d) The effect of reducing both B and RA on HS and C: ______________________

ISBN: 978-1-98-856693-1

Human Sustainability

Key Question: How can human sustainability be used to manage finite resources, in the face of a continually growing population?

The human population

- In the last 60 years, the human population has increased from fewer than 3 billion people to over 7.9 billion. Since the 1950s, improvements in medicine and access to more food have allowed the world's population to grow at a rate of almost 2% each year.
- Many scientists believe growth of this magnitude is not sustainable and that the human population has already surpassed the planet's carrying capacity. They predict the inevitable collapse of food supplies and populations in the near future. Current predictions suggest the human population will reach at least 9.7 billion by 2050.
- As the human population grows, it uses more **resources**. Even with careful resource management and more efficient use, the rate of resource use will continue to increase. This means that eventually either the resource will run out, or will need to be replaced with another resource before that happens.
- In many countries, initiatives have been taken to lower birth rates in an attempt to relieve pressure on resources.

Year	Population (billions)	Year	Population (billions)
1850	1.26	1960	3.01
1900	1.65	1970	3.68
1910	1.75	1980	4.44
1920	1.86	1990	5.31
1930	2.07	2000	6.12
1940	2.30	2010	6.93
1950	2.52	2016	7.4

Population growth

- Births, deaths, immigrations (movements into the population), and emigrations (movements out of the population) are events that determine the number of individuals in a population.
- Population growth depends on the number of individuals being added to the population due to births and immigration, and the number being lost through deaths and emigration (right).

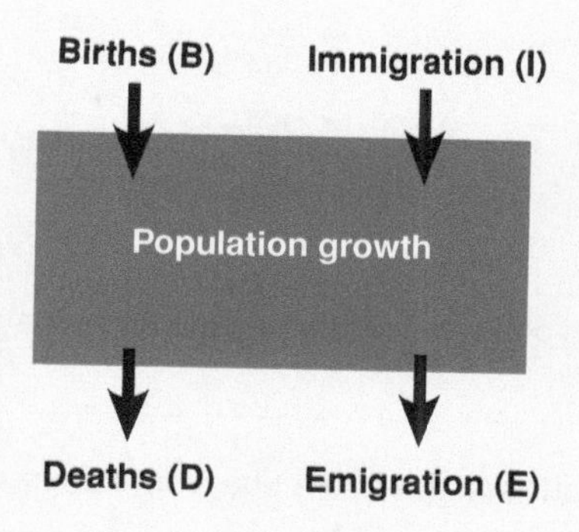

Resource use

- An example of the human population affecting resources is the consumption of coal in the last 200 years (right). Most of the energy consumed by humans originates from coal, either by direct use for heat or using it to fuel power stations that produce electricity.
- As the human population has increased, so has the consumption of coal, and other energy resources. Some of this demand is because our modern technology requires high energy inputs. However, technology has helped increase food supplies, living standards, life expectancy, and the human population itself.

Year	~ Coal consumption ($\times 10^{18}$ J)	Year	~ Coal consumption ($\times 10^{18}$ J)
1840	1	1940	41
1860	5	1960	50
1880	12	1980	70
1900	25	2000	100
1920	39	2015	150

1. What is the rate of the human population growth since 1950? __________

2. What will the human population be in 2050? __________

3. Produce an equation that could be used to calculate the population growth (N) of a certain population, e.g a country's population growth. D = deaths, B = births, I = immigration, and E = emigration

____

4. (a) How would the equation for the entire global human population differ? __________

____

(b) Write the equation for the entire global human population: __________

____

ISBN: 978-1-98-856693-1

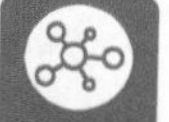

5. Use the data on the previous page to produce a graph to show the growth of the human population and the consumption of coal since 1840. You will need a left and right Y axis:

6. What type of growth curve do both human population and coal consumption show? ___

7. Use your equation from question 3 to complete the following:

(a) A town has a population of 70,230 in the year 2010. Over the next five years, 6556 people move into the town for work, but 4096 move to other parts of the country. A baby boom sees the birth of 5225 babies but there are also 4978 deaths. What is the population of the town in 2015?

(b) What is the percentage growth over the 5 years? ___

(c) The town uses water from a reservoir that holds 200 million L and is replenished at a rate of 60 million L a day. In 2010, the town used 46 million L per day. Calculate the average water use, per person, per day.

(d) How much water would be used per day in 2015 if each person used the same amount of water as in 2010?

(e) Assuming the town underwent the same rate of growth every 5 years into the future, when would the reservoir begin to fill more slowly than it was being used, i.e. the tipping point at which the water supply become unsustainable?

(f) At the end of 2025, the town introduces measures to extend the life of the water supply by asking people to cut their water use by 10%. Under these new measures, when will the water supply become unsustainable?

ISBN: 978-1-98-856693-1

135 Human Impact on the Ocean

Key Question: What impact has human activity had on ocean environments?

Less than two centuries ago the oceans must have seemed to people to be an inexhaustible **resource**. However, after years of exploiting this resource we are finally realizing that even the ocean has its limits and that we, as a species, have begun to exceed them.

Ocean acidification occurs when excess atmospheric carbon dioxide reacts with water to form a weak acid and lowers the pH. Increasing carbon dioxide emissions, leading to climate change, are driving the increasing acidification. Marine organisms whose shells are constructed from calcium carbonate, a weak base, are growing more slowly or growing thinner shells. The lower pH is pushing some organisms out of their range of tolerance, deceasing their ability to survive in their local conditions.

Fishing has provided food for people for thousands of years. However, fish stocks have plummeted as the human population has increased and fishing has become a major global industry. Many fish species have been fished so intensively that they are no longer economic. Others are on the brink of collapse. Fishing techniques have become so sophisticated, and efforts are on such a large scale, that hundreds of tonnes of fish can be caught by one vessel, on one fishing cruise.

Pollution is a major problem in parts of the oceans. Activities causing pollution range from deliberate dumping of rubbish from ships, to runoff from the land and contaminated discharge into rivers that lead to the sea. An estimated 12.7 million tonnes of plastic finds its way into the sea each year. Plastic can have severe detrimental effects on marine life, especially those that mistake plastic bags for jellyfish or other prey species. Extremely small microplastics are now found in every corner in the world.

Cargo ships carry ballast water in their hulls to keep them stable when empty. As the cargo is loaded, the ballast water is pumped out to maintain stability and buoyancy. This has led to many marine organisms being unintentionally transported around the globe. This can be disastrous for local marine environments when the organism is an invasive species. Newer ships are able to discharge ballast and replace it out at sea, where potentially invasive organisms would die in the open ocean.

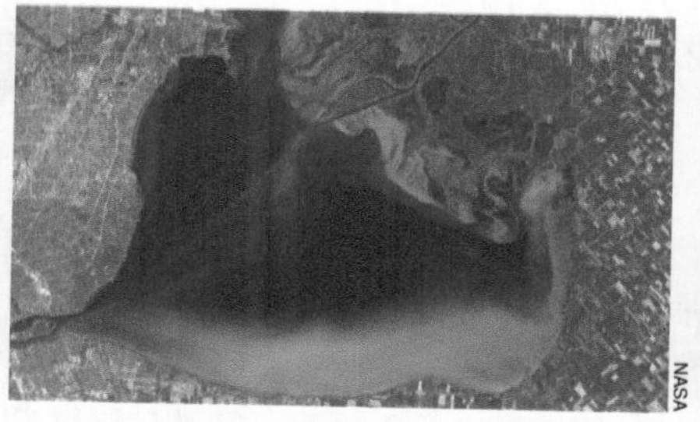

NASA

Runoff from the land into the ocean has caused problems with eutrophication (nutrient enrichment). Combined with increasing surface water temperatures, this has led to large algal blooms along coastlines. In some cases, these blooms make it dangerous for swimming. The algae often produce toxins that are concentrated by filter feeding organisms, e.g. clams. This makes them dangerous to eat and the public is often warned against collecting shellfish, taking away an important food resource.

Sea bed mining and drilling has had an impact on bottom dwelling marine organisms. Sea bed mining often uses dredges to vacuum up material from the sea floor, disturbing bottom dwelling organisms. Oil spills can affect the seabed and coastline for hundreds of kilometers. Although technology has made oil spills while drilling less likely, it remains a significant risk. Accidents can still occur, with catastrophic consequences, as the 2010 Deepwater Horizon oil spill in the Gulf of Mexico (above) demonstrated.

1. Paraphrase the information above to describe three impacts of human activity on the ocean:

(a) ______________________________

____

(b) ______________________________

____

(c) ______________________________

____

ISBN: 978-1-98-856693-1

136 Fishing and Sustainability

Key Question: How can fishing be managed so that fish stocks are maintained?

- Fishing is an ancient human tradition. It provides food and is economically, socially, and culturally important. Today, it is a worldwide **resource** extraction industry. Fisheries have a history of unsustainable stock management, globally. The depletion of fish stocks has made it necessary to implement careful management strategies. Decades of overfishing in all of the world's oceans has pushed commercially important species, such as cod (right), into steep decline.
- According to the United Nation's Food and Agriculture Organization (FAO), almost half the ocean's commercially targeted marine fish stocks are either heavily or over-exploited. Without drastic changes to the world's fishing operations, many fish stocks will soon be effectively lost.

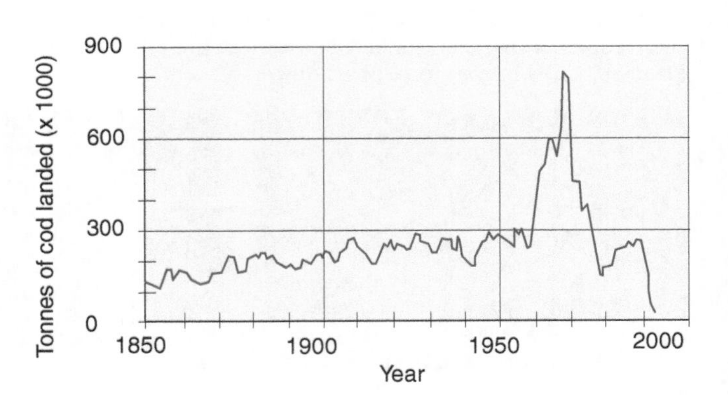

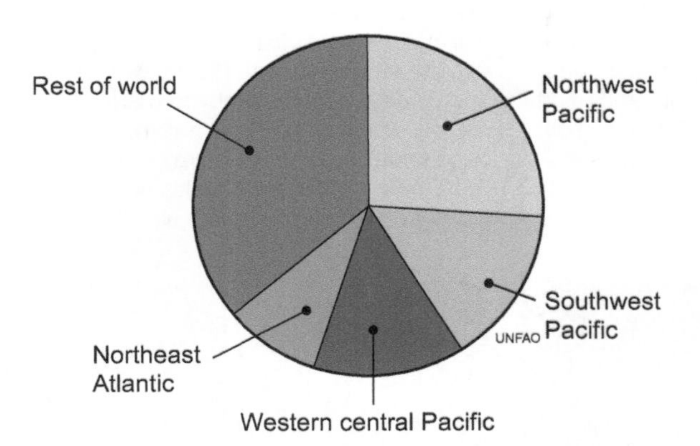

The single largest fishery is the Northwest Pacific, taking 26% of the total global catch.

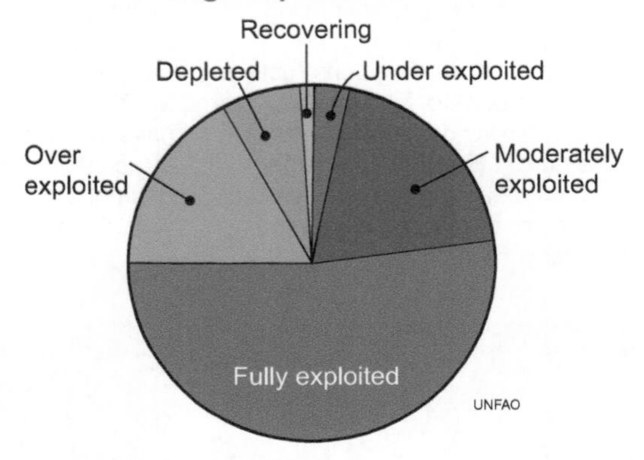

52% of the world's fished species are already fully exploited. Any increase in catch from these species would result in over-exploitation. 7% of the fish species are already depleted and 17% are over-exploited.

Part of the problem with fishing is by-catch, i.e. the fish that are not wanted. Even if thrown back, these fish or other marine organisms often don't survive. Techniques to reduce bycatch include changing hook design and attaching devices called pingers to the line or net that frighten away non-target organisms.

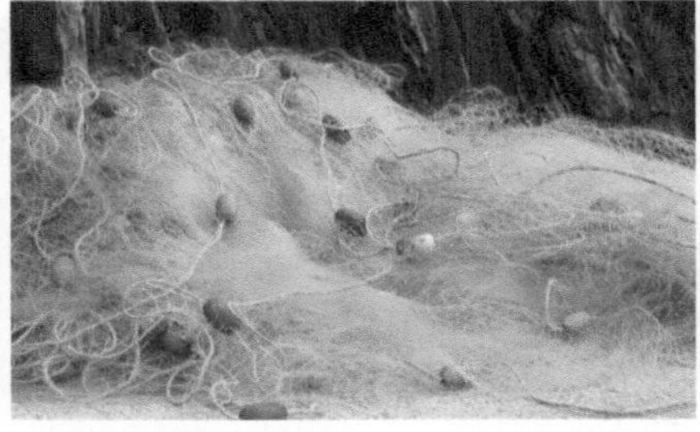

Different fish species are fished with different kinds of lines or nets. In particular, the mesh size of the net can be changed so that small fish can swim through it and larger fish are caught. This can help to ensure that young fish survive to breeding age or that the wrong species of fish are not caught in the net.

New types of net designs are constantly being tested. One of the newest net designs is called Precision Seafood Harvesting. It consists of a PVC liner towed by a trawler and forms a tunnel of water that reduces stress and damage to target fish, increasing catch efficiency. Holes allow unwanted fish to escape.

1. What percentage of fish stocks are depleted, overexploited, or fully exploited? ______________________

2. (a) What is bycatch? ______________________

   (b) Name two ways bycatch can be reduced: ______________________

____

ISBN: 978-1-98-856693-1

How do scientists use data to measure sustainable fishing?

- The **sustainable** harvesting of any food **resource** requires that its rate of harvest is no more than its replacement rate. If the harvest rate is higher than the replacement rate, then it follows that the food resource will continually reduce at ever increasing percentages (assuming a constant harvest rate), and eventually be lost. Scientists can collect data and use mathematical calculations, such as maximum sustainable yield, to establish how many fish can be harvested without affecting future populations.
- The maximum sustainable yield (MSY) is the maximum amount of fish that can be taken without affecting the stock biomass and replacement rate. Calculating an MSY relies on obtaining precise data about a population's age structure, size, and growth rate. If the MSY is incorrectly established, unsustainable quotas may be set, and the fish stock may become depleted.
- Scientists often use biomass, the total weight of all fish stock, as a useful measure for the "amount" of fish present. Biomass increases due to fish reproduction and growth rates, which can differ for each fish species. Biomass decreases due to fish death, both natural and caused by fishing.
- MSY biomass (B_{MSY}) is calculated at 50% of the maximum (unfished) biomass of an ecosystem and identifies the most effective amount of fish harvesting / fishing.
- Under ideal conditions, harvesting at this rate (B_{MSY}) should be able to continue indefinitely. However, the growth rate of a population is likely to fluctuate from year to year.
- If a population has below-average growth for several years while the take remains the same, there is a high risk of population collapse because an ever-increasing proportion of the population will be taken with each harvest.

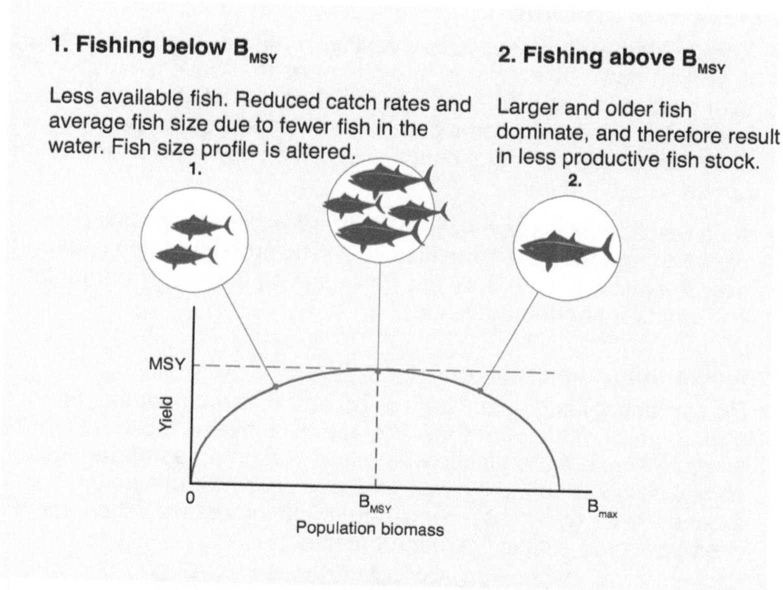

1. Fishing below B_{MSY}

Less available fish. Reduced catch rates and average fish size due to fewer fish in the water. Fish size profile is altered.

2. Fishing above B_{MSY}

Larger and older fish dominate, and therefore result in less productive fish stock.

3. What is the maximum sustainable yield? ___

4. A fish population consists of about 3.5 million individuals. A study shows that about 1.8 million are of breeding age.

(a) Researchers want to know the maximum sustainable yield for the population so that it can be fished sustainably. What factors will they need to know to accurately determine the MSY?

(b) Should these smaller non-breeding individuals be included in the catch? Explain your reasoning: ___

(c) It is found that the larger a breeding individual is, the more fertile it is. What implications might this have on the harvesting method for these fish and the viability of the fishery?

ISBN: 978-1-98-856693-1

137 Plastics in the Ocean

Key Question: How has plastic waste from human activity impacted the environment, and in what ways can it be remediated?

Plastic is a problem

- The problem with plastic is its stability. In nature, organic material is broken down by enzymes and microbes that have evolved over billions of years to deal with the chemical bonds found in nature. Very few organisms can degrade plastic because the chemical bonds in most plastics are not similar to the chemical bonds found in nature.
- As a result, plastics can remain in the environment for hundreds of years, and the vast quantities of plastic products thrown away over the last half a century are now causing large environmental and waste management issues.

Marine species, such as the turtle above, can mistake plastic for jellyfish and be harmed when eating it. Additionally, plastic can become entangled.

Concentrating the problem

- Human activity is global. There is no part of the planet that is not affected in some way by human activity. Even remote parts of the world are affected by activities thousands of kilometres away. The circulation of the oceans tends to concentrate plastic waste into certain areas of the ocean. The surface water of the oceans circulates in giant whirlpools called gyres. In the same way that you can concentrate debris in a small pool by swirling the water around, these gyres also concentrate floating debris. When this happens with floating plastic, giant areas of the ocean become plastic "garbage patches".

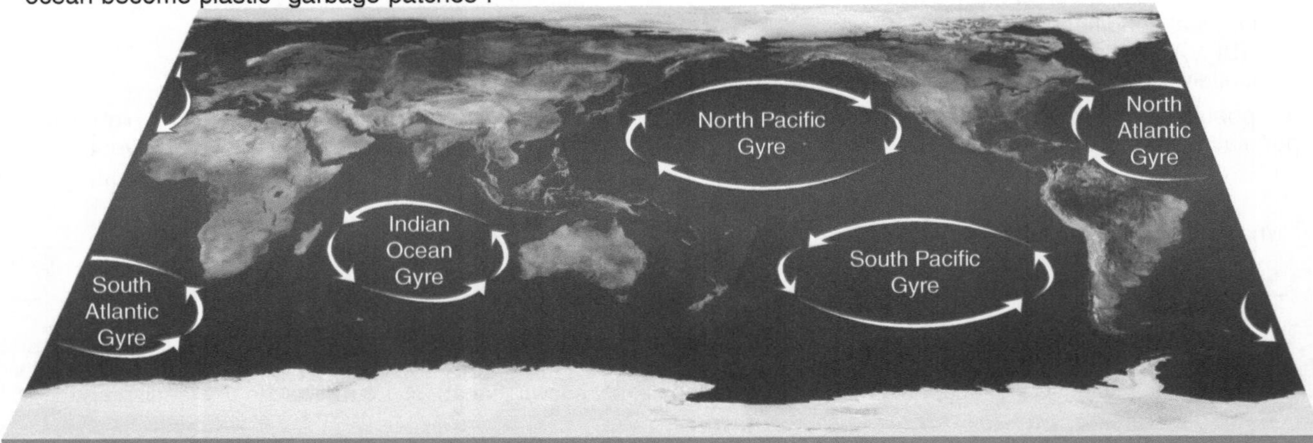

The **Great Pacific Garbage Patch** is an area within the North Pacific Gyre. Although given the name "garbage patch", most of the debris is not easily visible. The patches contain concentrations of waste and debris (mostly plastic) that are normally found in the ocean. The area covers around 1.2 million km^2, although definitions of the extent vary and the concentration of debris changes with the seasons. This makes an accurate estimate difficult.

1. Why do plastics persist in the environment? ______________________

____

2. (a) How does plastic waste become concentrated in certain areas of water? ______________________

____

____

(b) Some islands in the middle of the North Pacific Ocean are very isolated, yet it they have a massive problem with plastic washing up on its beaches. Explain how this happens:

____

____

3. Describe some potential problems created by plastic waste in the oceans: ______________________

____

____

ESS3.C SC

ISBN: 978-1-98-856693-1

Plastic in the Pacific

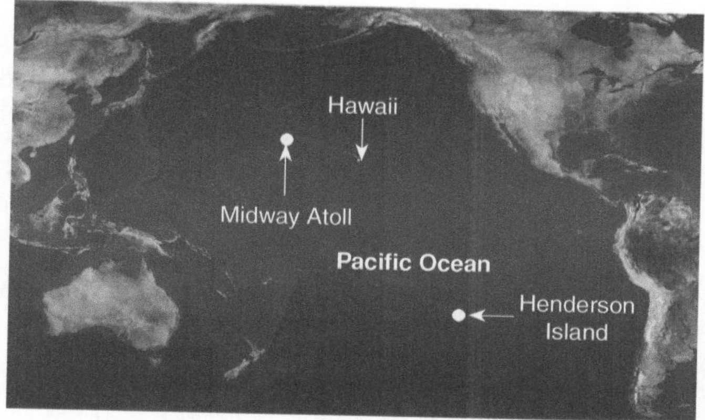

- In the South Pacific, plastic is concentrated by the South Pacific Gyre, a huge system of ocean currents that rotates in an anti-clockwise direction. In the North Pacific, plastic is concentrated by the North Pacific Gyre, which rotates in a clockwise direction.
- The effect of plastic in the marine environment can be dramatically seen on islands near the centre of these gyres. Henderson Island and Midway Atoll are two of these.

Henderson Island

- Henderson Island sits in the South Pacific Ocean. It is part of the Pitcairn group and is about 5000 km from the nearest significant land mass. The island is small, at only 37.3 km^2, and uninhabited. A study in 2017, led by Jennifer Lavers, measured the amount of plastic on the island's beaches. Her team measured the amount of plastic already on the beach, and then cleared a control area to measure the rate at which plastic accumulated (below).

Site	Mean density on beach (items per m^2)	Rate of accumulation (items km^{-1} d^{-1})	Estimated total debris on beach (items)		Estimated island total including buried items and back beach (items)	
			Number	Mass (kg)	Number	Mass (kg)
North Beach	30.3	13,316	812,116	2985	7,634,052	4,744
East Beach	239.4	–	3,053,901	12,611	30,027, 343	12,857
Total			3,866,017	15,597	37,661,395	17,601

Lavers, JL. 2017. Exceptional and rapid accumulation of anthropogenic debris on one of the world's most remote and pristine islands. https://www.pnas.org/doi/10.1073/pnas.1619818114

Midway Atoll

- Midway Atoll (land area 6.2 km^2) is in the North Pacific Ocean, 2,400 km west of Hawaii (the nearest significant land), and near the centre of the North Pacific Gyre. As with Henderson Island, the circulation of the ocean washes vast quantities of plastic onto the beaches. The National Oceanic and Atmospheric Administration (NOAA) regularly removes plastic debris from the beaches. Since 1999, they have removed 125 tonnes of plastic.
- On both these islands, and many others, plastic is mistaken for food by seabirds who eat it or feed it to their young. Every year on Midway Island, thousands of young albatrosses die from ingesting plastic products. The proportion of plastic deposited in the ocean is expected to increase at a rate of 4.8% each year until 2025, and at a rate of 3% from 2025 to 2050. At this rate, the ratio of plastic mass to fish mass could be roughly 1:1 by 2050. Microplastics and nanoplastics, tiny pieces of plastic including microbeads, enter the food chain and concentrate toxins, which accumulate in the fish that eat them. Nanoplastics can enter cells and affect their functioning.

Duncan Wright

Plastic in dead albatross chick, Midway Atoll.

Plastic debris on beach, Henderson Island.

Discarded nets can trap and drown marine mammals, reptiles, and birds (above).

4. Explain how plastic thrown away in a city on the west coast of North America can end up in a Laysan albatross chick on Midway Atoll:

5. What effect do micro and nanoplastics have on the animals that ingest them?

ISBN: 978-1-98-856693-1

Solving the problem

- Increasingly, degradable plastics are being produced. These may be photodegradable (break down in sunlight) or made from a blend of sugars and other chemicals, and can break down within 45 days. Although many degradable plastics break down into smaller pieces, those pieces still persist in the environment.
- Most plastic products are stamped with a number (1-7) to indicate what material they are made from, for recycling purposes. Plastic types 1 and 2 are the most commonly recycled plastics. Type 4 is less commonly recycled, while types 3, 5, 6, and 7 are unlikely to be recycled.

Plastic eating bacteria

- PET (Polyethylene terephthalate) plastic is widely used to make bottles. A few fungal species are know to digest PET, but until recently no bacteria were known to do so.
- However, in 2016 a Japanese research group collected 250 samples of sludge from a PET bottle recycling plant. They incubated these sludge samples with very thin PET film. After 15 days, they found that the PET film had vanished in some of the samples, indicating that something was breaking it down.
- Further analysis found that the bacterium *Ideonella sakaiensis* was responsible. This was the first bacterium shown to digest PET plastic. It does this by secreting the enzyme PETase, which breaks the PET molecule down into its single monomers. The enzyme MHETase then breaks the monomers down into compounds the bacteria can use.
- The technology is still in its early stages. If used commercially, it is predicted the bacteria could degrade more than 50 million tonnes of PET plastic annually. This is close to the global production of PET plastic. Currently, only 2.2 tonnes is recycled annually.

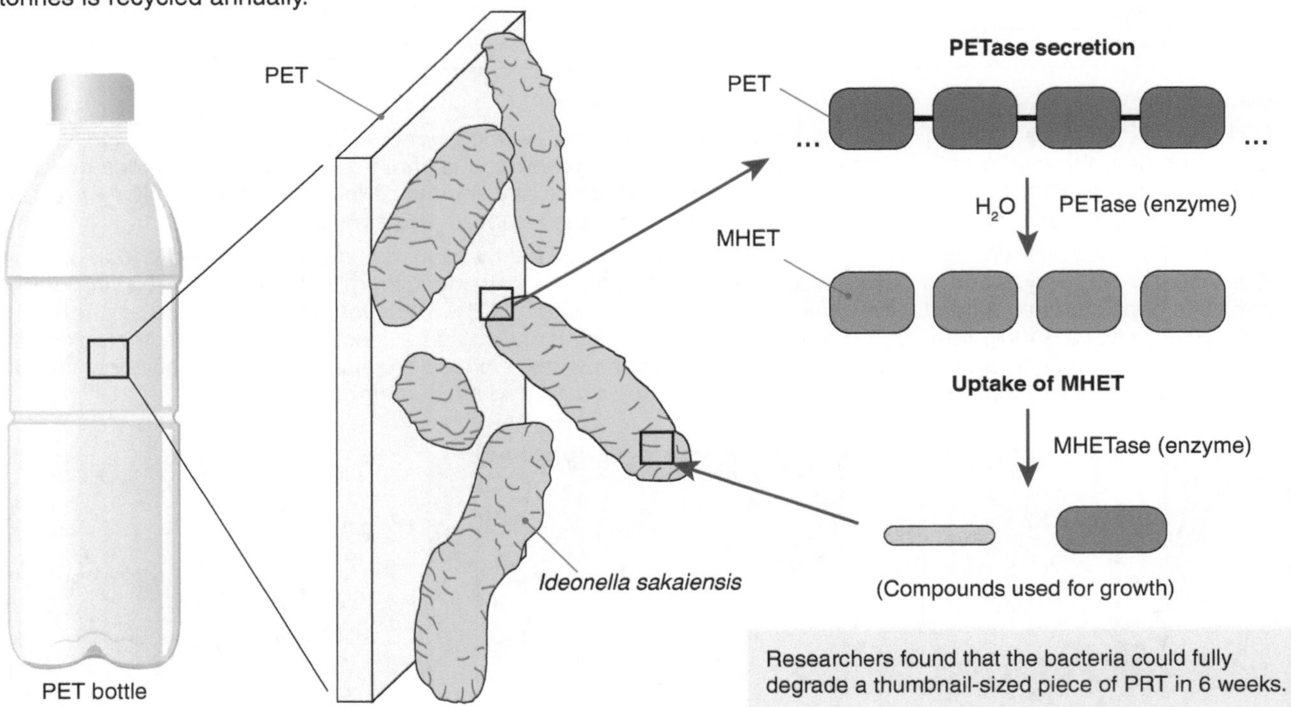

Researchers found that the bacteria could fully degrade a thumbnail-sized piece of PRT in 6 weeks.

6. (a) Briefly describe how the bacteria *Ideonella sakaiensis* was found and isolated: ______________________

(b) Evaluate the potential of this technology in reducing PET plastic waste: ______________________

ISBN: 978-1-98-856693-1

138 The Problem With Oil

Key Question: What impact do oil spills have on the environment, and how can we prevent or reverse this impact?

Oil and oil spills

- **Oil** is arguably one of the most important chemicals in human economics. It provides energy for transport and electricity and the raw materials for many consumer products, including plastics. Billions of dollars a year are spent on removing it from the ground and billions more obtained in revenue from its sale.
- However, crude oil is a very toxic substance and removing it from reservoirs is fraught with difficulty and danger. Some of the greatest man-made environmental disasters have occurred because of the search for and transport of oil.
- For example, the Deepwater Horizon disaster in 2010 produced an oil slick that, at its peak, covered 6500 km^2 of ocean.

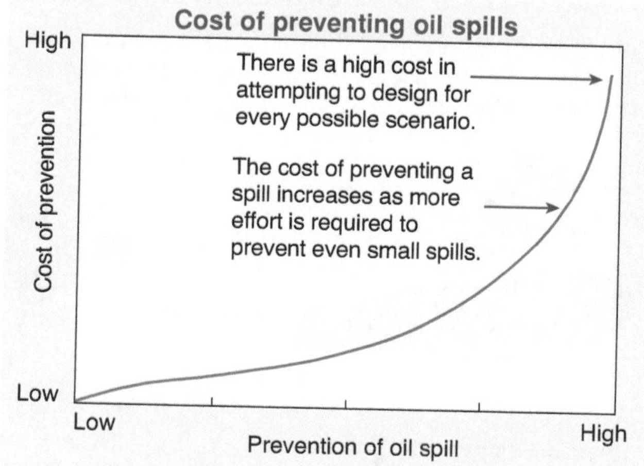

Cost of preventing oil spills

- Preventing oil spills is important, as oil is extremely damaging to the environment. However, the cost of prevention is high.
- At some point, the cost of measures taken to prevent oil spills outweighs the benefit of preventing spills (the reduction of damage to the environment).
- A cost-benefit analysis done soon after the Exxon Valdez grounding in 1989 found it cost less to clean up the mess than to prevent the spill. Of course this doesn't take into account that any oil spill is detrimental to the environment.

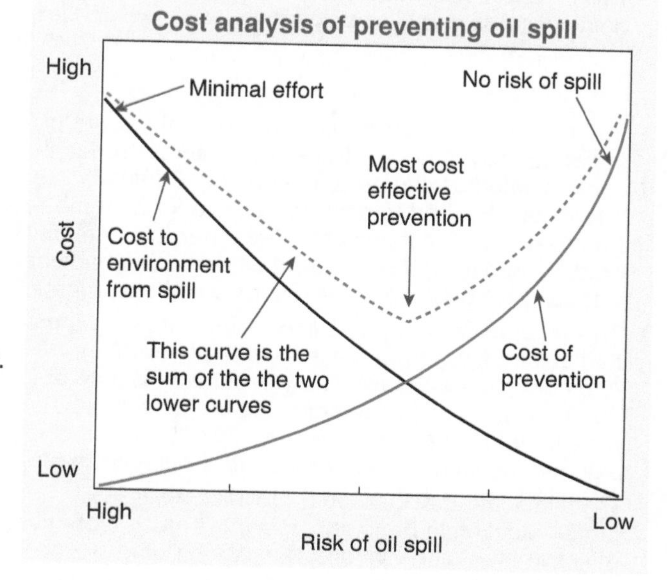

1. Why is oil an important resource?

2. Why does the cost of preventing an oil spill increase rapidly close to 100% prevention?

3. How does a cost-benefit analysis help us decide what level of risk is acceptable when dealing with oil and oil spills?

ISBN: 978-1-98-856693-1

Cleaning up oil spills

- Oil is difficult to remove once it is in the environment. New technologies are helping to quickly clean up oil spills and reduce their harm. In water, oil slicks can be contained using floating booms, and chemical dispersants can help break up the slick. Bioremediation, using organisms such as oil eating bacteria, was used in the Deepwater Horizon oil spill in the Gulf of Mexico in 2010

Using bacteria to metabolize hydrocarbons

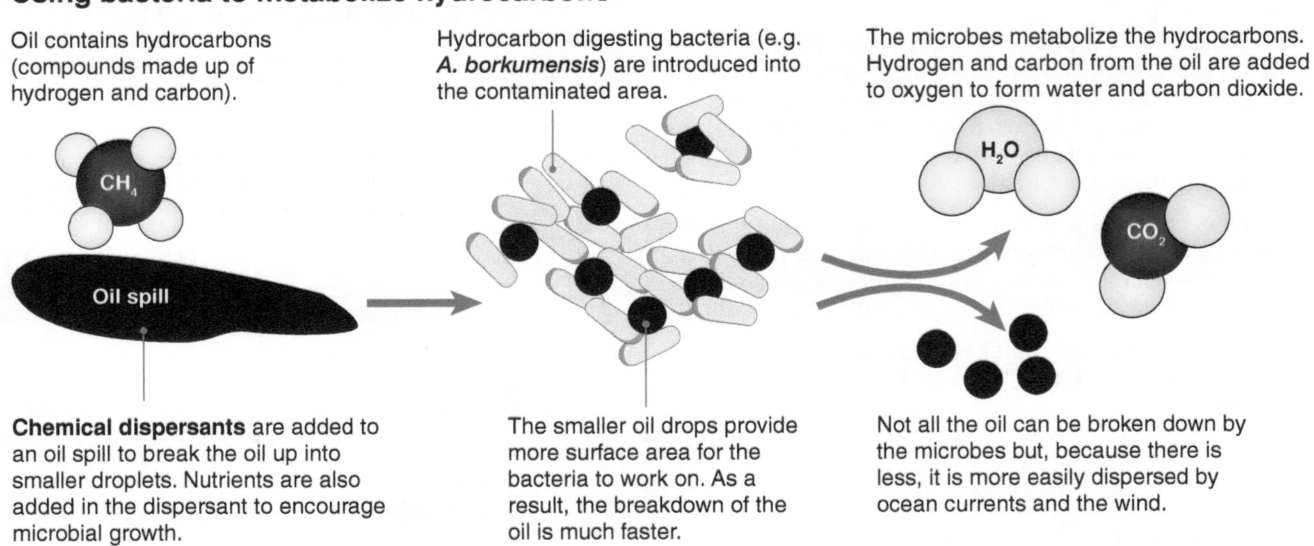

- In 2008, an oil spill occurred near Gujarat (Western India) due to a crude oil trunk line rupture. Crude oil contaminated a wide area of farmland. Oil-soaked soil was excavated and transported off site for bioremediation (removal of the contaminant). Oilzapper (a commercial product containing five different oil degrading bacteria) was applied to the soil. The results are shown (right).
- This is an example of *ex-situ* bioremediation (treatment that occurs away from the initial site of pollution). According to the Energy and Resources Institute of India, 5000 hectares of oil-contaminated cropland has been reclaimed in India and more than 26,000 tonnes of oily sludge has been successfully treated with Oilzapper.
- Trials indicate that Oilzapper provides 90.2-96% biodegradation in 5 months, making it much more cost effective than other options, such as building sludge storage pits and waiting for *in-situ* degradation in the soil.

Total petroleum hydrocarbon (TPH) in contaminated soil after treatment with Oilzapper

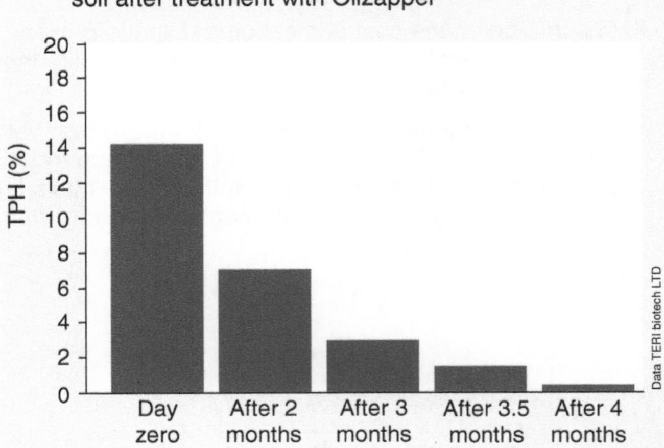

4. List some technological solutions to oil spills: ______

5. Outline how hydrocarbon-metabolizing bacteria are used to clean up an oil spill: ______

6. (a) How long did it take for the bacteria in Oilzapper to remove the oil in the Gujarat soil? ______

   (b) Evaluate the effectiveness of oilzapper as a bioremediation tool: ______

ISBN: 978-1-98-856693-1

139 Human Impact on the Land

Key Question: How has human activity impacted the land?

▶ Before ten thousand years ago, humans were a hunter-gatherer species. The change to a sedentary agricultural lifestyle meant that land needed to be cleared and protected from wildlife for the exclusive use of humans and their livestock. This was the start of humans dominating the planet. One third of the world's land area is now dedicated exclusively to producing food for humans, other parts are mined for **resources,** and forests are cleared for timber.

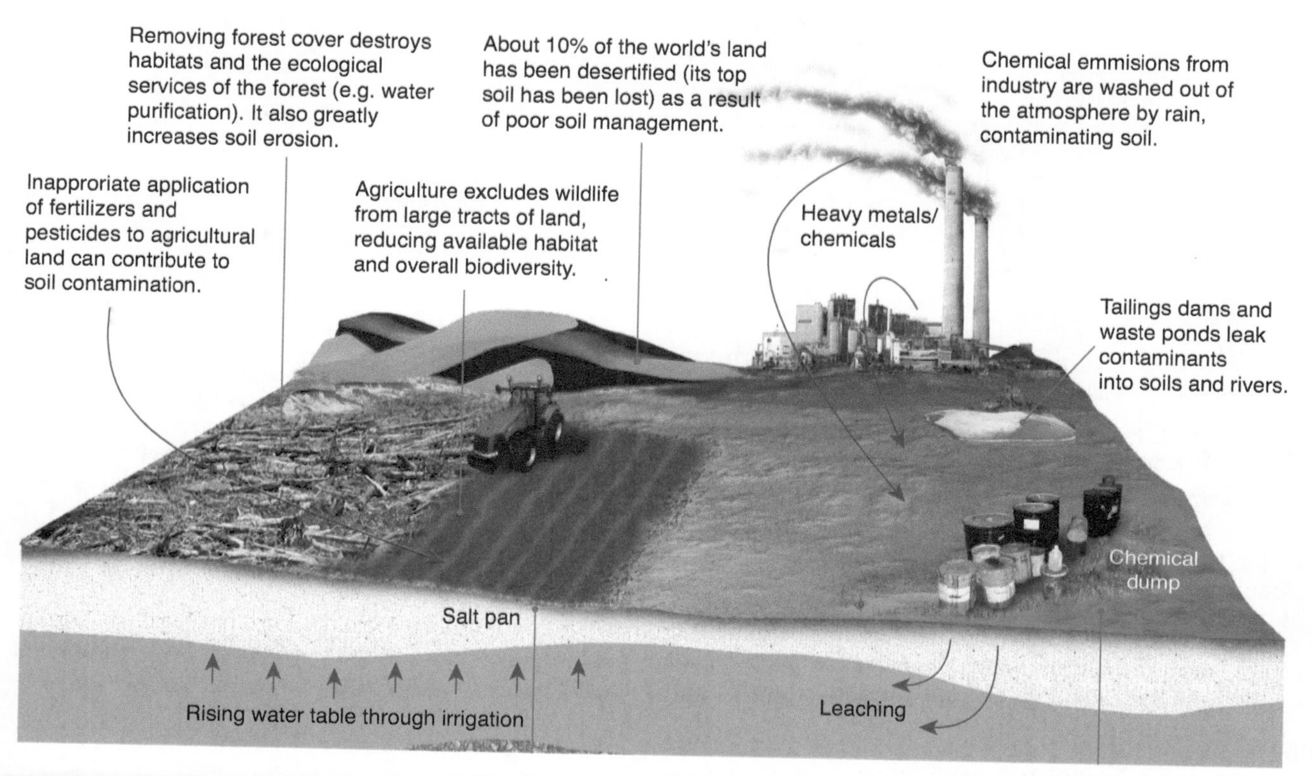

Deforestation is a major threat to wildlife. Deliberate destruction, such as logging, removes thousands of hectares of habitat a year, but accidental destruction by forest fires also destroys huge tracts of forest each year.

Urban sprawl is the development of large areas of land for housing. As the human population grows, especially around cities and in wealthier countries, more houses are needed. These often use undeveloped or previously agricultural land.

Humans produce a huge amount of waste. Not all is or can be recycled and so it is dumped in landfills. If landfills are not carefully managed, they can leach toxic chemicals into soils and groundwater. Even well managed sites occupy land.

1. Why was the change from humans being a hunter/gatherer society to an agricultural one an important milestone in human-environment interactions?

ISBN: 978-1-98-856693-1

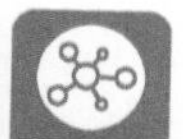

Desertification and Salinization

▸ Agriculture, **deforestation**, **pollution**, land mismanagement, and impacts from human induced climate change, have reduced the amount of fertile and usable land. Existing productive land needs to feed ever more people due to population growth and an increasing **resource** footprint from "developing" countries as they improve their economic situation. All this is against a backdrop of climate change induced drought, which is rapidly speeding up the process of desertification.

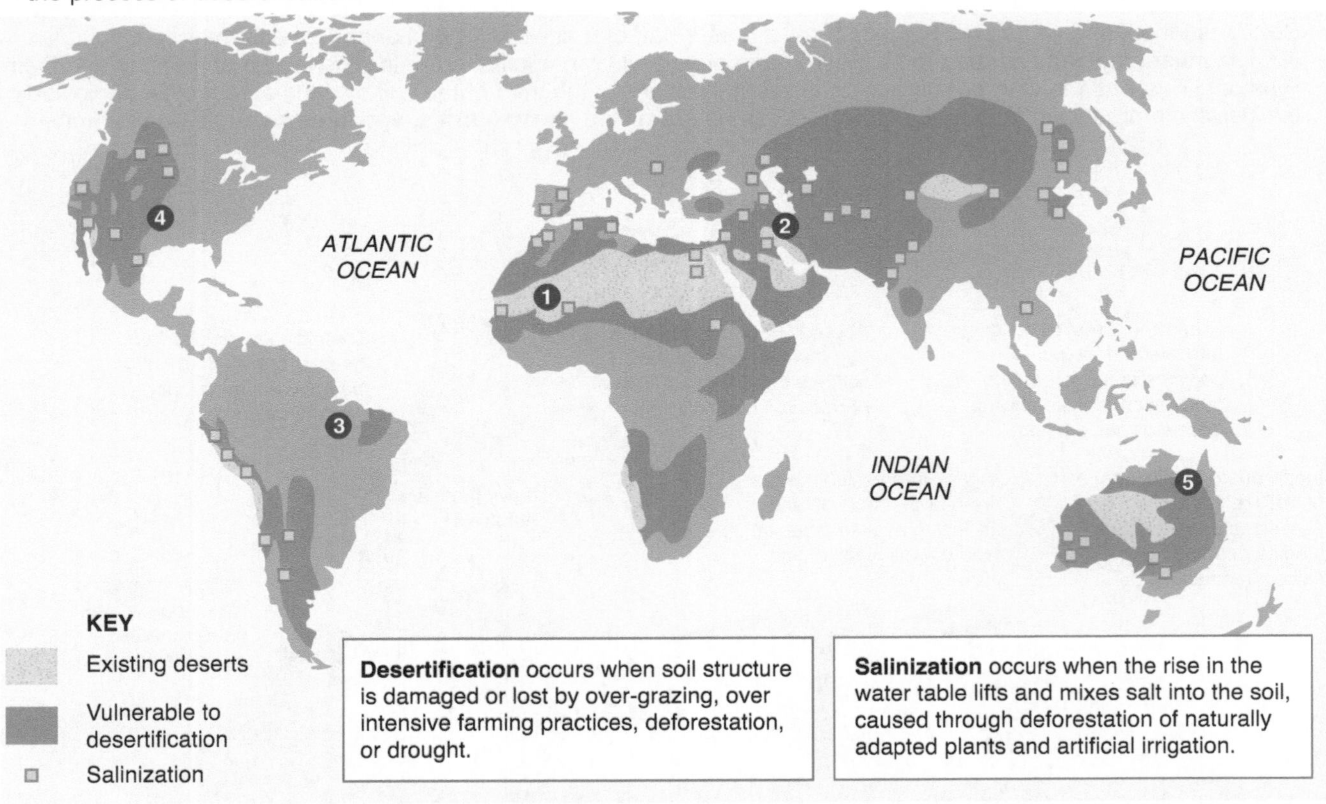

❶ **Africa Sahel region:** Demand for land and resources due to population growth has increased logging and land clearance for farming. This has resulted in loss of productive soil and increased desertification in an area already at risk from drought and dust storms.

❷ **Uzbekistan and Kazakhstan:** Intensive farming and agricultural irrigation in traditionally dry lands have shrunk the nearby Aral sea, lifting up salt and leaving extensive areas unusable due to salinization.

❸ **Amazon rainforest:** Deforestation and fires are turning the tropical forest in this equatorial area into arid, dry, and unproductive land due to desertification.

❹ **Western and southwestern United States:** Intensive farming, climate change, and prolonged droughts are leading to desertification of once productive land.

❺ **Australia:** Clearance of native vegetation and irrigation of dry farmland are degrading land due to salinization.

2. Explain how human-induced salinization develops: ______________________________

____

____

3. (a) What is desertification? ______________________________

(b) Outline the main causes of desertification? ______________________________

____

(c) What risks are associated with desertification? ______________________________

____

____

____

ISBN: 978-1-98-856693-1

140 Deforestation

Key Question: How can we use new technology to help track and reduce deforestation?

Deforestation

- At the end of the last glacial period, about 10,000 years ago, forests covered an estimated 6 billion hectares; about 45% of the Earth's land surface. Forests currently cover about 4 billion hectares of land (31% of Earth's surface). They include the cooler temperate forests of North and South America, Europe, China, and Australasia, and the tropical forests of equatorial regions. Over the last 5000 years, the loss of forest cover is estimated at 1.8 billion hectares. 5.2 million hectares have been lost in the last 10 years alone. Temperate regions, where human civilizations have historically existed the longest, e.g. Europe, have suffered the most but now the vast majority of **deforestation** is occurring in the tropics. Intensive clearance of forests during settlement of the most recently discovered lands has extensively altered their landscapes.

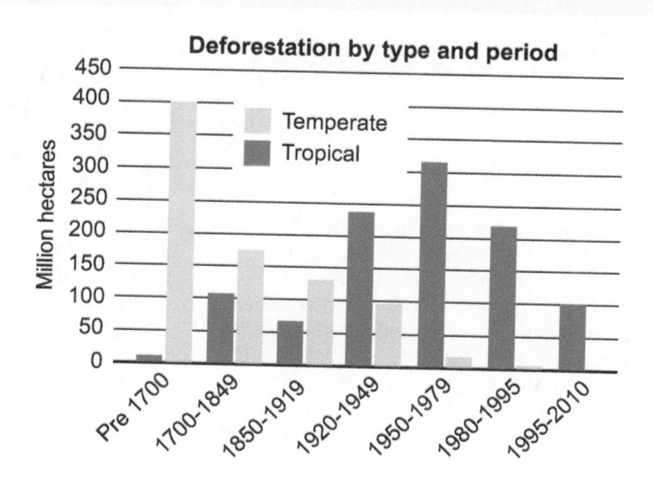

Causes of deforestation

- Deforestation is a result of many interrelated causes, which often center around socioeconomic drivers. In many tropical regions, the vast majority of deforestation is the result of subsistence farming. Poverty and a lack of secure land can be partially solved by clearing small areas of forest and producing family plots. However, huge areas of forests have been cleared for agriculture, including ranching and production of palm oil plantations. These produce revenue for governments through taxes and permits, producing an incentive to clear more forest. Just 14% of deforestation is attributable to commercial logging (although combined with illegal logging it may be higher).

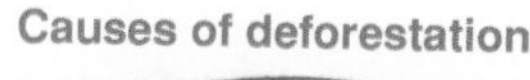

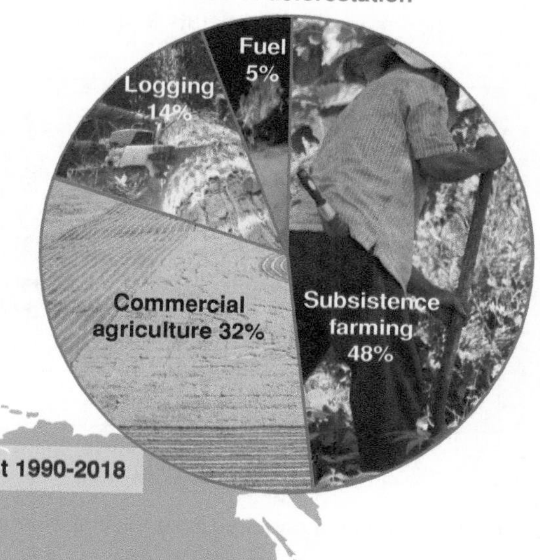

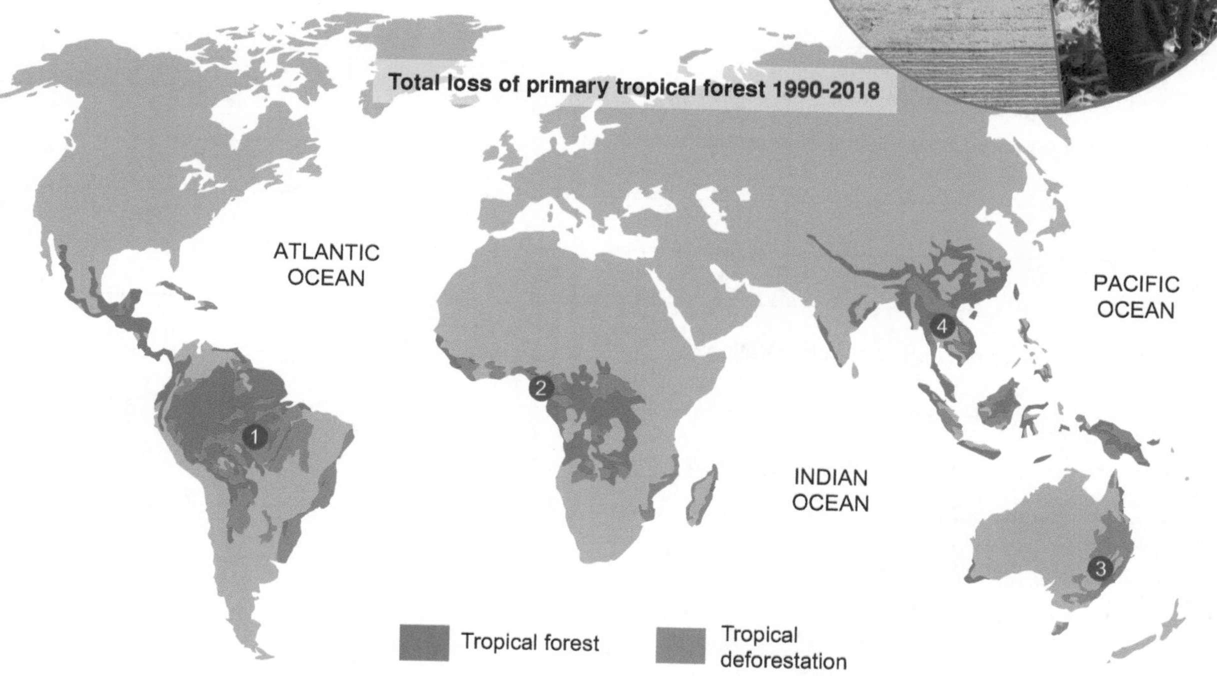

- It is important to distinguish between deforestation involving primary (old growth) forest, and deforestation in plantation forests. Plantations are regularly cut down and replaced and can artificially inflate a country's apparent forest cover or rate of deforestation. The loss of primary forests is far more important, as these are refuges of high biodiversity, including rare species, many of which are endemic to relatively small geographical regions

1. In small groups, or individually, locate and identify one of the regions in the map above and research the causes of deforestation for that area, along with any factors involved, and what, if any, conservation projects are underway.

ISBN: 978-1-98-856693-1

Reducing deforestation

Commercial plantations are specifically planted and grown for the production of timber or timber-based products. These forests are virtual monocultures, containing a specific timber tree, such as *Pinus radiata* (Monterey or radiata pine). These trees have often been selectively bred to produce straight-trunked, uniform trees that grow quickly and can be easily harvested and milled.

Government regulations and public education are key parts to solving **deforestation**. It is easy to tell a country to stop cutting down trees, but if the people of that country have no other way of making money or obtaining wood, what are they to do? Similarly, government regulation only works if people stick to the rules and the rules are strictly enforced.

Technology can help reduce deforestation by helping to monitor the reduction or growth of forests. Global Forest Watch 2.0 is a real-time interactive forest monitoring system produced by Google, in partnership with the University of Maryland and the UN Environment Program. It uses satellite technology and data sharing to track legal and illegal logging, helping law enforcement officials.

2. Describe the trend in temperate and tropical deforestation over the last 300 years: ______________________________

3. What are some of the causes of deforestation? ______________________________

4. Deforestation in temperate regions has largely stabilized and there has been substantial forest regrowth. However, these second growth forests differ in structure and composition from the forests that were lost. Why might this be of concern?

____

5. (a) How do commercial tree plantations help reduce deforestation? ______________________________

(b) How can technology help prevent deforestation? ______________________________

6. What must happen in order for regulations to halt deforestation? ______________________________

ISBN: 978-1-98-856693-1

141 The Availability of Land

Key Question: What solutions can be used so that all humans, our activities, and wildlife have enough room to coexist?

- There is a finite amount of land on Earth. The Earth has a land area of about 148.5 million km^2. 57 million km^2 is used for agriculture, of which 15.4 million km^2 is cropland (as opposed to pasture). About 54% of the world's population lives in urban areas, which occupy 2.5 million km^2. 46% of the land area is defined as wilderness and has just 2.4% of the world's population of 7.8 billion.
- As the population grows, more land will need to be developed for **resource** extraction, landfill, urban development, or cropping. Alternatively, instead of developing land, cities could become taller and denser, housing more people in high rise towers. There are also plans to develop high rise agricultural towers which would reduce the need to expand farmlands. A tower such the Willis Tower (Sears Towers) has 416,000 m^2 of floor space (41.6 hectares) that could be used to grow crops using hydroponics.

1. (a) Calculate the density of humans on the Earth's land surface (in humans per square kilometer):

   (b) 57 million km^2 of land is used for feeding the world's population. Taking this into account (people can't live on that land) what is the density of humans per square kilometer?

   (c) Now, consider that 46% of the land's surface contains just 2.4% of the human population. What is the density of humans per square kilometer in the land that is left?

   (d) Calculate the density of humans in urban areas:

2. Use the data to complete the table (a) and graph (b) to show available arable land (used for crop production) per person:

(a)

Year	Arable land (million km^2)	Population (billions)	Arable land per person (km^2 per person)
1960	14.4	3.01	
1970	15.1	3.68	
1980	15.2	4.44	
1990	16.1	5.31	
2000	16.0	6.12	
2010	15.8	6.93	

(b)

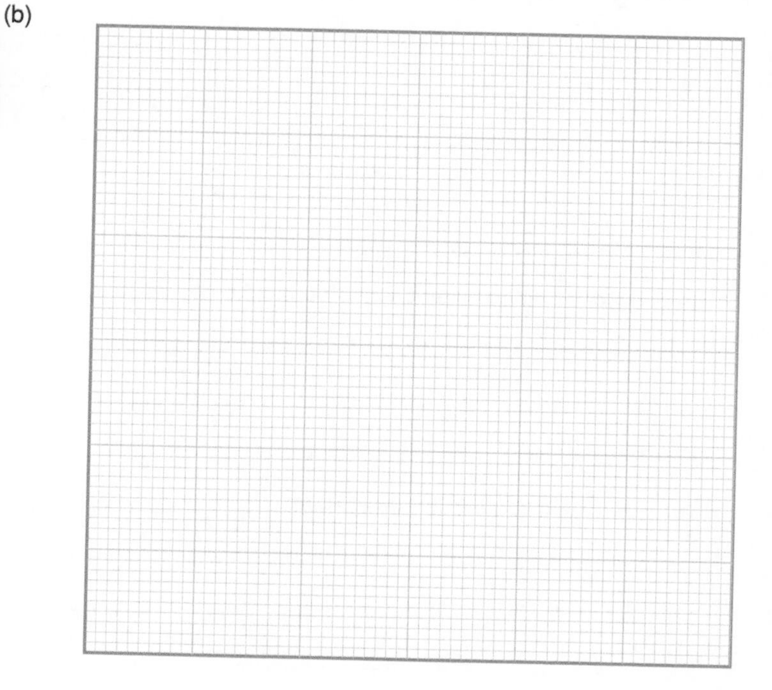

ISBN: 978-1-98-856693-1

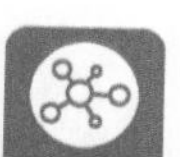

142 Urbanization

Key Question: How does urbanization impact the environment?

Issues with urbanization

- Urbanization describes the movement of people out of rural areas into cities. In the United States, an urban area is an area with more than 386 people per square km (1000 people per square mile).
- In 2007 (by UN estimate), the world passed the milestone of more people living in cities and urban areas than in rural areas. Today, approximately 4.1 billion people live in urban areas and 3.4 billion are designated rural. Urbanization has occurred more quickly in industrialized nations.
- Having thousands or millions of people in one place presents challenges for waste disposal, both solid rubbish and sewage. New York city produces more than 14 million tonnes of rubbish a year. Although most Western cities have effective waste systems involving a complex system of transport and disposal, many cities in developing countries do not. Large amounts of rubbish and sewage are still dumped directly into rivers and the sea. Rivers such as the Ganges (India) and the Citarum (Indonesia) act as open waste dumps and are the most polluted in the world. Rubbish that is not dumped may be incinerated. While this produces useful energy, it also produces a large amount of air **pollution** (including greenhouse gases) if not filtered carefully.
- Cities are transport hubs. People commute to and from them everyday, often many kilometers. Most of this transport relies on fossil fuels, mostly as diesel and gasoline in cars, trucks, and buses. Burning fossil fuels produces CO_2 which contributes to climate change. However, it also produces various other polluting gases, such as NO_2 and CO, which contribute to smog (right).

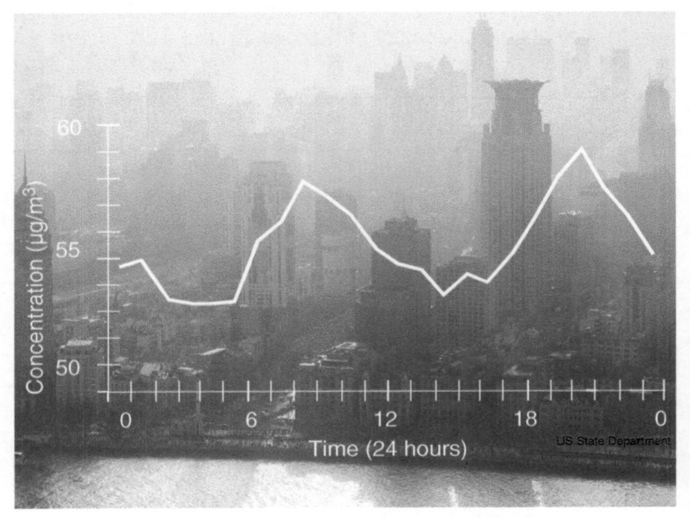

Graph above: Average daily variation in fine particulate matter ($PM_{2.5}$) in Shanghai, December 2011–July 2014 $PM_{2.5}$ poses a health risk. Background image: Smog, Shanghai cityscape.

1. What are some of the reasons people move into urban areas? ______

2. (a) How does air pollution change during the day in Shanghai? ______

   (b) How would you explain this pattern? ______

ESS3.C SC

ISBN: 978-1-98-856693-1

Stormwater surges and flooding

- Cities are known as concrete jungles for good reason. Aside from the buildings, much of the ground is covered with concrete or asphalt, e.g. roads, sidewalks, and carparks. This aids safety and ease of movement, but these surfaces are also impervious to water. Water from rainfall cannot soak naturally into the ground and moves directly, without treatment, into stormwater drains and then into streams and rivers. This has a number of consequences:
- Urban runoff includes pollutants that have accumulated on hard surfaces, including sediment, bacteria, metals, plastics, and residues from vehicle exhausts.
- As runoff increases, the amount of water that soaks into the soil (groundwater recharge) reduces, so urban development can result in a low water table.
- Any blockages to water into stormwater drainage can very quickly lead to surface flooding. The flow rate of rivers that pass through cities can rise and fall very quickly due to the sudden stormwater inflows after rain (right). Natural drainage systems show a much more moderate response to rainfall.

A culvert discharging stormwater after heavy rain (Illinois).

Stream flooding before and after urbanization

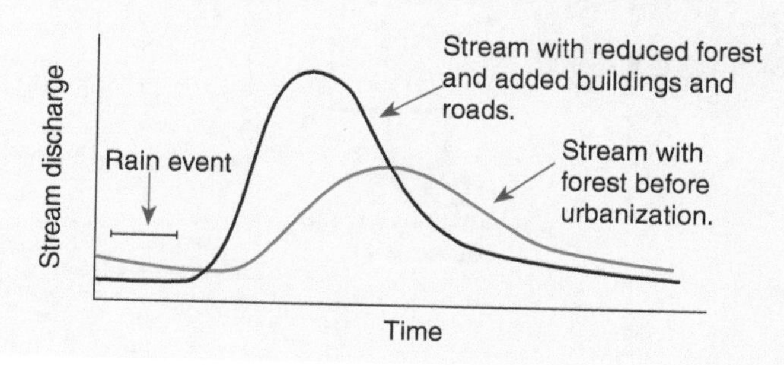

3. Describe the (often unintended) consequences of urbanization on the environment: ______________________________

4. How does urbanization affect stormwater surge and flooding? ______________________________

5. What are some possible positive effects of urbanization on the environment and world's resources? ______________________________

ISBN: 978-1-98-856693-1

143 Technology For Remediation

Key Question: How can new technologies help to remediate contaminated sites?

- Land that has been used for industry, such as mining, must be remediated when the **resource** runs out. **Remediation** is the removal of contaminants in order to make the area safe for human use.
- The method of remediation used depends on the extent and type of contamination (below). For example, polluted top soil can be removed and treated off-site, or plants and bacteria may be placed *in situ* to absorb and break down the contaminants. A treated area is monitored over many years to ensure that no further leaching of contaminants occurs. The remediated land can then be used for other purposes.

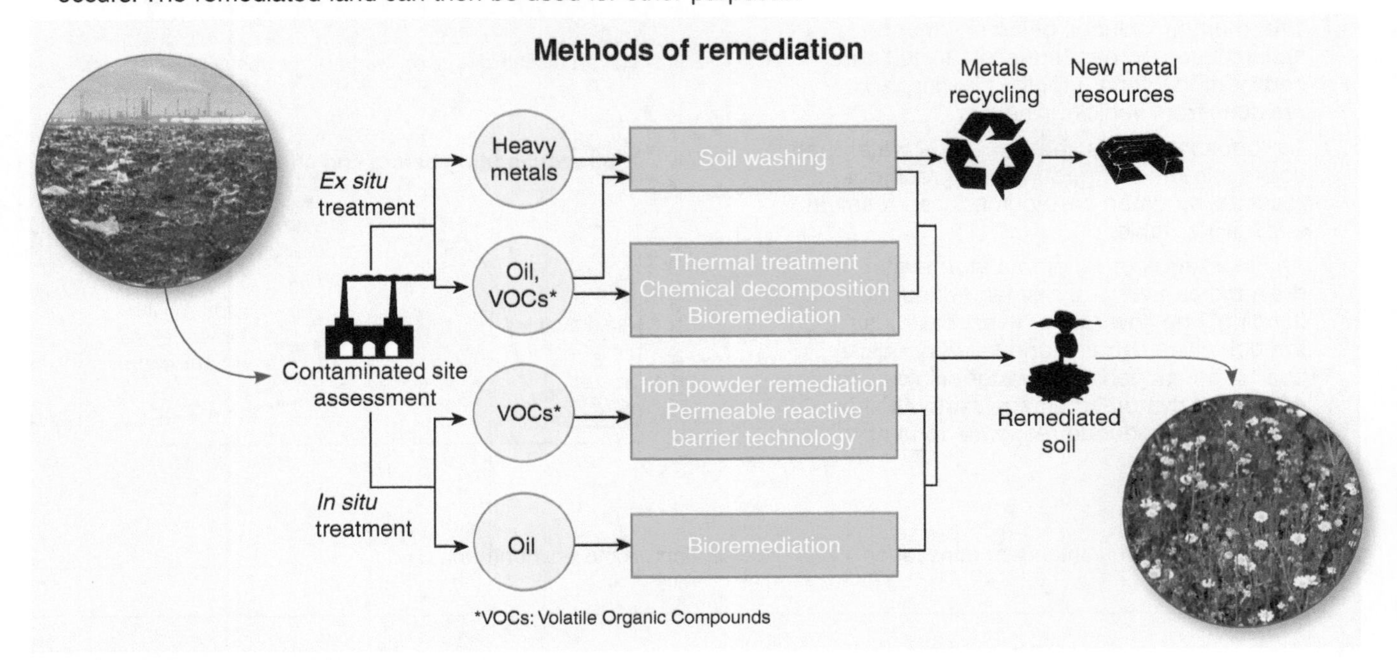

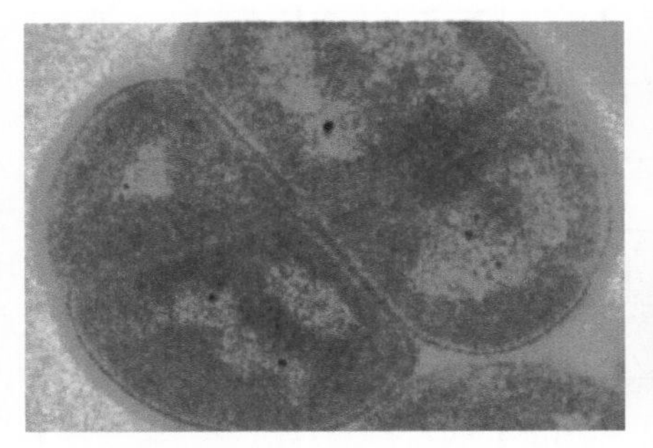

Bioremediation is the use of biological techniques to extract contaminants. Bacteria have great potential to do this and a number have been genetically engineered to digest contaminants. One such bacteria is *Deinococcus radiodurans*. It is one of the most radiation resistant organisms known and has been engineered to digest mercury and toluene in radioactive waste.

Technologies to remove contaminants can be quite simple. In areas with petroleum-based contaminants, water can be purified using activated carbon (highly granulated carbon). Contaminants adhere to the carbon granules and its very high surface area allows for a high rate of adsorption. Activated carbon is commonly used in household water purifiers.

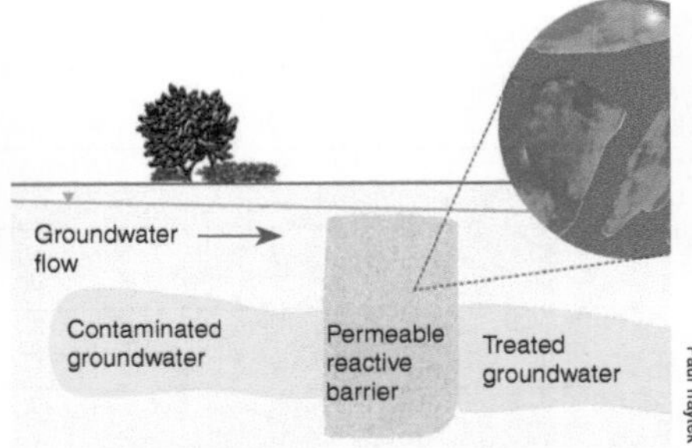

Permeable reactive barriers are new technologies that are a cost effective way of treating contaminated water *in situ*. The barrier is placed between the contaminated site and the groundwater. Water can move through the barrier from the site to the groundwater, but contaminants are either blocked or neutralized by the barrier.

1. Explain the purpose of environmental remediation: ____________________

2. Describe a technology for environmental remediation: ____________________

  ESS3.C  SC

ISBN: 978-1-98-856693-1

144 Evaluating Technological Solutions

Key Question: What are the advantages and disadvantages of different remediation technologies?

Different technology solutions for different remediation problems

- A wide range of new technology has been developed to minimize or reverse environmental damage caused by polluting contaminants. The effectiveness of their application is dependent on many factors.
- Companies, organizations, or governments must select the most appropriate contamination **remediation** technology based on ease of use, cost, urgency of operation, location of contamination, political, legal, moral, and social pressure, and availability of the technology, amongst other factors.

Land contamination remediation technologies

Bioremediation and phytoremediation are examples of technologies that are used to restore land to its original state in place (*in situ*). Bioremediation utilizes bacteria, fungi, or plant processes to breakdown specific contaminants into safe by products, while phytoremediation specifically uses plants to uptake, stabilize, or degrade contaminants.

Ex situ (away from site) remediation technologies

Some remediation technologies are used at locations away from the original contamination. Thermal treatment vaporizes and separates the contaminant at high temperatures, while land farming contains and treats the contaminants by a variety of methods in lined, leach-proof bins. *Ex situ* remediation tends to be expensive, but more thorough than in situ remediation.

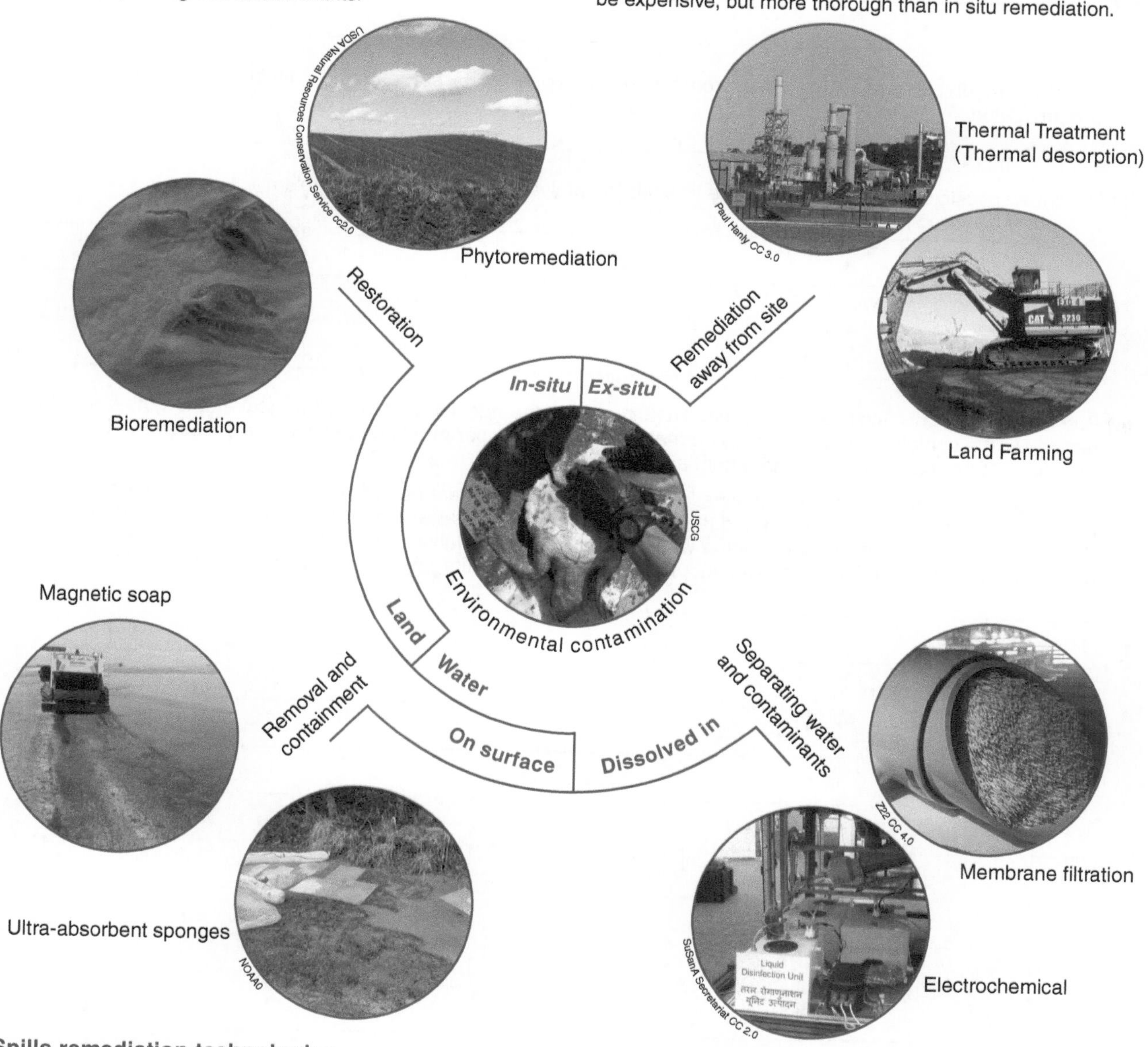

Oil Spills remediation technologies

Limiting the extent of environmental damage is driving the innovation of new technology to effectively clean up and remove harmful oil spills. Sponges have been developed to absorb more than 30 times their weight in oil, and properties of cleaning magnetic soaps can switched off and on to control the remediation process.

Water contamination remediation technologies

Contaminants, such as heavy metals and industrial chemicals, can make water harmful to human and animal health, so prompt removal is vital. Membrane filtration can remove contaminant molecules that have different sizes and characteristics from water, while electrochemical technology uses electricity to attract and draw out charged contaminant particles.

ISBN: 978-1-98-856693-1

SC   ESS3.C   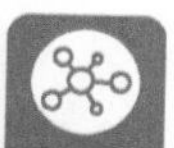

Evaluating environmental remediation solutions

1. Your challenge is to evaluate a selected type of **remediation** technology to tackle environmental contamination caused by human activity, such as oil spills, heavy metal contamination, or volatile organic compounds in ground water (pesticides, paint thinners, petrol etc.). Your class will be divided into groups.

   (a) Your class will be presented with ONE environmental contamination scenario. Write it here:

   (b) Each group will analyze how the pollutants produced from human activity contribute to environmental contamination. Describe the scope of the problem and potential harmful effects from it:

   (c) Select a remediation technology, either from the previous page or research, that is suitable to address the contamination:

   (d) Describe specific steps that you think are needed to resolve the contamination problem:

   (e) Present your group's findings to the class. The class must then decide together what goal and targets are required to remediate the contamination. You may find that there are a number of different opinions expressed, and compromises may have to be made to reach agreement among the groups.

   Your teacher will assign different remediation technologies to different groups to research. Work in your groups and evaluate a solution to reach the agreed target. Students can find starter ideas in the **BIOZONE Resource Hub**. Consider and prioritize a range of criteria when evaluating your solution. This includes cost, safety, reliability, and aesthetics (how something looks). You should also take into account any social, cultural, and environmental impacts.

   (f) Finish with a "contamination remediation summit". Each group should present their findings and recommendations to the whole class.

ISBN: 978-1-98-856693-1

145 Review Your Understanding

Key Question: How can our Earth and its resources sustain more people?

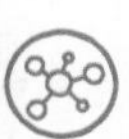

Vision of possible future city as a solution for increasing human population

▸ At the beginning of the chapter you were asked how we might respond to utilizing Earth's finite resources, against the trend of increasing human population. Use what you have learned from this chapter to summarize the key issue and possible solutions.

1. Summarize why Earth may experience a larger demand on its resources in future: ______

2. Discuss how land could be preserved for food production, as well as "wilding" space for other species to occupy, despite the predicted future growth in human population:

3. Identify ONE issue created by increasing population, research, and summarize your findings of a possible solution:

ISBN: 978-1-98-856693-1

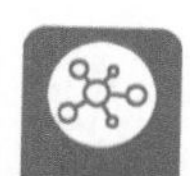

146 Summing Up

Computational simulation of the relationship between natural resource use, human sustainability, and biodiversity.

- The effect of human activities on **resources**, **biodiversity**, and **sustainability** is complex. By looking at specific areas and simplifying their interactions it is possible to produce simple mathematical models that help to show how a sustainable system might work.
- Below are the parameters of a hypothetical system. Your task is to set up a spreadsheet, as shown, and use it to simulate the effect of using different types of energy resources in the environment. You will do this by entering different combinations of parameters into the spreadsheet you have created and recording the outputs.
- As part of this task you will need to find the model that provides the most food and shelter, while remaining sustainable. At the end of the exercise, attach all your notes, answers, and spreadsheet printouts here.
- The spreadsheet is also available in the BIOZONE Resource Hub.

Energy resource

The system has three energy sources. The removal of the energy sources damages the biodiversity of the environment, e.g. by mining, in a different amount , i.e energy source A is easier to mine than energy source C and so mining does less damage the environment and biodiversity. The amount of damage is the same per unit of energy mined and is an arbitrary scale. 1.0 is equal to no damage.

Table 1

Energy source	Damage to biodiversity caused by extraction (per energy unit)
A	1.1
B	1.25
C	1.6

An average person uses **10 units of food a day** and **6 units of shelter/heat**.

The environment and biodiversity can replenish themselves by **15%** each day.

The environment and biodiversity are given a starting health value of 1000 and are deemed to be healthy, provided they remain at or above **60% of the original health** value.

Food and shelter

The two most basic human needs are food and shelter/warmth. The energy sources can be used to produce food and shelter. However the energy sources produce food and shelter with different efficiencies. Also, the production of food and shelter damages the biodiversity of the environment in some way, e.g. plowing a field, or clearing land for a house, or burning fuel for heat, as shown below.

Table 2

Energy source used	Units of energy source needed to produce 1 unit of food	Damage done to biodiversity during production of food
A	8	1.6
B	6	1.2
C	2	1.1

Table 3

Energy source used	Units of energy source needed to maintain 1 unit of shelter/heat	Damage done to biodiversity during maintenance of shelter/heat
A	9	1.2
B	5	1.3
C	3	1.15

- To carry out the simulation you need to set up a spreadsheet. The instructions given below are for setting up the spreadsheet using Microsoft Excel.

1. Open the spreadsheet and enter the energy source data shown in table 1 above, starting in the top corner (cell A1) of the spreadsheet:

	A	B
1	Energy source	Extraction effect on biodiversity per unit extracted
2	A	1.1
3	B	1.25
4	C	1.6
5		

2. Now, enter the data for food production and shelter underneath. Be sure to take account of the cell numbers the data are being entered in to:

	A	B	C
7	Food production (energy source used)	Energy units needed	Effect on biodiversity per food unit produced
8	A	8	1.6
9	B	6	1.2
10	C	2	1.1
11			
13	Shelter/heat (energy source used)	Energy units needed	Effect on biodiversity per shelter/heat unit used
14	A	9	1.2
15	B	5	1.3
16	C	3	1.15

ISBN: 978-1-98-856693-1

3. Enter the number of food units and shelter/heat units used by a person per day (see 4(a) below). Again, these are arbitrary. The number of units can be changed during the simulation to work out the maximum number that is sustainable.

4. (a) To run the simulation, you must enter formulae to calculate the effect on the environment of using each energy source into the appropriate cells. Be careful to enter the formulae correctly or the simulation may not run as expected! The formulae are shown below. Make sure that when you have entered the formula, the cell is formatted to show the numerical result.

F	G	H	I
	Units of food used by average person per day		Units of heat/shelter used by average person per day
	10		6
	Food energy source		Shelter/heat energy source
Extraction effect on environment /biodiversity	C		C
Energy units needed	=IF(G6=A2,B2, IF(G6=A3,B3, IF(G6=A4,B4)))		=IF(I6=A2,B2, IF(I6=A3,B3, IF(I6=A4,B4)))
Effect on biodiversity	=IF(G6=$A$8,B8, IF(G6=$A$9,B9, IF(G6=$A$10,B10))		=IF(I6=A14,B14, IF(I6=A15,B15, IF(I6=A16,B16)))
	=IF(G6=$A$8,C8, IF(G6=$A$9,C9, IF(G6=$A$10,C10))		=IF(I6=A14,C14, IF(I6=A15,C15, IF(I6=A16,C16)))

(b) Create a cell where the original health/starting value of the environment can be entered. The rate at which the environment can replenish itself (as a percentage) must also be entered.

ormula Bar

	G	H
12	Original environment/ biodiversity health	1000
13		
14	Rate of biodiversity replenishment (%)	15

(c) Finally, the output cells must have their formulae entered. Again make sure that each formula is entered correctly. If you change the layout of the spreadsheet, then you must make sure the reference cells in the formula are correct.

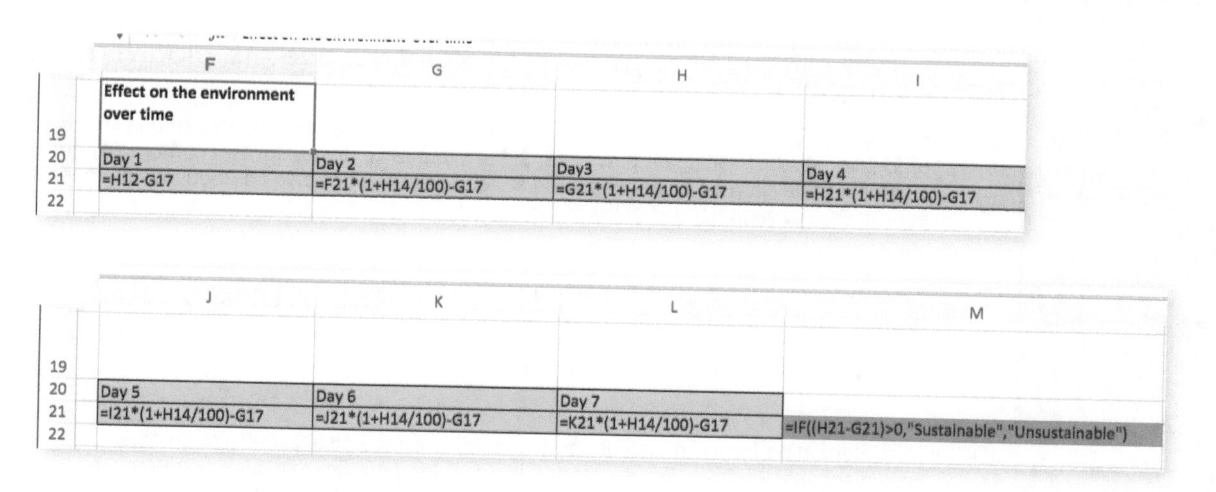

	F	G	H	I
19	Effect on the environment over time			
20	Day 1	Day 2	Day3	Day 4
21	=H12-G17	=F21*(1+H14/100)-G17	=G21*(1+H14/100)-G17	=H21*(1+H14/100)-G17
22				

	J	K	L	M
19				
20	Day 5	Day 6	Day 7	
21	=I21*(1+H14/100)-G17	=J21*(1+H14/100)-G17	=K21*(1+H14/100)-G17	=IF((H21-G21)>0,"Sustainable","Unsustainable")
22				

5. If you have created the spreadsheet correctly, you can now change the energy source for food production and shelter/heat. The image below shows the output for the first 4 days for using energy source A for both food production and shelter/heat, if you have entered everything correctly.

Effect on the environment over time			
Day 1	Day 2	Day3	Day 4
829.40	783.21	730.09	669.01

The sustainability value is tracking down. It will soon be unsustainable (<60% of 1000)

6. (a) Run the simulation by changing the food energy source (G6) and shelter/heat energy source (I6). Find the sustainability of an A and A, B and B, and C and C energy source scenario.

(b) Try combinations of energy sources, e.g. A and C or C and A, to see how sustainability and biodiversity are affected.

(c) Using these combinations, what is the maximum food units and shelter/heat units a person can use and remain sustainable? There may be many possible answers.

(d) Now try changing the rate at which the biodiversity replenishes or the value for the environment's original health. How do these affect the simulation?

ISBN: 978-1-98-856693-1

CHAPTER 12

Global Climate Change

Anchoring Phenomenon

Seashells by the seashore: Why are seashells getting thinner and more fragile? 147 155

How can climate models be used to predict future trends?

☐ 1 Define the terms climate and climate modeling. Explain the three main purposes of climate modeling. 148

☐ 2 Investigate how climate models have developed in complexity and accuracy. Explain the importance of considering how multiple elements influence each other in climate models. Research one component of a climate model, in depth. 149

☐ 3 Link the impact of climate change to the severity of hurricanes. Interpret data to explain the links between extreme weather events and climate change. Discuss how accuracy of climate change models assist with effective resource management. Analyze data to consider how the combination of multiple climate models adds to accuracy. 150

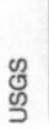

☐ 4 Compare data from historical and current sea level measurements. Describe causes of sea level rise, and the particular vulnerability to United States populations. Calculate and compare rates of sea level rise over 20 and 100 year periods. 150

☐ 5 Use climate modeling data to provide an evidence-based forecast of potential climate change rates. Describe potential future changes to crop yields. 156

How is climate change likely to effect our oceans, biodiversity and land use?

☐ 6 Define the term ocean acidification. Describe the trend in ocean acidification and link to probable causes. Investigate how water pH is affected by dry ice (frozen carbon dioxide). Use data to develop an evidence-based statement to link dissolved carbon dioxide in the surrounding oceans and pH of the water. 151

☐ 7 Describe some effects of climate change on the physical environment. Link changes in migratory patterns of birds to the impacts on food availability. Discuss the link between local extinction of some alpine species and climate change. Research specific species and the impacts of climate change upon them. 152

☐ 8 Use information from climate change data to discuss the possible effects on different crop plant species from climate change induced temperature rise. Link climate change induced distribution changes of crop pests to the impact on agriculture. 153

Boris Radosavljevic CC 2.5

How can technology be used to slow or reverse climate change impacts?

☐ 9 Discuss similarities and differences between different types of carbon capture technology. Discuss some of the limitations of carbon storage technology. Define carbon negative cement manufacture and calculate carbon absorption rates. Analyze a proposed carbon capture technology for possible limitations. 154

147 Seashells by the Seashore

Key Question: Why are seashells getting thinner and more fragile?

What's in a seashell?

- The photos below show calcium carbonate and a seashell reacting in hydrochloric acid. Notice that a gas is being produced during the reaction. In both cases, when the gas was tested, it proved to be carbon dioxide.

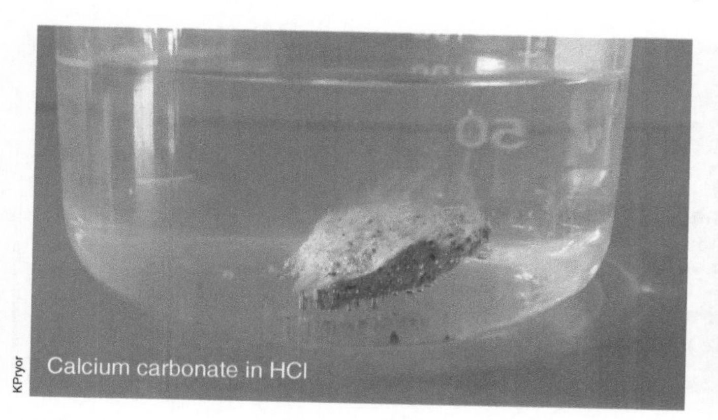

- Carbon dioxide gas is produced when carbonates react with acids. For the reaction of calcium carbonate with hydrochloric acid, the equation is $2HCl + CaCO_3 \rightarrow CaCl_2 + CO_2 + H_2O$.
- The reaction solutions were tested to identify any ions present. Calcium can be identified by adding sodium hydroxide. A white precipitate (solid) of calcium hydroxide forms. It remains, even if excess sodium hydroxide is added. Both solutions produced positive results for calcium ions.

Thin seashells

- Studies of many marine organisms with calcium carbonate shells have shown their shells appear to have become thinner over time. The graph below compares shell weight in the planktonic foraminifera *Globerigina bulloides* (below) over time. Bars indicate ±1 standard deviation of the mean.

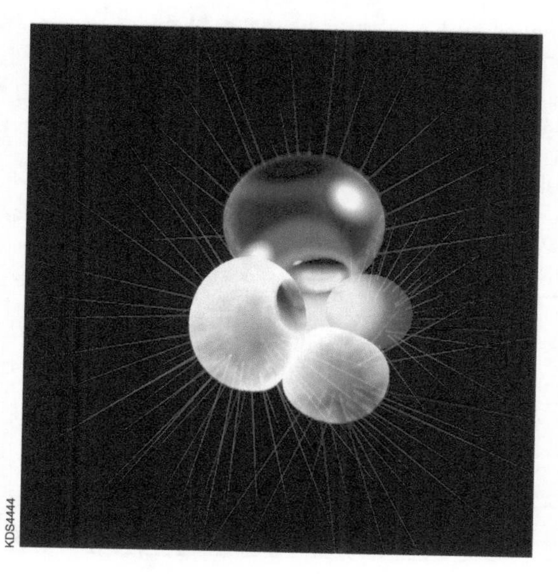

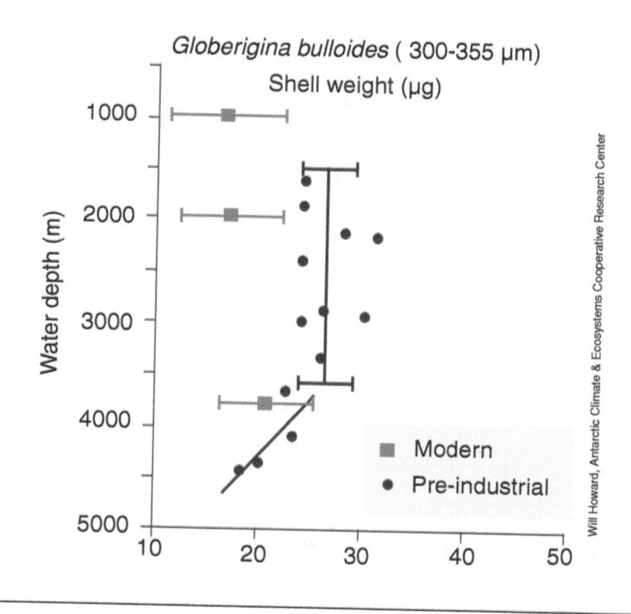

1. What are seashells mostly made of? ______________________

2. In groups, discuss what might be causing sea shells to become thinner. Summarize your ideas: ______________________

ISBN: 978-1-98-856693-1

148 What is Climate Modeling?

Key Question: How can scientists use climate models to predict long term climate patterns?

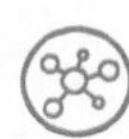

What is a climate model?

- **Climate** refers to the statistics of weather conditions (wind, precipitation, temperature, etc) at a location over a long period of time. Climate is the result of interactions among the Earth's systems. The complexity of these interactions makes climate difficult to understand and predict.
- Scientists use **models** to break the Earth's climate systems into components (parts) that can be more easily studied and understood. As the knowledge about a system grows, more components can be added so that it more closely represents the real system.
- Models used to understand climate are called **climate models**. They are mathematical representations and are very complex because the many different factors affecting the climate must be accounted for.
- The factors affecting the climate are interconnected. A change in one factor has an effect on another. Scientists manipulate the various components of the model and see what the outcome is.

Models can assist scientists when making connection between extreme weather events and climate change.

Mircea Madau public domain

What are climate models used for?

- To understand the present climate, including the factors contributing to it, and to project climatic conditions into the future.
- To investigate how natural processes or human activity may affect climate.
- To predict the effect of certain activities so that changes can be recommended to help prevent or slow down further climate change.
- Climate data is used by a wide range of people, such as farmers, who use the data to plan ahead for changing rainfall patterns by changing crop types or adjusting their livestock management practices.
- Cities can plan and implement strategies to manage water supplies and protect infrastructure through periods of low rainfall and flooding.
- The energy sector uses the data to forecast energy use. For example, energy use increases in a heat wave because people use fans and air conditioning to keep cool. Energy production can be increased to meet demand. In the long term, if global warming continues, more electricity capacity may be needed to meet the increase in demand.

The hydroelectric energy produced by the Hoover dam (above) varies depending on energy demands.

1. What is climate? ______________________________

2. (a) What is climate modeling? ______________________________

   (b) What are the three main purposes of climate modeling? ______________________________

3. How is climate modeling data used? ______________________________

  ESS2.D ESS3.D SSM SC

ISBN: 978-1-98-856693-1

149 The History of Climate Modeling

Key Question: How have climate models changed over time to allow scientists to make better predictions?

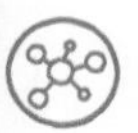

Climate models have become more sophisticated over time

- **Climate models** have been in use since the 1950s, but these very early versions really only modeled the weather in a particular region.
- The diagrams below show how the sophistication of climate models has changed over time. Note how the complexity has increased as more elements are incorporated into the models.

Early models in the 1970s were very simple and factored in only a few components, such as incoming sunlight, rainfall, and CO_2 concentration, due to limited knowledge about **climate change** mechanisms at that stage.

Over the next decade the models became more complex, as computers were becoming more functional, and other climate change components were added, such as clouds, land surface features, and ice.

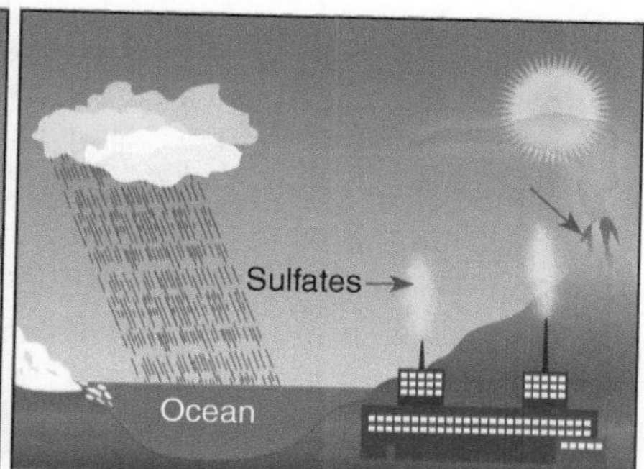

In 1988, the Intergovernmental Panel on Climate Change (IPCC) was established, to analyze climate data and inform the international community about their findings. The First Assessment Report (FAR) was release in 1990 and SAR in 1995.

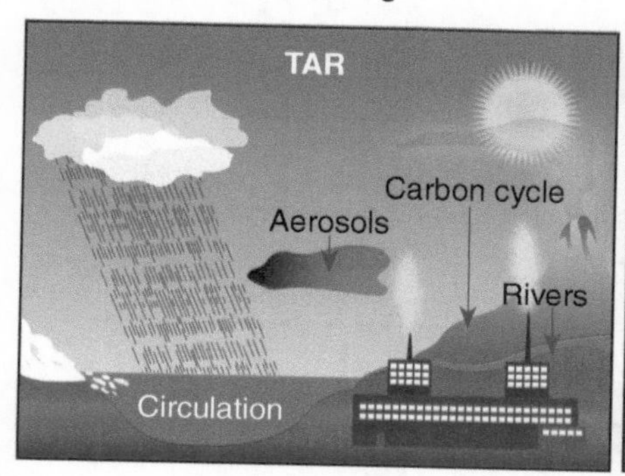

By 2001, the Third Assessment (TAR), was becoming more sophisticated, including adding the effect of atmospheric constituents such as aerosols and the carbon cycle, as well as factoring in the circulation patterns of the oceans.

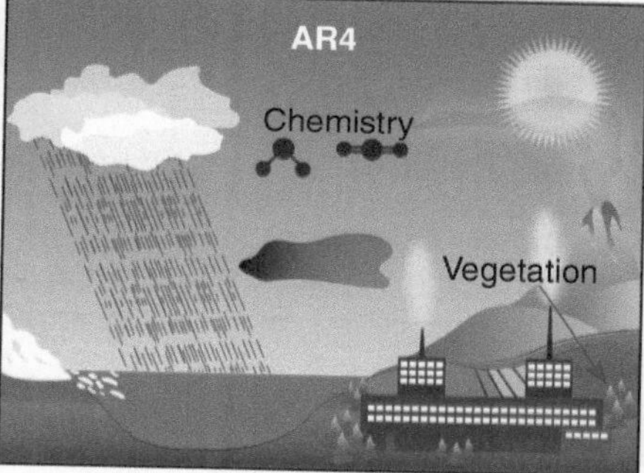

The Fourth Assessment (AR4) benefited from increased knowledge about factors contributing to the climate and also developments in computing and mathematics that allowed accurate prediction of more complicated scenarios.

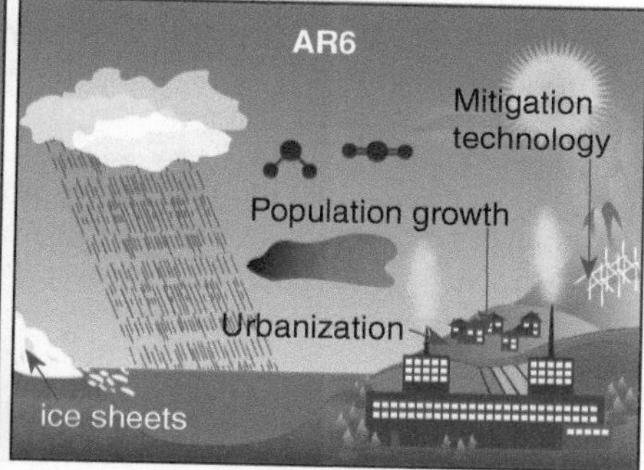

By 2021, the Sixth Assessment Report (AR6) findings from 40 different models were synthesized together, and factored in the "human element", including population growth, urbanization, and technological advancements in mitigation.

1. (a) How has the complexity of climate models changed over time? ______________________

____

____

____

(b) What has been the significance of this? ______________________

____

____

____

____

ISBN: 978-1-98-856693-1

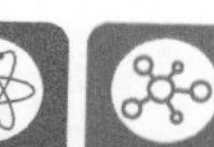

What should a climate model include?

Climate models predict climate change more accurately when the model incorporates all the factors contributing to climate change. Some components influencing climate, e.g. the ocean and **atmosphere,** have their own models to better understand how the individual components can be influenced. Data from these separate models can provide more detailed information about the climate model, as a whole. As we have already seen, climate models have become more complicated over time. Most now incorporate the following components:

- Atmosphere: This includes cloud cover, air pressure, water vapor, and gas concentrations.
- Oceans: Oceans have a key role in climate regulation. They help to buffer (neutralize) the effects of increasing levels of greenhouse gases in the atmosphere by acting as a carbon sink. They also act as a heat store, preventing rapid rises in global atmospheric temperature.
- Ice sheets and sea ice (the **cryosphere**): These factors influence how much of the Sun's heat is reflected or retained. Increased ice levels reflect more heat away from Earth. Less ice allows more heat to be retained.
- Biogeochemical cycles: Levels of some atmospheric compounds can greatly influence climate change. Carbon is the most significant, but others such as nitrogen, phosphorus, and sulfur can also influence climate.
- **Biosphere**: The level of plant cover on Earth has a significant impact on the amount of carbon in the atmosphere. During photosynthesis, plants utilize carbon dioxide from the atmosphere to produce carbohydrates, effectively removing a major greenhouse gas from the atmosphere.
- Human activity: Human activity has increased the rate of **climate change**, especially through the actions of deforestation and carbon emissions into the atmosphere. The addition of **greenhouse gases** into the atmosphere through human activity is driving current climate change.
- External influences: These include energy variations from the Sun, e.g. through sunspot cycles, and levels of carbon dioxide and other aerosols released during volcanic eruptions.

2. Scientists often use models that combine many of the features above, rather than focusing on them individually. How might this contribute to the accuracy of the climate models?

____

____

____

____

3. (a) Working in pairs or small groups, select one component of a climate model and research its significance to climate change. Summarize your findings below and report back to the class.

(b) Once all the presentations have been made, determine if any factor(s) has a larger influence than another. Record your answer on a separate piece of paper.

ISBN: 978-1-98-856693-1

Models of Climate Change

Key Question: How can climate models prepare us for future events?

Hurricane Katrina over the Gulf of Mexico, 2005

NASA: GSFC public domain

Flooding in New Orleans due to Hurricane Katrina

In 2005, Hurricane Katrina caused catastrophic damage, along the Gulf coast from central Florida to Texas. 1464 people died. New Orleans suffered severe flood damage because large volumes of water from Lake Pontchartrain were pushed against the city's levee system and flood walls, causing them to fail in 53 places. Since 2022, numerous other **hurricanes** greater than Category 1 have made landfall on continental United States.

A key factor in the formation of a hurricane is a sea surface temperature of at least 27°C. Environmental Protection Agency (EPA) records show sea surface temperature has increased since the 1900s, especially in the past three decades. This information can be placed into **climate models** to predict the strength and frequency of storm events, where both factors are forecasted to show an increasing trend currently, and in the near future.

1. Predict the effect of increasing surface sea temperature on the frequency and strength of hurricanes:

2. Some climate models forecast an increased frequency of damaging hurricanes. Suggest how this information can help the engineers and officials of New Orleans better protect their city and their people:

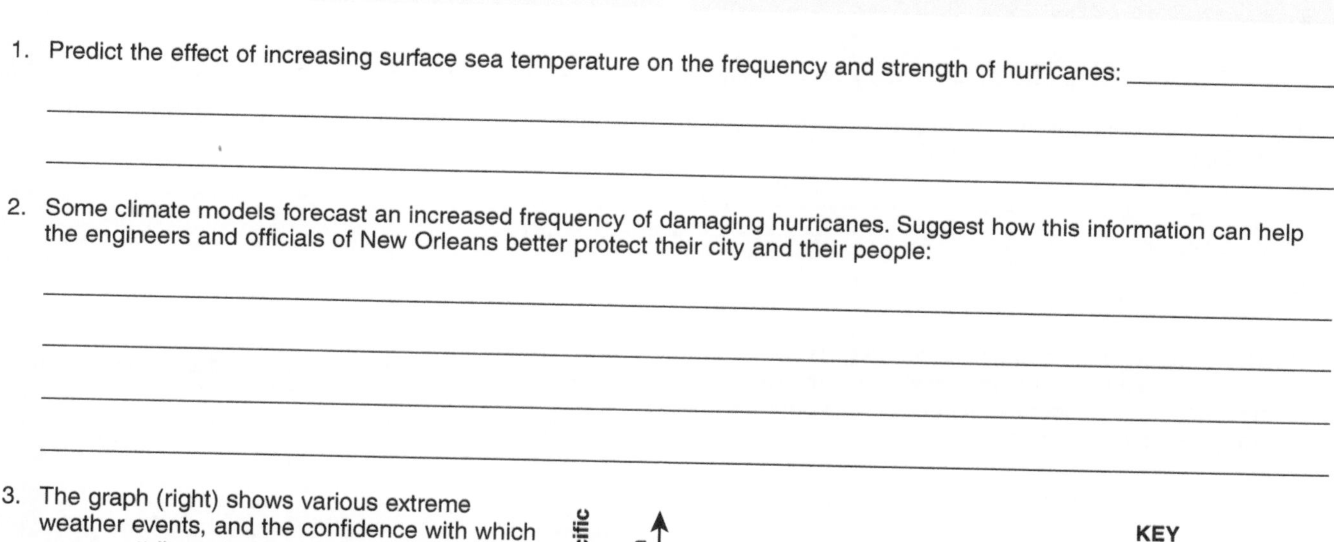

3. The graph (right) shows various extreme weather events, and the confidence with which we can attribute their occurrence to climate change.

   (a) Which types of events can be most confidently assigned to climate change?

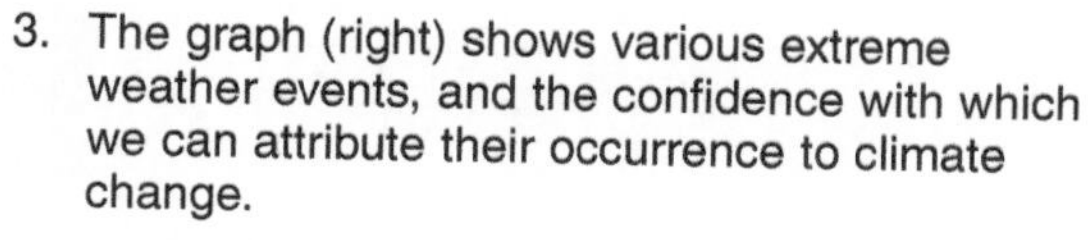

   (b) Suggest why there is such a range in the ability to assign events to climate change:

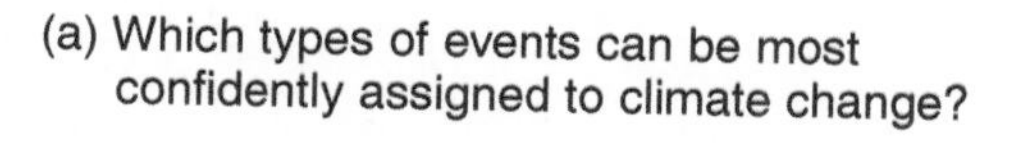

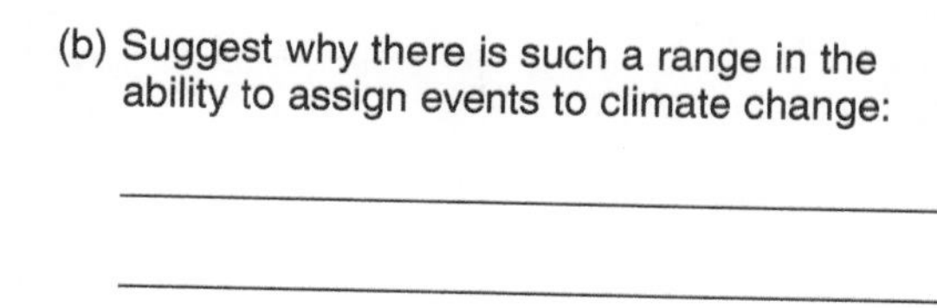

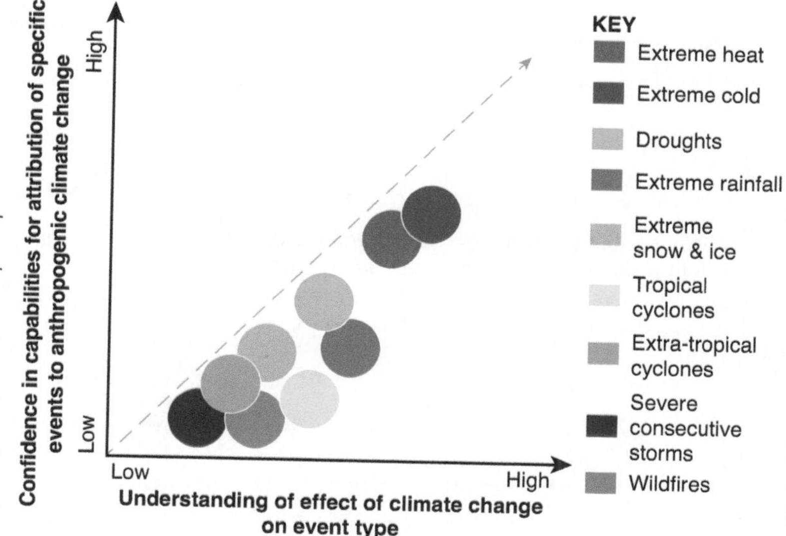

ISBN: 978-1-98-856693-1

SC

SSM

ESS3.D
ESS2.D

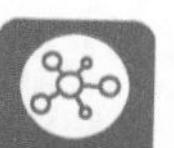

How are climate models tested?

- To see how well **models** work, scientists enter existing data from years gone by and see how accurately their models predict the climate changes that have already occurred. If the models recreate historical trends accurately, we can have confidence that they will also accurately predict future trends in climate change.
- The graph on the right shows an example of how **climate models** are tested. The orange-yellow lines represent data from 14 models and 58 different simulations. The red line represents the average of all 58 simulations. The black line represents the average actual (observed) data for the same period. The gray vertical lines represent large volcanic eruptions during the period.

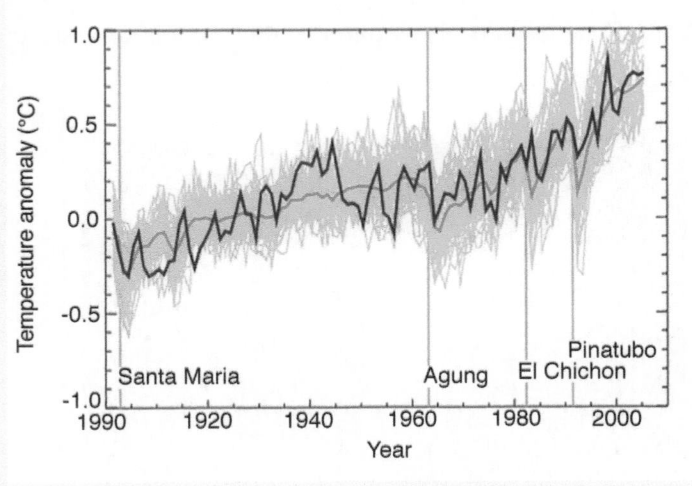

Randall, *et.al*, 2007: Climate Models and Their Evaluation. In: Climate Change 2007: The Physical Science Basis. Contribution of Working Group I to the Fourth Assessment Report of the Intergovernmental Panel on Climate Change

4. (a) How do scientists test the accuracy of their climate models? ______________________

   (b) How do accurate models help manage resources effectively? ______________________

   (c) Study the testing results on the graph above. Do you think the average data from the models accurately reflects the historical data? Why or why not?

5. (a) The graph (right) shows estimated, recorded, and projected model data of sea level rise. Why does the most recent recorded data have the narrowest range of sea level rise?

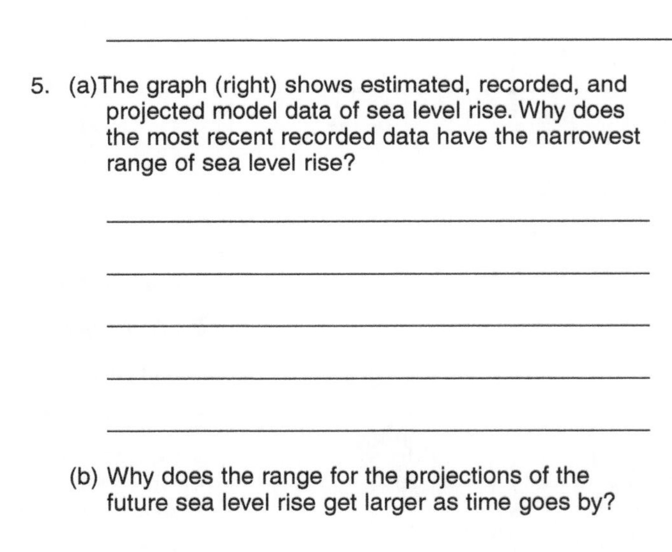

   (b) Why does the range for the projections of the future sea level rise get larger as time goes by?

Estimated, recorded, and predicted sea level change

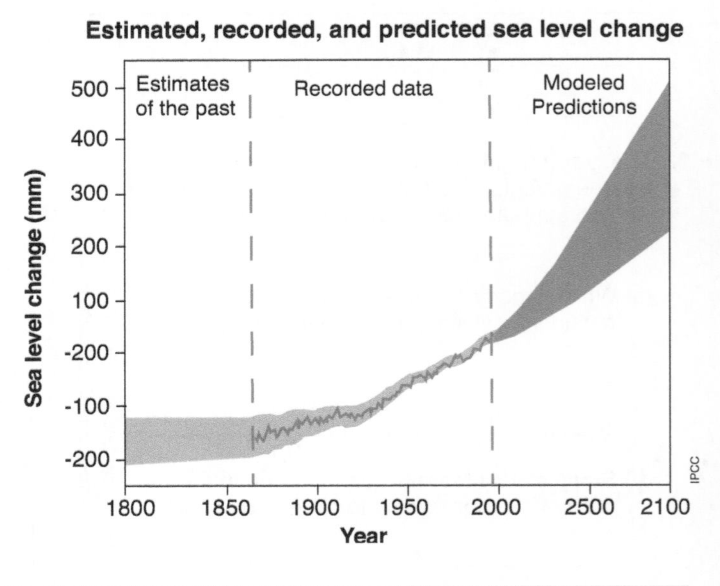

ISBN: 978-1-98-856693-1

What causes sea level rise?

- The increase in global temperature is linked to a rise in global sea level. Sea level rise occurs because of two main factors, thermal expansion and melting ice. When water heats up it expands and takes up more space. Around 24 million km^3 of water is stored in permanent snow, glaciers, and ice caps of the **cryosphere**. When these melt, they add to the volume of water in the oceans. Sea level rise will not only affect people living in coastal communities, but also Earth's systems. Many models have been developed to predict sea level rise under different scenarios in order to determine its effect.

What effect will sea level rise have in the US?

- In 2010, around 39% of the US population (around 123 million people) lived in counties directly on the shoreline. This population has continued to increase to over 40% in 2021. Rising sea levels therefore represent a significant hazard to the US. Large cities such as New York (right) are in danger of becoming inundated (flooded) as sea levels rise. Other large cities, such as San Francisco and Los Angeles, are at sea level, or close to it. In New York, a sea level rise of only a few meters would inundate thousands of hectares of highly developed land. Airports, ports, railroads, housing developments, highways, factories and industry would be damaged.

NASA

6. (a) Describe the causes of sea level rise: ______

   (b) Why is the US so vulnerable to a rise in sea level? ______

7. Some calculations estimate global mean sea level has increased between 10-20 cm over the last 100 years. However, for the last 20 years the rate of sea level rise has been around 3.2 mm per year.

   (a) Calculate the average rate of sea level change per year for the last 100 years: ______

   (b) How does this compare to the mean sea level change over the last 20 years: ______

   (c) What factor could be contributing to the change observed in 7(b)? ______

8. (a) Study the graph on the right. What does it show? ______

   (b) What is the worst case scenario? ______

   (c) What is the best case scenario? ______

Predicted global sea level rise under a number of scenarios

Observed | Scenarios

Global sea level rise (cm above 1992): 200, 160, 120, 80, 40, 0, -40

Year: 1900, 1950, 2000, 2050, 2100

Global Sea Level Rise Scenarios for the United States National Climate Assessment, NOAA (2012)

ISBN: 978-1-98-856693-1

151 Ocean Acidification

Key Question: How does the increasing amount of carbon dioxide in the atmosphere affect the pH of the ocean?

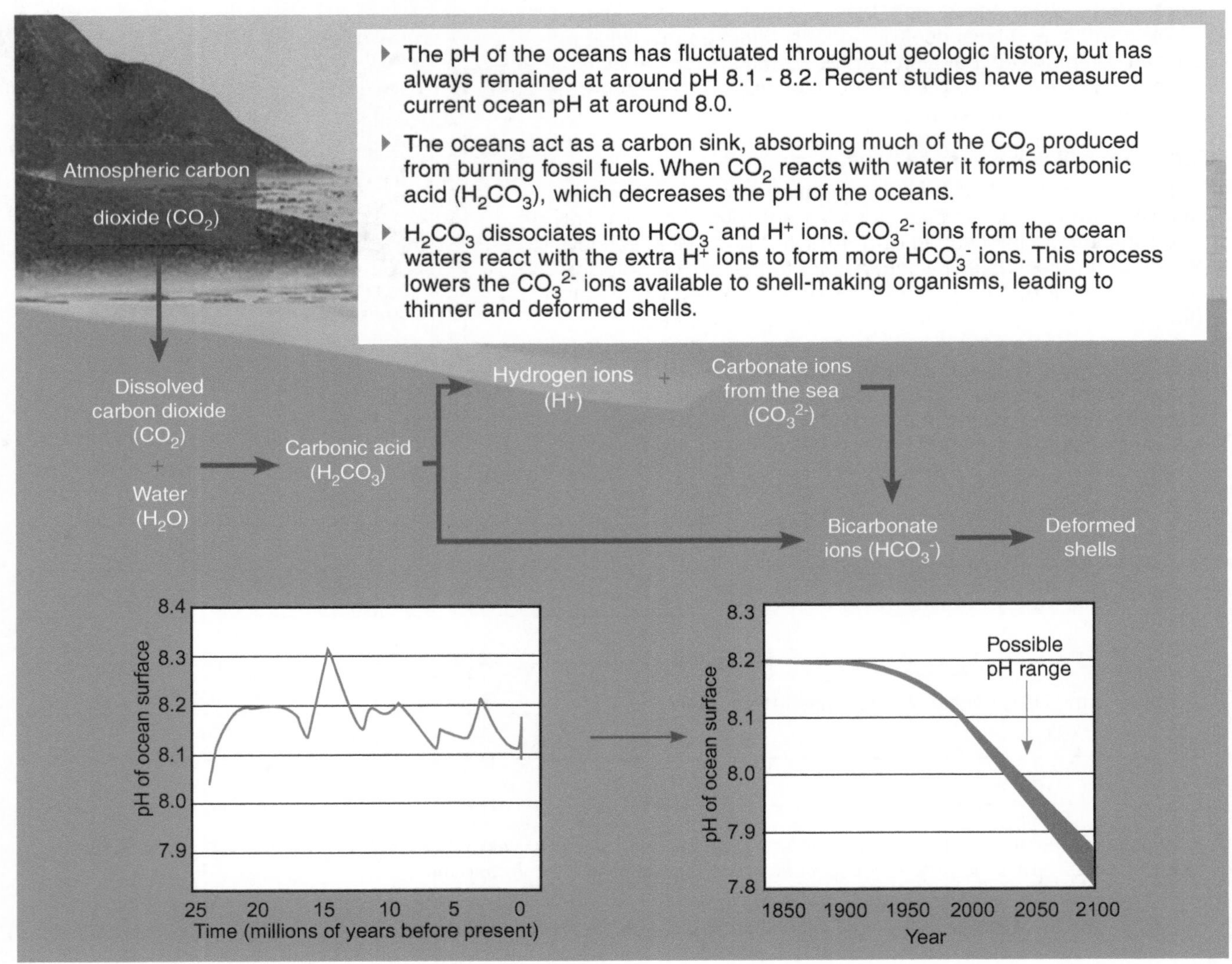

- The pH of the oceans has fluctuated throughout geologic history, but has always remained at around pH 8.1 - 8.2. Recent studies have measured current ocean pH at around 8.0.
- The oceans act as a carbon sink, absorbing much of the CO_2 produced from burning fossil fuels. When CO_2 reacts with water it forms carbonic acid (H_2CO_3), which decreases the pH of the oceans.
- H_2CO_3 dissociates into HCO_3^- and H^+ ions. CO_3^{2-} ions from the ocean waters react with the extra H^+ ions to form more HCO_3^- ions. This process lowers the CO_3^{2-} ions available to shell-making organisms, leading to thinner and deformed shells.

- pH is a logarithmic scale, so even a small change in pH represents a large change in H^+ concentration. Some areas of the ocean, e.g. areas of increased human activity or underwater volcanic eruptions are more affected by pH change than others.

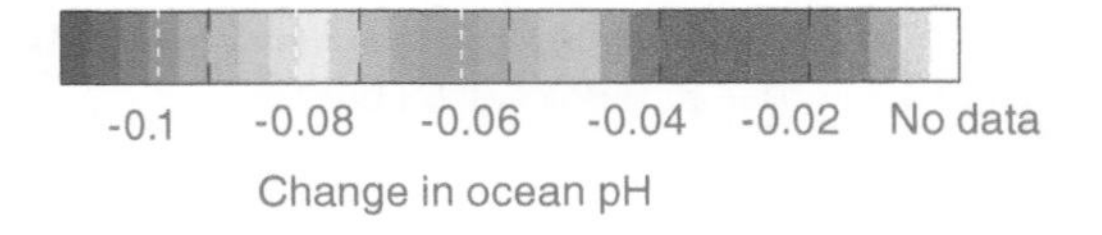

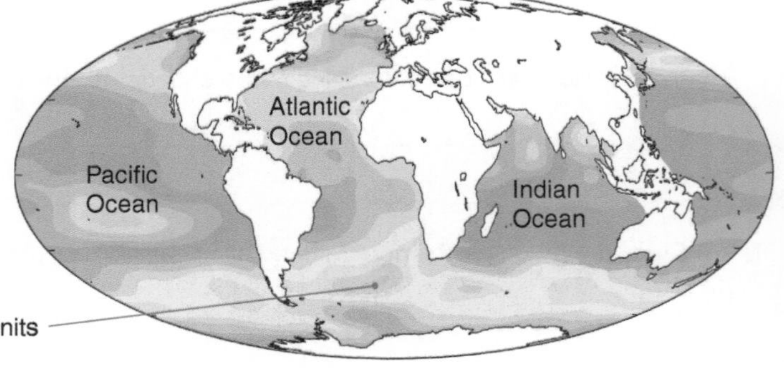

1. (a) What does the term "ocean acidification" mean? ______________________________

____

(b) Describe the trend in ocean pH since the 1850s: ______________________________

____

2. What do you think is causing this? ______________________________

____

ISBN: 978-1-98-856693-1

CO_2 and water

- In this section, you will use dry ice (solid CO_2) to determine the effect of CO_2 on pH. The change in pH will be measured using universal indicator (a solution that changes color as pH changes - see the color guide below).

< 3 Strong acid	3-6 Weak acid	7 Neutral	8-11 Weak base	> 11 Strong base

Investigation 12.1 Investigating how dry ice affects pH

See appendix for equipment list.

Wear protective eyewear and insulated gloves when handling dry ice.

Work in pairs or small groups for this investigation.

1. Pour 100 mL of tap water into two conical flasks. Label one as control and one as test.
2. Add a few drops of universal indicator into both flasks. Swirl to mix.
3. If the solution turns orange, add a few drops of 1 mol/L NaOH solution to both flasks to neutralize. Swirl to mix. Your solution should be green.
4. Use tongs to add a small lump of dry ice into the test beaker only.
5. Observe what occurs in each flask. Record your observations below (paste photos if you want):

3. (a) What happened to the pH of the solution in the test flask?

(b) What was responsible for this change? Provide evidence:

(c) Suggest why this happens?

4. Explain the likely effect of the decreasing pH of the seas on animals with shells based on calcium carbonate:

ISBN: 978-1-98-856693-1

Carbon dioxide and pH

- Recall that in the **carbon cycle** the oceans were a large reservoir of carbon because carbon dioxide from the atmosphere dissolves into them. This is evident in the plot, right, which shows how the ocean constantly exchanges CO_2 with the atmosphere.
- The effect of carbon dioxide on water can be seen by bubbling it through water containing a pH indicator. Bromothymol blue is an indicator that is blue in basic (alkaline) solutions, blue/green in neutral water and yellow/green in acidic solutions. Adding carbon dioxide to water containing bromothymol blue causes the solution to turn yellow/green as the carbon dioxide dissolves into the water.

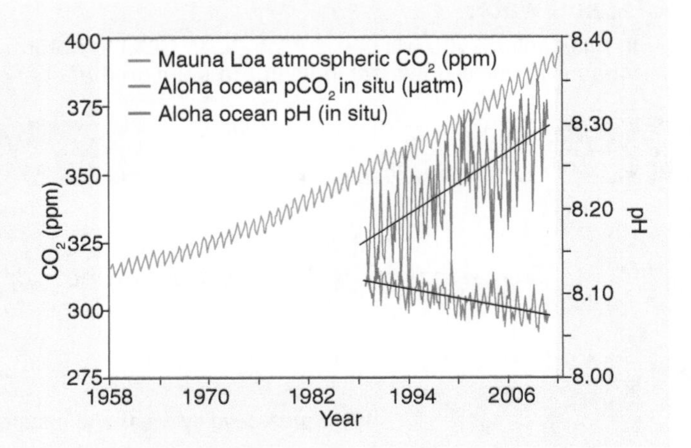

5. (a) What do you notice about the peak and dips in ocean and atmospheric CO_2 in the graph above? ______________

   (b) What does this pattern indicate? ______________

   (c) What is the trend over time in the CO_2 concentration in both reservoirs? ______________

- The graphs below show the effect of carbon dioxide on ocean water. The top row shows dissolved CO_2 at three locations and the bottom row shows ocean pH at the same locations. Vertical scales are the same in each case:

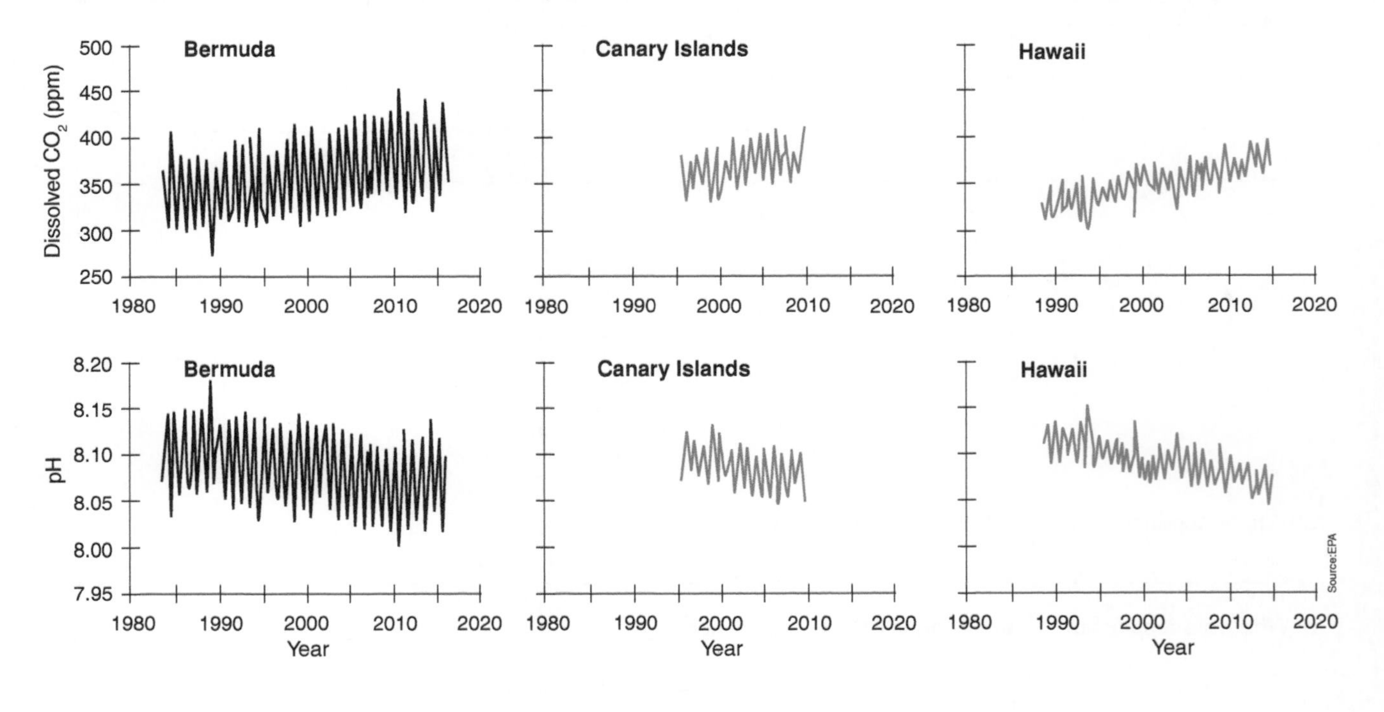

6. (a) Are the oceans acidic or basic? ______________

   (b) What is the pattern in the data at each location? ______________

   (c) What does this suggest about the effect of increasing dissolved CO_2 on the pH of the oceans? ______________

ISBN: 978-1-98-856693-1

152 Biodiversity and Climate Change

Key Question: How is climate change contributing to shifts in the distribution, behavior, and viability of plant and animal species?

- **Climate change** is changing the habitats of organisms. This may have profound effects on the biodiversity of specific regions, as well as on the planet overall. As temperatures rise, organisms may be forced to move to areas better suited to their temperature tolerances. Those that cannot move or tolerate the temperature change may face extinction (loss of all individuals).
- Changes in precipitation as a result of climate change will also affect where organisms can live. Long term changes in **climate** will ultimately result in a shift in vegetation zones as some habitats contract and others expand.

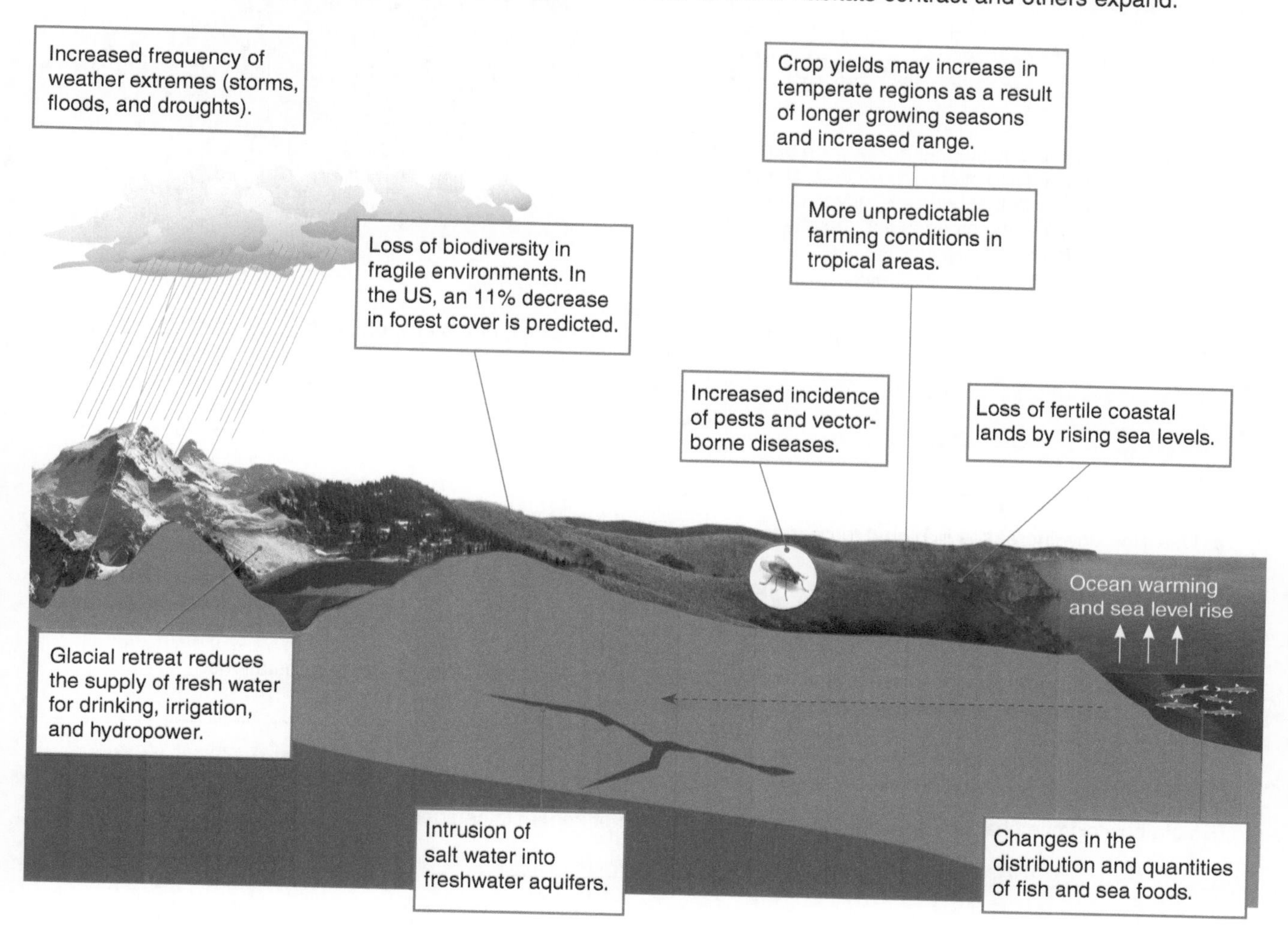

Studies of the distributions of butterfly species in many countries show their populations are shifting. Surveys of Edith's checkerspot butterfly (*Euphydryas editha*) in western North America have shown it to be moving north and to higher altitudes.

Sex ratios of reptiles are affected by the temperature. In turtles, males are produced at low incubation temperatures and females are produced at higher temperatures. Any rises in global temperatures could significantly affect populations.

An Australian study in 2004 found the center of distribution for the AdhS gene in *Drosophila*, which helps survival in hot and dry conditions, had shifted 400 kilometers south in the last twenty years.

ISBN: 978-1-98-856693-1

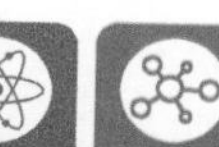

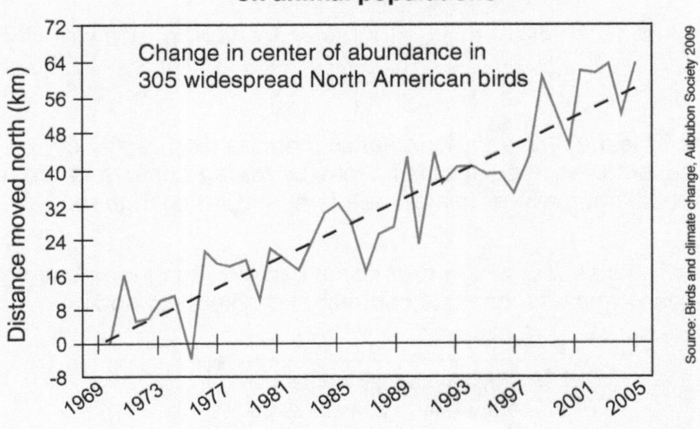

A number of studies indicate that animals are beginning to be affected by increases in global temperatures. Data sets from around the world show that birds are migrating up to two weeks earlier to summer feeding grounds and are often not migrating as far south in winter.

Animals living at altitude are also affected by warming climates and are being forced to shift their normal range. As temperatures increase, the snow line increases in altitude, pushing alpine animals to higher altitudes. In some areas of North America, this has resulted in the local extinction of the North American pika (*Ochotona princeps*).

1. Describe some of the likely effects of climate change on physical aspects of the environment: ______________________

2. (a) Describe how increases in global temperatures have affected some migratory birds: ______________________

   (b) Explain how these changes in migratory patterns might affect food availability for these populations: ______________________

3. Explain how climate change could lead to the local extinction of some alpine species: ______________________

4. Describe the effects of climate change on three named animal examples:

   (a) ______________________

   (b) ______________________

   (c) ______________________

ISBN: 978-1-98-856693-1

153 Climate Change and Agriculture

Key Question: How will climate change influence where crops can be grown, as well as the impact of pests and diseases on them?

- The impacts of **climate change** on agriculture and horticulture will vary around the globe because of local **climate** and geography. In some regions, temperature changes will increase the growing season for existing crops or enable a wider variety of crops to be grown.
- Changes in temperature or precipitation patterns may benefit some crops, but have negative effects on others. Increasing atmospheric CO_2 levels will enhance the growth of some crops, but rising nighttime temperatures may affect seed set and fruit production.

Effects of increases in temperature on crop yields

Studies on the grain production show that maximum daytime temperatures have little effect on crop yield. However, minimum night time temperatures lower crop (rice) yield by as much as 5% for every 0.5°C increase in temperature.

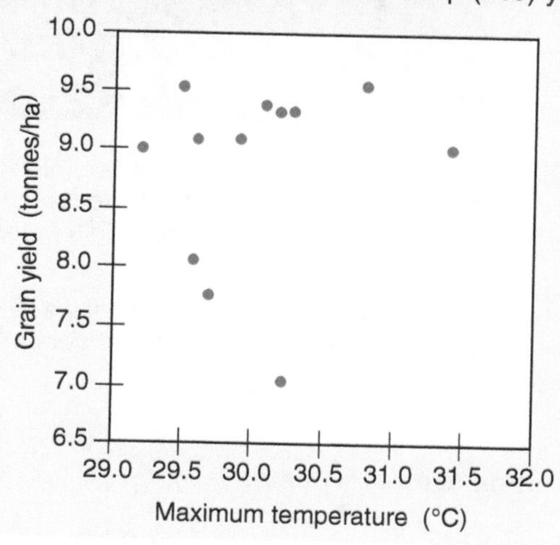

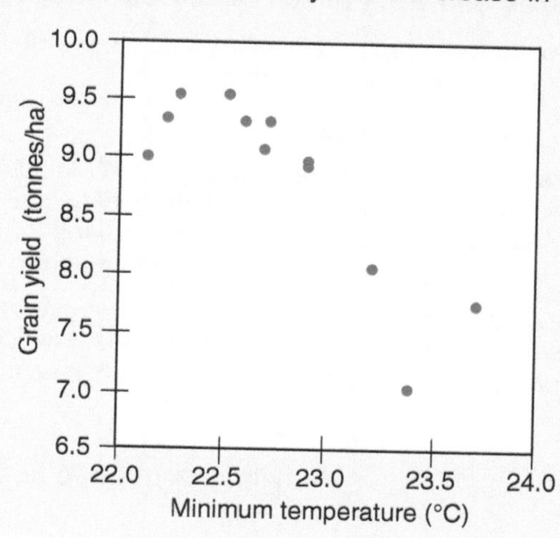

Source: Peng S. *et al.* PNAS 2004

Possible effects of increases in temperature on crop damage

The fossil record shows that global temperatures rose sharply around 56 million years ago (the Paleocene-Eocene Thermal Maximum (PETM)). Studies of fossil leaves with insect browse damage indicate that leaf damage peaked at the same time. This gives some historical evidence that, as temperatures rise, plant damage caused by insects also rises. This could have implications for agricultural crops.

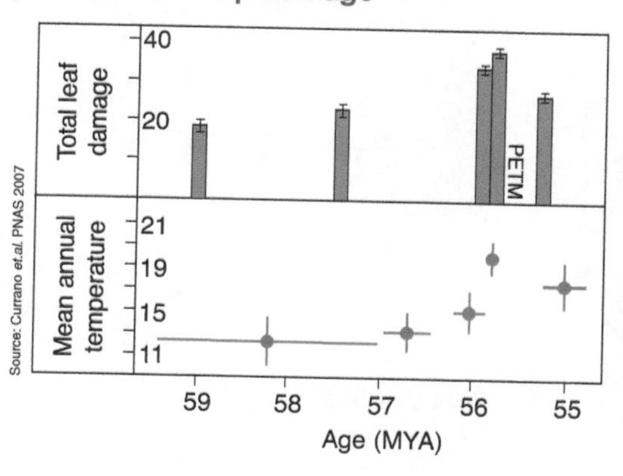

Source: Currano *et.al.* PNAS 2007

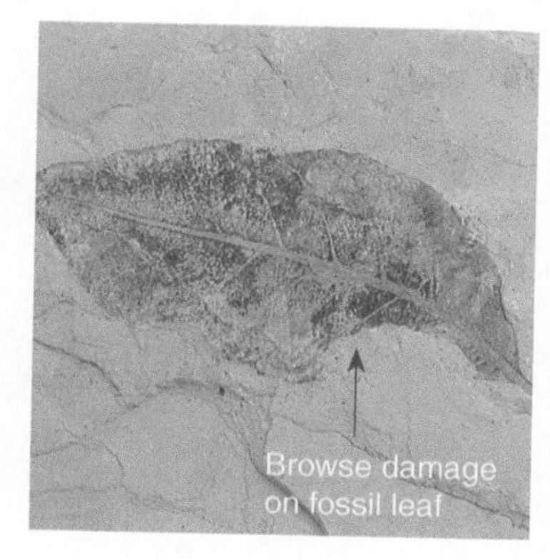

1. What minimum temperature produces the best grain yield in rice? ______________________

2. Suggest why climate change might benefit some agricultural crops, while disadvantaging others: ______________________

____

____

____

____

3. What evidence is there that climate change might influence the distribution or number of crop pests and so affect agriculture?

____

____

____

ISBN: 978-1-98-856693-1

154 Technological Solutions to Climate Change

Key Question: How can technology and innovation help slow climate change?

How can new technologies be used to slow climate change?

- If **greenhouse gas** production was to completely stop today, the Earth's temperature would still continue to rise slightly. To prevent continued **climate change**, climate scientists agree that we need to reduce our level of greenhouse gas emissions to slow the most damaging effects.
- There are many possible ways to achieve this. They include improving energy efficiency, increasing the use of renewable energy sources, and using carbon capture technologies.
- We can also capture carbon naturally by planting more trees and reducing the rate of deforestation.

Tree plantation, USA

USDA Natural Resources Conservation Service cc2.0

Large-scale carbon producers

- Burning fossil fuels in power stations to generate electricity accounts for about 40% of global carbon dioxide emissions. Even power stations using high quality coal and oil release huge volumes of CO_2. Systems that capture the CO_2 produced, so that it can be stored or used for other purposes, are beginning to address this problem. Some CO_2 capture systems are shown in the diagram below.
- Other large contributors are the transport industry (30%) and the manufacture of cement and concrete (5-10%). Concrete is the final set product of cement mixed with water and gravel. New types of cement and cement manufacturing techniques aim to reduce the emissions produced during manufacturing.

Schematics of three possible carbon capture systems

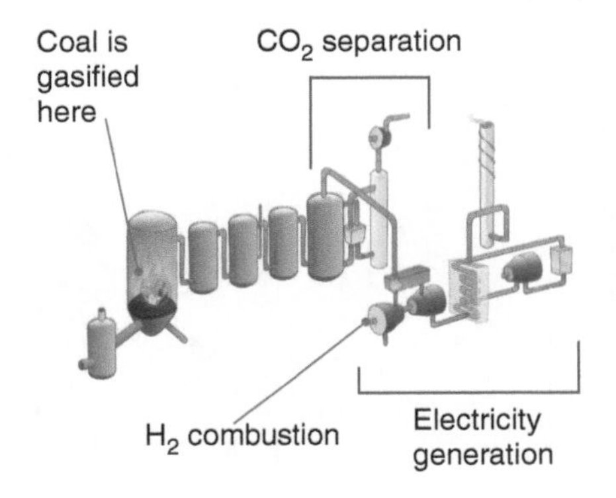

Pre-combustion capture:
The coal is converted to CO_2 and H_2 using a gasification process. The CO_2 is recovered while the H_2 gas is combusted.

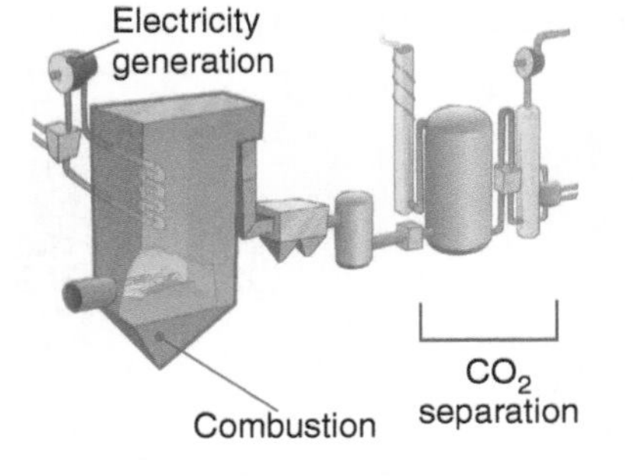

Post combustion capture:
CO_2 is washed from the flue gas after combustion. It is then passed to a desorber to re-gasify the CO_2, where it is then compressed for storage.

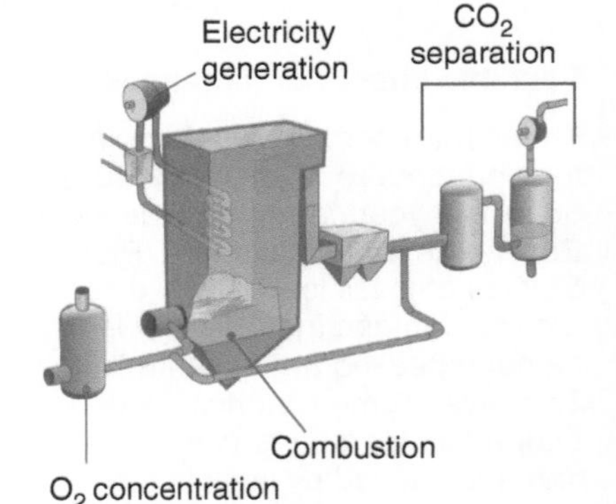

Oxyfuel combustion:
Concentrated O_2 is used in the furnace, producing only CO_2 gas in the flue gas. This is then compressed for storage. Compressed CO_2 is useful as a inexpensive, nonflammable pressurized gas, e.g. for inflation and for carbonated water.

1. Describe the differences and similarities of the three types of carbon dioxide capture systems described above:

ISBN: 978-1-98-856693-1

Storing captured CO_2

- Captured CO_2 can be injected into porous rock layers between non-porous rock layers. Power stations near to injection sites can pipe the recovered CO_2 to the injected well. Other stations will need to transport the CO_2 to the site. The transportation of the CO_2 will produce less CO_2 than is captured by the power station, making the option viable.

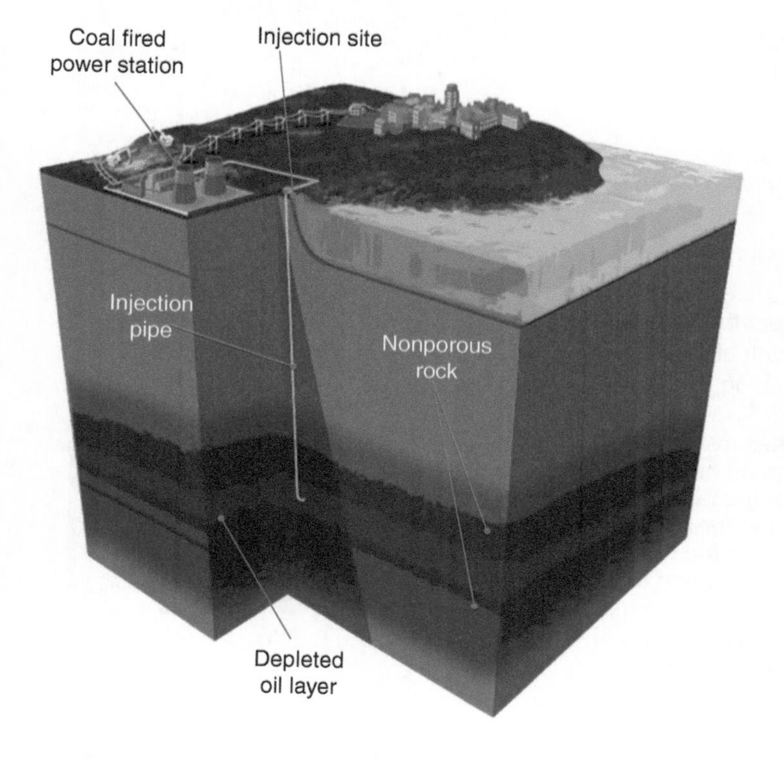

CO_2 can be stored by injecting it into empty oil wells or other deep geological formations. CO_2 can also be released into deep ocean waters (above), or it can be reacted with minerals to form solid carbonates. CO_2 can also be used in synthetic fuels production.

Deep ocean storage of CO_2 risks lowering ocean pH. Storing CO_2 in geological formations risks the sudden release of large quantities of CO_2 if the rock is unstable, which could kill animal life.

2. Describe how captured carbon dioxide might be used or stored: ______________________

3. Discuss some of the potential problems with capturing and storing carbon dioxide: ______________________

4. (a) Some technologies are being developed that are drawing carbon dioxide gas directly from the air (shown below), separating and storing the carbon dioxide, and then releasing the "CO_2 free" air. Explain what natural process this is attempting to replicate?

   (b) What might be some advantages and disadvantages of this technology?

Fans draw in the air
Released CO_2-free air
Filtering
Filtering is heated to release the captured CO_2
Released CO_2-free air
Stored CO_2

ISBN: 978-1-98-856693-1

Case study: Lowering emissions in the cement industry

- Cement and concrete are essential to the building industry and the global economy. 4.1 billion tonnes of cement were produced in 2015. This is expected to increase to 4.8 billion tonnes by 2030. This is important to the global climate because producing one tonne of cement also produces about one tonne of CO_2 (and uses the equivalent of 200 kg of coal).
- The most common cement used is called Portland cement, which is very strong when set. It requires a lot of energy to make it. 40% of the CO_2 emissions come from burning fossil fuels to heat limestone ($CaCO_3$) and other minerals to 1400 °C. At this temperature, the limestone breaks down and releases CO_2. This step produces about 50% of the CO_2 emissions. Portland cement reabsorbs about half of this CO_2 as it hardens over the lifetime of the cement.
- Reducing the CO_2 emissions for cement manufacture can be done at three steps in the process:

• Reducing the amount of fossil fuels needed to heat the raw materials.
• Reducing the amount of CO_2 released by the raw materials.
• Increasing the amount of CO_2 absorbed when setting.

- New types of cement that use magnesium silicates instead of limestone are being trialed. These do not need to be heated to such high temperatures and do not release CO_2 when heated. Total CO_2 emissions are up to 0.5 tonnes per tonne of cement produced (half that of Portland cement). During setting, CO_2 is absorbed at a greater rate than in traditional cement (about 1.1 tonnes per tonne of cement produced). This type of cement is called carbon negative cement because it absorbs more CO_2 than is produced making it (about 0.6 tonnes of CO_2 absorbed for every tonne of cement produced).

Cement factory

5. (a) Approximately how many tonnes of CO_2 were produced by the cement industry in 2015? ____________

(b) Where is this CO_2 produced in the manufacture of cement? ____________

(c) Explain why carbon negative cement is carbon negative: ____________

(d) Based on the 2015 figures, how much carbon would carbon negative cement absorb? ____________

6. The Centre for Climate Repair, based at the University of Cambridge, UK, has proposed an idea to mitigate (prevent or reverse) climate change. Technology would be used to fertilize the oceans to encourage more algae growth, which could then absorb more CO_2. What could be some potential issues with"greening' the ocean, as a mitigation technology?

ISBN: 978-1-98-856693-1

155 Review Your Understanding

Key Question: Why are seashells getting thinner and more fragile?

- At the beginning of this chapter, you were shown some evidence that seashells contained calcium carbonate. You were also shown data that showed the shells of certain shell-making marine organisms were becoming thinner over time.
- During this chapter, you will have become familiar with the concept of pH and acidification.
- You should now be able to explain exactly why the shells of some marine organisms are becoming thinner and where this phenomenon is likely to have the greatest impact.

1. Explain to your class why the shells of calcium carbonate shell-building marine organisms are likely to become thinner in coming decades. Discuss the chemistry around this phenomenon, and what conditions seem to affect it. Discuss how this shell thinning phenomenon might affect the survival of shell-building creatures. If you prefer, you can present your discussion as a slide presentation or poster.

2. Ocean acidification may not affect only shell-building activity. What other impacts might ocean acidification have on the marine community? Use the resources on the **BIOZONE Resource Hub** to develop a more detailed discussion.

ISBN: 978-1-98-856693-1

156 Summing Up

1. The graphs below show data for past and current CO_2 concentrations and temperature, and models for CO_2 and temperature for the future.

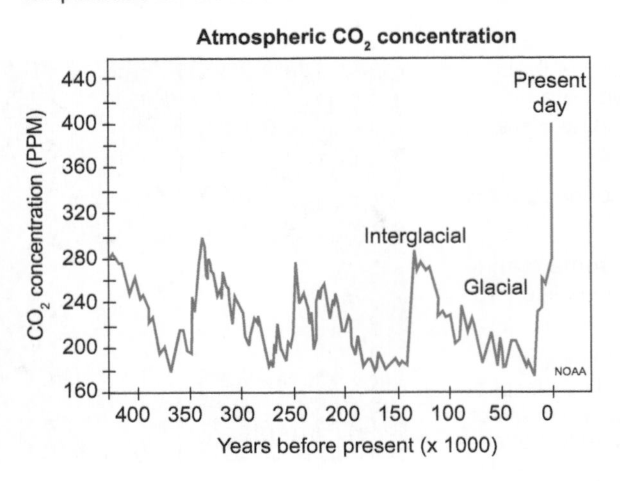

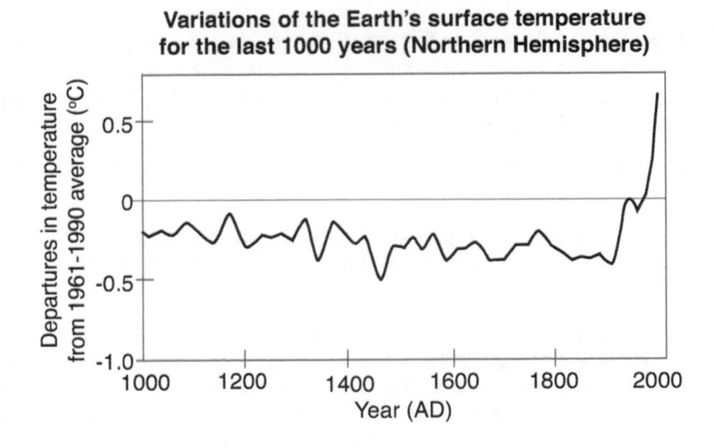

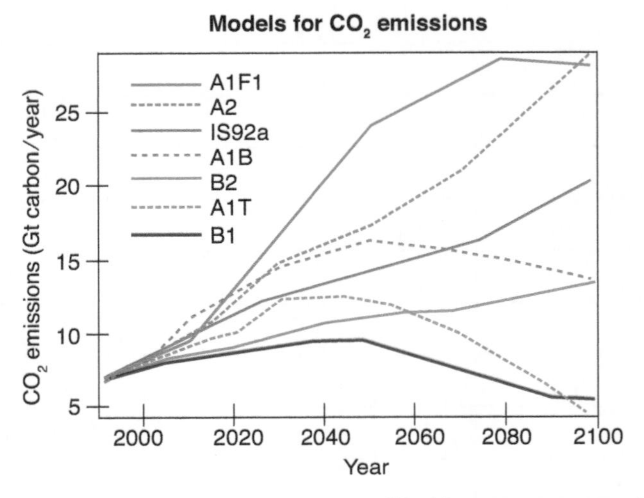

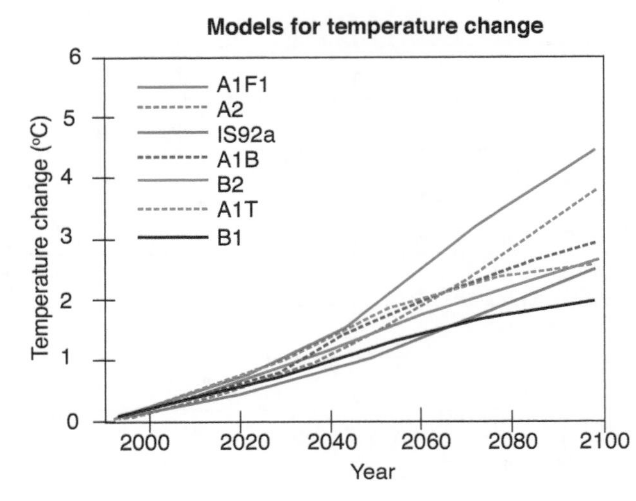

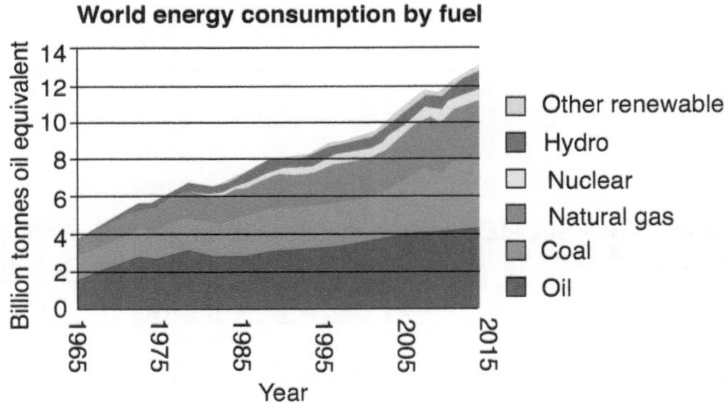

Use the graphs above to make an evidence-based forecast of the future rate of climate change, including your analysis of whether or not the rate will increase or decrease. You may use extra sources of information to further research your analysis. You may also use extra paper to write your analysis. Attach it to this page:

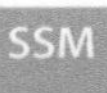

ISBN: 978-1-98-856693-1

2. The data below shows the expected temperature, precipitation changes, and grain yield for wheat grown in the Eastern Washington area over the next 65 years. The data was produced using the CCSM3 global climate model (which predicts more warming and less precipitation globally, although not necessarily locally).

	Baseline	2020	2040	2080
Precipitation (mm)	535.8	549.9	543.9	588.3
Mean temperature °C	8.5	10.2	11.2	12.0
Yield (kg) No CO_2 effect	5713	6022	5116	5209
Yield (kg) CO_2 effect	5713	6546	6034	7033

Cladio O. Stockle et al

The data below shows the percentage crop yield response of wheat and other crop plants to changes in the environment including temperature and CO_2 changes.

Crop	Temperature (+1.2°C)	CO_2 increase (380 to 440 ppm)	Temperature, and CO_2 and irrigation
Wheat	-6.7	+6.8	+0.1
Corn (midwest)	-4.0	+1.0	-3.0
Soybean	-3.5	+7.4	+3.9
Cotton	-5.7	+9.2	+3.5

(a) Describe the change in rainfall expected in the Eastern Washington area over the next 65 years:

(b) Describe the change in temperature expected in the Eastern Washington area over the next 65 years:

(c) Describe the effect on grain yield the change in climate will have, including effects of increased CO_2:

(d) Plants carry out photosynthesis, producing organic molecules. The chemical equation for photosynthesis is:

$$6CO_2 + 6H_2O \rightarrow C_6H_{12}O_6 + 6O_2$$

Why does the grain yield increase with more atmospheric CO_2?

(e) How will a change in temperature affect other crops grown in the USA?

(f) How will a change in CO_2 affect other crops grown in the USA?

(g) What overall effect might there be on crop yield due to climate change. How might this affect farmers and consumers?

ISBN: 978-1-98-856693-1

Appendix 1: English/Spanish Glossary

Each glossary term is first provided in English (black text) with the Spanish translation directly beneath (blue text).

absorption spectrum: The fraction of the spectrum absorbed by a gaseous material as electromagnetic radiation passes through it.

espectro de absorción: La fracción del espectro absorbida por un material gaseoso a medida que la radiación electromagnética pasa a través de él.

accuracy: The correctness of a measurement; how close a measured value is to the true value.

exactitud:La exactitud de una medición; qué tan cerca está un valor medido del valor verdadero.

adhesion: The tendency of certain dissimilar molecules to cling to one another at the surface.

adhesión: La tendencia de ciertas moléculas disímilares a aferrarse unas a otras en la superficie.

albedo: A measure of how much light hits a surface and is reflected without being absorbed.

albedo: Una medida de cuánta luz golpea una superficie y se refleja sin ser absorbida.

apparent retrograde motion: An illusion whereby planets appear to move across the night sky in one direction and then in reverse, before returning to move in the original direction again.

movimiento retrógrado aparente: Es una ilusión por la cual los planetas parecen moverse a través del cielo nocturno en una dirección y luego en reversa, antes de volver a moverse en la dirección original nuevamente.

assumption: A statement that is assumed to be true but is not (or cannot be) tested.

presunción: Una afirmación que se supone que es verdadera pero que no se prueba (o no se puede).

asthenosphere: The upper layer of the Earth's mantle, which lies below the lithosphere.

astenosfera: La capa superior del manto de la Tierra, que se encuentra debajo de la litosfera.

atmosphere: The envelope of gases surrounding Earth.

atmósfera: La envoltura de gases que rodea la Tierra.

atomic nuclei: The central part of an atomic consisting of the protons and neutrons.

núcleos atómicos: La parte central de un atómo que consiste en los protones y neutrones.

Big Bang theory: The prevailing theory of how the observable universe formed, from its first moments to the current era.

Teoría del Big Bang: La teoría predominante de cómo se formó el universo observable, desde sus primeros momentos hasta la era actual.

biodiversity: The amount of biological variation present in a region; includes genetic, species, and habitat diversity.

biodiversidad: La cantidad de variación biológica presente en una región; incluyiendo diversidad genética, de especies y de hábitat.

biome: Major regional ecological community of plants and animals.

bioma: Importante comunidad ecológica regional de plantas y animales.

biosphere: A combination of all parts of the Earth that support life, from the depth of the ocean to a few km into the atmosphere. Also called the ecosphere.

bíosfera: Una combinación de todas las partes de la Tierra que sustentan la vida, desde la profundidad del océano hasta unos pocos kilómetros en la atmósfera. También llamada ecosfera.

carbon cycle: The process by which carbon is exchanged between living organisms, the Earth and its atmosphere.

ciclo del carbono: El proceso por el cual el carbono se intercambia entre los organismos vivos, la tierra y su atmósfera.

climate: Long term trends or patterns in the weather of a given area.

clima: Tendencias a lo largo o modelos en el clima de una área determindada.

climate change: A change in patterns of climate, such as temperature and rainfall, that is attributed to human activity, including the use of fossil fuels.

cambio climático: Un cambio en los patrones de clima, como la temperatura y las precipitaciones, que se atribuye a la actividad humana, incluido el uso de combustibles fósiles.

climate model: Mathematical or computation model that predicts future changes to the climate.

modelo climático: Modelo matemático o computacional que predecen cambios futuros en el clima.

coal: A brown/black sedimentary rock formed by compression of plant material over a long period. Rich in carbon and can be burned as a fuel source.

carbón: Una roca sedimentaria marrón / negra formada por la compresión de material vegetal durante un largo período. Rico en carbono y se puede quemar como fuente de combustible.

coevolution: Evolution that occurs among interdependent species as a result of specific interactions.

coevolución: Evolución que ocurre entre especies interdependientes como resultado de interacciones específicas.

cohesion: The tendency of certain like-molecules to cling together due to attractive forces.

cohesión: La tendencia de ciertas moléculas similares a aferrarse entre ellos debido a las fuerzas de atracción.

constructive mechanisms: Factors that build features on earth's surface, including deposition of sediments, tectonic uplift, and volcanic eruptions.

mecanismos constructivos: Factores que construyen características en la superficie de la tierra, incluida la deposición de sedimentos, la elevación tectónica y las erupciones volcánicas.

continental crust: The part of the Earth's crust that "floats" on the mantle and forms the continents.

corteza continental: La parte de la corteza terrestre que "flota" en el manto y forma los continentes.

continental drift: The movement of the continents, relative to each other.

deriva continental: El movimiento de los continentes, relativos entre ellos mismo.

control: A component of an experiment that is isolated from the effects of the independent variable. It demonstrates that any change to the dependent variable must come from the independent variable.

control: Componente de un experimento aislado de los efectos de la variable independiente. Demuestra que cualquier cambio en la variable dependiente debe provenir de la variable independiente.

controlled variable: Another word for independent variable. The variable being controlled or changed by the experimenter.

variable controlada: Otra palabra para variable independiente. La variable que está siendo controlada o cambiada por el experimentador

convection: Process of heat transfer through the earth's mantle caused by hotter, less dense material rising from the central core outwards, while cooler, denser material sinks back towards the core

convección: Proceso de transferencia de calor a través del manto de la tierra causado por material más caliente y menos denso que se eleva desde el núcleo central de la tierra hacia afuera, mientras que el material más frío y denso se hunde hacia el núcleo de la tierra.

convergent boundary: A tectonic boundary where two plates are moving toward each other and colliding.

borde convergente: Un borde tectónico donde dos placas se mueven una hacia la otra y chocan.

coral reef: underwater ecosystem composed of millions of tiny animals called polyps that have a skeleton composed of calcium carbonate.

arrecife de coral: ecosistema submarino compuesto por millones de pequeños animales llamados pólipos que tienen un esqueleto compuesto de carbonato de calcio.

cosmic microwave background: Electromagnetic radiation left over from the early stages of the Big Bang that has had its wavelength stretched into the microwave region

fondo cósmico de microondas: Radiación electromagnética sobrante de las primeras etapas del Big Bang que ha tenido su longitud de onda estirada en la región de microondas

crust: The outermost layer of the Earth, composed of a great variety of igneous, metamorphic, and sedimentary rocks.

corteza: La capa más externa de la Tierra, compuesta por una gran variedad de rocas ígneas, metamórficas y sedimentarias.

cryosphere: The frozen part of the world's water, e.g. sea ice and glaciers.

Criosfera: La parte congelada del agua del mundo, por ejemplo, el hielo marino y los glaciares.

data: A set of values of qualitative or quantitative variables, collected through observation.

datos: Conjunto de valores de variables cualitativas o cuantitativas, recogidos a través de la observación.

deforestation: The removal of forests by cutting, burning or other large scale activity by humans, usually to make way for crops or monoculture plantations.

deforestación: La eliminación de bosques por cortar los árboles, quemar o otros actividades a gran escala por parte de los seres humanos, generalmente para dar paso a cultivos o plantaciones de monocultivos.

dependent variable: The variable being tested and measured in an experiment, whose value depends on that of the independent variable.

variable dependiente: La variable que se está probando y midiendo en un experimento, de que su valor depende del de la variable independiente.

deposition: Geological process that adds sediments and soil to the land by wind, or water and ice flow.

deposición: Proceso geológico que agrega sedimentos y suelo a la tierra por el viento, o el flujo de agua y hielo.

descriptive statistics: Also called summary statistics, these are brief descriptors that help summarize features of data.

estadística descriptiva: También llamadas estadísticas resumidas, estas son descriptores breves que ayudan a resumir las características de los datos.

destructive forces: Forces that remove features on the Earth's surface, including weathering, erosion or sudden landslides.

fuerzas destructivas: Fuerzas que eliminan las características en la superficie de la Tierra, incluida la intemperie, la erosión o los deslizamientos repentinos de tierra.

dipole: A molecule that has both negative and positive charges.

dipolo: Una molécula que tiene cargas negativas y positivas.

displacement: An immediate response to devastation caused by a natural disaster that forces large numbers of people to migrate from one area to another.

desplazamiento: Una respuesta inmediata a la devastación causada por un desastre natural que obliga a un gran número de personas a migrar de un área a otra.

divergent boundary: A tectonic boundary where two plates are moving away from each other and new crust is forming from magma rising the surface, between the two plates.

borde divergente: Un borde tectónico donde dos placas se alejan una de la otra y se forma una nueva corteza a partir del magma que sube la superficie, entre las dos placas.

Doppler effect: The change in frequency of sound or light of an object due to its movement, relative to the observer.

Efecto Doppler: El cambio en la frecuencia del sonido o la luz de un objeto debido a su movimiento, en relación con el observador.

drought: Prolonged period of time without rainfall.

sequía: Período prolongado de tiempo sin lluvias.

English/Spanish Glossary

earthquake: The sudden movement of the ground along fault lines.

terremoto: El movimiento repentino del suelo a lo largo de las líneas de falla.

eccentricity: A measure of how circular a planet's orbit is.

excentricidad: Una medida de cuán circular es la órbita de un planeta.

ecosystem services: Services provided by earth that humans use, including food and water, but also habitats and areas for humans to enjoy nature.

servicios ecosistémicos: Servicios proporcionados por la tierra que los humanos utilizan, incluidos los alimentos y el agua, pero también hábitats y áreas para que los humanos disfruten de la naturaleza.

El Niño: A recurring climate pattern involving changes in the temperature of waters in the central and eastern tropical Pacific Ocean.

El Niño: Un patrón climático recurrente que implica cambios en la temperatura de las aguas en el Océano Pacífico tropical central y oriental.

electrical energy: Energy that arises from the movement of electrically charged particles.

energía eléctrica: Energía que surge del movimiento de partículas cargadas eléctricamente.

electromagnetic radiation: Waves formed by oscillating electric and magnetic fields at right angle to each other, moving through space. Consist of short wavelength gamma rays, to long wavelength radio waves.

radiación electromagnética: Ondas formadas por campos eléctricos y magnéticos oscilantes en ángulo recto entre sí, moviéndose a través del espacio. Consisten en rayos gamma de longitud de onda corta, a ondas de radio de longitud de onda larga.

element: A pure substance consisting of only one type of atom.

elemento: Una sustancia pura que consiste en un solo tipo de átomo.

Energy Return on Energy Invested (ERoEI): A method of analyzing and comparing different fuels to compare the energy costs of production with the amount of energy available from the fuel source.

Retorno de la energía sobre la energía invertida (ERoEI): Un método de análisis y comparación de diferentes combustibles para comparar los costos de producción de energía con la cantidad de energía disponible de la fuente de combustible.

equinox: The name given to the period of time when the Sun crosses directly over the equator, normally around 21st March and September.

equinoccio: El nombre dado al período de tiempo en que el Sol cruza directamente sobre el ecuador, normalmente alrededor del 21 de marzo y septiembre.

erosion: The action of surface processes (water, wind or ice) that removes soil, rock, or dissolved material from one location and transports it to another location.

erosión: La acción de los procesos superficiales (agua, viento o hielo) que elimina el suelo, la roca o el material disuelto de un lugar y lo transporta a otro lugar.

eruption: The release of material from a volcano, e.g. lava, gas, ash.

erupción: La liberación de material de un volcáno, por ejemplo, lava, gas, cenizas.

event horizon: The boundary around a black hole beyond which events will not affect the outside universe. Light falling into the black hole beyond the event horizon cannot re-emerge from it.

horizonte de eventos: El borde alrededor de un agujero negro más allá del cual los eventos no afectarán al universo exterior. La luz que cae en el agujero negro más allá del horizonte de eventos no puede resurgir de él.

exoplanet: A planet outside our solar system

exoplaneta: Un planeta fuera de nuestro sistema solar.

fault: A fracture of the Earth's crust, between different rock masses.

Falla: Una fractura de la corteza de la Tierra, entre diferentes mases de rocas.

flood: An overflow of water on to land that is normally dry.

inundación: Un desbordamiento de agua en la tierra que normalmente está seca.

fossil fuel: A natural fuel such as coal or gas, formed in the geological past from the remains of living organisms.

combustible fósil: Un combustible natural como el carbón o el gas, formado en el pasado geológico a partir de los restos de organismos vivos.

geosphere: The portion of the Earth system that includes the Earth's interior, rocks and minerals, landforms and the processes that shape the Earth's surface.

geosfera: La porción del sistema de la Tierra que incluye el interior de la Tierra, las rocas y los minerales, los accidentes geográficos y los procesos que dan forma a la superficie de la Tierra.

global warming: The gradual heating of the Earth, attributed to human activities such as the burning of fossil fuels.

Calentamiento global: El calentamiento gradual de la Earth, atribuido a actividades humanas como la quema de combustibles fósiles.

graph: A diagram that is used to present scientific data, usually with two variables on an x and y axis. It allows relationships between variables to be clearly visualized.

gráfico: Un diagrama que se utiliza para presentar datos científicos, generalmente con dos variables el x y la y. Permite visualizar claramente las relaciones entre variables.

gravity: The force that pulls a body towards the surface of a planet.

gravedad: La fuerza que jala un cuerpo/objecto hacia la superficie de un planeta.

Great Oxygenation Event (GOE): Initial rise in free oxygen produced by photosynthetic life on Earth.

Gran Evento de Oxigenación (GOE): Aumento inicial del oxígeno libre producido por la vida fotosintética en la Tierra.

greenhouse effect: The retention of solar energy in the Earth's atmosphere by gases that absorb heat and prevent it being released back into space.

efecto invernadero: La retención de la energía solar en la atmósfera de la Tierra por gases que absorben el calor y evitan que se libere de nuevo en el espacio.

---

greenhouse gas: Any gas in the atmosphere that causes the retention of heat in the Earth's atmosphere. Major gases are water vapor and carbon dioxide.

gases de efecto invernadero: Cualquier gas en la atmósfera que cause la retención de calor en la atmósfera de la Tierra. Los principales gases son el vapor de agua y el dióxido de carbono.

---

heat energy: The energy that results from the movement of particles such as individual atoms moving against each other.

energía térmica: La energía que resulta del movimiento de partículas como átomos individuales que se mueven uno contra el otro.

Hertzsprung Russell diagram: Scatter plot which plots the luminosity of stars against their effective temperature or spectral class.

Diagrama de Hertzsprung Russell: Diagrama de dispersión que traza la luminosidad de las estrellas contra su temperatura efectiva o clase espectral.

---

hurricane: A tropical storm characterised by extremely high, sustained winds.

huracán: Una tormenta tropical caracterizada por vientos extremadamente altos y sostenidos.

---

hydrologic cycle: Also known as the water cycle. Describes that way in which water circulates between the Earth and its atmosphere.

ciclo hidrológico: También conocido como el ciclo del agua. Describe la forma en que el agua circula entre la Tierra y su atmósfera.

---

hydrosphere: All the waters on the Earth's surface, such as lakes and seas.

hidrosfera: Todas las aguas de la superficie de la Tierra, como lagos y mares.

---

hypothesis: A tentative explanation, or proposition, that can be tested by scientific experimentation.

hipótesis: Una explicación tentativa, o proposición, que puede ser probada por experimentación científica.

---

ice age: A geological period when there are substantial ice sheets and glaciers on the planet.

glaciación: Un período geológico en el que hay capas de hielo y glaciares sustanciales en el planeta.

---

igneous rock: Rock formed from the cooling of molten rock.

roca ígnea: Roca formada a partir del enfriamiento de la roca fundida.

---

independent variable: The variable being set by the experimenter which is assumed to have a direct effect upon the dependent variable.

variable independiente: La variable establecida por el experimentador que se supone que tiene un efecto directo sobre la variable dependiente.

---

inner core: The innermost layer of the Earth; a solid mass of mostly iron and nickel.

núcleo interno: La capa más interna de la Tierra; una masa sólida de hierro y níquel en su mayoría.

---

interglacial: A warmer period between glaciations in an ice age.

interglacial: Un período más caliente entre glaciaciones en una edad de hielo.

Kepler's laws: Rules that describe the motion of planets in a solar system.

Leyes de Kepler: Reglas que describen el movimiento de los planetas en un sistema solar.

---

light spectra: The color of light waves that depend on their wavelength.

espectros de luz: El color de las ondas de luz que dependen de su longitud de onda.

---

lithosphere: The rigid outer part of the Earth, consisting of the crust and upper mantle.

litosfera: La parte exterior rígida de la Tierra, que consiste en la corteza y el manto superior.

---

lunar rocks: Rocks that originate from the Moon and that have been collected by manned or unmanned missions.

rocas lunares: Rocks que se originan en la Luna y que han sido recogidos por misiones tripuladas o no tripuladas.

---

magma: Molten rock below the ground.

magma: Roca fundida bajo tierra.

---

main sequence star: Star that sits within the main band of stars plotted on a Hertzsprung-Russell diagram. The star is in it middle part of its life span.

estrella de la secuencia principal: Estrella que se encuentra dentro de la banda principal de estrellas trazada en un diagrama de Hertzsprung-Russell. La estrella se encuentra en la mitad de su vida útil.

---

mantle, Earth's: The mostly solid bulk of Earth's interior, which lies between the dense, super-heated core and the crust.

manto, tierra: La mayor parte sólida del interior de la Tierra, que se encuentra entre el núcleo denso y sobrecalentado y la corteza.

---

mean: The sum of the data divided by the number of data entries; a measure of central tendency in a normal distribution.

significar / promedio: La suma de los datos dividida por el número de entradas de datos; una medida de tendencia central en una distribución normal.

---

mechanical energy: Energy that arises from the motion of an object.

energía mecánica: Energía que surge del movimiento de un objeto.

---

median: The middle number in an ordered sequence of numbers. For an odd number of values, it is the average of the two middle numbers.

mediana: El número medio en una secuencia ordenada de números. Para un número impar de valores, es el promedio de los dos números medios.

---

metamorphic rock: Rocks that change from one format to another, e.g. as a result of heat and/or pressure.

roca metamórfica: Rocas que cambian de un formato a otro, por ejemplo, como resultado del calor y/o la presión.

English/Spanish Glossary

meteorite: A fragment of rock or iron from outer space that has survived both passage through the Earth's atmosphere and impact with Earth's surface.

meteorito: Un fragmento de roca o hierro del espacio exterior que ha sobrevivido tanto al paso a través de la atmósfera de la Tierra como al impacto con la superficie de la Tierra.

---

migration: Movement from one place to another.

migración: Movimiento de un lugar a otro.

---

mineral: Naturally occurring compound with an ordered structure.

mineral: Compuesto natural con una estructura ordenada.

---

mitigation: A way of reducing the impact of a negative event.

mitigación: Una forma de reducir el impacto de un evento negativo.

---

mode: The value that occurs most often in a data set.

modo: El valor que se produce con mayor frecuencia en un conjunto de datos.

---

model: A conceptual, mathematical or physical representation of a real-world phenomenon.

modelo: Una representación conceptual, matemática o física de un fenómeno del mundo real.

---

natural hazard: A phenomenon that has the potential to disrupt everyday human life.

riesgo natural: Un fenómeno que tiene el potencial de interrumpir la vida humana cotidiana.

---

natural resource: Resources from the Earth's environment that can be used by humans.

recurso natural: Recursos del medio ambiente de la Tierra que pueden ser utilizados por los humanos.

---

nebula: A cloud of interstellar gas and dust.

nebulosa: Una nube de gas y polvo interestelar.

---

negative feedback: A mechanism where a change the output of a system acts to oppose changes to the input of a system (prevents deviation from the norm).

comentarios negativos: Un mecanismo en el que un cambio en la salida de un sistema actúa para oponerse a los cambios en la entrada de un sistema (evita la desviación de la norma).

---

newton (N): Unit of force. The force required to accelerate a 1kg object by 1 m/s^2

newton (N): Unidad de fuerza. La fuerza requerida para acelerar un objeto de 1 kg en 1 m/s^2

Newton's law of gravitation: A rule stating that all matter in the universe it attracted to all other matter with a force that is proportional to both of their masses and inversely proportional to the square of their distances apart.

La ley de la gravitación de Newton: Una regla que establece que toda la materia en el universo atrae a toda la otra materia con una fuerza que es proporcional a sus dos masas e inversamente proporcional al cuadrado de sus distancias separadas.

---

non-renewable resource: Resources from the Earth that cannot be replaced, e.g. fossil fuels such as oil and gas.

recurso no renovable: Recursos de la Tierra que no pueden ser reemplazados, por ejemplo, combustibles fósiles como el petróleo y el gas.

---

nucleon: A particle found in the nucleus of an atom; either a proton or a neutron.

nucleón: Una partícula que se encuentra en el núcleo de un átomo; ya sea un protón o un neutrón.

---

nucleosynthesis: The production of new atomic nuclei by the nuclear processes in stars, e.g. fusion, or supernova.

nucleosíntesis: La producción de nuevos núcleos atómicos por los procesos nucleares en las estrellas, por ejemplo, la fusión o la supernova.

---

observation: The activity of watching or recording what is happening in a given, often experimental, setting.

observación: La actividad de observar o registrar lo que está sucediendo en un entorno dado, a menudo experimental.

---

oceanic crust: Part of Earth's crust that is rich in basalt, relatively dense, and geologically young. Found under ocean basins. **corteza oceánica**; Parte de la corteza terrestre que es rica en basalto, relativamente densa y geológicamente joven. Se encuentra bajo las cuencas oceánicas.

---

oil: A liquid fossil fuel formed by intense

heat and pressure on the remains of ancient, dead marine organisms.

aceite: Un combustible fósil líquido formado por el intenso calor y la presión sobre los restos de antiguos organismos marinos muertos.

---

orbit: The path an object takes in space, going around another object.

órbita: La ruta que toma un objeto en el espacio, rodeando a otro objeto.

---

outer core: The liquid part of the Earth's interior that surrounds the inner core and gives rise to the magnetic field.

núcleo externo: La parte líquida del interior de la Tierra que rodea el núcleo interno y da lugar al campo magnético.

P-wave: A longitudinal seismic wave produced by an earthquake. Also known as a pressure wave, it is able to move through solid and liquid media. The fastest moving seismic wave.

Onda P: Una onda sísmica longitudinal producida por un terremoto. También conocida como onda de presión, es capaz de moverse a través de medios sólidos y líquidos. La onda sísmica de movimiento más rápido.

---

planet: A celestial body that orbits the sun.

planeta: Un cuerpo celeste que orbita alrededor del sol.

---

plate tectonics: The theory that describes how the Earth's crust is divided into pates/parts that move about due to convection currents in the mantle.

tectónica de placas: La teoría que describe cómo la corteza terrestre se divide en patés/partes que se mueven debido a las corrientes de convección en el manto.

---

pollution: The introduction of a contaminant into the natural environment that has harmful or poisonous effects.

contaminación: La introducción de un contaminante en el medio natural que tenga efectos nocivos o venenosos.

---

positive feedback: A destabilizing mechanism, in which the output of the system causes the initial response to escalate.

comentarios positivos: Un mecanismo desestabilizador, en el que la salida del sistema hace que la respuesta inicial se intensifique.

---

precision: How close repeated measurements are to each other, i.e. repeatability.

precisión: Qué tan cerca están las mediciones repetidas entre sí, es decir, la repetibilidad.

---

prediction: What is expected to happen if the hypothesis of an experiment or scenario is true.

predicción: Lo que se espera que suceda si la hipótesis de un experimento o escenario es cierta.

---

qualitative data: Non-numerical data that describes qualities or characteristics.

datos cualitativos: Datos no numéricos que describen cualidades o características.

---

quantitative data: Numerical data expressing a certain quantity, amount, or range.

datos cuantitativos: Datos numéricos que expresan una determinada cantidad, cantidad o rango.

---

radioactive decay: The process by which an unstable atomic nucleus loses energy through radiation.

desintegración radiactiva: El proceso por el cual un núcleo atómico inestable pierde energía a través de la radiación.

---

radiometric dating: A method for determining the age of an object based on the proportion of a radioactive isotope within it and the half-life of that isotope.

datación radiométrica: Un método para determinar la edad de un objeto basado en la proporción de un isótopo radiactivo dentro de él y la vida media de ese isótopo.

---

raw data: experimental data that is collected in the field or laboratory and has not yet been processed.

datos brutos: datos experimentales que se recogen en la industriao laboratorio y que aún no se han procesado.

---

red shift: The increase in wavelength of light rays (and shift of absorption spectrum towards the red end of the spectrum) due to the movement of a light emitting object away from the observer.

desplazamiento al rojo: El aumento de la longitud de onda de los rayos de luz (y el desplazamiento del espectro de absorción hacia el extremo rojo del espectro) debido al movimiento de un objeto emisor de luz lejos del observador.

---

remediation: The use of biological agents, such as bacteria or plants, to remove or neutralize contaminants, as in polluted soil or water.

remediación: El uso de agentes biológicos, como bacterias o plantas, para eliminar o neutralizar contaminantes, como en el suelo o el agua contaminados.

---

renewable resource: Resources from earth that are not used up, e.g. wind, waves, solar energy.

recurso renovable: Recursos de la tierra que no se agotan, por ejemplo, viento, olas, energía solar.

---

resource: Anything used for human activity.

recurso: Cualquier cosa utilizada para la actividad humana.

---

rock cycle: Series of processes that create rocks in the Earth's crust and change them from one form into another.

ciclo de la roca: Serie de procesos que crean rocas en la corteza terrestre y las cambian de una forma a otra.

S-wave: A transverse seismic wave produced during an earthquake that is unable to move through a liquid medium.

Onda S: Una onda sísmica transversal producida durante un terremoto que no puede moverse a través de un medio líquido.

---

satellite: An object in space that orbits around another object.

satélite: Un objeto en el espacio que orbita alrededor de otro objeto.

---

scientific method: The processes applied to the way in which scientists discover how the universe works. It involves a specific way of asking questions, observing, measuring, and interpreting data to formulate hypotheses and theories.

método científico: Los procesos aplicados a la forma en que los científicos descubren cómo funciona el universo. Implica una forma específica de hacer preguntas, observar, medir e interpretar datos para formular hipótesis y teorías.

---

season: Time division of the year, characterised by the tilt of the Earth, that causes alternate heating and cooling.

estación: División temporal del año, caracterizada por la inclinación de la Tierra, que provoca calentamiento y enfriamiento alternativos.

---

sedimentary rock: Rock formed from compressed, buried sediments.

roca sedimentaria: Roca formada a partir de sedimentos comprimidos y enterrados.

---

snowball earth: A period of time when Earth was almost completely covered in ice.

tierra bola de nieve: Un período de tiempo en el que la Tierra estaba casi completamente cubierta de hielo.

---

soil: Loose mixture of materials on Earth's surface in which plants grow; composed of rock particles, organic matter and clay.

suelo: Mezcla suelta de materiales en la superficie de la Tierra en la que crecen las plantas; compuesto por partículas de roca, materia orgánica y arcilla.

---

solar system: A system composed of a sun and the celestial bodies that orbit it.

sistema solar: Un sistema compuesto por un sol y los cuerpos celestes que lo orbitan.

---

solstice: The name given to the period of time when the Sun crosses directly over the Tropic of Cancer or Tropic of Capricorn, normally around 21st June and December.

solsticio: El nombre dado al período de tiempo en que el Sol cruza directamente sobre el Trópico de Cáncer o Trópico de Capricornio, normalmente alrededor del 21 de junio y diciembre.

---

star: A luminous sphere held together by its own gravity that, for most that for most of its life, comprises 75% hydrogen and 25% helium. Nuclei fusion in the core converts hydrogen to helium.

estrella: Una esfera luminosa unida por su propia gravedad que, durante la mayor parte de su vida, comprende un 75% de hidrógeno y un 25% de helio. La fusión de núcleos en el núcleo convierte el hidrógeno en helio.

---

stellar: Referring to a star or stars

estelar: Refiriéndose a una estrella o estrellas

---

stratosphere: The layer of the Earth's atmosphere above the troposphere, extending to about 50 km above the Earth's surface.

estratosfera: La capa de la atmósfera de la Tierra sobre la troposfera, que se extiende a unos 50 km sobre la superficie de la Tierra.

---

subduction zone: The place where two tectonic plates meet and one moves under the other, into the mantle.

zona de subducción: El lugar donde dos placas tectónicas se encuentran y una se mueve debajo de la otra, en el manto.

Sun: The star at the center of our solar system.

Sol: La estrella en el centro de nuestro sistema solar.

---

sunspot cycle: The 11 year cycle in which sunspots grow and fade on the surface of the Sun.

ciclo de manchas solares: El ciclo de 11 años en el que las manchas solares crecen y se desvanecen en la superficie del Sol.

---

sustainability: The ability of the earth to maintain itself without depletion of non-renewable resources.

sostenibilidad: La capacidad de la tierra para mantenerse sin agotamiento de recursos no renovables.

---

sustainable development: Development of industry or use of Earth's resources such that they are not depleted beyond a level at which they can be renewed.

desarrollo sostenible: Del desarrollo de la industria o la utilización de los recursos de la Tierra, de modo que no se agoten más allá de un nivel en el que puedan renovarse.

---

table: A way of presenting data in a structured format that allows relationships and trends to be easily recognized.

mesa: Una forma de presentar los datos en un formato estructurado que permite reconocer fácilmente las relaciones y tendencias.

---

terrestrial rocks: Rocks that originated on Earth

rocas terrestres: Rocks que se originaron en la Tierra

Theia: A Mars sized protoplanet that collided with Earth 4.4 billion years ago, producing our moon from the collision debris.

Theia: Un protoplaneta del tamaño de Marte que colisionó con la Tierra hace 4.400 millones de años, produciendo nuestra luna a partir de los escombros de la colisión.

---

transform boundary: A region where two tectonic plates, side by side, slide past each other.

límite de transformación: Una región donde dos placas tectónicas, una al lado de la otra, se deslizan una sobre la otra.

---

tricellular model: A model of atmospheric circulation that uses three cells in each hemisphere to explain weather and climatic conditions at certain latitudes.

modelo tricelular: Un modelo de circulación atmosférica que utiliza tres células en cada hemisferio para explicar el clima y las condiciones climáticas en ciertas latitudes.

---

troposphere: The lowest layer of Earth's atmosphere.

troposfera: La capa más baja de la atmósfera de la Tierra.

---

tsunami: Waves caused by movements of the sea floor due to earthquakes or landslides.

tsunami: Olas causadas por movimientos del fondo marino debido a terremotos o deslizamientos de tierra.

---

uranium-lead dating: Radiometric dating technique that uses the ratios of uranium and lead isotopes to calculate the age of a mineral.

datación uranio-plomo: Técnica de datación radiométrica que utiliza las proporciones de isótopos de uranio y plomo para calcular la edad de un mineral.

---

variable: A measurable property that changes over time, or can take on different values.

variable: Una propiedad medible que cambia con el tiempo o puede tomar diferentes valores.

---

weathering: Breakdown of rocks and minerals over time by physical, chemical, and biological processes.

meteorización: Descomposición de rocas y minerales a lo largo del tiempo por procesos físicos, químicos y biológicos.

---

zircon: The common name for the mineral containing zirconium silicate and trace amounts of uranium and thorium.

circón: El nombre común para el mineral que contiene silicato de circonio y trazas de uranio y torio.

Appendix 2: Equipment List

1: Science Practices

INVESTIGATION 1.1
Investigating surface area and dissolving time

Per student/pair
Limestone ($CaCO_3$) chips
1 mol/L HCl
3 x 200 mL beakers
Timer
Electronic balance
Mortar and pestle

2: The Universe and its Stars

INVESTIGATION 2.1
Modeling expansion

Per student/pair
Rubber bands
Thumb tacks

INVESTIGATION 2.2
Measuring the size of the Sun

Per student/pair
Aluminum foil
Push pin
Card (to make a frame for the foil)
Ruler

3: Earth and the Solar System

INVESTIGATION 3.1
Elliptical orbits

Per pair/group
String (15 cm)
Two thumbtacks
Pencil
Corkboard or card

INVESTIGATION 3.2
Modeling orbits 1

Per pair
1 bowl
4-5 balls of various sizes
4-5 clothes pegs
Sheet of material to cover bowl

INVESTIGATION 3.3
Modeling orbits 2

Per student/pair
Computer

INVESTIGATION 3.4
Parallax

Per group of four
Protractor (a 180° is easiest to use)
Corkboard or thick card
Tape
Push pins
Plastic straw
Measuring tape

4: The History of Planet Earth

INVESTIGATION 4.1
Modeling half-lives

Per pair/group
M&M's®
Lidded container

5: Earth Materials and Systems

INVESTIGATION 5.1
Modeling ice sheet melting

Per pair/group
2 x Florence or Erlenmeyer flasks
Black paint
Aluminum foil
Ice cubes
2 x thermometers
60W tungsten lamp (optional)
Timer

6: Plate Tectonics

INVESTIGATION 6.1
Continental drift

Per student/pair
Scissors
Tape or paste

INVESTIGATION 6.2
Modeling drift over time

Per student/pair
Scissors
Tape or paste

7: The Roles of Water in the Earth's Surface Processes

INVESTIGATION 7.1
Determining properties of rocks

Per pair/group
Samples of sedimentary, igneous, and metamorphic rock
Graduated cylinder
Electronic balance

INVESTIGATION 7.2
Investigating frost wedging

Plaster of paris
3 x balloons
Graduated cylinder
3 x Disposable containers
Freezer

INVESTIGATION 7.3
Modeling the process of erosion

Per group
1 x plastic tray (at least A3 in size) with a water inlet and outlet
Hose and connectors
Substrate (gravel, silt, sand, clay)
Large rocks
Vegetation

8: Weather, Climate, and Biogeography

INVESTIGATION 8.1
Measuring energy

Per student/pair
Torch
Clamp stand
Protractor
Grid paper

INVESTIGATION 8.2
Modeling carbon cycle changes

Per student/pair
Computer
Spreadsheet application e.g. Excel

9: Natural Resources

INVESTIGATION 9.1
Investigating soil types 1

Per student/pair
Samples of sand, silt, and clay.
Measuring cylinders
Stirring rods

INVESTIGATION 9.2
Investigating soil types 2

Per student/pair
Three different soil samples.
Measuring cylinders
Stirring rods

12: Global Climate Change

INVESTIGATION 12.1
Investigating how dry ice affects pH

Per pair/group
250 mL conical flasks
Universal indicator
Dry ice
1 Mol/L NaOH

Appendix 3: Rearranging Equations

Rearranging Equations

Often, we need to rearrange equations so that the "unknown" term is easier for us to work out.

We do this by moving one term at a time until we have the "unknown" on its own, on one side of the equation.

Example 1

Let's start by rearranging $M = \frac{a^3}{T^2}$ to work out T.

First, we multiply both sides by T^2 and cancel out those on the right. This moves T^2 to the left.

$$T^2 M = \frac{a^3 \cancel{T^2}}{\cancel{T^2}}$$

Next, divide both sides by M and cancel out those on the left. This moves M to the right, leaving us with T^2 on the left.

$$\frac{T^2 \cancel{M}}{\cancel{M}} = \frac{a^3}{M}$$

Now we just have to find T, knowing T^2.
T is the square root of the right hand side.

$$T = \sqrt{\frac{a^3}{M}}$$

Example 2

Now, let's rearrange $M = \frac{4\pi^2 a^3}{GT^2}$ to work out T

First, we multiply both sides by T^2 and cancel out those on the right.
This moves T^2 to the left hand side.

$$T^2 M = \frac{(4\pi^2 a^3)\cancel{T^2}}{G\cancel{T^2}}$$

Next, divide both sides by M and cancel those on the left.
This moves M to the right hand side.

$$\frac{T^2 \cancel{M}}{\cancel{M}} = \frac{(4\pi^2 a^3)}{GM}$$

Now, we just need to find T, knowing T^2.

T is the square root of the right hand side.

$$T = \sqrt{\frac{(4\pi^2 a^3)}{GM}}$$

Credits

We acknowledge the generosity of those who have provided photographs or diagrams for this edition including: Scott McDougall for the image of the comet • Dartmouth College Electronic Microscope Facility

We also acknowledge the photographers that have made their images available through Pixabay (pixabay.com) or Wikimedia Commons under Creative Commons Licences 2.0, 2.5, 3.0, or 4.0:
• Marlith • Coyau • Barfooz • Jan Fjaldowski • Brocken Inaglory • Dartmouth Electron Microscope Facility (Public Domain) • Dicklyon • Andrew Pontzen and Fabio Governato • Judy Schmidt • ALMA (ESO/NAOJ/NRAO)/E. O'Gorman/P. Kervella • Gregory H. Revera • Gregory H. Revera • Tobias 1984 • H. Raab • G310Luke • Valerio Pillar • Yosemite • Rakot13 • Bigest • Hcrepin • Graeme Churchard • Ashley Dace • Charles Robert Knight • Meteorite Recon cc 3.0 • Mike Beauregard • BenAveling • Gunnar Ries • Hartman and Neukum 2001 • Eugen Zibsio • Andrzej Mireck • Kochendes_wasser02 • Acagastya • Till Niermann • katorisi • Eurico Zimbres • Ed Hawkins • Efbrazil • Wknight94 talk • Hullwaren • Bob Metcalf • Sharon Loxton • Wawny • Cunningham- Saigo • United nations Logan Abassi cc2.0 • US Coastguard Public domain • Oxfam East Africa cc2.0 • Govt of Kiribati cc 3.0 • SuSanA cc 2.0 • Evancez CC 4.0 Shahee Ilyas CC3.0 • hughe82 cc3.0 • Edwin S • Doug Kerr • Precision Seafood Harvesting • Ravedave • Paul Traytek • Chongkian • Duncan Wright • Paul Hanly • Z22 • Boris Radosavljevic • Mircea Madau (public domain) • Walter siegmund • KDS4444 • California High-Speed Rail Authority • National Park Service • Swain, Sing, Touma, & Diffenbaugh • Tuxyso

Contributors identified by coded credits are:
BH: Brendan Hicks (University of Waikato), **KP**: Kent Pryor, **USDE**: U.S. Department of Energy, **UNFAO**: Food and Agriculture Organization of the United Nations, **NASA**: National Aeronautics and Space Administration, **JPL**: Jet Propulsion Laboratory, **NOAA**: National Oceanic and Atmospheric Administration, **ESA**: European Space Agency, **ESO**: European Southern Observatory, **RA**: Richard Allan, **USGS**: United States Geological Survey, **USDA**: United States Department of Agriculture, **USFW**: United States Fish and Wildlife Service, **CSIRO**: Commonwealth Scientific and Industrial Research Organisation, **IPCC**: Intergovernmental Panel on Climate Change, **NPS**: National Park Service

Royalty free images, purchased by Biozone International Ltd, are used throughout this book and have been obtained from the following sources: Corel Corporation from their Professional Photos CD-ROM collection; IMSI (Intl Microcomputer Software Inc.) images from IMSI's MasterClips® and MasterPhotos™ Collection, 1895 Francisco Blvd. East, San Rafael, CA 94901-5506, USA; ©1996 Digital Stock, Medicine and Health Care collection; © 2005 JupiterImages Corporation www.clipart.com; ©Hemera Technologies Inc, 1997-2001; ©Click Art, ©T/Maker Company; ©1994., ©Digital Vision; Gazelle Technologies Inc.; PhotoDisc®, Inc. USA, www.photodisc.com. • TechPool Studios, for their clipart collection of human anatomy: Copyright ©1994, TechPool Studios Corp. USA (some of these images were modified by BIOZONE) • Totem Graphics, for their clipart collection • Corel Corporation, for use of their clipart from the Corel MEGAGALLERY collection • 3D images created using Bryce, Vue 6, Poser, and Pymol • iStock images • Art Today • Dollar Photo Club.• Adobe Stock

Index